D1708367

3 3 3 3 3 3 3

Actex

Study Manual

Course 3

Examination of the Society of Actuaries

Exam 3

of the Casualty Actuarial Society

Volume I
(Survival Models, Contingent Payment Models)

2000 Edition

Michael A. Gauger, Ph.D.

Printed in the United States of America

ISBN: 1-56698-369-X

TABLE OF CONTENTS

Preface

This two-volume manual has been designed as a self-contained introduction to the topics covered by the new Course 3 Exam. It could also serve as a stand-alone text for a year-long University Course. We have endeavored to address all of the Learning Objectives set forth in the Report of the Joint CAS/SOA Working Group on Courses 3 and 4. Volume I is devoted to Survival Models (2 units) and Contingent Payment Models (6 units). As suggested in the Report of the Working Group, relevant business applications with contingent payments supplement the usual life insurance and annuity models. Volume II includes Aggregate Loss Models (4 units), Stochastic Processes (4 units), and Simulation (1 unit). The multiple-decrement model developed in Volume I is integrated with the treatment of continuous-time stochastic processes to describe the mathematics of "transition to the next state." Application of stochastic process theory is then made to contingent payment models in the Unit Review Questions.

Each of the 17 units contains Introductory Discussion, Condensed Review Notes, a Conceptual Review Test (to reinforce basic concepts and reasoning), a Computational Review Test (more central and elementary computations), and Unit Review Questions. In Volume I, many of the Unit Review Questions are from past SOA 150 exam. Additional questions have been created featuring business applications of contingent payment models to try to prepare the student for the style of question likely to be encountered on the Course 3 Examination. In Volume II some questions from past SOA 151 exams concerning aggregate loss and ruin models remain relevant and have been included. Most questions are newly-created, and, wherever possible, the questions are applied to business problems.

The Unit Review Questions in these two volumes are the best questions we can offer at this point for the student seeking to prepare for the Course 3 Exam. However, the Course 3 Sample Exam produced by the Working Group makes it clear that the style of exams is changing dramatically compared to the recent past. Fewer questions will involve heavy symbolic manipulation and parametric model algebra. Many questions will require integrating ideas from several topics and applying them to solve a problem set in a business context. Solutions will require reasoning from first principles. Memorizing lists of equations from parametric models, and being prepared to do heavy computation or algebra with these equations is not the way to prepare for the Course 3 Exam. Understanding concepts, being able to integrate ideas from different topics, and applying these things to business problems will be paramount.

We commend the Working Group for the care with which they have undertaken the design of this new course and for their adherence in the Sample Exam to the principles set forth in their report. It is clear that actuarial education is evolving in a new direction, with the result that successful exam candidates will have to demonstrate not only computational mathematic skill, but also conceptual understanding and an ability to apply these concepts to solve business problem.

We would like also to express appreciation to the peer review group who read the first draft of these manuals and made valuable suggestions for improvement. This group includes James W. Daniel, ASA, University of Texas; Samuel H. Cox, FSA, Georgia State University; Thomas N. Herzog, ASA, Department of HUD; and Brian Lowrey, Walter B. Lowrie, FSA, Dick London, FSA, and Jeyaraj (Jay) Vadiveloo, FSA, all of the Actuarial Science Program at the University of Connecticut.

Michael A. Gauger
July 1999

YOUR OPINION IS IMPORTANT TO US

We here at ACTEX are eager to provide you, the actuarial student, with helpful study material to assist you in gaining the necessary knowledge to become a successful actuary. In turn we would like your help in evaluating our manuals so we can help you meet that end. We invite you to provide us with a critique of this manual by sending this form to us at your convenience.

Course 3

In preparing for my exam I found this manual: (Check one)

☐ Very Good ☐ Good ☐ Satisfactory ☐ Unsatisfactory

I found the following helpful:

____

____

____

____

I found the following problems:
(Please be specific as to area, i.e., section, specific item, and/or page #)

____

____

____

____

To improve this manual I would:

____

____

____

____

Name: ______________________________

Address: ______________________________

____

Phone: __________________

(Please provide name and phone number in case clarification is needed)

Send to: Denise Rosengrant
ACTEX Publications
P.O. Box 974
Winsted, CT 06098

We appreciate your time and value your input. THANK YOU!

ACTEX
MAD RIVER BOOKS ORDER FORM

This form may be used to order copies of the following textbooks:

_____ *A Guide to Actuarial Mathematics: Life Contingencies and Ruin Theory for the Actuarial Student*, Batten and London ($60.00)
_____ *Solutions to Bowers' Actuarial Mathematics: Life Contingencies and Ruin Theory*, Gauger, ($15.00)
_____ An Introduction to Actuarial Models and Modeling: An Interactive Approach, Jones, ($60.00)

Payment can be made by check or by credit card. Credit card orders can also be placed by fax, phone, or e-mail.

Name ____

Address ____

____

City ______________________ State ______ Zip Code __________

Phone (Day) ______________________________

Method of Payment:

❑ Check/Money Order ❑ Visa ❑ Mastercard ❑ American Express ❑ Discover

				-					-					-				

Expiration Date ______/______

Signature ________________________________

Total	
Connecticut Residents Add 6% Sales Tax	
Foreign Shipping *See Below*	
TOTAL AMOUNT	

Foreign shipping charges:

Africa, Asia, Australia and the Middle East please add	40% of order total
Europe please add	25% of order total
Mexico, South America, Central America, Caribbean please add	20% of order total

Mail you orders to ACTEX Publications, P.O. Box 974, Winsted, CT 06098. Please indicate "Check Enclosed" or provide the necessary credit card information. Credit card orders may be faxed to 860-738-3152, phoned to 1-800-282-2839, or e-mailed to retail@actexmadriver.com. Prices include postage on U.S. and Canadian orders. All Connecticut orders must add 6% for sales tax. Foreign orders must be paid in U.S. funds drawn on a U.S. bank. Thank you!

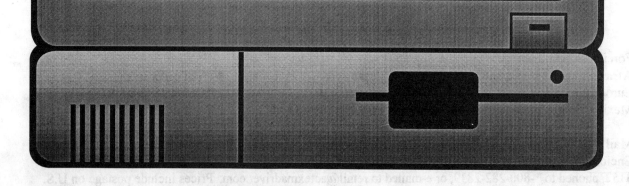

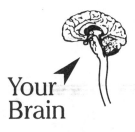

SECTION I

SURVIVAL MODELS

INTRODUCTORY NOTE

This section of the manual contains two units: Survival Models and Other Uses of Survival Models. For each unit there is a package of five items:

(1) ***Introductory Notes.*** While not as complete as many textbooks, it is designed to cover all the learning objectives set forth in the SOA - Working Group Report on Course 3.

(2) ***Condensed Review Notes and Advanced Topics.*** These notes constitute a list of the major relations with additional comments on more exotic topics. They should be useful as a reference when solving the Unit Review Questions, and as a final checklist of facts you should be familiar with for the exam.

(3) ***Conceptual Review Test.*** This material should be used in conjunction with reading and rereading the Introductory notes.

(4) ***Computational Review Test.*** These questions are more elementary than the Unit Review Questions and emphasize very basic calculations related to the unit reading.

(5) ***Unit Review Questions.*** This is a compilation of past SOA exam questions which still appear to be relevant, and newly created questions to reflect the new learning objectives and syllabus.

UNIT 1: ACTUARIAL SURVIVAL MODELS

Why a Survival Model Is Necessary

Consider a plan of life insurance issued to an individual who pays annual premiums to the insurer for as long as she survives after the issue of the policy in return for a benefit, B (the face value), paid to her beneficiary upon her death. Pricing of this plan (i.e., calculating the annual premium) is a matter of balancing the "value" of the insurer's inflow, the premiums, with the "value" of its outflow, the benefit. In interest theory you learned to value a payment which is certain. It's present value was calculated by multiplying the payment amount by a discount factor at an appropriate rate of interest and for the appropriate number of years until the payment was due. However, in the life insurance example above, the premium and benefit payments are not certain. They are contingent on the occurrence of random events. Each possible premium payment is contingent on the policyholder's survival at the time it falls due. Hence both the number of premiums paid and their total present value are random variables (at issue). The timing of the death benefit payment is contingent on the time of death of the policyholder. Its present value is random since it must be discounted for a random (at issue) number of years.

So we are presented with the problem of valuing a series of contingent payments. Disassociating this problem from the life insurance discussion, let's see how to handle a simple example. Let i be the effective annual rate of interest and let $v = (1+i)^{-1}$ be the corresponding discount factor. Consider a single payment, P, due in n years only if a random event E occurs. The present value is $P \cdot v^n$ if E occurs, and is $0 \cdot v^n$ if E does not occur. In other words, the present value is a discrete random variable having two values:

<u>Present Value Random Variable</u>

Possible Value	Probability
$P \cdot v^n$	$Pr(E)$
$0 \cdot v^n$	$1 - Pr(E)$

Since insurers deal with large groups of individuals they are concerned with the average or expected value of variables like the one above. In actuarial mathematics this expected value is referred to as an actuarial present value. Since the expected value of a discrete random variable is a sum, over all possible values, of value times the corresponding probability, we see that the expected present value of this single contingent payment is

$$\underbrace{P}_{\text{amount}} \cdot \underbrace{v^n}_{\text{discount}} \cdot \underbrace{Pr(E)}_{\text{probability}} .$$

Going back to the life insurance example, the random events of interest concern the random future lifetime of the insured after issue of the contract. A probability model for this random lifetime is known as a survival model.

The Tabular (Discrete) Survival Model of Insurance Practice

Consider a group of 10,000,000 newborn lives which is to be followed until the last death occurs. For each age x we denote by ℓ_x (read: number[1] living at age x) the number of lives from this group which are still surviving. At age 0 we have $\ell_0 = 10{,}000{,}000$. As x increases deaths occur and the function ℓ_x decreases, gradually at first, then more rapidly. In insurance practice one typically has a table of ℓ_x values at integral ages such as the one on the following page. In theoretical (continuous) survival models ℓ_x is assumed to be a differentiable (hence continuous), decreasing function of x. There is a final age, ω, by which all lives are assumed to perish. Thus $\ell_\omega = 0$ and $[0, \omega]$ is the domain of the ℓ_x function. Here we will introduce some of the important ideas in terms of the practical, tabular models before considering the theoretical ones and their connection with the tabular ones.

There are three important types of probabilities with regard to a newborn known to have survived to age x which are defined as ratios of life table values. We should first explain the d_x column. A d_x value is defined as the number of x-year-olds who will die in the next year. Since an x-year-old will either survive the next year (and be counted in ℓ_{x+1}) or die during it (and be counted in d_x) it follows that $\ell_x = d_x + \ell_{x+1}$, or equivalently, $d_x = \ell_x - \ell_{x+1}$.

Important Probabilities

Notation	Definition	Calculation as a Ratio of Table Values
${}_np_x$	$Pr(x$ survives to age $x+n)$	$\frac{\ell_{x+n}}{\ell_x}$
${}_nq_x$	$Pr(x$ dies before age $x+n)$	$1 - \frac{\ell_{x+n}}{\ell_x}$
${}_{n\vert m}q_x$	$Pr(x$ dies between ages $x+n$ and $x+n+m)$	$\frac{\ell_{x+n} - \ell_{x+n+m}}{\ell_x}$

---

1 At the beginning of this study the actual number is random, so ℓ_x is mathematically the expected number of survivors.

An Illustrative Life Table

x	ℓ_x	d_x	x	ℓ_x	d_x
0	10,000,000	204,200	50	8,950,994	52,990
1	9,795,800	13,126	51	8,898,004	57,125
2	9,782,674	11,935	52	8,840,879	61,621
3	9,770,739	10,943	53	8,779,258	66,547
4	9,759,796	10,150	54	8,712,711	71,793
5	9,749,646	9,555	55	8,640,918	77,423
6	9,740,091	9,058	56	8,563,495	83,494
7	9,731,033	8,661	57	8,480,001	90,058
8	9,722,372	8,458	58	8,389,943	97,156
9	9,713,914	8,257	59	8,292,787	104,655
10	9,705,657	8,250	60	8,188,132	112,669
11	9,697,407	8,243	61	8,075,463	121,213
12	9,689,164	8,333	62	7,954,250	130,291
13	9,680,831	8,422	63	7,823,959	139,892
14	9,672,409	8,608	64	7,684,067	149,993
15	9,663,801	8,794	65	7,534,074	160,626
16	9,655,007	8,979	66	7,373,448	171,728
17	9,646,028	9,164	67	7,201,720	183,212
18	9,636,864	9,348	68	7,018,508	195,044
19	9,627,516	9,628	69	6,823,464	207,229
20	9,617,888	9,906	70	6,616,235	219,527
21	9,607,982	10,184	71	6,396,708	231,945
22	9,597,798	10,558	72	6,164,763	244,248
23	9,587,240	10,929	73	5,920,515	256,358
24	9,576,311	11,300	74	5,664,157	267,971
25	9,565,011	11,669	75	5,396,186	278,929
26	9,553,342	12,133	76	5,117,257	288,972
27	9,541,209	12,690	77	4,828,258	297,809
28	9,528,519	13,245	78	4,530,476	305,218
29	9,515,274	13,892	79	4,225,258	310,810
30	9,501,382	14,537	80	3,914,448	314,330
31	9,486,845	15,274	81	3,600,118	315,514
32	9,471,571	16,102	82	3,284,604	314,041
33	9,455,469	16,925	83	2,970,563	309,770
34	9,438,544	17,933	84	2,660,793	302,506
35	9,420,611	18,935	85	2,385,287	292,168
36	9,401,676	20,120	86	2,066,119	278,802
37	9,381,556	21,390	87	1,787,317	262,539
38	9,360,166	22,745	88	1,524,778	243,675
39	9,337,421	24,277	89	1,281,103	222,592
40	9,313,144	25,891	90	1,058,511	199,815
41	9,287,253	27,676	91	858,696	175,973
42	9,259,577	29,631	92	682,723	151,749
43	9,229,946	31,751	93	530,974	127,890
44	9,198,195	34,125	94	403,084	105,096
45	9,164,070	36,656	95	297,988	84,006
46	9,127,414	39,339	96	213,982	74,894
47	9,088,075	42,350	97	139,088	66,067
48	9,045,725	45,590	98	73,021	49,289
49	9,000,135	49,141	99	23,732	23,732

The expressions in terms of life table values correspond to the relative frequencies with which the associated events occurred. Each of the ℓ_x lives at age x is viewed as a trial of an experiment. The numerator corresponds to the number of times the given event occurred. There are ℓ_{x+n} survivors at age $x+n$, $\ell_x - \ell_{x+n}$ deaths prior to age $x+n$, and $\ell_{x+n} - \ell_{x+n+m}$ deaths between ages $x+n$ and $x+n+m$ from the group of ℓ_x survivors at age x.

In actuarial mathematics the "$_{n|}$" notation is used to denote something which is deferred for n years. In the symbol $_{n|m}q_x$ death is deferred for n years and then occurs within the next m years. If a life insurance contract is issued to (25) today ((x) denotes a newborn life known to be alive at age x) and premiums are due at ages $25, 26, 27, \ldots$ then $_0p_{25}, {_1p_{25}}, {_2p_{25}}, \ldots$ are the corresponding payment-probabilities. The age intervals $[25,26], [26,27], \ldots$ are known as the $1^{st}, 2^{nd}, \ldots$ policy years. The probabilities $_{0|1}q_{25}, {_{1|1}q_{25}}, \ldots$ give the likelihood of death in the $1^{st}, 2^{nd}, \ldots$ policy year respectively.

One-year periods are fundamental in many models, so the symbols $_1p_x$, $_1q_x$ and $_{n|1}q_x$ are commonly shortened to p_x, q_x and $_{n|}q_x$. Following are some of the basic relations that are frequently exploited.

$$p_x = \frac{\ell_{x+1}}{\ell_x},\ q_x = \frac{d_x}{\ell_x},\ {_{n|}q_x} = \frac{d_{x+n}}{\ell_x}$$

$$_np_x + {_nq_x} = 1 \quad \text{((}x\text{) either lives the next } n \text{ years or passes away in this period)}$$

$$_{n|m}q_x = \frac{\ell_{x+n} - \ell_{x+n+m}}{\ell_x} = \frac{\ell_{x+n}}{\ell_x} \cdot \frac{\ell_{x+n} - \ell_{x+n+m}}{\ell_{x+n}} = {_np_x} \cdot {_mq_{x+n}}$$

(multiplicative law of probability for the intersection of events)

$$\begin{aligned} _np_x &= \frac{\ell_{x+n}}{\ell_x} = \frac{\ell_{x+1}}{\ell_x} \cdot \frac{\ell_{x+2}}{\ell_{x+1}} \cdots \frac{\ell_{x+n}}{\ell_{x+n-1}} \\ &= p_x p_{x+1} \cdots p_{x+n-1} \\ &= (1-q_x)(1-q_{x+1}) \cdots (1-q_{x+n-1}) \end{aligned} \quad \left.\right\} \text{fundamental importance of 1-year periods}$$

$$_np_0 = \frac{\ell_n}{\ell_0} \Rightarrow \ell_n = \ell_0 \cdot {_np_0} = \ell_0 \cdot p_0 \cdot p_1 \cdot p_2 \cdot \cdots \cdot p_{n-1}$$

$$\Rightarrow \ell_n = \ell_0\,(1-q_0)(1-q_1)\cdots(1-q_{n-1})$$

This final relation is the basis of table construction for modeling the survival of a given population. The one-year mortality rates $q_0, q_1, q_2, \ldots$ are estimated from a statistical study on the group. These estimates together with a chosen ℓ_0 value can then be used to successively generate $\ell_1, \ell_2, \ldots$. The number ℓ_0 is typically chosen to be large so that a smooth pattern of survival can be exhibited with a whole number of lives at each integral age. The numbers $\ell_0, \ell_1, \ldots$ themselves are irrelevant since probabilities are calculated as ratios of ℓ_x values. Multiplying every entry in the table by the same constant does not change the probability model.

The Theory of Survival Models

The basis of a survival model is a random lifetime variable and its corresponding distribution. The lifetime of a randomly selected newborn from a given population is commonly denoted by X, and is assumed to be a continuous random variable whose probability is spread over an interval $[0, \omega]$ [2]. You are familiar with having this distribution given in terms of either the probability density function, $f_X(x)$, or the distribution function, $F_X(x)$. Since $X \geq 0$ we have

$$F_X(x) = Pr(X \leq x) \;=\; Pr(\text{newborn dies before age } x) \;=\; \int_0^x f_X(s)\,ds.$$

It is a continuous, increasing function with $F(0) = 0$ and $F(\omega) = 1$. From the verbal description of "death prior to age x" you see that this is the same as ${}_xq_0$ defined in the tabular model.

For a continuous random variable $f_X(x)$ is not itself a probability. However, the picture

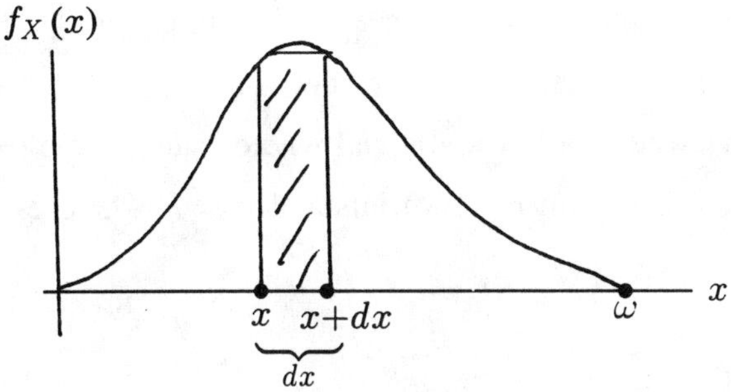

suggests the approximation

$$\begin{aligned} f_X(x)\,dx \;&=\; \text{area of rectangle} \approx \text{area under density above } [x, x+dx] \\ &\approx\; Pr(\text{newborn dies in the } \underbrace{\text{interval } [x, x+dx]}_{\text{"next instant after age } x\text{"}}). \end{aligned}$$

One has the standard relation $f_X(x) = F'_X(x)$. Keep in mind the following picture.

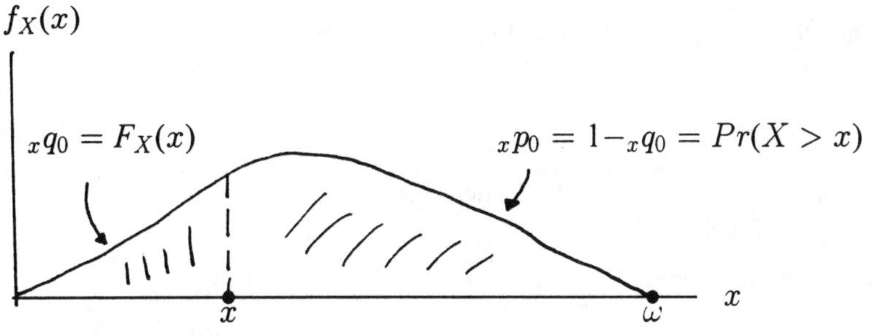

In actuarial mathematics there are three additional, equivalent, ways of specifying this distribution.

---

2 Occasionally $\omega = \infty$ is allowed.

The survival function $s_X(x)$[3] is defined as the probability that a newborn survives to age x. Since this is the event that $X > x$ we have

$$s_X(x) \;=\; Pr(X > x) \;=\; 1 - Pr(X \leq x) \;=\; 1 - F_X(x).$$

It is a continuous, decreasing function with $s_X(0) = 1$ and $s_X(\omega) = 0$. Suppose for example that $s_X(75) = .12$ so that $F_X(75) = .88$. Then 88% of newborns are expected to die prior to age 75, whereas 12% of newborns are expected to survive to age 75. The relations above indicate that if one of $f_X(x)$, $s_X(x)$ or $F_X(x)$ is given the other two may be easily calculated. Notice that $s_X(x)$ is the same as ${}_xp_0$ encountered in the tabular model.

There are two other functions, $\mu(x)$ (the force of mortality at age x) and ℓ_x (the life table), which are equivalent ways of specifying the probability distribution of X. They are not as clearly related to the distribution but are interchangeable with $f_X(x)$, $s_X(x)$, and $F_X(x)$. First we will introduce the life table in a theoretical way. For a group of ℓ_0 newborns let $\mathcal{L}_x$ be the random number of survivors at age x. Each newborn is viewed as a Bernoulli trial where "success" is survival to age x. Hence $\mathcal{L}(x)$ has a binomial distribution based on $n = \ell_0$ trials and $p = Pr(\text{"success"}) = s_X(x)$. Now define ℓ_x as the expected number of survivors:

$$\ell_x \;=\; E\left[\mathcal{L}_x\right] \;=\; \underbrace{n \cdot p}_{\text{binomial}} \;=\; \ell_0\, s_X(x).$$

This clearly shows that ℓ_x can be created from the probability distribution of X. Turning the tables you see that $s_X(x) = \frac{\ell_x}{\ell_0}$ allows calculation of the probability distribution from the ℓ_x function. In later chapters, as an aid in understanding insurance processes, we will occasionally adopt a deterministic view of ℓ_x. In this mode we assume people cooperate fully, dying exactly as scheduled in the ℓ_x function, so that there are exactly ℓ_x survivors at each age x.

Finally, we define $\mu(x)$, the force of mortality[4] at age x, by

$$\mu(x) \;=\; \underbrace{\frac{f(x)}{s_X(x)} \;=\; -\,\frac{s'(x)}{s_X(x)} \;=\; -\left[(ln(s_X(x))\right]'}_{\text{mathematically equivalent}}\;.$$

Integrating this differential equation leads to the relation

$$s_X(x) = e^{-\int_0^x \mu(s)\,ds}$$

---

[3] Other notations include $S(x)$ or $s(x)$, $S_X(x)$.

[4] Also called the hazard function in more general survival models (see Unit II to follow) or the intensity rate in stochastic processes.

showing that the probability distribution of X can be calculated from the force of mortality. The function $\mu(x)$ is positive, continuous and $\int_0^{\omega} \mu(x)\,dx = \infty$ so that $s_X(\omega) = 0$. Conversely, $\mu(x)$ is defined in terms of this probability distribution. Thus the 5 functions $f_X(x)$, $s_X(x)$, $F_X(x)$, ℓ_x, $\mu(x)$ are completely interchangeable.

Example 1 If $\mu(x) = \frac{2}{100-x}$ for $0 \le x < 100$, find the other 4 functions.

Solution
$$-\int_0^x \mu(s)\,ds = \int_0^x -\frac{2}{100-s}\,ds = 2\,ln(100-s)\Big|_0^x = ln\left[\left(\frac{100-x}{100}\right)^2\right].$$

Hence $s_X(x) = \left(\frac{100-x}{100}\right)^2$. Also $\ell_x = \ell_0\left(\frac{100-x}{100}\right)^2$,

$$F_X(x) = 1 - \left(\frac{100-x}{100}\right)^2 = \frac{200x - x^2}{10{,}000}, \text{ and } f_X(x) = -2\left(\frac{100-x}{100}\right)\left(-\frac{1}{100}\right) = \frac{200-2x}{10{,}000}. \quad \square$$

Before leaving the general theory it is helpful to understand the meaning of $\mu(x)$ and its usefulness in density functions. Let us compare it to q_x, the probability that x dies in the next year. Since ℓ_x is proportional to $s_X(x)$ and since $\mu(x) = -\frac{s_X'(x)}{s_X(x)}$, we also have $\mu(x) = -\frac{\ell_x'}{\ell_x}$. Hence

$$q_x = \frac{d_x}{\ell_x} = \frac{\ell_x - \ell_{x+1}}{\ell_x} = -\underbrace{\frac{(\ell_{x+1}-\ell_x)/(x+1-x)}{\ell_x}}_{\substack{\text{average rate of change}\\ \text{of } \ell_x \text{ relative to } \ell_x}} = -\frac{\text{chordal slope}}{\ell_x}$$

$$\mu(x) = -\frac{\ell_x'}{\ell_x} = \underbrace{-\lim_{t\to 0}\frac{(\ell_{x+t}-\ell_x)/(x+t-x)}{\ell_x}}_{\substack{\text{instantaneous rate of change}\\ \text{of } \ell_x \text{ relative to } \ell_x}} = -\frac{\text{tan slope}}{\ell_x}$$

Using the differential approximation $\ell_x' \approx \frac{\Delta \ell_x}{\Delta x}$ leads to

$$\mu(x)\cdot\Delta x \approx \frac{-\Delta\ell_x}{\ell_x} = \frac{\ell_x - \ell_{x+\Delta x}}{\ell_x} = {}_{\Delta x}q_x,$$

the probability that x dies in the "next instant" Δx.

What is the meaning of $q_x = .008$ versus the meaning of $\mu(x) = .008$? If $q_x = .008$ then for every 1000 survivors to age x, 8 are expected to die in the next year. With $\mu(x) = .008$ we still have an annual rate, but we should only use it for short-term projections. For example, viewing a week as $\Delta x = \left(\frac{1}{52}\right)^{nd}$ of a year, there would be $8 \cdot \frac{1}{52}$ expected deaths in the next week for every 1000 lives reaching age x.

Going back to $\mu(x) = \frac{f_X(x)}{s_X(x)}$ we can obtain $f_X(x) = s_X(x)\mu(x)$, which is turn is ${}_xp_0\,\mu(x)$ since $s_X(x)$ is the probability that a newborn survives to age x. Recall that $f_X(x)\cdot(dx)$ is approximately the probability that a newborn dies between ages x and $x+dx$. This would require the newborn to survive to age x (probability ${}_xp_0$) and then (x) to die in the next instant (probability $\mu(x)\,dx$). Hence we have

$$f_X(x)\,dx \;=\; {}_xp_0(\mu(x)\,dx) \;\approx\; Pr(\text{newborn dies in } [x, x+dx]).$$

The Future Lifetime of (x)

Consider a newborn having lifetime model X and suppose we know that he has survived to age x. Typically x will be the age at issue of some insurance contract. Then T, his future lifetime, satisfies $X = x + T$.

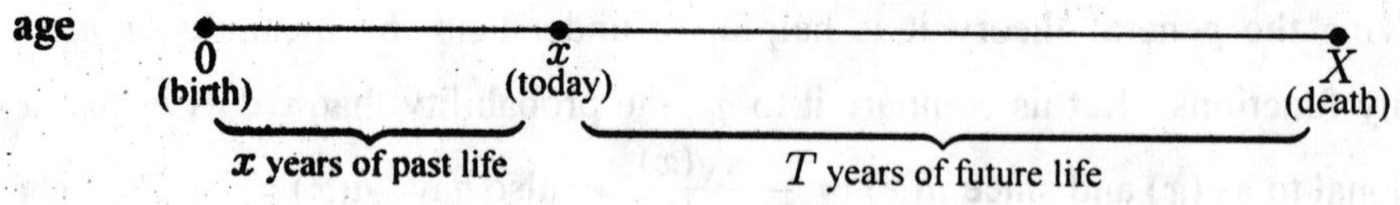

We are given that $X > x$, so

$$T = X - x|_{X>x} \qquad (\text{“}|_{X>x}\text{” is read “given } X > x.\text{”})$$

Since T is a function of X, its density (denoted $f_T(t)$) and distribution function (denoted $F_T(t)$) should be related to those of X:

$$\begin{aligned}
F_T(t) &= Pr(T \le t) = Pr(X - x \le t \mid X > x)\\
&= Pr(X \le x+t \mid X > x)\\
&= \frac{Pr(x < X \le x+t)}{Pr(X > x)} \qquad \text{(definition of conditional probability)}\\
&= \frac{F_X(x+t) - F_X(x)}{s_X(x)}
\end{aligned}$$

$$f_T(t) = \frac{d}{dt}[F_T(t)] = \frac{d}{dt}\left[\frac{F_X(x+t) - F_X(x)}{s_X(x)}\right] = \frac{f_X(x+t)}{s_X(x)}$$

Using $f_X(x) = {}_xp_0 \cdot \mu(x)$ and $s_X(x) = {}_xp_0$ the above formula for $f_T(t)$ reduces to the analogous form ${}_tp_x\mu(x+t)$ which has an intuitive explanation:

$$
\begin{aligned}
f_T(t)\,dt \;\approx\; Pr(t \le T \le t{+}dt) &= Pr((x) \text{ dies in age interval } [x{+}t, x{+}t{+}dt]) \\
&= Pr\left(\Big\{\underbrace{(x) \text{ survives to age } x{+}t}_{E}\Big\} \cap \Big\{\underbrace{(x) \text{ dies prior to age } x{+}t{+}dt}_{F}\Big\}\right) \\
&= Pr(E)\cdot Pr(F\,|\,E) \;=\; {}_tp_x \cdot Pr((x{+}t) \text{ dies in the next instant } dt) \\
&= {}_tp_x \cdot (\mu(x{+}t)\,dt).
\end{aligned}
$$

Example 2 Suppose $\mu(x) = \frac{2}{100-x}$ for $0 \le x < 100$ as in the first example and let $x = 40$. Find $f_T(t)$ and $F_T(t)$.

Solution First $0 \le X \le 100$, so $T = X - 40$ satisfies $0 \le T \le 100 - 40 = 60$. On the domain $t \in [0, 60]$ we have, from the above and Example 1,

$$
\begin{aligned}
f_T(t) &= {}_tp_{40} \cdot \mu(40{+}t) \;=\; \frac{\ell_{40+t}}{\ell_{40}} \cdot \mu(40{+}t) \\
&= \frac{\ell_0\left(\frac{100-40-t}{100}\right)^2}{\ell_0\left(\frac{100-40}{100}\right)^2} \cdot \frac{2}{100-40-t} \\
&= \left(\frac{60-t}{60}\right)^2 \cdot \frac{2}{60-t} \;=\; \frac{2(60-t)}{60^2}, \\
F_T(t) &= Pr(T \le t) \;=\; {}_tq_{40} \;=\; 1 - {}_tp_{40} \;=\; 1 - \frac{\ell_{40+t}}{\ell_{40}} \\
&= 1 - \left(\frac{60-t}{60}\right)^2 \;=\; \frac{120t - t^2}{3600}.
\end{aligned}
$$

□

The continuous variable T is the complete future lifetime of (x) whereas $K = [T]$ (greatest integer) is a discrete random variable known as the curtate future lifetime. For example, if $x = 30$ and $X = 73.67$ then $T = 43.67$ and $K = 43$. If x is the age at issue, then $K{+}1$ is the policy year during which death occurs. In Unit I of Contingent Payment Models you will study discrete and continuous insurance models. In the discrete models both the benefit amount and the time of payment are functions of the discrete variable K. In continuous ones they are both functions of T. In practice a death benefit is typically paid within a few business days of the death. This is reasonably close to a continuous model assuming that the benefit is paid T years from the issue at age x. However, the tabular model is more suitable for a discrete model assuming that the benefit is paid at the end of the policy year during which death occurs, that is, $K{+}1$ years from the issue at age x. In the following section here and in the Contingent Payment Model material you will see the relation between these two types of models.

First let's describe the probability function of K which is denoted by $f_K(k)$.

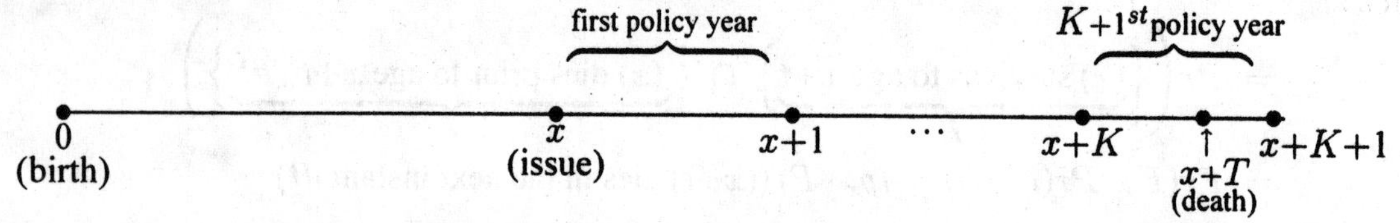

$$f_K(k) = Pr(K=k) = Pr(k \leq T < k+1)^5 = {}_{k|}q_x = \frac{d_{x+k}}{\ell_x}$$

(definition in discrete case) (see the diagram above)

Example 3 Given the following portion of a life table, find the distribution of K for $x = 90$.

x	90	91	92	93
ℓ_x	100	87	52	0
d_x	13	35	52	—

Solution $\quad f_K(k) = \dfrac{d_{90+k}}{\ell_{90}} \quad$ for $\quad k = 0,1,2$

k	0	1	2
$f_K(k)$	$\frac{13}{100}$	$\frac{35}{100}$	$\frac{52}{100}$

← the d_x row divided by ℓ_{90}

Rewriting $f_K(k) = \dfrac{d_{x+k}}{\ell_x}$ as $\dfrac{\ell_{x+k}}{\ell_x} \cdot \dfrac{d_{x+k}}{\ell_{x+k}} = {}_kp_x \cdot q_{x+k}$, we can see the similarity with $f_T(t) = {}_tp_x \cdot \mu(x+t)$. Recall that $\mu(x+t)$ and q_{x+t} are instantaneous and average annual rates of mortality at age $x+t$, respectively. □

The UDD Assumption as a Bridge from Tabular (Discrete) Models to Continuous Ones

The ideas here will be introduced in the context of Example 3, a 3-year, discrete survival model for 90-year-olds. In terms of this example the table gives us 4 points on the graph of ℓ_x versus x for $x \geq 90$. The UDD assumption (uniform distribution of deaths over each year of age) linearly interpolates among these 4 points to obtain the complete graph of ℓ_x for all x between 90 and 93:

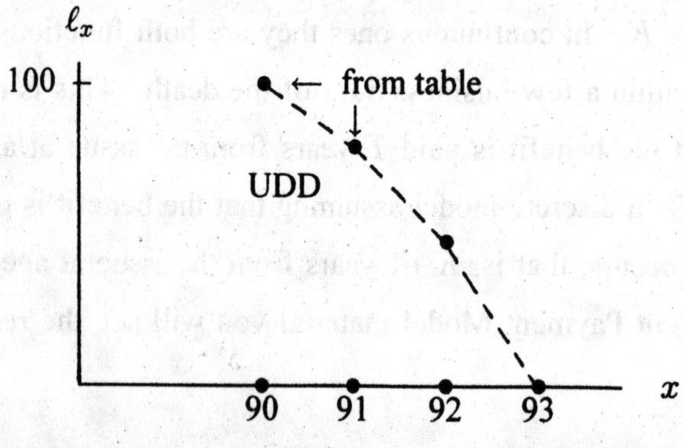

5 Technically ${}_{k|}q_x = Pr(k < T \leq k+1)$. This is the same as $Pr(k \leq T < k+1)$ since T is a continuous random variable. This fact is used occasionally without additional explanation.

UDD: $\ell_{x+t} = (1-t)\ell_x + (t)\ell_{x+1}$ $\left(\begin{array}{c}\text{linear interpolation, where} \\ x \text{ is an integer, and } 0 \le t \le 1\end{array}\right)$

$$= \ell_x - t(\ell_x - \ell_{x+1})$$

$$= \ell_x - t \cdot d_x$$

$$\ell_{x+t} = \begin{cases} 100 - 13t & x = 90, \quad 0 \le t \le 1 \\ 87 - 35t & x = 91, \quad 0 \le t \le 1 \\ 52 - 52t & x = 92, \quad 0 \le t \le 1 \end{cases}$$

The UDD gets its name from the relation $\ell_{x+t} = \ell_x - t \cdot d_x$ which implies that if a year of age is divided into m equal parts, then $\frac{1}{m^{th}}$ of the annual deaths occur during each subperiod. (Two other methods of interpolating among the tabular data are developed in the Condensed Review Notes to follow: the constant force assumption and the Balducci assumption.)

Now let T be the complete future lifetime of a 90-year-old from Example 3, where we have extended the life table to a continuous model via the UDD assumption. For $0 \le t \le 3$ we have

$$f_T(t) = {}_tp_{90} \cdot \mu(90+t) = \frac{\ell_{90+t}}{\ell_{90}} \cdot -\frac{\ell'_{90+t}}{\ell_{90+t}} = -\frac{\ell'_{90+t}}{\ell_{90}}$$

$$= \begin{cases} \frac{13}{100} & 0 < t < 1 \\ \frac{35}{100} & 1 < t < 2 \\ \frac{52}{100} & 2 < t < 3 \end{cases}.$$

The derivative does not exist at $t = 0, 1, 2, 3$ due to the "corners" on the ℓ_x graph at ages 90, 91, 92, 93.

(Discrete)
Density of K

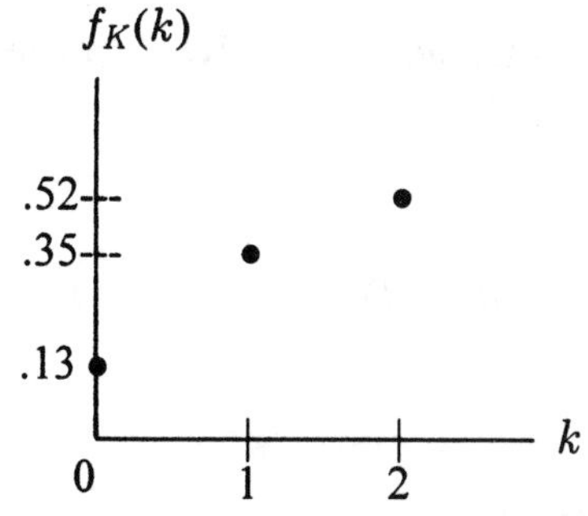

(Continuous)
Density of T Assuming UDD

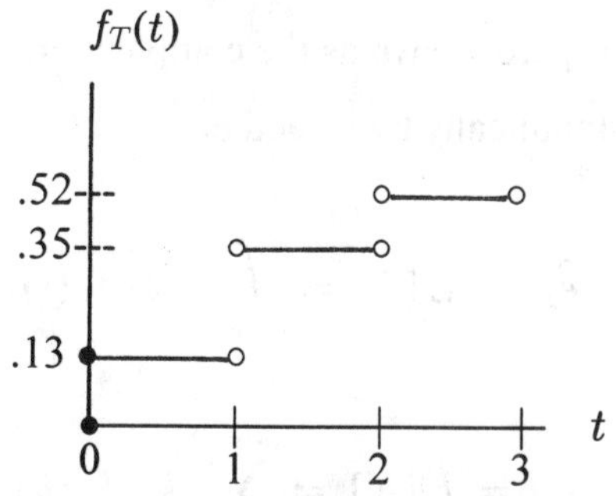

Distribution Function of T Assuming UDD

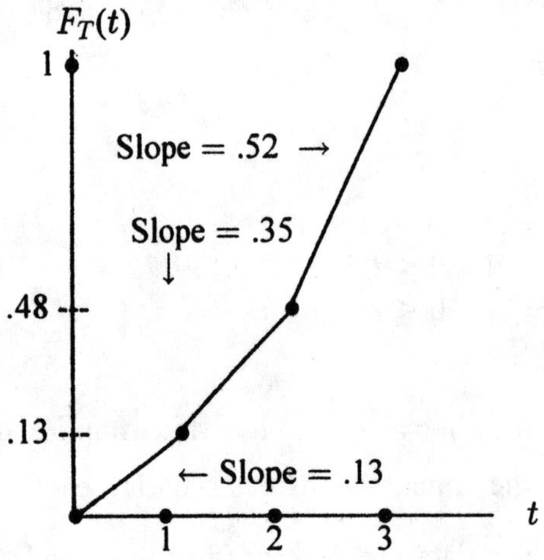

The following is a brief explanation of the theoretical side of the simple idea above. If T and K are the complete and curtate future lifetimes of x, then $S = T - K$ is the fractional part of the final policy-year of life. For example if issue is at $x = 30$ and $X = 73.17$ then $T = 43.17$, $K = 43$ and $S = .17$. Under the UDD assumption it can be proven that S and K are independent variables and S is uniformly distributed on the interval $[0, 1)$. This result is exploited in Unit I of Contingent Payment Models to give a simple relation between insurance premiums calculated for related discrete and continuous models. For example

$$\underbrace{E[v^T]}_{\substack{\text{Actuarial present}\\ \text{value of \$1 at death;}\\ \text{continuous model}}} = E\left[v^{K+S}\right] = \overbrace{\underbrace{E[v^{K+1}]}_{\substack{\text{Actuarial present}\\ \text{value of \$1 at end of}\\ \text{policy year of death;}\\ \text{discrete model}}} \cdot \underbrace{E\left[v^{S-1}\right]}_{\substack{\text{Equal to } i/\delta \text{ as a}\\ \text{result of } S \text{ being}\\ \text{uniform on [0,1)}}}}^{\text{due to independence}}.$$

Life Expectancy

$E[T]$ and $E[K]$ are known as the complete and curtate life expectancies, respectively, at age x. They are denoted symbolically by $\mathring{e}_x$ and e_x:

$$\mathring{e}_x = E[T] = \int_0^{\omega-x} t \cdot f_T(t)\,dt = \int_0^{\omega-x} t \cdot {}_tp_x\mu(x+t)\,dt$$

$$e_x = E[K] = \sum_{k=0}^{\omega-x-1} k \cdot f_K(k) = \sum_{k=0}^{\omega-x-1} k \cdot {}_kp_x q_{x+k}\,.$$

These formulas can be simplified a bit using integration by parts and summation by parts. From $\mu(x+t) = \frac{-\ell'_{x+t}}{\ell_{x+t}}$ it follows that

$$\ell'_{x+t} \;=\; -\,\ell_{x+t}\mu(x+t).$$

Dividing by ℓ_x leads to

$$\frac{d}{dt}\left(\frac{\ell_{x+t}}{\ell_x}\right) \;=\; -\,\frac{\ell_{x+t}}{\ell_x}\cdot\mu(x+t),$$

or equivalently $\frac{d}{dt}({}_tp_x) = -\,{}_tp_x\mu(x+t)$. If we let $u = t$ and $dv = {}_tp_x\mu(x+t)\,dt$, then using integration by parts we are lead to

$$\overset{\circ}{e}_x = \int_0^{\omega-x} t\cdot{}_tp_x\mu(x+t)\,dt \underset{\text{"parts"}}{\overset{\uparrow}{=}} \int_0^{\omega-x} {}_tp_x\,dt = \int_0^{\omega-x}\frac{\ell_{x+t}}{\ell_x}\,dt = \frac{\int_0^{\omega-x}\ell_{x+t}\,dt}{\ell_x},$$

which has a nice interpretation with the deterministic view of the life table. The integral in the numerator has a Riemann sum explanation as the total future lifetime of the ℓ_x lives at age x since there are ℓ_{x+t} lives at age $x+t$ and, in the next instant dt, they live approximately $\ell_{x+t}\cdot dt$ years as a group. The total future lifetime of the group divided by the number in the group should represent an "average" future lifetime.

An analogous summation by parts results in

$$e_x = \sum_{k=0}^{\omega-x-1} k\cdot{}_kp_xq_{x+k} = \sum_{k=0}^{\omega-x-1}{}_{k+1}p_x = \frac{\ell_{x+1}}{\ell_x}+\cdots+\frac{\ell_{\omega-1}}{\ell_x} = \frac{\ell_{x+1}+\ell_{x+2}+\cdots+\ell_{\omega-1}}{\ell_x}.$$

When the UDD assumption is satisfied by ℓ_{x+t}, recall that $T = K + S$ were S is uniformly distributed over the interval [0,1). So in this case

$$\overset{\circ}{e}_x \;=\; E[T] \;=\; E[K+S] \;=\; E[K]+E[S] \underset{\text{UDD}}{\overset{\uparrow}{=}} e_x+\tfrac{1}{2}.$$

Example 4 Find the complete and curtate life expectancies at age 90 for the survival model in Example 3 assuming UDD.

Solution By the above

$$e_{90} \;=\; \frac{\ell_{91}+\ell_{92}}{\ell_{90}} \;=\; \frac{87+52}{100} \;=\; 1.39 \text{ (years)}$$

$$\overset{\circ}{e}_{90} \;=\; e_{90}+\tfrac{1}{2} \;=\; 1.89 \text{ (years)}$$

□

There is an analogous development of $\overset{\circ}{e}_{x:\overline{n}|}$, the expected number of years[6] lived by (x) before age $x+n$, and of $e_{x:\overline{n}|}$, the expected number of complete[7] years lived by (x) in the next n years:

$$\widetilde{T} = \begin{cases} T \text{ if } T \leq n \\ n \text{ if } T \geq n \end{cases} = \text{number of years lived by } (x) \text{ in the next } n \text{ years; a function of } T \text{ (the value of } T \text{ has been censored at the right.)}$$

$$\widetilde{K} = \begin{cases} K \text{ if } K \leq n-1 \\ n \text{ if } K \geq n \end{cases} = \text{number of completed years lived by } (x) \text{ in the next } n \text{ years; a function of } K$$

$$\overset{\circ}{e}_{x:\overline{n}|} = E[\widetilde{T}\,] = \int \widetilde{t} \cdot f_T(t)\,dt = \int_0^n {}_tp_x\,dt$$

$$e_{x:\overline{n}|} = E[\widetilde{K}\,] = \sum \widetilde{k} \cdot f_K(k) \underset{\text{"parts"}}{\overset{\uparrow}{=}} \sum_{k=0}^{n-1} {}_{k+1}p_x = \frac{\ell_{x+1} + \cdots + \ell_{x+n}}{\ell_x}$$

Example 5 Compute $\overset{\circ}{e}_{50:\overline{25}|}$ for the survival model in Example 1.

Solution From the above we need to evaluate $\int_0^{25} {}_tp_{50}\,dt$. In the referenced example we saw

$$\ell_x = \ell_0\left(\frac{100-x}{100}\right)^2,$$

so ${}_tp_{50}$ reduces to

$$\frac{\ell_{50+t}}{\ell_{50}} = \frac{\ell_0(100-50-t)^2/100^2}{\ell_0(100-50)^2/100^2} = \left(\frac{50-t}{50}\right)^2.$$

Hence

$$\overset{\circ}{e}_{50:\overline{25}|} = \int_0^{25} \frac{(50-t)^2}{2500}\,dt = -\frac{1}{2500}\,\frac{(50-t)^3}{3}\Bigg|_0^{25} = 14.58\overline{3}\,.$$

That is, on average, a 50-year-old lives $14.58\overline{3}$ years between ages 50 and 75. □

Select Mortality and the Underwriting Process

An applicant for life insurance typically provides the insurer with extensive information regarding personal health, occupation, family history, income, and so on. (A lot more is known than just the survival of a newborn to age x today.) The underwriter examines this information to see that the risk in insuring the applicant is appropriate for the life table used in pricing. In the absence of such an evaluation, many people would postpone buying life insurance until they contracted a fatal illness or reached old age. The mortality experience with such a group would be quite severe in comparison with the pricing mortality model.

6 fractional parts of years count
7 fractional parts do not count

Suppose ℓ_x ($x = 0, 1, 2, \dots$) is a life table developed from estimates of $q_0, q_1, q_2, \cdots$, obtained from a statistical study of a group of insured (i.e., underwritten) lives. Consider for example the value of q_{25}, the probability that an insured 25-year-old will die in the next year. The q_{25}-values for individuals underwritten at ages 0, 1, 2, ..., 24, 25 are respectively denoted by $q_{[0]+25}$, $q_{[1]+24}$, ..., $q_{[25]}$. The value q_{25} is an "average" of the mortality rates at age 25 for these 26 subgroups. Some of them will be above q_{25} and others below. Intuitively one would expect

$$q_{[0]+25} > q_{[1]+24} > \cdots > q_{[24]+1} > q_{[25]},$$

since the further age 25 is from the age of underwriting, the more the chance that the individual will develop a fatal illness, or perhaps a risky lifestyle by attainment of age 25.

A select mortality table is based on the above idea. A typical mathematical model of this idea is given in the following discussion illustrating the construction of a select and ultimate table based on

(i) a 3-year select period, and

(ii) 85%, 90%, 95% and 100% of general mortality in policy years 1, 2, 3 and 4^+, respectively.

Suppose we have the following portion of a life table for insured lives.

x	21	22	23	24	25	26
ℓ_x	1200	1150	1090	1020	940	850
q_x	.0416	.0522	.0642	.0784	.0957	

With a 3-year select period an individual underwritten at age 21 would be subject to mortality rates

$$q_{[21]} = .85q_{21}, \quad q_{[21]+1} = .90q_{22}, \quad q_{[21]+2} = .95q_{23},$$

at ages 21, 22, and 23. She would experience general mortality from age 24 onward.

A select and ultimate table has a row for each issue age. The mortality pattern for an individual issued life insurance at age 21 is illustrated across the row labeled [21] for the first three years and then down the ultimate column (labeled ℓ_{x+3}) from age 24 onward.

$[x]$	$\ell_{[x]}$	$\ell_{[x]+1}$	$\ell_{[x]+2}$	ℓ_{x+3}	$x+3$
				1200	21
				1150	22
				1090	23
21	1181.64	1139.79	1086.27	1020	24
22				940	25
				850	26

ultimate portion with mortality undifferentiated by age at issue

The entries across the row for issue at age 21 are calculated as follows:

(i) $\frac{\ell_{24}}{\ell_{[21]+2}} = p_{[21]+2} = 1 - q_{[21]+2} = 1 - .95q_{23} = 1 - (.95)(.0642) = .938991$

$\Rightarrow \ell_{[21]+2} = \frac{\ell_{24}}{.938991} = \frac{1020}{.938991} = 1086.27$

(ii) $\frac{\ell_{[21]+2}}{\ell_{[21]+1}} = p_{[21]+1} = 1 - q_{[21]+1} = 1 - .90q_{22} = 1 - (.90)(.0522) = .953043$

$\Rightarrow \ell_{[21]+1} = \frac{\ell_{[21]+2}}{.953043} = \frac{1086.27}{.953043} = 1139.79$

(iii) $\frac{\ell_{[21]+1}}{\ell_{[21]}} = p_{[21]} = 1 - q_{[21]} = 1 - .85q_{21} = 1 - (.85)(.0416) = .964583$

$\Rightarrow \ell_{[21]} = \frac{\ell_{[21]+1}}{.964583} = \frac{1139.79}{.964583} = 1181.64$

CONDENSED REVIEW NOTES AND ADVANCED TOPICS

X = random lifetime (age at death) of a newborn

Definitions: 5 equivalent ways of specifying the distribution

$F_X(x) = Pr(X \le x)$ – the probability a newborn dies before age x

$s_X(x) = Pr(X > x)$ – the probability a newborn survives to age x

$f_X(x) = F'_X(x)$ – the p.d.f.; assumed $\neq 0$ if $x \in [0, \omega]$

$\mu(x) = \frac{-s'_X(x)}{s_X(x)} = -[ln\,(s_X(x))]' = \frac{f_X(x)}{s_X(x)}$ – the force of mortality at age x

$\ell_x = E[\mathcal{L}(x)] = s_X(x) \cdot \ell_0$ – the expected number of survivors at age x from a cohort of ℓ_0 newborns where $\mathcal{L}(x)$ is the random number of survivors

Important Relations

$$F_X(x) + s_X(x) = 1, \quad F_X(x) = \int_0^x f_X(s)\,ds \quad \left(\int_{-\infty}^0 f_X(s)\,ds = 0\right),$$

$$f_X(x) = F'_X(x) = -s'_X(x), \quad \mu(x) = \frac{-\ell'_x}{\ell_x}, \quad s_X(x) = e^{-\int_0^x \mu(s)ds},$$

$$s_X(x) = \frac{\ell_x}{\ell_0} = \text{expected fraction of newborns surviving at age } x$$

Example Given that $\mu(x) = \frac{r}{\omega - x}$ for $0 \le x < \omega$ and $r > 0$ find $s_X(x)$, $F_X(x)$, $f_X(x)$ and ℓ_x.

Solution A useful trick to speed up the calculation of $s_X(x)$ from $e^{-\int_0^x \mu(s)\,ds}$ is as follows: if $\mu(x) = c\frac{p'(x)}{p(x)}$ for some function $p(x)$ then $-\int_0^x \mu(s)\,ds = -c\,ln\,(p(s))\Big|_{s=0}^{x} = c \cdot ln\left(\frac{p(0)}{p(x)}\right)$, hence $s_X(x) = exp\left(c \cdot ln\left(\frac{p(0)}{p(x)}\right)\right) = \left[\frac{p(0)}{p(x)}\right]^c$. If $\mu(x) = \frac{r}{\omega - x}$ let $p(x) = \omega - x$. Then $p'(x) = -1$, $c = -r$ and, by the above, $s_X(x) = \left(\frac{\omega}{\omega - x}\right)^{-r} = \left(1 - \frac{x}{\omega}\right)^r$. Finally $F_X(x) = 1 - \left(1 - \frac{x}{\omega}\right)^r$, $f_X(x) = F'_x(x) = \frac{r}{\omega}\left(1 - \frac{x}{\omega}\right)^{r-1}$ and, using $\ell_0 = \omega^r$, $\ell_x = \ell_0 s_X(x) = (\omega - x)^r$. □

Standard Actuarial Probability Symbols

${}_tp_x$ – the probability of survival to age $x + t$ given survival to age x

${}_tq_x$ – the probability of death before age $x + t$ given survival to age x

${}_{s|t}q_x$ – the probability of death between ages $x + s$ and $x + s + t$ given survival at age x.

Note: When $t = 1$ the t is suppressed; also ${}_xp_0 = s_X(x)$

Relations

Life Table: $_tp_x = \frac{\ell_{x+t}}{\ell_x}$, $\quad _tq_x = \frac{\ell_x - \ell_{x+t}}{\ell_x} = \frac{_td_x}{\ell_x}$, $_{s|t}q_x = \frac{\ell_{x+s} - \ell_{x+s+t}}{\ell_x} = \frac{_td_{x+s}}{\ell_x}$

Internal: $\quad 1 = {_tp_x} + {_tq_x}$, $_{s|t}q_x = {_sp_x} \cdot {_tq_{x+s}}$,

$$_{s+t}p_x = {_sp_x} \cdot {_tp_{x+s}}, \quad {_np_x} = p_x \cdot p_{x+1} \cdots p_{x+n-1} \text{ (}n\text{ integer)}$$

$$1 = {_{0|}q_x} + {_{1|}q_x} + \cdots + {_{\omega-x-1|}q_x}, \quad {_nq_x} = {_{0|}q_x} + {_{1|}q_x} + \cdots + {_{n-1|}q_x}$$

Future Lifetime of (x) - Continuous Model

T = random future lifetime of (x) = $X - x|_{X>x}$

$$F_T(t) = Pr(T \le t) = Pr(X - x \le t | X > x) = Pr(X \le x + t) | X > x)$$

$$= \frac{Pr(x < X \le x + t)}{P(X > x)} = \frac{F_X(x+t) - F_X(x)}{S_X(x)}$$

$$s_T(t) = Pr(T > t) = Pr(X > x+t) | X > x) = \frac{Pr(X > x+t)}{Pr(X > x)} = \frac{s_X(x+t)}{s_X(x)}$$

$$f_T(t) = \left(F_T(t)\right)' = \frac{d}{dt}\left[\frac{F_X(x+t) - F_X(x)}{s_X(x)}\right] = \frac{f_X(x+t)}{s_X(x)}$$

$$F_T(t) = {_tq_x} = \frac{\ell_x - \ell_{x+t}}{\ell_x} = 1 - s_T(t)$$

$$s_T(t) = {_tp_x} = \frac{\ell_{x+t}}{\ell_x} = e^{-\int_0^t \mu(x+s)ds}$$

Example Suppose $\mu(x) = \frac{2}{80 - x}$ for $0 \le x < 80$. Calculate the survival function for the future lifetime of (20).

Solution From the preceding example where $\mu(x) = \frac{r}{\omega - x}$ we see that $s_X(x) = \left(1 - \frac{x}{80}\right)^2 = \left(\frac{80 - x}{80}\right)^2$. Since $s_T(t)$ can be calculated as $_tp_x = \frac{\ell_{x+t}}{\ell_x} = \frac{s_X(x+t)}{s_X(x)}$ we have

$$s_T(t) = \frac{s(20+t)}{s(20)} = \left(\frac{80 - (20+-t)}{80}\right)^2 \Big/ \left(\frac{80 - 20}{80}\right)^2 = \left(\frac{60 - t}{60}\right)^2 = \left(1 - \frac{t}{60}\right)^2. \quad \square$$

Note the similar form to the original survival function. We could also have noticed that $\mu(20+t) = \frac{2}{60 - t} = \frac{p'(t)}{p(t)}r$ and used the same trick as above to conclude that $S_T(t) = \left(1 - \frac{t}{60}\right)^2$.

This is possible since $_tp_{20} = S_T(t) = exp\left(-\int_0^t \mu(20+s)\,ds\right)$.

Density Functions

$$f_X(x) \;=\; s_X(x)\mu(x) \;=\; {}_xp_0 \cdot \mu(x)$$

$$f_T(t) \;=\; s_T(t)\cdot\mu(x+t) \;=\; {}_tp_x \cdot \mu(x+t)$$

$$f_X(x)\cdot\Delta x \;\approx\; Pr(X \in [x, x+\Delta x]) \;=\; Pr(\{\text{newborn survives to age } x\} \cap \{x \text{ dies in next instant}\})$$
$$=\; {}_xp_0 \cdot (\mu(x)\cdot\Delta x)$$

$$f_T(t)\cdot(\Delta t) \approx Pr(T \in [t, t+\Delta t]) = Pr(\{(x) \text{ survives to age } x+t\} \cap \{x+t \text{ dies in the next instant}\})$$
$$=\; {}_tp_x \cdot (\mu(x+t)\cdot\Delta t)$$

Comparison of $\mu(x)$ and q_x

$$q_x \;=\; \frac{\ell_x - \ell_{x+1}}{\ell_x} \;=\; \frac{-(\ell_{x+1}-\ell_x)}{((x+1)-x)}/\ell_x \;=\; \text{average rate of change of } -\ell_x \text{ relative to } \ell_x$$
$$=\; -\text{chordal slope}/\ell_x$$

$$\mu(x) = \frac{-\ell'_x}{\ell_x} \;=\; \lim_{\Delta x\to 0} -\frac{(\ell_{x+\Delta x}-\ell_x)}{\Delta x}/\ell_x \;=\; \text{instantaneous rate of change of } -\ell_x \text{ relative to } \ell_x$$
$$=\; -\text{tangent slope}/\ell_x$$

q_x = probability that (x) dies within one year

$\mu(x)\Delta x \approx$ probability that (x) dies in the " next instant"

Curtate Future Lifetime of (x) - Discrete Model

$K = [T]$ = number of *completed* years of future life after age x

$$f_K(k) \;=\; Pr(K=k) \;=\; Pr(k \le T < k+1) \;=\; Pr(k < T \le k+1)$$
$$=\; {}_{k|}q_x \;=\; {}_kp_x \cdot q_{x+k} \;=\; \frac{d_{x+k}}{\ell_x} \;=\; \int_k^{k+1} f_T(t)\,dt$$

$$F_K(k) \;=\; Pr(K \le k) \;=\; Pr(T < k+1) \;=\; Pr(T \le k+1) \;=\; {}_{k+1}q_x$$

$$s_K(k) \;=\; Pr(K > k) \;=\; Pr(T \ge k+1) \;=\; Pr(T > k+1) \;=\; {}_{k+1}p_x$$

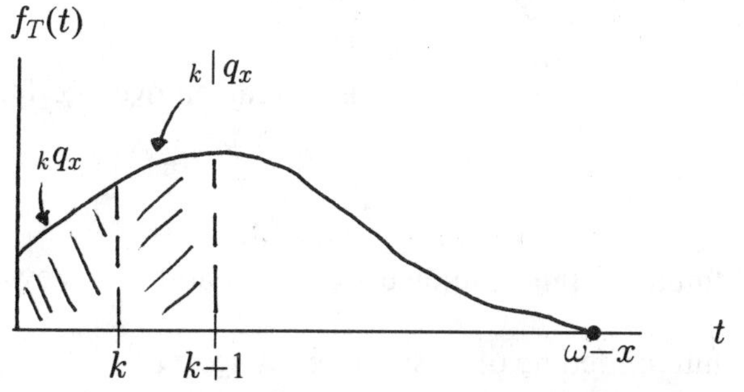

$S \;=\; T-K \;=\;$ fractional part of final policy year of life

UDD Fact: If $\ell_{x+t} = \ell_x - t\cdot d_x$ x integral, $t \in [0,1]$ then K, S are independent and $S \sim U(0,1)$.[8]

---

8 S is uniformly distributed over (0, 1).

Random Survivorship Model Versus Life Table

$\mathcal{L}(x) \;=\;$ random number of survivors at age x among ℓ_0 newborns having independent lifetimes distributed like X.

$\mathcal{L}(x) \;\sim\; B(n = \ell_0, p = s_X(x))$ – binomial distribution

$$\ell_x = E[\mathcal{L}(x)] = \textit{expected} \text{ number of survivors at age } x \text{ among } \ell_0 \text{ newborns}$$
$$= n \cdot p \text{ (binomial)} = \ell_0 \cdot s_X(x)$$

$$Var(\mathcal{L}(x)) = n \cdot p(1-p) \text{ (binomial)} = \ell_0 \cdot s_X(x)(1 - s_X(x))$$
$$= \ell_0 \cdot \frac{\ell_x}{\ell_0}\left(1 - \frac{\ell_x}{\ell_o}\right) = \frac{\ell_x(\ell_0 - \ell_x)}{\ell_0}$$

${}_n\mathcal{D}_x \;=\;$ random number of ℓ_0 newborns dying between ages x, $x+n$

$$\sim B\Big(n = \ell_0, p = Pr(X \in [x, x+n]) = s_X(x) - s_X(x+n)\Big)$$

$${}_nd_x = E[{}_n\mathcal{D}_x] = np\text{(binomial)} = \ell_0\left(\frac{\ell_x}{\ell_0} - \frac{\ell_{x+n}}{\ell_0}\right) = \ell_x - \ell_{x+n}$$

Life Table Functions and Relations

(x, m, n whole numbers)

$${}_nd_x = \ell_x - \ell_{x+n}, \quad {}_1d_x = d_x = \ell_x - \ell_{x+1}, \quad \ell_x = d_x + \ell_{x+1},$$

$$\ell_x = d_x + d_{x+1} + \cdots + d_{\omega-1}, \quad {}_np_x = \frac{\ell_{x+n}}{\ell_x}, \quad {}_1p_x = p_x = \frac{\ell_{x+1}}{\ell_x},$$

$${}_nq_x = \frac{{}_nd_x}{\ell_x} = \frac{d_x + d_{x+1} + \cdots + d_{x+n-1}}{\ell_x}, \quad {}_1q_x = q_x = \frac{d_x}{\ell_x}, \quad {}_np_x + {}_nq_x = 1,$$

$${}_{n|m}q_x = {}_np_x \cdot {}_mq_{x+n} = \frac{\ell_{x+n} - \ell_{x+n+m}}{\ell_x}, \quad {}_{n|}q_x = {}_{n|}{}_1q_x = \frac{d_{x+n}}{\ell_x},$$

$$1 = {}_{0|}q_x + {}_{1|}q_x + \cdots + {}_{\omega-x-1|}q_x, \; {}_np_x = p_x \cdot p_{x+1} \cdots p_{x+n-1} = (1-q_x)(1-q_{x+1})\cdots(1-q_{x+n-1})$$

$$\ell_x = \ell_0 \cdot p_0 \cdot p_1 \cdots p_{x-1} = \ell_0(1-q_0)(1-q_1)\cdots(1-q_{x-1}), \quad \ell_x = \frac{\ell_{x+1}}{p_x} = \frac{\ell_{x+1}}{1-q_x},$$

$L_x = \int_x^{x+1} \ell_y dy = \int_0^1 \ell_{x+t}\, dt =$ number of years lived by the cohort of ℓ_0 newborns between ages x, $x+1$

$\underset{\text{UDD}}{=} \ell_{x+1} + \frac{1}{2} \cdot d_x$ (1 full year for each survivor at age $x+1$ plus $\frac{1}{2}$ year on average for each death in $[x, x+1]$)

$T_x = \int_x^{\omega} \ell_y dy = \int_0^{\omega - x} \ell_{x+t}\, dt =$ total future lifetime after age x of the cohort of ℓ_0 newborns

$=$ total future lifetime of ℓ_x survivors at age x.

$$= L_x + L_{x+1} + \cdots$$

$$\underset{\text{UDD}}{=} (\ell_{x+1} + \tfrac{1}{2}d_x) + (\ell_{x+2} + \tfrac{1}{2}d_{x+1}) + \cdots + \; = \; \tfrac{1}{2}\ell_x + \ell_{x+1} + \ell_{x+2} + \cdots + \ell_{w-1}$$

$$Y_x = \int_x^{\omega} T_y \, dy = \int_0^{\omega - x} T_{x+t} \, dt \quad \Big(\text{used in calculating } Var(T)\Big)$$

$$\ell'_x = -\,\ell_x \cdot \mu(x), \quad L'_x = \ell_{x+1} - \ell_x = -\,d_x, \quad T'_x = -\,\ell_x, \quad Y'_x = -\,T_x$$

The Central Rate of Death

$$m_x \equiv \text{central rate of death at age } x \equiv \frac{\int_0^1 {}_tp_x \mu(x+t)\, dt}{\int_0^1 {}_tp_x \, dt} = \frac{\int_0^1 \ell_{x+t}\, \mu(x+t)\, dt}{\int_0^1 \ell_{x+t}\, dt} = \frac{d_x}{L_x}$$

Comparison with q_x:

(i) $q_x = \frac{d_x}{\ell_x} < \frac{d_x}{L_x} = m_x$, since $L_x < \ell_x$

(ii) q_x = ratio of deaths to number living at age x

m_x = ratio of deaths to total number of person-years lived between ages x, $x+1$ by the ℓ_x survivors at age x.

(iii) In the q_x calculation each of the ℓ_x lives contributes one unit to the denominator regardless of how much of the year she lived. In the m_x calculation, each of the ℓ_{x+1} survivors contributes 1 unit to the denominator, but the d_x deaths contribute only the fraction of the year for which they survived. Thus L_x is the person-years of "exposure" to death for the group.

Life Expectancy

I. *Complete life expectancy at age* x = $E[T] = \mathring{e}_x$ (standard actuarial symbol)

$$= \underbrace{\int_0^{\omega-x} t \cdot f_T(t)\, dt}_{\text{(most basic)}} = \underbrace{\int_0^{\omega-x} {}_tp_x \, dt}_{\text{(often easier)}} \text{ (integration by parts)}$$

$$= \frac{\int_0^{\omega-x} \ell_{x+t}\, dt}{\ell_x} = \frac{T_x}{\ell_x} = \frac{\textit{total future lifetime of } \ell_x \textit{ survivors}}{\textit{number of survivors at age x}}$$

$$E[T^2] = \underbrace{\int_0^{\omega-x} t^2 \cdot f_T(t)\, dt}_{\text{(most basic)}} = \underbrace{\int_0^{\omega-x} 2t \cdot {}_tp_x \, dt}_{\text{(often easier)}} \text{ (integration by parts)}$$

$$= 2 \cdot \frac{Y_x}{\ell_x} \text{ (second integration by parts)}$$

$$Var(T) = E[T^2] - \Big(E[T]\Big)^2 = 2 \cdot \frac{Y_x}{\ell_x} - \left(\frac{T_x}{\ell_x}\right)^2$$

Example

1. <u>de Moivre's Law</u>. In this case $\ell_x = \omega - x$ and $f_X(x) = \frac{1}{\omega}$ for $0 \le x \le \omega$. Thus X has a uniform distribution on $[0, \omega]$. Similarly T is uniform on $[0, \omega - x]$. Thus $\overset{\circ}{e}_x = E[T] = \frac{\omega - x}{2}, Var(T) = \frac{(\omega - x)^2}{12}$

2. <u>Constant Force</u>. If $\mu(x) = \mu \;\; 0 \le x < \infty$ then $f_X(x) = \mu e^{-\mu x}$ is the exponential distribution. Similarly $f_T(t) = \mu e^{-\mu t}$ is the same exponential distribution. Thus $\overset{\circ}{e}_x = E[T] = \frac{1}{\mu}, \;\; Var(T) = \frac{1}{\mu^2}$.

3. <u>Generalization of de Moivre</u>. If $\mu(x) = \frac{r}{\omega - x}$ for $0 \le x < \omega$ and $r > 0$ then $E[T] = \frac{\omega - x}{r+1}, Var(T) = \frac{(\omega - x)^2 r}{(r+1)^2\,(r+2)}$. Notice that $r = 1$ gives de Moivre's law.

□

II. ***Curtate life expectancy at age x*** $= E[K] = e_x$ **(standard actuarial symbol)**

$$= \sum_{k=0}^{\omega-x-1} k \cdot f_K(k) = \sum_{k=0}^{\omega-x-1} {}_{k+1}p_x \text{ (summation by parts)}$$

$$= \frac{\ell_{x+1} + \ell_{x+2} + \cdots \ell_{\omega-1}}{\ell_x}$$

$$E[K^2] = \sum_{k=0}^{\omega-x-1} k^2 \cdot f_K(k) = \sum_{k=0}^{\omega-x-1} (2k+1) \cdot {}_{k+1}p_x \text{ (summation by parts)}$$

$$= \frac{1 \cdot \ell_{x+1} + 3 \cdot \ell_{x+2} + 5 \cdot \ell_{x+3} + \cdots}{\ell_x}$$

UDD Relation:

$$\overset{\circ}{e}_x = E[T] = E[K+S] = E[K] + E[S] = e_x + \tfrac{1}{2}$$

$$Var(T) = Var(K+S) = Var(K) + Var(S) = Var(K) + \tfrac{1}{12}$$

$$\left(S, K \text{ independent: } S \sim U(0,1),\; E[S] = \tfrac{1}{2}, Var(S) = \tfrac{1}{12}\right)$$

Expected Age at Death given survival to age x $= x + E[T] \underset{\text{UDD}}{=} x + \frac{\ell_{x+1} + \cdots + \ell_{\omega-1}}{\ell_x} + \frac{1}{2}$

Temporary Life Expectancy

$\overset{\circ}{e}_{x:\overline{n}|}$ = **expected number of years lived by (x) in the next n years**

$$= E[\tilde{T}] \text{ where } \tilde{T} = g(T) = \begin{cases} T & \text{if } T \le n \\ n & \text{if } T > n \end{cases}$$

$$= \int_0^n t \cdot f_T(t)\,dt + \int_n^{\omega-x} n \cdot f_T(t)\,dt = \int_0^n t \cdot f_T(t)\,dt + n \cdot {}_np_x$$

$$= \int_0^n {}_tp_x\,dt \text{ (integration by parts)} = \frac{T_x - T_{x+n}}{\ell_x}$$

$e_{x:\overline{n}|}$ = expected number of *whole* years lived by (x) in the next n years

$$= E[\widetilde{K}] \text{ where } \widetilde{K} = g(K) = \begin{cases} K & \text{if } K = 0, 1, \ldots, n-1 \\ n & \text{if } K = n, n+1 \end{cases}$$

$$= \frac{\ell_{x+1} + \cdots + \ell_{x+n}}{\ell_x} \text{ (summation by parts)}$$

UDD Relation: $\mathring{e}_{x:\overline{n}|} = e_{x:\overline{n}|} + \frac{1}{2} \cdot {}_nq_x$ (those who die in the next n years live on average $\frac{1}{2}$ year longer than their curtate lifetime)

The Function a(x)

$a(x)$ = average fractional part of year $[x, x+1]$ lived by an (x) who dies in the next year

$$= E[T|T \leq 1] \quad \text{where } f_T(t|T \leq 1) = \frac{f_T(t)}{q_x} \text{ for } t \in [0,1]$$

$$= \int_0^1 t \cdot f_T(t|T \leq 1)\,dt = \int_0^1 t \cdot \frac{{}_tp_x \cdot \mu_{x+t}}{q_x}\,dt$$

$$= \frac{1}{\ell_x \cdot q_x}\left[-t\ell_{x+t}\Big|_0^1 + \int_0^1 \ell_{x+t}\,dt\right]$$

$$= \frac{1}{d_x}[-\ell_{x+1} + L_x] = \frac{L_x - \ell_{x+1}}{d_x}$$

Interpretation: L_x is the total years lived during $[x, x+1]$. The survivors at age $x+1$ live ℓ_{x+1} years during this period, so the d_x who die live $L_x - \ell_{x+1}$ years in this period. Consider $\mathring{e}_{x:\overline{1}|}$, the average time lived in the next year by x. This is the overall average for the ℓ_x group. Now divide ℓ_x in two subgroups:

(1) a life in the d_x group lives on average $a(x)$ years in the next year; and

(2) a life in the ℓ_{x+1} group lives exactly 1 year in the next year.

Thus $\mathring{e}_{x:\overline{1}|}$ should be a weighted average of the subgroup averages, $a(x)$ and 1, where the weights, q_x and p_x, correspond to the fractions of the ℓ_x group belonging to the subgroups, that is,

$$\mathring{e}_{x:\overline{1}|} = q_x \cdot a(x) + p_x \cdot 1.$$

So instead of calculating $a(x)$ as above it might be more efficient to use this new relation and a simpler calculation $\mathring{e}_{x:\overline{1}|} = \int_0^1 {}_tp_x\,dt$.

Example

Calculate $\mathring{e}_{x:\overline{1}|}$ and $a(x)$ when $\ell_{x+t} = \ell_x - td_x$ (UDD) and when $\mu(x+t) = \mu$ (constant force).

Solution

UDD. $\overset{\circ}{e}_{x:\overline{1}|} = \int_0^1 {}_tp_x\, dt = \int_0^1 1 - tq_x\, dt = 1 - \frac{1}{2}q_x$, so

$$a(x) = \frac{[\overset{\circ}{e}_{x:\overline{1}|} - p_x]}{q_x} = \frac{[1 - \frac{1}{2}q_x - p_x]}{q_x} = \frac{\left(\frac{1}{2}q_x\right)}{q_x} = \frac{1}{2}.$$

Constant Force. ${}_tp_x = e^{-\mu t}$ so $\overset{\circ}{e}_{x:\overline{1}|} = \int_0^1 e^{-\mu t}\, dt = \frac{(1-e^{-\mu})}{\mu}$ and

$$a(x) = \frac{[\overset{\circ}{e}_{x:\overline{1}|} - p_x]}{q_x} = \frac{[(1-e^{-\mu})/\mu - e^{-\mu}]}{(1-e^{-\mu})} = \frac{1-(1+\mu)e^{-\mu}}{\mu(1-e^{-\mu})} = \begin{cases} .49167 & \mu = .100 \\ .49917 & \mu = .010 \\ .49995 & \mu = .001 \end{cases}$$ □

Fractional Age Assumptions

(i.e., methods of interpolation from $\ell_0, \ell_1, \ell_2, \ldots$ to ℓ_x at all ages)

x integral, $t \in [0, 1]$

	UDD (linear)	Constant Force (exponential)	Balducci (hyperbolic)
ℓ_{x+t}	$(1-t)\ell_x + t\ell_{x+1}$	$\ell_x^{(1-t)} \cdot \ell_{x+1}^t$	$\frac{1}{\ell_{x+t}} = \frac{1-t}{\ell_x} + \frac{t}{\ell_{x+1}}$
	$= \ell_x - t \cdot d_x$	$= \ell_x e^{-\mu t}$,	
	$= \ell_x(1-tq_x)$	$= \ell_x(p_x)^t$ where	$\Rightarrow \ell_{x+t} = \ell_x\left[\frac{p_x}{p_x+tq_x}\right]$
		$\mu = -\ln p_x$	
${}_tp_x$	$1 - tq_x$	p_x^t	$\frac{p_x}{p_x + tq_x}$
${}_yq_{x+t}$ $(y+t \le 1)$	$\frac{y \cdot q_x}{1 - t \cdot q_x}$	$1 - e^{-\mu y}$	$\frac{y \cdot q_x}{1-(1-y-t)\cdot q_x}$
$\mu(x+t)$	$\frac{q_x}{1 - t \cdot q_x}$ (increasing)	μ (constant)	$\frac{q_x}{1-(1-t)\cdot q_x}$ (decreasing)
$f_T(t)$ $t \in [0,1]$	q_x	$\mu e^{-\mu t}$	$\frac{p_x \cdot q_x}{\left(1-(1-t)\cdot q_x\right)^2}$

In general, *under the UDD assumption*

$$f_T(t) = {}_tp_x \cdot \mu(x+t) = {}_{k+s}p_x\mu(x+k+s) = {}_kp_x \cdot {}_sp_{x+k} \cdot \mu(x+k+s)$$
$$= {}_kp_x \cdot q_{x+k} = {}_{k|}q_x \text{ for all } t \in [k, k+1)$$

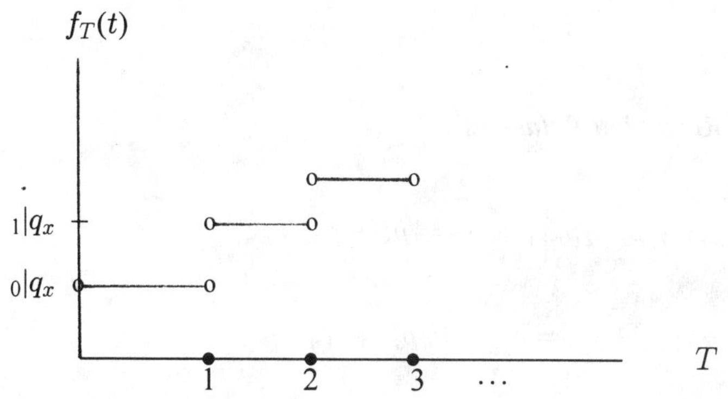

Example Given a q_x value derive expressions for $\overset{\circ}{e}_{x:\overline{1}|}$ under the three interpolation assumptions.

Solution

UDD: ${}_tp_x = 1 - tq_x$, $\overset{\circ}{e}{}^{UDD}_{x:\overline{1}|} = \int_0^1 1 - tq_x \, dt = 1 - \frac{1}{2}q_x$

C.F.: ${}_tp_x = p_x^t$, $\overset{\circ}{e}{}^{CF}_{x:\overline{1}|} = \int_0^1 p_x^t \, dt = -\dfrac{(1-p_x)}{lnp_x} = \dfrac{-q_x}{ln(1-q_x)}$

Bald: ${}_tp_x = \dfrac{p_x}{p_x + tq_x}$, $\overset{\circ}{e}{}^{Bald}_{x:\overline{1}|} = \int_0^1 \dfrac{p_x}{p_x + tq_x} dt = \dfrac{-(1-q_x)}{q_x} \cdot ln(1-q_x)$ □

Comparison

		$\overset{\circ}{e}_{x:\overline{1}|}$ with $q_x = .01$	$\overset{\circ}{e}_{x:\overline{1}|}$ with $q_x = .05$
method	UDD	.99500	.97500
	CF	.99499	.97479
	Bald	.99498	.97457

Analytic Mortality Laws

Gompertz :	$\mu(x) = Bc^x$	$\ell_x = \ell_0 \cdot g^{c^x - 1}$	where $B = -ln(c)\,ln(g)$
Makeham :	$\mu(x) = A + Bc^x$	$\ell_x = \ell_0 \cdot s^x \cdot g^{c^x - 1}$	where $A = -ln(s)$
			$B = -ln(c)\,ln(g)$
Weibull :	$\mu(x) = kx^n$	$\ell_x = \ell_0\, e^{-ux^{n+1}}$	where $u = \dfrac{k}{n+1}$

Derivatives

$$\frac{d}{dt}\left({}_tp_x\right) = -\,{}_tp_x \cdot \mu(x+t) \qquad \frac{d}{dx}\left({}_tp_x\right) = {}_tp_x \cdot (\mu(x) - \mu(x+t))$$

Recursion Relations

$$e_x = p_x + {}_2p_x + {}_3p_x + \cdots = p_x + p_x \cdot p_{x+1} + p_x \cdot {}_2p_{x+1} + \cdots = p_x + p_x \cdot e_{x+1}$$

$$e_x = p_x + \cdots + {}_np_x + {}_np_x \cdot p_{x+n} + {}_np_x \cdot {}_2p_{x+n} + \cdots = e_{x:\overline{n|}} + {}_np_x \cdot e_{x+n}$$

$$\mathring{e}_x = \int_0^{\omega-x} {}_tp_x\,dt = \int_0^n {}_tp_x\,dt + \int_n^{\omega-x} {}_np_x \cdot {}_{t-n}p_{x+n}dt = \mathring{e}_{x:\overline{n|}} + {}_np_x \cdot \mathring{e}_{x+n}$$

CONCEPTUAL REVIEW TEST

1. If X is the random lifetime of a newborn express $s_X(65)$ in words where $s_X(x)$ is the survival function.

2. If $f_X(x)$ is the probability density function of X interpret $\int_{25}^{35} f_X(x)\,dx$ in terms of the age at death of a newborn.

3. If $(x) = (15)$, what is the relation between X and the future lifetime $T = T(15)$ of (15)?

4. If T is the future lifetime of (15) and $f_T(t)$ is its p.d.f., one way to express the probability that (15) dies between ages 25 and 35 is as $\int_{10}^{20} f_T(t)\,dt$. Write it also in terms of a deferred death probability (i.e., ${}_{t|u}q_x$) and as a ratio of integrals involving the newborn's density function $f_X(x)$, relying on the definition of conditional probability (i.e., $Pr(25 \leq X < 35 \,|\, X > 15)$).

5. If (25) dies at age 58.6, then what are T, the complete future lifetime of (25), and K, the curtate future lifetime of (25)?

6. Interpret $\ell_{25} \cdot \mu(25) \cdot \Delta x$ in terms of an expected number of deaths among ℓ_0 newborn lives.

7. If $(x) = (25)$, the probability $f_K(10) = Pr(K = 10)$ is the probability that (25) will die between ages 35 and 36. Express it in terms of a deferred death probability, in terms of $f_T(t)$, the p.d.f. of $T(25)$, and in terms of life table symbols.

8. If $\omega = 100$, explain why $\int_0^{75} {}_tp_{25} \cdot \mu(25+t)\,dt = 1$.

9. Interpret the life table ratios $\frac{d_{35}}{\ell_{35}}$, $\frac{\ell_{35} - \ell_{40}}{\ell_{25}}$, and $\frac{\ell_{60}}{\ell_0}$ as probabilities.

10. Explain the relation between $\mathcal{L}(60)$, the random number of ℓ_0 newborns surviving at age 60, and ℓ_{60}.

11. (a) Assuming $\omega = 100$, interpret $\int_0^{40} \ell_{60+t}\,dt$ in terms of the deterministic view of a life table using a Riemann sum approach based on the idea that the ℓ_{60+t} survivors at age $60 + t$ live approximately $\ell_{60+t} \cdot \Delta t$ total years between ages $60 + t$ and $60 + t + \Delta t$.

    (b) If $\ell_{60} = 2000$ and $\int_0^{40} \ell_{60+t}\,dt = 35{,}000$, then what is $\mathring{e}_{60}$, the complete life expectancy of a 60-year-old?

    (c) If the uniform distribution of deaths assumption is made, then what is e_{60}, the curtate life expectancy of a 60-year-old?

12. $K \leq 21$ is equivalent to what in terms of T? Express $Pr(K \leq 21)$ in terms of life table values.

CONCEPTUAL REVIEW TEST SOLUTIONS

1. $s_X(65)$ is the probability that a newborn survives to age 65 or, alternately, the probability that a newborn's death occurs after age 65.

2. $\int_{25}^{35} f_X(x)dx$ is the probability that a newborn dies between ages 25 and 35.

3. $T = X - 15|_{X>15}$

4. $$Pr(15 \text{ dies between 25 and 35}) = {}_{10|10}q_{15} = Pr(25 \leq X < 35 \,|\, X > 15)$$
$$= \frac{Pr(\{25 \leq X \leq 35\} \cap \{X > 15\})}{Pr(X > 15)} = \frac{Pr(25 \leq X \leq 35)}{Pr(X > 15)} = \frac{\int_{25}^{35} f_X(x)dx}{\int_{15}^{\omega} f_X(x)dx}$$

5. $T = 58.6 - 25 = 33.6$ years, $K = [T] = [33.6] = 33$ where [ ] denotes the "greatest integer function."

6. $\mu(25) \cdot \Delta x$ is approximately the probability that a 25-year-old will die in the "next instant," i.e., between ages 25 and 25+ Δx. So since ℓ_{25} is the expected number of newborns surviving at age 25, $\ell_{25}(\mu(25)\Delta x)$ is approximately the expected number of newborns dying between ages 25 and 25+Δx.

7. $f_K(10) = Pr(K = 10) = {}_{10|}q_{25} = Pr(10 \leq T < 11) = \int_{10}^{11} f_T(t)dt = \frac{d_{35}}{\ell_{25}}$, the relative frequency with which 25-year-olds die between ages 35 and 36.

8. ${}_tp_{25}\mu(25+t)\Delta t$ is approximately the probability that (25) dies between ages $25 + t$ and $25 + t + \Delta t$, thus $\int_0^{75} {}_tp_{25}\mu(25+t)dt$ is the probability that (25) dies between ages $25 + 0$ and $25 + 75 = 100$. Since this is certain, the integral is one. More formally, $f_T(t) = {}_tp_{25}\mu(25+t)$ for $0 \leq t \leq 75$, hence $1 = \int_0^{75} f_T(t)dt$.

9. $$\frac{d_{35}}{\ell_{35}} = Pr\Big((35) \text{ dies between ages 35 and 36}\Big)$$
$$\frac{\ell_{35} - \ell_{40}}{\ell_{25}} = Pr\Big((25) \text{ dies between ages 35 and 40}\Big)$$
$$\frac{\ell_{60}}{\ell_0} = Pr(\text{a newborn survives to age 60})$$

10. Considering each newborn as a Bernoulli trial with "success" interpreted as survival to age 60, $\mathcal{L}(60)$ is a binomial random variable having $n = \ell_0$ trials and $p = Pr(\text{success}) = {}_{60}p_0$. ℓ_{60} is the expected number of survivors at age 60 and is given for a binomial variable by $n \cdot p = \ell_0 \cdot {}_{60}p_0$.

11. (a) $\int_0^{40} \ell_{60+t}dt$ is the total number of years lived after age 60 by the ℓ_{60} survivors at age 60.

(b) $\overset{\circ}{e}_{60} = \frac{\text{total future lifetime of } \ell_{60} \text{ lives}}{\ell_{60}} = \frac{35{,}000}{2000} = 17.5$ years.

(c) $\overset{\circ}{e}_{60} = e_{60} + \frac{1}{2}$ under the UDD assumption, so $e_{60} = 17$.

12. $K \leq 21$ means $K = 0, 1, 2, \ldots, 21$, or $0 \leq T < 22$. $Pr(K \leq 21) = \frac{{}_{22}d_x}{\ell_x}$.

COMPUTATIONAL REVIEW TEST

1. If $s_X(x) = \left(1 - \frac{x}{100}\right)^2$ for $0 \le x < 100$, find $F_X(75)$, $f_X(75)$ and $\mu(75)$.

2. If $\ell_{25} = 1000$, $\ell_{28} = 955$, $q_{25} = .010$ and $p_{27} = \frac{955}{975}$, what is q_{26}?

3. If the p.d.f. of the lifetime X of a newborn is given by $f_X(x) = \frac{2x}{6400}$ for $0 \le x \le 80$, find ${}_{20}q_{40}$ using the conditional probability $Pr(40 \le X \le 60 \,|\, X > 40)$.

4. If $f_X(x)$ is the same as in Question 3 and $(x) = (40)$, give an expression for the p.d.f of $T = T(40)$ using the relation between distribution functions $Pr(T \le t) = Pr(X - 40 \le t \,|\, X > 40)$.

5. (a) If $\ell_{65} = 100$ and $\ell_{66} = 80$, calculate $\ell_{65.5}$ under the UDD, constant force and Balducci assumptions.

   (b) Express ${}_{.5}q_{65.5}$ as a fraction for the 3 cases above.

6. If $\mu(x) = \frac{1}{50 - (x/2)}$ for $0 \le x \le 100$, find an expression for ℓ_x in terms of x using the relation between the survival function and the force of morality and assuming $\ell_0 = 10{,}000$.

7. Compute the complete future life expectancy of a newborn (i.e., $\mathring{e}_0$) for the life table given in Question 6.

8. If $f_X(x)$ is as in Questions 6 and 7, and K is the curtate future lifetime of (40), then what is $f_K(40)$?

COMPUTATIONAL REVIEW TEST SOLUTIONS

1. $F_X(75) = 1 - s_X(75) = 1 - \left(\frac{1}{4}\right)^2 = \frac{15}{16}$; $f_X(75) = -s'_X(75) = \frac{2}{100}\left(1 - \frac{75}{100}\right) = \frac{1}{200}$;
$\mu(75) = \frac{f_X(75)}{s_X(75)} = \frac{\left(\frac{1}{200}\right)}{\left(\frac{1}{16}\right)} = \frac{8}{100}$.

2. $.010 = q_{25} = \frac{d_{25}}{\ell_{25}} = \frac{d_{25}}{1000} \quad \Rightarrow \quad d_{25} = 10 \quad \Rightarrow \quad \ell_{26} = \ell_{25} - d_{25} = 990$
$\frac{955}{975} = p_{27} = \frac{\ell_{28}}{\ell_{27}} = \frac{955}{\ell_{27}} \quad \Rightarrow \quad \ell_{27} = 975$. Thus $q_{26} = \frac{d_{26}}{\ell_{26}} = \frac{990 - 975}{990} = \frac{15}{990}$.

3. $_{20}q_{40} = Pr(40 \le X \le 60 \mid X > 40) = \frac{\int_{40}^{60} f_X(x)dx}{\int_{40}^{80} f_X(x)dx} = \frac{\frac{36}{64} - \frac{16}{64}}{\frac{64}{64} - \frac{16}{64}} = \frac{20}{48}$.

4. $F_T(t) =$ distribution function of $T = Pr(X - 40 \le t \mid X > 40)$

$$= \frac{Pr(40 \le X \le 40{+}t)}{Pr(40 \le X)} = \frac{\int_{40}^{40+t} \frac{2x}{6400}\,dx}{\int_{40}^{80} \frac{2x}{6400}\,dx} = \frac{\left(\frac{40+t}{80}\right)^2 - \left(\frac{40}{80}\right)^2}{1 - \left(\frac{40}{80}\right)^2};$$

$f_T(t) = F'_T(t) = \frac{4}{3} \cdot 2 \cdot \frac{40+t}{80} \cdot \frac{1}{80}$ for $0 \le t \le 80 - 40$.

5. (a) UDD: $\ell_{65.5} = \frac{1}{2} \cdot \ell_{65} + \frac{1}{2} \cdot \ell_{66} = 90$

Balducci: $\frac{1}{\ell_{65.5}} = \frac{1}{2} \cdot \frac{1}{\ell_{65}} + \frac{1}{2} \cdot \frac{1}{\ell_{66}} = \frac{1}{2}\left(\frac{1}{100} + \frac{1}{80}\right)$, hence $\ell_{65.5} = \frac{8000}{90} = 88.\overline{8}$

Constant force: $p_x = e^{-\int_0^1 \mu_x(s)ds}$ implies $\mu = -ln\, p_{65} = -ln\left(\frac{80}{100}\right)$,

hence $\ell_{65.5} = \ell_{65} \cdot e^{-.5\mu} = 100 \cdot \left(\frac{80}{100}\right)^{.5} = 89.4427$

(b) $_{.5}q_{65.5} = \frac{\ell_{65.5} - \ell_{66}}{\ell_{65.5}} = \frac{10}{90}$, $\frac{8.\overline{8}}{88.\overline{8}}$, or $\frac{9.4427}{89.4427}$
(UDD) (Balducci) (Constant force)

6. $\int_0^x \mu(s)\,ds = \int_0^x \frac{2}{100 - s} \cdot ds = -2\,ln(100 - s)\Big|_0^x = -ln\left[\left(\frac{100-x}{100}\right)^2\right]$, thus
$s_X(x) = e^{-\int_0^x \mu(s)ds} = \left(\frac{100-x}{100}\right)^2$. Finally $\ell_x = \ell_0 \cdot s_X(x) = 10{,}000 \cdot \left(\frac{100-x}{100}\right)^2 = (100-x)^2$.

7. This can be done via $E[X] = \int_0^{100} x \cdot f(x)dx$ once $f(x)$ is obtained as
$-s'(x) = \frac{2}{100}\left(1 - \frac{x}{100}\right)$, or alternately,

$$\mathring{e}_0 = \frac{T_0}{\ell_0} = \frac{\int_0^{100}(100-x)^2\,dx}{10{,}000} = \frac{-(100-x)^3}{30{,}000}\Bigg|_0^{100} = 33.\overline{3}.$$

8. $f_K(40) = Pr(K = 40) = Pr\Big((40)$ dies between 80 and 81$\Big)$

$$= \frac{d_{80}}{\ell_{40}} = \frac{\ell_{80} - \ell_{81}}{\ell_{40}} = \frac{20^2 - 19^2}{60^2} = \frac{39}{3600}$$

UNIT REVIEW QUESTIONS

The following questions are taken from SOA exams given prior to the year 2000 syllabus. Questions under the new syllabus may be quite different. Nevertheless, these old questions remain an excellent source for mastering the basic theory.

1. You are given the survival function $s_X(x) = \dfrac{\sqrt{100-x}}{10}$ for $0 \le x \le 100$. Calculate $F_X(75)$, $f_X(75)$, and $\mu(75)$.

	$F_X(75)$	$f_X(75)$	$\mu(75)$
(A)	0.2	0.02	0.04
(B)	0.5	0.01	0.02
(C)	0.5	0.01	0.04
(D)	0.2	0.02	0.02
(E)	0.5	0.02	0.04

2. You are given: $_{1|}q_{x+1} = 0.095$ $\quad$ $_{2|}q_{x+1} = 0.171$ $\quad$ $q_{x+3} = 0.200$

Calculate $q_{x+1} + q_{x+2}$.

(A) 0.15 (B) 0.20 (C) 0.25 (D) 0.27 (E) 0.30

3. You are given the following information:

(i) K = probability that (x) dies in the first $\frac{1}{3}$ of the year, under the Balducci assumption.

(ii) L = probability that (x) dies in the last $\frac{2}{3}$ of the year, under the uniform distribution of deaths assumption.

(iii) $\ell_x = 9$

(iv) $\ell_{x+1} = 6$

Calculate $K + L$.

(A) $\frac{19}{63}$ (B) $\frac{1}{3}$ (C) $\frac{23}{63}$ (D) $\frac{11}{28}$ (E) $\frac{23}{56}$

4. If K is the curtate future lifetime of (96), calculate $Var(K)$, given the following life table:

x	ℓ_x
96	180
97	130
98	73
99	31
100	0

(A) .39 (B) .53 (C) .91 (D) 1.11 (E) 1.50

5. Mortality follows de Moivre's Law and $\overset{\circ}{e}_{16} = 42$. Calculate $Var\Big(T(16)\Big)$.
(Answer to nearest integer)

(A) 595 (B) 588 (C) 505 (D) 472 (E) 300

6. You are given the survival function $s_X(x) = \frac{9000 - 10x - x^2}{9000}$ for $0 \leq x \leq 90$.
Calculate the exact value of $q_{50} - \mu(50)$.

(A) $\frac{-1}{600}$ (B) $\frac{-1}{6000}$ (C) 0 (D) $\frac{1}{6000}$ (E) $\frac{1}{600}$

7. If $\ell_x = 10(100 - x)^2$, calculate $Var(T(x))$.

(A) $(100 - x)^2/18$ (B) $(100 - x)/3$ (C) $(100 - x)^3/6$ (D) $(100 - x)^2/6$ (E) $(100 - x)^2/3$

8. You are given: $\mu(x) = \frac{x}{100}$. Calculate ${}_{20|10}q_5$.

(A) $\frac{e^5 - 1}{e^6}$ (B) $\frac{e^4 - 1}{e^6}$ (C) $\frac{e^3 - 1}{e^6}$ (D) $\frac{e^2 - 1}{e^6}$ (E) $\frac{e - 1}{e^6}$

9. You are given the following extract from a 2-year select-and-ultimate mortality table:

$[x]$	$\ell_{[x]}$	$\ell_{[x]+1}$	ℓ_{x+2}	$x+2$
92	...	...	6300	94
93	...	...	5040	95
94	...	...	3024	96

The following relationships hold for all x:

(i) $2 \cdot q_{[x]+1} = 3 \cdot q_{[x+1]}$ (ii) $3 \cdot q_{x+2} = 4 \cdot q_{[x+1]+1}$

Calculate $\ell_{[94]}$.

(A) 4800 (B) 4851 (C) 4985 (D) 5103 (E) 5166

10. Calculate ${}_{20}p_{40}$, given that $\mu(x) = kx$ for all $x > 0$, and ${}_{10}p_{35} = .81$.

(A) .36 (B) .41 (C) .45 (D) .59 (E) .66

11. You are given ${}_{t|}q_x = 0.10$, for $t = 0,1,\ldots 9$. Calculate ${}_2p_{x+5}$.

(A) 0.40 (B) 0.60 (C) 0.72 (D) 0.80 (E) 0.81

12. You are given:

(i) Deaths are uniformly distributed over each year of age.

(ii)

x	ℓ_x
35	100
36	99
37	96
38	92
39	87

Which of the following are true?

I. $_{1|2}q_{36} = .091$

II. $m_{37} = .043$

III. $_{.33}q_{38.5} = .021$

(A) I and II only (B) I and III only (C) II and III only (D) I, II and III
(E) The correct answer is not given by (A), (B), (C) or (D)

13. You are given:

(i) Deaths are uniformly distributed over each year of age.
(ii) $\mu(45.5) = .50$

Calculate $\overset{\circ}{e}_{45:\overline{1|}}$.

(A) .40 (B) .50 (C) .60 (D) .70 (E) .80

14. You are given:

(i) $q_{70} = .040$
(ii) $q_{71} = .044$
(iii) Deaths are uniformly distributed over each year of age.

Calculate $\overset{\circ}{e}_{70:\overline{1.5|}}$.

(A) 1.435 (B) 1.445 (C) 1.455 (D) 1.465 (E) 1.475

15. You are given that $q_x = .25$.

Based on the constant force of mortality assumption, the force of mortality is $\mu_x^A(s)$, $0 < s < 1$. Based on the uniform distribution of deaths assumption, the force of mortality is $\mu_x^B(s)$, $0 < s < 1$. Calculate the smallest s such that $\mu_x^B(s) \geq \mu_x^A(s)$.

(A) .4523 (B) .4758 (C) .5001 (D) .5242 (E) .5477

16. For a 2-year select and ultimate mortality table, you are given:

(i) $q_{96} = .350$, $q_{97} = .475$, $q_{98} = .675$
(ii) $q_{[x]} = .5q_x$ for all x
(iii) $q_{[x]+1} = .5q_{x+1}$ for all x
(iv) $\ell_{[96]} = 10{,}000$

Calculate $\ell_{[97]}$.

(A) 4047 (B) 4076 (C) 4094 (D) 4136 (E) 4158

17. For a two-year select-and-ultimate mortality table, you are given:

(i) $q_{[x]} = (1-2k)q_x$
(ii) $q_{[x]+1} = (1-k)q_{x+1}$
(iii) $\ell_{[32]} = 90$
(iv) $\ell_{32} = 100$
(v) $\ell_{33} = 90$
(vi) $\ell_{34} = 63$

Calculate $\ell_{[32]+1}$.

(A) 82 (B) 83 (C) 84 (D) 85 (E) 86

18. You are given:

(i) $\mathring{e}_{x:\overline{1}|} = F$ under the uniform distribution of deaths assumption
(ii) $\mathring{e}_{x:\overline{1}|} = G$ under the Balducci assumption
(iii) $q_x = .1$

Calculate $1000(F - G)$.

(A) .00 (B) .24 (C) 1.00 (D) 1.76 (E) 2.52

19. A survival function, $s_X(x)$, is defined as follows:

$$s_X(x) = \left(1 - \frac{x}{\omega}\right)^r \quad 0 \le x < \omega, \quad r > 0$$

For age y, $0 \le y < \omega$, you are given:

(i) $\mu_y = .1$
(ii) $\mathring{e}_y = 8.75$

Calculate r.

(A) 1 (B) 3 (C) 5 (D) 7 (E) 9

20. You are given that $q_x = .1200$.

Which of the following are true?

I. ${}_{1/3}q_{x+1/2} = .0426$ under the uniform distribution of deaths assumption.
II. ${}_{1/3}q_x = .0435$ under the Balducci assumption.
III. ${}_{1/2}q_x = .0619$ under the constant force of mortality assumption.

(A) I and II only (B) I and III only (C) II and III only (D) I, II and III
(E) The correct answer is not given by (A), (B), (C) or (D)

21. You are given:

(i) $q_x = .04$
(ii) $\mu_x(t) = .04 + .001644t,\ 0 \le t \le 1$
(iii) $\mu_y(t) = .08 + .003288t,\ 0 \le t \le 1$

Calculate q_y.

(A) .0784 (B) .0792 (C) .0800 (D) .0808 (E) .0816

22. For a two-year select-and-ultimate mortality table, you are given:

$[x]$	$\ell_{[x]}$	$\ell_{[x]+1}$	ℓ_{x+2}	$x+2$
30	1000	998	995	32
31	996	994	988	33
32	994	990	982	34
33	987	983	970	35

Which of the following are true?

I. ${}_2p_{[31]} > {}_2p_{[30]+1}$ II. ${}_{1|}q_{[31]} > {}_{1|}q_{[30]+1}$ III. ${}_2q_{[33]} > {}_2q_{[31]+2}$

(A) None (B) I only (C) II only (D) III only
(E) The correct answer is not given by (A), (B), (C), or (D)

23. Assume mortality follows de Moivre's law, for $0 \le x \le \omega$.

Which of the following expressions equal $\mu(x)$?

I. $\dfrac{1}{2\overset{\circ}{e}_x}$

II. ${}_{n|}q_x,\ 0 \le n \le \omega - x - 1$

III. $\dfrac{m_x}{1 + .5m_x},\ x \le \omega - 1$

(A) I and II only (B) I and III only (C) II and III only (D) I, II and III
(E) The correct answer is not given by (A), (B), (C) or (D)

24. Which of the following can serve as survival functions for $x \geq 0$?

I. $s_X(x) = exp[x - .7(2^x - 1)]$ II. $s_X(x) = \frac{1}{(1+x)^2}$ III. $s_X(x) = exp(-x^2)$

(A) I and II only (B) I and III only (C) II and III only (D) I, II and III
(E) The correct answer is not given by (A), (B), (C) or (D)

25. Deaths are assumed to be uniformly distributed over each year of age. The distribution function of the curtate future lifetime of (x) is

k	0	1	2	3	4	5	6
$F_k(k)$	.05	.15	.35	.60	.75	.85	1.00

Calculate $\overset{\circ}{e}_{x:\overline{5}|}$.

(A) 3.100 (B) 3.475 (C) 3.625 (D) 3.850 (E) 4.275

26. You are given:

$$s_X(x) = \left(1 - \frac{x}{\omega}\right)^\alpha,\ 0 \leq x < \omega, \text{ where } \alpha \text{ is a positive constant.}$$

Calculate $\mu_x \cdot \overset{\circ}{e}_x$.

(A) $\frac{\alpha}{\alpha+1}$ (B) $\frac{\alpha\omega}{\alpha+1}$ (C) $\frac{\alpha^2}{\alpha+1}$ (D) $\frac{\alpha^2}{\omega-x}$ (E) $\frac{\alpha(\omega-x)}{(\alpha+1)\omega}$

27. You are given:
(i) $q_{60} = .30$
(ii) $q_{61} = .40$
(iii) f is the probability that (60) will die between ages 60.5 and 61.5 under the uniform distribution of deaths assumption.
(iv) g is the probability that (60) will die between ages 60.5 and 61.5 under the Balducci assumption.

Calculate $10{,}000(g - f)$.

(A) 0 (B) 85 (C) 94 (D) 178 (E) 213

28. You are given $\mu(x) = \sqrt{\frac{1}{80 - x}},\ 0 \leq x < 80.$

Calculate the median future lifetime of (20).

(A) 5.25 (B) 6.08 (C) 8.52 (D) 26.08 (E) 30.00

29. You are given:

(i) $_tp_x = (0.8)^t, t \geq 0$
(ii) $\ell_{x+2} = 6.4$

Calculate T_{x+1}.

(A) 4.5 (B) 7.2 (C) 28.7 (D) 35.9 (E) 44.8

30. For a ten-year select-and ultimate table, you are given:

(i) $\ell_{[30]+t} = \frac{\sqrt{60}}{9}\left(1 - \frac{t}{100}\right), 0 \leq t < 10$

(ii) $\ell_{30+t} = \frac{\sqrt{70-t}}{10,}, 10 \leq t \leq 70$

Calculate $\overset{\circ}{e}_{[30]}$.

(A) 21.0 (B) 39.0 (C) 42.0 (D) 45.5 (E) 48.5

31. You are given:

(i) $\mu_{35+t} = \mu, 0 \leq t \leq 1$
(ii) $p_{35} = .985$
(iii) μ'_{35+t} is the force of mortality for (35) subject to an additional hazard, $0 \leq t \leq 1$.
(iv) $\mu'_{35+t} = \mu + c, 0 \leq t \leq .5$
(v) The additional force of mortality decreases uniformly from c to 0 between age 35.5 and age 36.

Determine the probability that (35) subject to the additional hazard will not survive to age 36.

(A) $0.015e^{-.25c}$ (B) $0.015e^{.25c}$ (C) $1 - 0.985e^{-c}$ (D) $1 - 0.985e^{-.5c}$ (E) $1 - 0.985e^{-.75c}$

32. You are given:

(i) $s_X(x) = \frac{\sqrt{k^2 - x}}{k}, \ 0 \leq x \leq k^2, \ k > 0$
(ii) $\overset{\circ}{e}_{40} = 2\overset{\circ}{e}_{80}$

Calculate $\overset{\circ}{e}_{60}$.

(A) 10 (B) 20 (C) 30 (D) 40 (E) 50

Use the following information for Questions 33-36.

For a select-and-ultimate mortality table with a one-year select period, you are given:

x	$\ell_{[x]}$	$d_{[x]} = q_{[x]}\ell_{[x]}$	$\mathring{e}_{[x]}$
85	1000	100	5.225
86	850	100	

Assume deaths are uniformly distributed over each year of age.

33. Which of the following is correct?

	$p_{[85]}$	$p_{[86]}$	p_{86}
(A)	10/100	100/100	100/850
(B)	90/100	75/90	75/85
(C)	90/100	75/85	75/90
(D)	90/100	75/85	100/100
(E)	90/100	75/100	75/90

34. Calculate $\int_2^\infty {}_tp_{[85]}\,dt$.

(A) 1.775 (B) 3.245 (C) 3.450 (D) 3.754 (E) 3.950

35. Calculate $\mathring{e}_{[87]}$.

(A) 3.45 (B) 3.75 (C) 4.15 (D) 4.40 (E) 4.60

36. Calculate $\mathring{e}_{[86]}$.

(A) 3.45 (B) 3.75 (C) 4.15 (D) 4.40 (E) 5.00

Use the following information for Questions 37-40.

You are given:

$$s_X(x) = \frac{(10-x)^2}{100}, \quad 0 \le x \le 10$$

37. Calculate the average number of years of future lifetime of the ℓ_1 survivors of the group at age 1.

(A) 2.37 (B) 2.43 (C) 2.70 (D) 2.92 (E) 3.00

38. Calculate the difference between the force of mortality at age 1, and the probability that (1) dies before age 2.

(A) .007 (B) .010 (C) .012 (D) .016 (E) .024

39. Calculate the average number of years lived between ages 1 and 2 by those of the survivorship group who die between those ages.

(A) .461 (B) .473 (C) .484 (D) .490 (E) .500

40. Instead of using $s_X(x)$ within each year of age, use the constant force of mortality assumption to calculate the average number of years lived between ages 1 and 2 by those of the survivorship group who die between those ages.

(A) .461 (B) .480 (C) .490 (D) .500 (E) .508

Use the following information for Questions 41-44.

You are given:

(i) T is the random variable for the future lifetime of (x).
(ii) The p.d.f. of T is $f_T(t) = 2e^{-2t}$, $t \geq 0$.

41. Calculate $\overset{\circ}{e}_x$.

(A) 0.5 (B) 2.0 (C) 10.0 (D) 20.0 (E) 30.0

42. Calculate $Var[T]$.

(A) 0.25 (B) 0.50 (C) 1.00 (D) 2.00 (E) 4.00

43. Calculate $m(x)$, the median future lifetime of (x).

(A) $\frac{e^{-4}}{2}$ (B) $\frac{e^{-2}}{2}$ (C) $\frac{ln\,2}{2}$ (D) $\frac{ln\,4}{2}$ (E) 1

44. Calculate m_x, the central-death-rate at age x.

(A) $\frac{e^{-2}}{2}$ (B) e^{-2} (C) $2e^{-2}$ (D) 1 (E) 2

SOLUTIONS TO UNIT REVIEW QUESTIONS

1. $F_X(75) \;=\; 1 - s(75) \;=\; 1 - \dfrac{\sqrt{100-75}}{10} \;=\; 1 - \frac{1}{2} \;=\; .5.$

Now $f_X(x) \;=\; -\,s'_X(x) \;=\; -\frac{1}{10}\cdot\frac{1}{2}\,\dfrac{-1}{\sqrt{100-x}};\; f_X(75) = \dfrac{1}{20\sqrt{100-75}} = \frac{1}{100} = .01.$

Also $f_X(75) \;=\; s_X(75)\mu(75)$ so $\mu(75) \;=\; \dfrac{f_X(75)}{s_X(75)} = \dfrac{1/100}{1/2} \;=\; \frac{1}{50} = .02.$ ANSWER B

2. Consider the table below based on ${}_{1|}q_{x+1} = .095$ and $.171 = {}_{2\,|}\,q_{x+1}$. Then from

age	living	deaths
$x+1$	1000	
$x+2$	$\uparrow$	95
$x+3$	ℓ_{x+3}	171

$.200 = q_{x+3} = \dfrac{171}{\ell_{x+3}}$ we obtain $\ell_{x+3} = 855$.
Thus $\ell_{x+2} = 855 + 95 = 950$, and
$d_{x+1} = 1000 - 950 = 50$. Hence
$q_{x+1} + q_{x+2} = \dfrac{50}{1000} + \dfrac{95}{950} = .05 + .10 = .15$

ANSWER A

3.

$$K \;=\; {}_{1/3}q_x \text{ (Balducci)} \;=\; \frac{\ell_x - \ell^{Bal}_{x+1/3}}{\ell_x} \;=\; \frac{9-\frac{54}{7}}{9} \;=\; \frac{9}{63}$$

$$L \;=\; {}_{1/3|2/3}q_x \text{ (UDD)} \;=\; \frac{\ell^{UDD}_{x+1/3} - \ell_{x+1}}{\ell_x} \;=\; \frac{8-6}{9} \;=\; \frac{2}{9} \;=\; \frac{14}{63}$$

Sum $K + L \;=\; \dfrac{9+14}{63} \;=\; \dfrac{23}{63}$ ANSWER C

<u>Balducci</u>

$$\frac{1}{\ell_{x+1/3}} \;=\; \frac{2}{3}\cdot\frac{1}{9} + \frac{1}{3}\cdot\frac{1}{6} \;=\; \frac{2}{27} + \frac{1}{18} \;=\; \frac{4+3}{54},\quad \ell_{x+1/3} \;=\; \frac{54}{7}$$

<u>UDD</u>

$$\ell_{x+1/3} \;=\; \frac{2}{3}\cdot 9 + \frac{1}{3}\cdot 6 \;=\; 8$$

4. $E[K] = \dfrac{\ell_{97} + \ell_{98} + \ell_{99}}{\ell_{96}} = \dfrac{130 + 73 + 31}{180} = \dfrac{234}{180} = 1.3$

$E[K^2] = \dfrac{1\cdot\ell_{97} + 3\cdot\ell_{98} + 5\cdot\ell_{99}}{\ell_{96}} = \dfrac{130 + 219 + 155}{180} = 2.8$

$Var(K) = 2.8 - 1.3^2 = 1.11$ ANSWER D

5. With de Moivre's Law $T \sim U(0, \omega - x) = U(0, \omega - 16)$.

In this case $42 = \overset{\circ}{e}_x = E[T] = \frac{\omega - 16}{2}$ implies $\omega = 100$.

Also $Var(T) = \frac{(\omega - 16)^2}{12} = \frac{84^2}{12} = 588$ for a uniform distribution. ANSWER B

6. $$q_{50} = \frac{\ell_{50} - \ell_{51}}{\ell_{50}} = \frac{s_X(50) - s_X(51)}{s_X(50)} = \frac{.66\overline{6} - .654\overline{3}}{.66\overline{6}} = .0185$$

$$\mu_{50} = \frac{-s'_X(50)}{s_X(50)} = \frac{(10 + 2 \cdot 50)/9000}{.66\overline{6}} = .018\overline{3}$$

$$q_{50} - \mu_{50} = .000167 = \frac{1}{6000}$$ ANSWER D

7. $$E[T] = \int_0^{100-x} {}_tp_x \, dt = \int_0^{100-x} \left(\frac{100 - x - t}{100 - x}\right)^2 dt$$

$$= \frac{-\frac{1}{3}(100 - x - t)^3 \Big|_{t=0}^{100-x}}{(100 - x)^2} = \frac{1}{3}(100 - x)$$

$$E[T^2] = \int_0^{100-x} 2t \, {}_tp_x \, dt = \int_0^{100-x} \frac{2t(100 - x - t)^2}{(100 - x)^2} dt$$

$$= -2\int_0^{100-x} \frac{-t(100 - x - t)^2}{(100 - x)^2} dt = -2\int_0^{100-x} \frac{[(100 - x - t) - (100 - x)](100 - x - t)^2}{(100 - x)^2} dt$$

$$= \frac{-2}{(100 - x)^2}\left[\int_0^{100-x} (100 - x - t)^3 \, dt - (100 - x)\int_0^{100-x} (100 - x - t)^2 \, dt\right]$$

$$= \frac{-2}{(100 - x)^2}\left[\frac{(100 - x)^4}{4} - \frac{(100 - x)^4}{3}\right] = \frac{(100 - x)^2}{6}.$$

$$Var(T) = E[T^2] - \left(E[T]\right)^2 = (100 - x)^2\left(\frac{1}{6} - \left(\frac{1}{3}\right)^2\right) = \frac{(100 - x)^2}{18}$$ ANSWER A

This problem is a special case of the more general situation where $\mu(x) = \frac{n}{\omega - x}$, $E[T] = \frac{\omega - x}{n + 1}$, and $Var(T) = \frac{(\omega - x)^2 \cdot n}{(n + 1)^2 \cdot (n + 2)}$

8. $${}_{20|10}q_5 = Pr(5 \text{ dies between ages 25 and 35}) = \frac{s_X(25) - s_X(35)}{s_X(5)}.$$

$s_X(x) = e^{-\int_0^x \mu(s)ds} = e^{-\int_0^x s/100 \, ds} = e^{-x^2/200}$; $s_X(25) = e^{-625/200}$,
$s_X(35) = e^{-1225/200}$, $s_X(5) = e^{-25/200}$. Thus

$${}_{20|10}q_5 = \frac{e^{-625/200} - e^{-1225/200}}{e^{-25/200}} = e^{-600/200} - e^{-1200/200} = e^{-3} - e^{-6} = \frac{e^3 - 1}{e^6}$$

ANSWER C

9. We are given $q_{[x+1]} = \frac{2}{3} q_{[x]+1}$, $q_{[x+1]+1} = \frac{3}{4} q_{x+2}$. To find $\ell_{[94]}$ we must find ${}_2p_{[94]} = p_{[94]} \cdot p_{[94]+1} = (1 - q_{[94]})(1 - q_{[94]+1})$.

Now $q_{[94]+1} = \frac{3}{4} \cdot q_{95} = \frac{3}{4} \cdot \frac{5040 - 3024}{5040} = \frac{3}{4} \cdot \frac{2}{5} = \frac{3}{10}$ and

$q_{[94]} = \frac{2}{3} \cdot q_{[93]+1} = \frac{2}{3} \cdot \frac{3}{4} \cdot q_{94} = \frac{1}{2} \cdot \frac{6300 - 5040}{6300} = \frac{1}{2} \cdot \frac{1}{5} = \frac{1}{10}$.

Thus $\left(1 - \frac{3}{10}\right)\left(1 - \frac{1}{10}\right) = \frac{7}{10} \cdot \frac{9}{10} = {}_2p_{[94]} = \frac{\ell_{96}}{\ell_{[94]}} = \frac{3024}{\ell_{[94]}}$.

Hence $\ell_{[94]} = \frac{100}{63} \cdot 3024 = 4800$. ANSWER A

10. ${}_tp_x = e^{-\int_x^{x+t} \mu(s)\,ds}$. Also $\int_x^{x+t} \mu(s)\,ds = \int_x^{x+t} ks\,ds = \frac{k}{2} s^2 \Big|_x^{x+t} = \frac{k}{2}(2tx+t^2)$.

Thus $.81 = {}_{10}p_{35} = e^{-k/2\,(2 \cdot 10 \cdot 35 + 10^2)} = e^{-400k}$. Also

$${}_{20}p_{40} = e^{-(k/2)(2 \cdot 20 \cdot 40 + 20^2)} = e^{-1000k} = \left(e^{-400k}\right)^{5/2} = .81^{5/2}$$

$$= (.81)^2(.9) = \left(\frac{9}{10}\right)^5 = .59049.$$

ANSWER D

11. If ${}_{t|}q_x = .10$ for $t = 0,1,\ldots,9$, an obvious choice for ℓ_{x+t} is $10 - t$. Thus

$${}_2p_{x+5} = \frac{\ell_{x+7}}{\ell_{x+5}} = \frac{10-7}{10-5} = \frac{3}{5}$$

ANSWER B

12. I. ${}_{1|2}q_{36} = Pr[(36)$ dies between ages 37 and 39$] = \frac{\ell_{37} - \ell_{39}}{\ell_{36}} = \frac{96 - 87}{99} = \frac{1}{11} = .091$, *true*.

II. $m_{37} = \frac{d_{37}}{L_{37}} \underset{\text{UDD}}{=} \frac{d_{37}}{\ell_{37} - \frac{1}{2}d_{37}} = \frac{4}{96 - \frac{1}{2} \cdot 4} = \frac{4}{94} = .043$, *true*.

III. ${}_{.33}q_{38.5} = \frac{\ell_{38.5} - \ell_{38.83}}{\ell_{38.5}} = \frac{(92 - \frac{1}{2} \cdot 5) - (92 - \frac{5}{6} \cdot 5)}{92 - \frac{1}{2} \cdot 5} = \frac{5/3}{89.5} = .0186$, *false*.

ANSWER A

13. Under the UDD assumption $\overset{\circ}{e}_{x:\overline{n}|} = e_{x:\overline{n}|} + \frac{1}{2} \cdot {}_nq_x$. So $\overset{\circ}{e}_{45:\overline{1}|} = e_{45:\overline{1}|} + \frac{1}{2} \cdot q_{45} = p_{45} + \frac{1}{2} \cdot q_{45}$ since $e_{x:\overline{n}|} = {}_1p_x + {}_2p_x + \cdots + {}_np_x$. Also, from the UDD assumption, $\mu(45.5) = \frac{q_{45}}{1 - \frac{1}{2} \cdot q_{45}}$, so $\frac{1}{2} = \frac{q_{45}}{1 - \frac{1}{2} \cdot q_{45}}$ implies $q_{45} = \frac{1}{2.5}$. Finally $\overset{\circ}{e}_{45:\overline{1}|} = p_{45} + \frac{1}{2} \cdot q_{45} = \frac{1.5}{2.5} + \frac{.5}{2.5} = .8$, ANSWER E.

ALTERNATE METHOD:

Use $\overset{\circ}{e}_{x:\overline{n}|} = \int_0^n {}_tp_x \, dt$ and the facts that $n = 1$ and ${}_tp_x = 1 - {}_tq_x = 1 - t \cdot q_x$ under UDD.

14. The starting point is to note that $\overset{\circ}{e}_{70:\overline{1.5}|} = \int_0^{1.5} {}_tp_{70} \cdot dt$. From the given $q_{70} = .040$ and $q_{71} = .044$, and the UDD assumption, we obtain $p_{70} = .960$, ${}_2p_{70} = (.960)(.956) = .91584$ and the piecewise linear picture below:

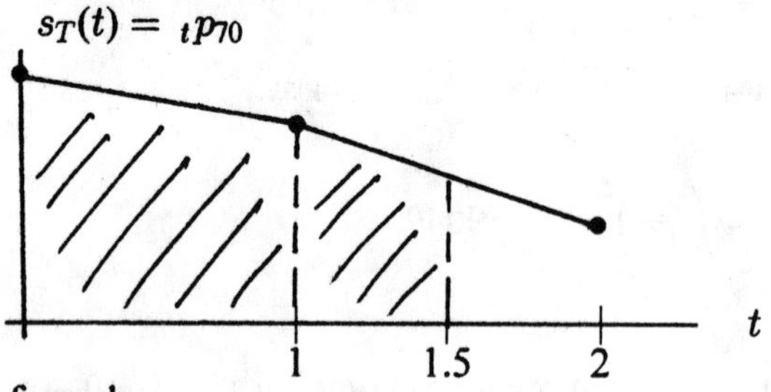

The corresponding formula,

$$ {}_tp_{70} = \begin{cases} 1 - t(.040) & 0 \le t \le 1 \\ (.96)(1-(t-1).044) & 1 < t < 2 \end{cases} $$

is based on ${}_tp_x = 1 - {}_tq_x = 1 - t \cdot q_x$ for $0 \le t \le 1$ under UDD. Finally

$$ \overset{\circ}{e}_{70:\overline{1.5}|} = \int_0^{1.5} {}_tp_{70} \, dt = \int_0^{1} {}_tp_{70} \, dt + \int_1^{1.5} {}_tp_{70} \, dt = .980 + .4747 = 1.4547, $$

ANSWER C

ALTERNATE GEOMETRIC METHOD:

$\overset{\circ}{e}_{70:\overline{1.5}|}$ is represented as the sum of the two shaded trapezoidal regions in the figure. Using the fact that the area of a trapezoid is the length of the base times the height at the midpoint of the base we have

$$ \overset{\circ}{e}_{70:\overline{1.5}|} = (1)\left(\frac{s_X(0) + s_X(1)}{2}\right) + \left(\frac{1}{2}\right)\left(\frac{s_X(1) + s_X(1.5)}{2}\right) $$

where $s_X(0) = 1$, $s_X(1) = {}_1p_{70} = .96$ and $s_X(1.5) = \frac{s_X(1) + s_X(2)}{2} = \frac{.96 + (.96)(.956)}{2}$.

15. Under UDD, $\mu(x+s) = \frac{q_x}{1 - sq_x}$ for $0 \le s \le 1$ and under constant force $\mu(x+s) = -\ln p_x$ for $0 \le s \le 1$. The graphs are shown below.

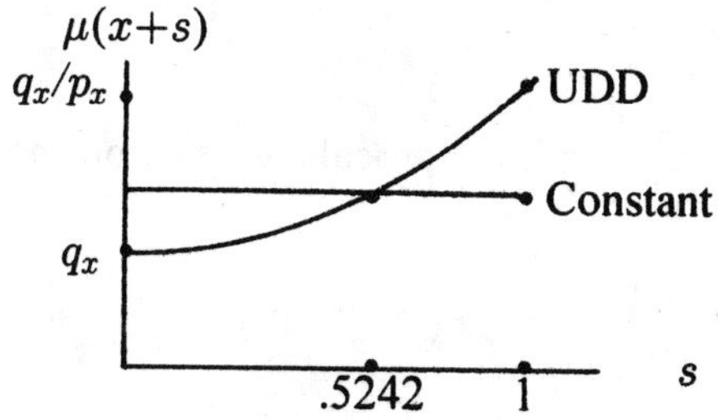

So $\mu^B(x+s) \ge \mu^A(x+s)$ translates into $\frac{.25}{1-.25s} \ge -\ln(.75)$, or $\frac{1}{4-s} \ge .2877 = \ln\left(\frac{4}{3}\right)$. This inequality has solution set $s \ge \frac{.1508}{.2877} = .5242$, **ANSWER D**

16. Proceeding as arrows in the diagram indicate

$$\begin{array}{ccccc} \ell_{[96]} & \rightarrow & \ell_{[96]+1} & \rightarrow & \ell_{98} \\ & & & & \downarrow \\ \ell_{[97]} & \leftarrow & \ell_{[97]+1} & \leftarrow & \ell_{99} \end{array}$$

$$\ell_{[96]+1} = (1 - q_{[96]})\ell_{[96]} = \left(1 - \tfrac{1}{2}q_{96}\right)10{,}000 = \left(1 - \tfrac{1}{2}(.350)\right)10{,}000 = 8250$$

$$\ell_{98} = (1 - q_{[96]+1})\ell_{[96]+1} = \left(1 - \tfrac{1}{2}(.475)\right)(8250) = 6290.625$$

$$\ell_{99} = (1 - q_{98})\ell_{98} = (1 - .675)6290.625 = 2044.453$$

$$\ell_{[97]+1} = \ell_{99}/(1 - q_{[97]+1}) = 2044.453/\left(1 - \tfrac{1}{2}(.675)\right) = 3085.967$$

$$\ell_{[97]} = \ell_{[97]+1}/(1 - q_{[97]}) = 3085.967/\left(1 - \tfrac{1}{2}(.475)\right) = 4047.170,$$

ANSWER A

17. Since there is a 2-year select period, the unknown $\ell_{[32]+1}$ sits in between the given $\ell_{[32]} = 90$ and $\ell_{34} = 63$ with

$$\begin{aligned} 63 = \ell_{34} &= \ell_{[32]} \cdot p_{[32]} \cdot p_{[32]+1} = (90)(1 - q_{[32]})(1 - q_{[32]+1}) \\ &= (90)(1 - (1-2k)\underset{\uparrow \atop \frac{100-90}{100}}{q_{32}})(1 - (1-k)\underset{\uparrow \atop \frac{90-63}{90}}{q_{33}}). \end{aligned}$$

This tedious quadratic equation in k has the solution $k = \frac{1}{6}$ so that

$$\ell_{[32]+1} = \ell_{[32]} \cdot p_{[32]} = 90\left(1 - \left(1 - 2 \cdot \tfrac{1}{6}\right)\tfrac{10}{100}\right) = 84,$$

ANSWER C

18. In general $\overset{\circ}{e}_{x:\overline{1}|} = \int_0^1 {}_tp_x dt$. Under the UDD assumption ${}_tp_x = 1 - tq_x = 1 - .1t$, which results in

$$F = \overset{\circ}{e}_{x:\overline{1}|} = \int_0^1 (1 - .1t)\,dt = 1 - .05 = .95.$$

Balducci's law, linear interpolation with reciprocals, gives a bit more complicated expression for ${}_tp_x = \ell_{x+t}/\ell_x$:

$${}_tp_x = \frac{\ell_{x+t}}{\ell_x} = \left(\frac{\ell_x}{\ell_{x+t}}\right)^{-1} = \left[\ell_x\left(\frac{1-t}{\ell_x} + \frac{t}{\ell_{x+1}}\right)\right]^{-1}$$

$$= \left[(1-t) + \frac{t}{p_x}\right]^{-1} = \left[1 - t + \tfrac{10}{9}t\right]^{-1} = 9[9+t]^{-1}$$

$$G = \overset{\circ}{e}_{x:\overline{1}|} = \int_0^1 9(9+t)^{-1}dt = 9\,ln(9+t)\Big|_0^1 = 9(ln\,10 - ln\,9) = .94825.$$

Hence $1000(F - G) = 1.755$, ANSWER D.

Note: See the example under the heading "Fractional Age Assumptions" in the Condensed Review Notes for Unit 1.

19. With $s_X(x) = \left(1 - \frac{x}{\omega}\right)^r$ it follows that

$$.10 = \mu(y) = \frac{-s'_Y(y)}{s_Y(y)} = \frac{r}{\omega}\left(1 - \frac{y}{\omega}\right)^{r-1} \Big/ \left(1 - \frac{y}{\omega}\right)^r = \frac{r}{\omega - y}$$

$$8.75 = \overset{\circ}{e}_y = \int_0^{\omega-y} {}_tp_y\,dt = \int_0^{\omega-y} \frac{s_Y(t+y)}{s_Y(y)}\,dt = \int_0^{\omega-y} \frac{(\omega-y-t)^r}{(\omega-y)^r}\,dt = \frac{\omega-y}{r+1}.$$

Notice then that $(.10)(8.75) = \frac{r}{\omega-y} \cdot \frac{\omega-y}{r+1} = \frac{r}{r+1}$, which results in $r = 7$, ANSWER D.

Note: See the third example under the heading "Life Expectancy" in the Condensed Review Notes for Unit 1.

20. With $q_x = .12$ we can use $\ell_x = 100$, $\ell_{x+1} = 88$.

I. $${}_{1/3}q_{x+1/2} = \frac{\ell_{x+1/2} - \ell_{x+5/6}}{\ell_{x+1/2}} \underset{\text{UDD}}{=} \frac{(\ell_x - \frac{1}{2}d_x) - (\ell_x - \frac{5}{6}d_x)}{\ell_x - \frac{1}{2}d_x}$$

$$= \frac{\frac{1}{3}d_x}{\ell_x - \frac{1}{2}d_x} = \frac{4}{94} = .042553 = .0426$$

So I is true (presuming "=" means "equal to 4 places")

II. $${}_{1/3}q_x = \frac{\ell_x - \ell_{x+1/3}}{\ell_x}$$

Under Balducci's law $\frac{1}{\ell_{x+1/3}} = \frac{2}{3}\frac{1}{\ell_x} + \frac{1}{3}\frac{1}{\ell_{x+1}} = \frac{2}{300} + \frac{1}{264}$, so $\ell_{x+1/3} = 95.652174$ and ${}_{1/3}q_x = .043478 = .0435$. II is also true.

III. ${}_{1/2}q_x = 1 - {}_{1/2}p_x$, and under constant force ${}_tp_x = e^{-\mu t} = (e^{-\mu})^t = p_x^t$. Hence ${}_{1/2}p_x = (.88)^{1/2}$ and ${}_{1/2}q_x = .061917 = .0619$. III is correct, ANSWER D

21. The data in (iii) alone is sufficient to find q_y using

$$q_y = 1 - p_y = 1 - e^{\int_0^1 \mu(y+t)dt}.$$

A short cut here results from observing that $\mu(y+t)$ is exactly double $\mu(x+t)$. Hence

$$p_y = e^{\int_0^1 \mu(y+t)dt} = e^{\int_0^1 2\mu(x+t)dt} = \left[e^{\int_0^1 \mu(x+t)dt}\right]^2 = p_x^2.$$

Thus

$$\begin{aligned} q_y &= 1 - p_y = 1 - p_x^2 = 1-(1-q_x)^2 \\ &= 1 - .96^2 = .0784. \end{aligned}$$

ANSWER A

22. I. $$\left.\begin{aligned} {}_2p_{[31]} &= \tfrac{988}{996} \text{ (bigger)} \\ {}_2p_{[30]+1} &= \tfrac{988}{998} \end{aligned}\right\} \Rightarrow \text{true}$$

II. $$\left.\begin{aligned} {}_{1|}q_{[31]} &= \frac{994-988}{996} = \frac{6}{996} \\ {}_{1|}q_{[30]+1} &= \frac{995-988}{998} = \frac{7}{998} \text{ (bigger)} \end{aligned}\right\} \Rightarrow \text{false}$$

III. $$\left.\begin{aligned} {}_2q_{[33]} &= \frac{987-970}{987} = \frac{17}{987} \\ {}_2q_{[31]+2} &= \frac{988-970}{988} = \frac{18}{988} \text{ (bigger)} \end{aligned}\right\} \Rightarrow \text{false}$$

ANSWER B

23. Under de Moivre's law $\ell_x = \omega - x$ and $T(x)$ is uniformly distributed over $[0, \omega - x]$. Hence

$$\mu(x) = \frac{-\ell_x'}{\ell_x} = \frac{1}{\omega - x}, \ \mathring{e}_x = E[T(x)] = \frac{\omega - x}{2},$$

$$\begin{aligned} {}_{n|}q_x &= \frac{\ell_{x+n} - \ell_{x+n+1}}{\ell_x} = \frac{1}{\omega - x}, \ L_x = \tfrac{1}{2}\ell_x + \tfrac{1}{2}\ell_{x+1} \text{ (UDD)} = \omega - x - \tfrac{1}{2} \\ m_x &= \frac{d_x}{L_x} = \frac{1}{\omega - x - .5}. \end{aligned}$$

I. $$\frac{1}{2\mathring{e}_x} = \frac{1}{2(\omega-x)/2} = \frac{1}{\omega-x}$$ correct

II. $${}_{n|}q_x = \frac{1}{\omega - x}$$ correct

III. $$\frac{m_x}{1+.5m_x} = \frac{2/(2\omega - 2x - 1)}{2(\omega - x)/(2\omega - 2x - 1)} = \frac{1}{\omega - x}$$ correct

ANSWER D

24. The basic properties of a survival function are: $s_X(0) = 1$, it must be non-increasing, and $\lim_{x\to\infty} s_X(x) = 0$.

I.
$$s_X(0) = e^0 = 1$$
$$s'_X(x) = exp(x - .7(2^x - 1))\underbrace{(x - .7(2^x - 1))'}_{1 - .7(2^x)ln2 = 1 - (.4852)2^x}$$

$\Rightarrow s'_X(0) = .5148 \Rightarrow$ increasing near 0

$\therefore$ not a survival function.

II.
$$\left.\begin{aligned} s_X(0) &= \frac{1}{(1+0)^2} = 1 \\ s'_X(x) &= -2(1+x)^{-3} < 0 \Rightarrow \text{decreasing} \\ \lim_{x\to\infty} s_X(x) &= \lim_{x\to\infty}\frac{1}{(1+x)^2} = \frac{1}{\infty} = 0 \end{aligned}\right\} s_X(x) \text{ is a survival function.}$$

III.
$$\left.\begin{aligned} s_X(0) &= e^0 = 1 \\ s'_X(x) &= (e^{-x^2})(-2x) < 0 \Rightarrow \text{decreasing} \\ \lim_{x\to\infty} s_X(x) &= e^{-\infty} = 0 \end{aligned}\right\} s_X(x) \text{ is a survival function.}$$

ANSWER C

25. The problem gives a discrete distribution (that of K), whereas $\overset{\circ}{e}_{x:\overline{5|}}$ is the expected value of a function of the continuous variable T. UDD is a bridge between these two situations, giving $\overset{\circ}{e}_{x:\overline{5|}} = e_{x:\overline{5|}} + \frac{1}{2}\cdot {}_5q_x = \sum_{k=1}^{5} {}_kp_x + \frac{1}{2}\cdot {}_5q_x$, by the standard UDD relation.

Now $F_K(k) = Pr(K \le k) = Pr(T < k+1) = {}_{k+1}q_x$, so ${}_{k+1}p_x = 1 - F_K(k)$, and therefore

$\overset{\circ}{e}_{x:\overline{5|}} = .95 + .85 + .65 + .40 + .25 + \left(\frac{1}{2}\right)(.75) = 3.475,$ ANSWER B

26. Working from first principles $\mu(x) = \dfrac{-s'_X(x)}{s_X(x)} = \dfrac{\alpha}{\omega - x}$,

$$\overset{\circ}{e}_x = \int_0^{\omega-x} {}_tp_x\,dt = \int_0^{\omega-x} \frac{s_X(x+t)}{s_X(x)}\,dt = \int_0^{\omega-x}\left(\frac{\omega-x-t}{\omega-x}\right)^{\alpha} dt = \frac{\omega-x}{\alpha+1}.$$

Thus $\mu(x)\cdot\overset{\circ}{e}_x = \left(\frac{\alpha}{\omega-x}\right)\left(\frac{\omega-x}{\alpha+1}\right) = \frac{\alpha}{\alpha+1}$. ANSWER A

Note: The model $\mu(x) = \dfrac{r}{\omega - x}$ has frequently occurred on past exams and several shortcuts can be learned. See the examples in the Unit Condensed Review Notes.

27. The probability that 60 dies between 60.5 and 61.5, ${}_{.5|}q_{60}$, can be calculated from $\dfrac{\ell_{60.5} - \ell_{61.5}}{\ell_{60}}$. The mid-year values $\ell_{60.5}$, $\ell_{61.5}$ are calculated here with an interpolation assumption from ℓ_{60}, ℓ_{61} and ℓ_{62}.

From $q_{60} = .30$, $q_{61} = .40$ it is easy to see that appropriate ℓ_x values are $\ell_{60} = 100$, $\ell_{61} = 70$, $\ell_{62} = 42$.

UDD: $\quad \ell_{60.5} = \dfrac{100+70}{2} = 85,\ \ell_{61.5} = \dfrac{70+42}{2} = 56,\ f = {}_{.5|}q_{60}^{UDD} = \dfrac{85-56}{100} = .29000$

Balducci: $\dfrac{1}{\ell_{60.5}} = \frac{1}{2} \cdot \frac{1}{100} + \frac{1}{2} \cdot \frac{1}{70} \ \Rightarrow \ \ell_{60.5} = 82.3529$. Similarly $\ell_{61.5} = 52.5000$, so

$$g = {}_{.5|}q_{60}^{Bal} = \frac{82.3529 - 52.5000}{100} = .29853$$

$\Rightarrow \ 10{,}000(g - f) = 85.3,$ ANSWER B

28. The median sought, $t_{.5}$, is the solution of $.5 = S(t_{.5}) = {}_{t_{.5}}p_{20} = exp\left(-\int_0^{t_{.5}} \mu(20+t)dt\right)$:

$-\int_0^{t_{.5}} \dfrac{1}{\sqrt{60-s}}\, ds = 2(\sqrt{60-t_{.5}} - \sqrt{60})$. Substituting into the above and taking a natural log of both sides results in $-ln2 = 2(\sqrt{60-t_{.5}} - \sqrt{60})$: $t_{.5} = 5.249$ ANSWER A

29. The key to this problem is recognizing that ${}_tp_x = .8^t$ assumes constant force with $e^{-\mu t} = .8^t$, $\mu = -ln(.8)$. Now $T_{x+1} = \int_{x+1}^{\infty} \ell_y\, dy$ is used in calculating $\overset{\circ}{e}_{x+1} = T_{x+1}/\ell_{x+1}$. Under a constant force assumption both $T(x)$ and $T(x+1)$ have the same exponential distribution. Hence $\dfrac{-1}{ln(.8)} = \dfrac{1}{\mu} = E[T(x+1)] = \overset{\circ}{e}_{x+1} = \dfrac{T_{x+1}}{\ell_{x+1}}$. Finally, $\ell_{x+2} = \ell_{x+1} \cdot p_{x+1}$ gives $\ell_{x+1} = 6.4/.8 = 8$ and $T_{x+1} = \dfrac{-8}{ln(.8)} = 35.85$. ANSWER D

30. A natural way to set this one up, due to the 10-year select period, is

$$\overset{\circ}{e}_{[30]} = \underbrace{\overset{\circ}{e}_{[30]:\overline{10}|}}_{\text{based on select mortality}} + {}_{10}p_{[30]} \cdot \underbrace{\overset{\circ}{e}_{40}}_{\text{ultimate mortality}}$$

(See the Unit Condensed Review Notes under the heading "Recursion Relations"). Now ${}_tp_{[30]} = \dfrac{\ell_{[30]+t}}{\ell_{[30]}} = 1 - \dfrac{t}{100}$ for $0 \le t \le 10$ so $\overset{\circ}{e}_{[30]:\overline{10}|} = \int_0^{10} \left(1 - \frac{t}{100}\right) dt = 9.5$, ${}_{10}p_{[30]} = 1 - \dfrac{10}{100} = .90$. Next, ${}_tp_{40} = \dfrac{\ell_{40+t}}{\ell_{40}} = \dfrac{\ell_{30+(10+t)}}{\ell_{30+10}} = \sqrt{\dfrac{60-t}{60}} = \left(1 - \frac{t}{60}\right)^{1/2}$, hence $\overset{\circ}{e}_{40} = \int_0^{60} \left(1 - \frac{t}{60}\right)^{1/2} dt = \dfrac{60}{1.5} = 40$. Substituting these results into the first relation results in $\overset{\circ}{e}_{[30]} = 9.5 + (.90)40 = 45.5$. ANSWER D

31. This question concerns the effect on q_x of an additional hazard rate of $\lambda(t)$ at age $x+t$ for $0 \le t \le 1$:

$$\underbrace{q'_x}_{\text{with additional hazard}} = 1 - p'_x = 1 - e^{-\int_0^1 \mu(x+t)+\lambda(t)\,dt}$$

$$= 1 - \underbrace{(e^{-\int_0^1 \mu(x+t)\,dt}}_{p_x})\underbrace{(e^{-\int_0^1 \lambda(t)\,dt}}_{\text{factor} < 1}).$$

The definition of $\lambda(t)$ in this problem is given graphically by

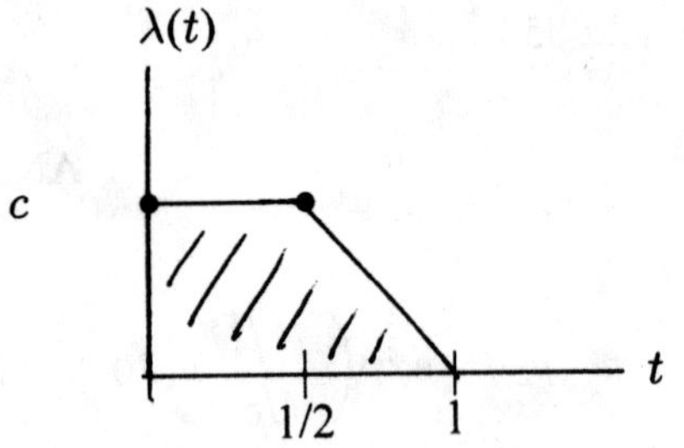

From simple geometry the shaded area is $\int_0^1 \lambda(t)\,dt = .75c$. Thus $q'_x = 1 - p_x e^{-.75c} = 1 - (.985)e^{-.75c}$. ANSWER E

32. The question can be done from first principles or from recognition that the survival model in the problem is a slightly disguised form of $s_X(x) = (1 - \frac{x}{\omega})^r$, discussed in the examples of the unit Condensed Review Notes. Here $s_X(x) = \frac{\sqrt{k^2 - x}}{k} = \left(1 - \frac{x}{k}\right)^{1/2}$ so $\mathring{e}_x = \frac{\omega - x}{r+1} = \frac{k-x}{1.5}$. From $\mathring{e}_{40} = 2\mathring{e}_{80}$ it follows that $\omega = k = 120$, hence $\mathring{e}_{60} = \frac{\omega - 60}{1.5} = \frac{60}{1.5} = 40$. ANSWER D

33-36. A useful point in this problem is the evaluation of $\int_0^n {}_tp_x\,dt$ when you are given a tabular survival model and told to assume UDD.

EXAMPLE:

x	50	51	52
ℓ_x	100	98	95

Under the UDD the survival function ${}_tp_{50},\ 0 \le t \le 2$ is piecewise linear as illustrated in the graph

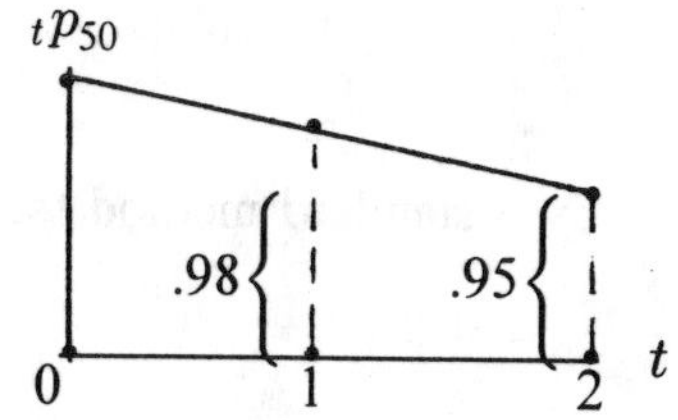

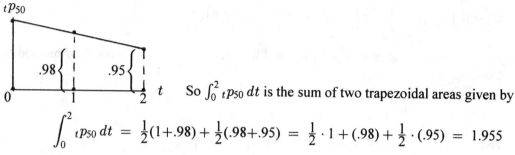

So $\int_0^2 {}_tp_{50}\,dt$ is the sum of two trapezoidal areas given by

$$\int_0^2 {}_tp_{50}\,dt = \tfrac{1}{2}(1+.98) + \tfrac{1}{2}(.98+.95) = \tfrac{1}{2}\cdot 1 + (.98) + \tfrac{1}{2}\cdot(.95) = 1.955$$

We are given $\ell_{[85]} = 1000$, $\ell_{86} = 1000 - 100 = 900$, $\ell_{[86]} = 850$ and $\ell_{87} = 850 - 100 = 750$ since the select period is 1 year. Hence

$$p_{[85]} = \frac{900}{1000} = .9,\ p_{[86]} = \frac{750}{850},\ p_{86} = \frac{750}{900}.$$

Question 33 has ANSWER C.

For this part the discussion above is relevant:

$$5.225 = \mathring{e}_{[85]} = \int_0^\infty {}_tp_{[85]}\,dt = \int_0^2 {}_tp_{[85]}\,dt + \int_2^\infty {}_tp_{[85]}\,dt.$$

By above

$$\int_0^2 {}_tp_{[85]}\,dt = \tfrac{1}{2}\cdot 1 + p_{[85]} + \tfrac{1}{2}\cdot {}_2p_{[85]}$$

$$= .50 + .90 + \tfrac{1}{2}\cdot p_{[85]}\cdot p_{86} = .50 + .90 + \tfrac{1}{2}(.75) = 1.775,$$

so $5.225 = 1.775 + \int_2^\infty {}_tp_{[85]}\,dt$: $\int_2^\infty {}_tp_{[85]}\,dt = 3.45$.

Question 34 has ANSWER C.

From standard life-expectancy recursion relations (see the end of the unit Condensed Review Notes)

$$\mathring{e}_{[86]} = \int_0^1 {}_tp_{[86]}\,dt + p_{[86]}\cdot\mathring{e}_{87} = \tfrac{1}{2}(1+p_{[86]}) + p_{[86]}\cdot\mathring{e}_{87} = \frac{800}{850} + \frac{750}{850}\cdot\mathring{e}_{87}$$

Going back to the above we had $5.225 = \mathring{e}_{\overline{85}|} = \mathring{e}_{[85]:\overline{2}|} + {}_2p_{[85]}\cdot\mathring{e}_{87} = 1.775 + 3.45$ so $\mathring{e}_{87} = \dfrac{3.45}{{}_2p_{[85]}} = \dfrac{3.45}{.75} = 4.60$. Hence $\mathring{e}_{[86]} = \dfrac{800}{850} + \dfrac{750}{850}(4.60) = 5$.

So Questions 35 and 36 are both ANSWER E.

37-40. $s_X(x) = \frac{(10-x)^2}{100}$ is of the form $\left(1 - \frac{x}{\omega}\right)^r$, for which the following can be written down from memory (see the examples in the Unit Condensed Review Notes):
$\overset{\circ}{e}_x = \frac{\omega - x}{r+1}$, $\mu(x) = \frac{r}{\omega - x}$, $\ell_x = (\omega - x)^r$.

For Question 37 we use $\overset{\circ}{e}_1 = \frac{\omega - 1}{r+1} = \frac{10-1}{3} = 3$. ANSWER E.

For Question 38 we use $\mu(1) = \frac{r}{\omega - 1} = \frac{2}{10-1} = \frac{2}{9}$ and $q_1 = 1 - \frac{\ell_2}{\ell_1} = 1 - \frac{8^2}{9^2} = \frac{17}{81}$.
Thus $\mu(1) - q_1 = \frac{2}{9} - \frac{17}{81} = \frac{1}{81} = .012$. ANSWER C.

For the final two questions we are asked to calculate $a(1)$. By a standard method (see Unit Condensed Review Notes)

$\overset{\circ}{e}_{1:\overline{1}|} = q_1 \cdot a(1) + p_1 \cdot 1$.

Here, using $q_1 = \frac{17}{81}$, $p_1 = \frac{64}{81}$, we have $a(1) = \frac{\overset{\circ}{e}_{1:\overline{1}|} - (64/81)}{(17/81)}$

The final two questions require calculations of $\overset{\circ}{e}_{1:\overline{1}|}$ (hence $a(1)$) under slightly different assumptions and result in slightly different values of $a(1)$.

Question 39 calculation of $\overset{\circ}{e}_{1:\overline{1}|}$ and $a(1)$:

$$\overset{\circ}{e}_{1:\overline{1}|} = \int_0^1 {}_tp_1\, dt = \int_0^1 S(1+t)/S(1)dt = \int_0^1 \left(1 - \tfrac{t}{9}\right)^2 dt = \frac{9^3 - 8^3}{243} = .8930$$

$$a(1) = \frac{.8930 - (64/81)}{(17/81)} = .490, \text{ ANSWER D.}$$

Question 40 calculation of $\overset{\circ}{e}_{1:\overline{1}|}$ and $a(1)$:
Here we use ${}_tp_1 = p_1^t$ (constant force assumption in place of the actual $S(1+t)/S(1)$) to calculate

$$\overset{\circ}{e}_{1:\overline{1}|} = \int_0^1 p_1^t\, dt = \frac{-q_1}{ln p_1} = .8909$$

$$a(1) = \frac{.8909 - (64/81)}{(17/81)} = .480, \text{ ANSWER B.}$$

41-44. The given T-density is exponential with parameter $\mu = 2$. From standard results the answer to Question 41 is $\overset{\circ}{e}_x = E[T] = \frac{1}{\mu} = .5$, ANSWER A, and the answer to Question 42 is $Var(T) = \frac{1}{\mu^2} = .25$, ANSWER A.

The survival function $S_T(t) = {}_tp_x = e^{-\mu t} = e^{-2t}$ reaches a value of .5 at the median time $t = \frac{ln(2)}{\mu} = \frac{ln(2)}{2}$. Question 43 has ANSWER C.

Finally, since a central rate is a weighted average of the force over an age interval, an assumption of constant force means $m_x = \mu = 2$. Question 44 has ANSWER E.

UNIT 2: OTHER USES OF SURVIVAL MODELS

Introduction

Survival models are widely used in finance, health, biology, medicine, and clinical studies as well as in mathematical areas such as multiple decrement models and stochastic processes. The notation and terminology vary from one context to the next but the mathematics of these models is unchanging.

The essential element of all applications is a random time, X, from some well-defined point in time (i.e., when $x = 0$) until some random event (called failure, death, etc.) occurs. So X is a positive-valued random variable. Survival is said to take place at time x if the event $X > x$ occurs, whereas failure by time x corresponds to $X \leq x$. X might be called a waiting time, a time until failure, or a time until event. The probability distribution of X describes the pattern of survival/failure.

Useful examples of survival models include:

(1) Time until failure of a particular brand of new car battery. The time count begins when the battery is put into service and failure is said to occur when it can no longer hold a sufficient charge. Modeling this distribution would be important in determining the cost of a warranty to be provided by the manufacturer.

(2) Time of residence for a newly admitted nursing home resident. The model for this time variable together with the distribution of daily costs during residence would be used to price an insurance plan providing nursing home care.

(3) Time after issue until a callable bond is called. Even though the bond is not certain to be called one could handle this mathematically by putting a significant part of the total probability of 1 as a point mass at or beyond the maturity time.

(4) Time after issue until a bond defaults. Again, it is not certain that a bond will default. It is probably even unlikely. But suppose we have a 20-year bond with a 5% chance of default. We could model the distribution of time until default by spreading 5% of the probability over the interval $[0, 20]$ in some economically reasonable way, and then putting the other 95% of probability in $(20, \infty)$ in any manner which is convenient.

(5) Time after issue until a mortgage or securitized pool of mortgages is repaid. The pattern of prepayments would govern how the probability is distributed.

(6) Time until a strike is settled.

(7) Time until a current member of an employee benefit plan leaves the plan due to retirement, death, disablement or withdrawal (euphemism for all other possible reasons).

(8) Time after a life insurance contract is issued until the policy owner dies or lapses the contract.

A survival model (i.e., probability distribution for X) in any context can be specified in a number of mathematically equivalent ways. The survival function, $s_X(x)$[9] $= Pr(X > x)$, gives the probability that the failure event has not occurred by time x. The distribution function, $F(x) = Pr(X \leq x) = 1 - s_X(x)$, gives the probability that the event has occurred by time x. The probability density function, $f(x) = F'(x) = -s'_X(x)$, is not itself a probability, but $f_X(x)(\Delta x)$ is approximately the probability that the failure event occurs in the instant $[x, x{+}\Delta x]$.

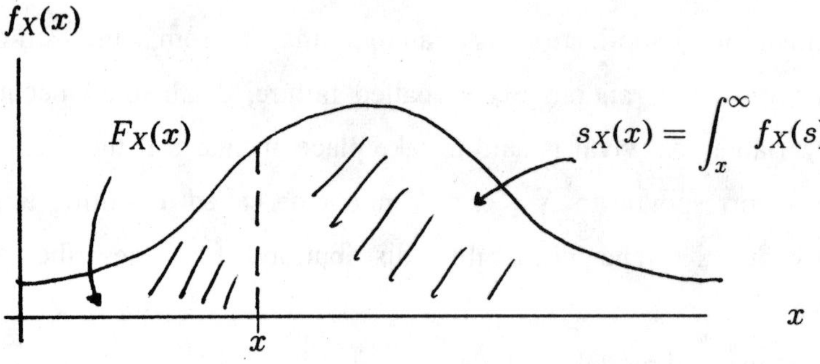

In actuarial survival models we also saw two other mathematically equivalent ways of describing the distribution: the force of mortality, $\mu(x)$, and the life table, ℓ_x. In non-actuarial models the terminology and notation differ. The term "force of mortality" is replaced by "hazard rate" or "intensity function" and it might be denoted by $h(x)$, $\lambda(x)$ or some other symbol depending on the tradition within the field of application. It is defined generically by $h(x) = \dfrac{f_X(x)}{s_X(x)} = \dfrac{-s'_X(x)}{s_X(x)} = -ln(s_X(x))'$. The survival function can be recreated from $h(x)$ via the relation $s_X(x) = exp(-\int_0^x h(s)\,ds)$. The definition can be rearranged in the form $f_X(x) = s_X(x)h(x)$ to enhance the understanding of the meaning of $h(x)$.

$$
\begin{aligned}
s_X(x)(h(x)\Delta x) = f_X(x)(\Delta x) &\approx Pr(x < X \leq x{+}\Delta x) \\
&= Pr(x < X \text{ and } X \leq x{+}\Delta x) \\
&= \underbrace{Pr(x < X)}_{s_X(x)} \cdot \underbrace{Pr(X \leq x{+}\Delta x | X > x)}_{\substack{h(x)\Delta x \,=\, \text{probability that} \\ \text{failure occurs in the next instant} \\ \text{(i.e., } \Delta x\text{) given survival at time } x}} \qquad \text{(multiplicative law of probability)}
\end{aligned}
$$

So $f_X(x)(\Delta x)$ is the unconditional probability of failure in $[x, x{+}\Delta x]$ whereas $h(x)(\Delta x)$ is the conditional probability of failure in the interval given survival to the start of the interval.

Even though these general models may have nothing to do with the survival of human lives we can think of $x = 0$ as corresponding to "birth" and the failure event as "death." X could then be

---

[9] In this Unit we use $s(x)$, $s_X(x)$, interchangeably when it should cause no confusion. One must be careful, however, with expressions involving survival functions of different distributions, for example, ${}_tp_x = s_T(t) = \dfrac{s_X(x+t)}{s_X(x)}$.

thought of as the "age" of death. We could then define $\ell_x = \ell_0 s_X(x)$, the life table, as a fifth way of describing the distribution of X and employ all the symbols and relations discussed in Unit one for actuarial survival models. For example,

$$s_X(x) = {}_xp_0 = p_0 \cdot p_1 \cdot \cdots \cdot p_{x-1} \qquad (x \text{ a whole number})$$

$${}_tp_x = \frac{\ell_{x+t}}{\ell_x} = \frac{s_X(x+t)}{s_X(x)} = Pr(X > x+t \,|\, X > x)$$

$${}_{n|m}q_x = \frac{\ell_{x+n} - \ell_{x+n+m}}{\ell_x} = Pr(x+n < X \leq x+n+m \,|\, X > x).$$

A sixth equivalent way of functionally describing the distribution of X is by giving the mean residual lifetime at "age" x, $mr\ell(x) = E[X - x|X > x]$. In actuarial models $X - x|_{X>x}$ was denoted by $T = T(x)$ and $\overset{\circ}{e}_x$ was used to denote $E[T]$. Thus

$$mr\ell(x) = \overset{\circ}{e}_x = \int_0^\infty {}_tp_x \, dt = \int_0^\infty \frac{s_X(x+t)dt}{s_X(x)}$$

and $E[X] = \overset{\circ}{e}_0 = \int_0^\infty s_X(t)\, dt$ (the area under the survival curve) is a special case. It can be shown that

$$h(x) = \left(\frac{d\overset{\circ}{e}_x}{dx} + 1\right) / \overset{\circ}{e}_x,$$

which allows creation of $h(x)$, $s_X(x)$, $F_X(x)$, $f_X(x)$ and ℓ_x from the function $\overset{\circ}{e}_x = mr\ell(x)$.

Example 1 Suppose $\overset{\circ}{e}_x = \frac{\omega - x}{2}$ for $0 \leq x \leq \omega$. Describe the distribution of X.

Solution From the above

$$h(x) = \frac{\dfrac{d\left(\frac{\omega - x}{2}\right)}{dx} + 1}{\left(\frac{\omega - x}{2}\right)} = \frac{\frac{1}{2}}{\left(\frac{\omega - x}{2}\right)} = \frac{1}{\omega - x}.$$

In the unit on actuarial survival models $\mu(x) = \frac{1}{\omega - x}$, or equivalently, $\ell_x = \omega - x$, $s_X(x) = 1 - \frac{x}{\omega}$, $f_X(x) = \frac{1}{\omega}$ for $0 \leq x \leq \omega$, was named de Moivre's law. In this model X is uniformly distributed over the interval $[0, \omega]$. □

In all of the preceding discussion we assumed that X was a continuous random variable. If X were discrete and $x_1, x_2, \ldots$ is a list of all the points having positive probability we have $\sum_i p(x_i) = 1$ where $p(x)$ is the probability function. The generic definitions of $s_X(x)$ and $F_X(x)$ are still valid, but $p(x) = Pr(X = x)$ cannot be obtained from $F'_X(x)$ or $-s'_X(x)$, instead

$$p(x_i) = s_X(x_{i-1}) - s_X(x_i) = F_X(x_i) - F_X(x_{i-1})$$

where $x_0 < x_1$ and $p(x_0) = 0$. The hazard function is defined by

$$h(x_j) = Pr(X = x_j | X \geq x_j) = \frac{p(x_j)}{p(x_j) + p(x_{j+1}) + \cdots} = \frac{s_X(x_{j-1}) - s_X(x_j)}{s_X(x_{j-1})} = 1 - \frac{s_X(x_j)}{s_X(x_{j-1})}$$

so that instead of the continuous model relation $s_X(x) = exp(-\int_0^x h(s)\,ds)$ one has

$$s_X(x) = \frac{s_X(x_1)}{s_X(x_0)} \cdot \frac{s_X(x_2)}{s_X(x_1)} \cdot \cdots \cdot \frac{s_X(x_j)}{s_X(x_{j-1})}, \qquad x_j \leq x < x_{j+1}$$

$$= [1 - h(x_1)][1 - h(x_2)] \cdots [1 - h(x_j)].$$

Example 2 Suppose $p(x) = .8^{x-1}(.2)$ for $x = 1, 2, 3, \ldots$. Calculate $s_X(x)$ and $h(x)$ for $x = 1, 2, \ldots$.

Solution

$$s_X(x) = p(x+1) + p(x+2) + \cdots$$

$$= .8^x(.2) + .8^{x+1}(.2) + \cdots$$

$$= .8^x(.2)[\underbrace{1 + .8 + .8^2 + \cdots}_{\text{geometric series}}]$$

$$= .8^x\left(\frac{.2}{1 - .8}\right) = .8^x$$

$$h(x) = \frac{p(x)}{p(x) + p(x+1) + \cdots} = \frac{p(x)}{s(x-1)} = \frac{.8^{x-1}(.2)}{.8^{x-1}} = .2 \qquad \text{(constant)}$$ □

Parametric Hazard Rate and Survival Models

Inspection of the survival function's graph does not typically lead to any insight on the failure mechanism. This mechanism is most obviously reflected in the hazard rate graph. For example, population hazard function's tend to have the shape in the figure. The rise at the left is

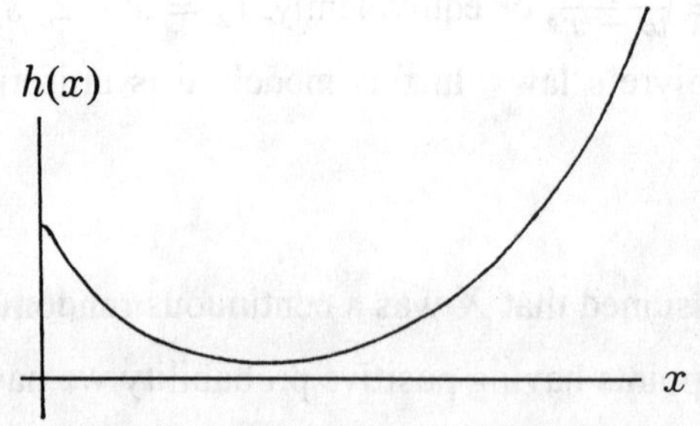

related to infant mortality, the hazard levels off and stabilizes in the middle age range, and then accelerates upward as a result of aging.

Investigators have developed a number of parametric families of models for hazard rates and survival functions. The hazard function for each family has a characteristic shape. Adjusting the parameters allows you to fine-tune the graph to your data. For example, the two-parameter Weibull family has a hazard function $h(x) = \alpha\lambda x^{\alpha-1}$ for $x \geq 0$ where α and λ are positive parameters. If $\alpha = 1$ the hazard rate is constant at λ, if $\alpha > 1$ it is an increasing function, and if $\alpha < 1$ it is a decreasing function.

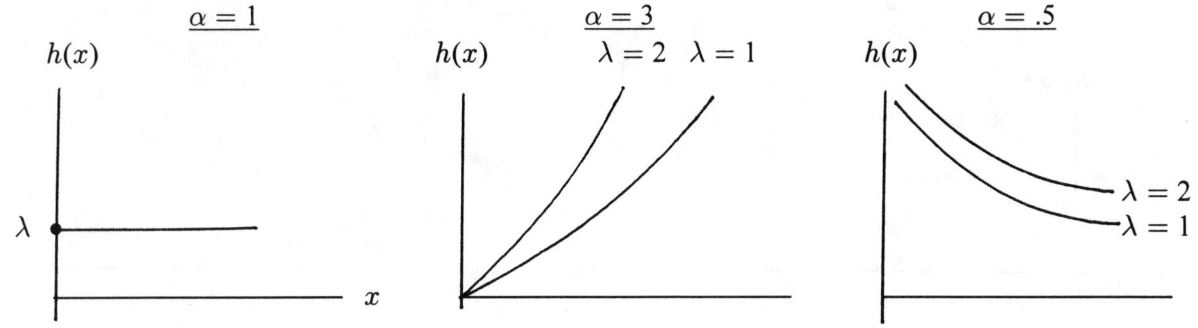

These graphs are flatter as α gets closer to 1 and steeper as α gets large or near zero.

The survival function for the Weibull family is

$$s_X(x) = e^{-\int_0^x h(s)\,ds} = e^{-\lambda x^\alpha}.$$

Between the choice of many popular parametric families and the tweaking of their parameters one can model a hazard rate graph of practically any shape. In addition there are other tricks for expanding the variety of shapes such as linear combinations. If a_1, a_2 are positive consider $h(x) = a_1 h_1(x) + a_2 h_2(x)$ where the $h_i(x)$ are hazard functions with corresponding survival functions $s_i(x)$. Hazard functions need only be positive, continuous and satisfy $\int_0^\infty h(x)\,dx = \infty$ (so that $s(\infty) = 0$). With the $a_i > 0$ the function $h(x)$ has these properties also. Furthermore

$$\begin{aligned} s_X(x) &= e^{-\int_0^x a_1 h_1(s) + a_2 h_2(s)\,ds}. \\ &= \left[e^{-\int_0^x h_1(s)\,ds}\right]^{a_1} \left[e^{-\int_0^x h_2(s)\,ds}\right]^{a_2} \\ &= (s_1(x))^{a_1} (s_2(x))^{a_2} \end{aligned}$$

If $a_1 + a_2 = 1$, $h(x)$ is a weighted average of $h_1(x)$ and $h_2(x)$.

Now suppose $h_1(x)$, $h_2(x)$ are Weibull hazard functions. Between the four parameters in these models and the positive numbers a_1, a_2, one has 5 (if $a_1 + a_2 = 1$) or 6 parameters to manipulate the shape of $h(x)$. The new $h(x)$ is not a Weibull hazard rate, but is a closely related hybrid.

$\alpha_1 = 2$, $\lambda_1 = \frac{1}{2}$, $h_1(x) = x$

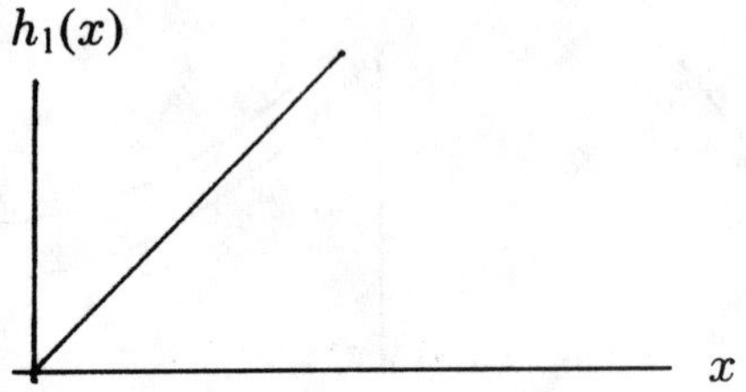

$\alpha_2 = \frac{1}{2}$, $\lambda_2 = 2$, $h_2(x) = x^{-1/2}$

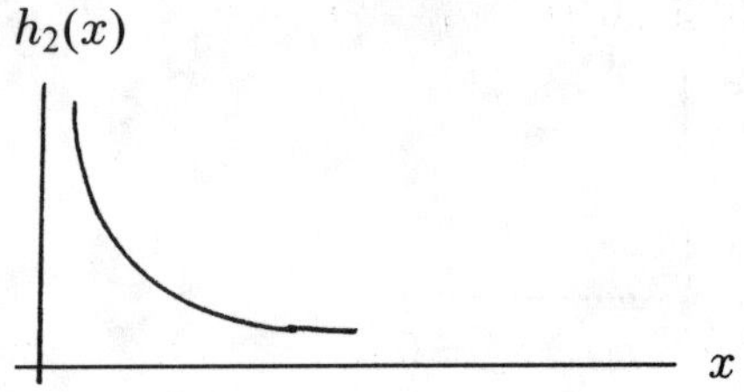

$$h(x) = \frac{1}{2}h_1(x) + \frac{1}{2}h_2(x) = \frac{1}{2}(x + x^{-1/2})$$

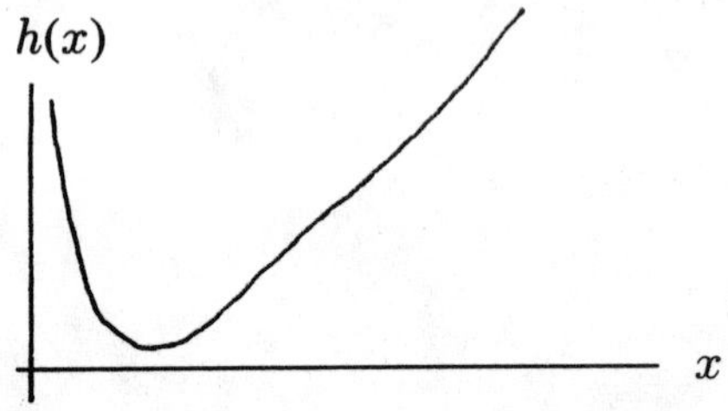

The new shape obtained is similar to a typical population hazard function illustrated earlier. This suggests that a population hazard function could be modeled as a positive linear combination of two Weibull hazard functions with 5 or 6 parameters available to fine tune the shape.

Regression Models for Survival with Covariate Data

These ideas are probably explained most easily in a simple example. Suppose we have a population of 50-year-old insured lives. Let X represent the future time until death (i.e., denoted $T(50)$ in actuarial models). Attempting to use one distribution for all these lives is not the best idea since we have additional (i.e., other related variables) information on these individuals that we know to affect survival. For example, women live longer than men and smokers die sooner than non-smokers. Formally, let's denote covariates (dependent variables) by Z_1, a sex indicator, and Z_2, a smoking indicator. By convention Z_1 is 0 for a female, 1 for a male and Z_2 is 0 for a non-smoker, and 1 for a smoker. We might be better served by modeling the conditional survival distributions of $X|_{Z_1, Z_2}$ for the four possible combinations of Z_1 and Z_2. Rather than using four totally separate survival models perhaps we can think of female non-smokers ($Z_1 = 0$, $Z_2 = 0$) as the baseline model and make simple adjustments to this model for the other three groups if there is high correlation between X, Z_1 and Z_2.

In the accelerated failure time model $ln(X)$ is regressed on Z_1, Z_2. That is,

$$ln(X) = \mu + \gamma_1 Z_1 + \gamma_2 Z_2 + \sigma W$$

where γ_1, γ_2 are regression coefficients and W is an error distribution ($E[W] = 0$, $\sigma_W = 1$) such as the standard normal. Hence

$$X|_{Z_1=z_1,\, Z_2=z_2} = e^{\gamma_1 z_1 + \gamma_2 z_2} \cdot e^{\mu+\sigma W}.$$

When $z_1 = z_2 = 0$ (i.e., female non-smokers, the baseline group) the conditional distribution is that of $e^{\mu+\sigma W}$. This baseline survival function is denoted by $s_0(x)$. The conditional survival functions for the other three groups are related to this one by

$$\begin{aligned} s(x|Z_1 = z_1, Z_2 = z_2) &= Pr(ln(X) > ln(x)|Z_i = z_i) \\ &= Pr(\mu + \gamma_1 z_1 + \gamma_2 z_2 + \sigma W > ln(x)) \\ &= Pr(\mu + \sigma W > ln(x) - \gamma_1 z_1 - \gamma_2 z_2) \\ &= Pr(e^{\mu+\sigma W} > x e^{-(\gamma_1 z_1 + \gamma_2 z_2)}) \\ &= s_0(x e^{-(\gamma_1 z_1 + \gamma_2 z_2)}) \end{aligned}$$

Aging for the group determined by $Z_1 = z_1$, $Z_2 = z_2$ is "accelerated" by the factor $e^{-(\gamma_1 z_1 + \gamma_2 z_2)}$ in comparison with aging for the baseline group. For example, suppose the regression resulted in $\gamma_1 = -.015$ and $\gamma_2 = -.040$.

Group	z_1	z_2	$e^{-(\gamma_1 z_1 + \gamma_2 z_2)}$
Male non-smoker	1	0	$e^{.015} = 1.0151$
Male smoker	1	1	$e^{.055} = 1.0565$
Female non-smoker	0	0	$e^{0} = 1$
Female smoker	0	1	$e^{.040} = 1.0408$

For $s_0(x)$ one could use either a parametric or tabular model. For male non-smokers the model would be $s_0(1.0151x)$, for male smokers it would be $s_0(1.0565x)$, and for female smokers $s_0(1.0408x)$.

As an alternative to the accelerated failure time model above where $ln(X)$ is regressed on Z_1, Z_2, the conditional hazard rate $h(x|Z_1 = z_1,\ Z_2 = z_2)$ could be modeled as a function of the covariates. In a muliplicative model known as proportional hazards the conditional hazard rate is assumed to be of the form

$$h(x|Z_1 = z_1, Z_2 = z_2) = h_0(x)exp(\beta_1 z_1 + \beta_2 z_2)$$

where $h_0(x)$ is the baseline hazard function corresponding to $z_1 = z_2 = 0$. In this form

$$ln(h(x|Z_1 = z_1, Z_2 = z_2)) = ln\, h_0(x) + \beta_1 z_1 + \beta_2 z_2$$

and β_1, β_2 are obtained from linear regression. As a result

$$\frac{h(x|Z_1 = a,\, Z_2 = b)}{h(x|Z_1 = c,\, Z_2 = d)} = \frac{h_0(x)e^{\beta_1 a + \beta_2 b}}{h_0(x)e^{\beta_1 c + \beta_2 d}} = e^{\beta_1(a-c)+\beta_2(b-d)}. \text{ (independent of } x\text{)}$$

If this last number were simply denoted by k, the hazard rates are proportional and the survival functions are related by

$$s(x|Z_1 = a,\, Z_2 = b) = exp\left(-\int_0^x h(s|Z_1 = a,\, Z_2 = b)\, ds\right)$$

$$= exp\left(-\int_0^x h(s|Z_1 = c,\, Z_2 = d)\, ds \cdot k\right)$$

$$= [s(x|Z_1 = c,\, Z_2 = d)]^k.$$

Censored and Truncated Random Variables

X is still a general survival model. It might be a parametric model or an empirical one. Here we want to set the stage for the problem of estimating various parameters, percentiles, etc. of this model from the data provided by a statistical study. The estimation problem can be split into two cases – complete data or incomplete data. By far, the simplest situation is the complete data or longitudinal study design. A study is conducted on a sample of n units (people, mice, batteries, electrical circuits, etc.). Each unit enters the study at $x = 0$ and is observed until the time of failure. One has a complete list of failure times $X_1 = x_1, \ldots, X_n = x_n$. If the goal is to find a maximum likelihood estimate of one or more parameters, the likelihood is $L = f(x_1)f(x_2)\cdots f(x_n)$ where each $f(x_i)$ is expressed in terms of the parameter(s). Complete data studies are practical only for small sample sizes and when all units are certain to fail within a fairly short amount of time.

By contrast consider the problem of estimating $q_0, q_1, q_2, \ldots\ q_{\omega-1}$ for a tabular survival model of human lives. Once ℓ_0 is chosen and the parameters are estimated, the table is constructed at integral ages from $\ell_n = \ell_0 \cdot p_0 \cdot p_1 \cdot \cdots \cdot p_{n-1} = \ell_0(1-q_0)(1-q_1)\cdots(1-q_{n-1})$, and then extended to fractional ages (i.e., a continuous model) by some interpolation assumption such as the UDD. A longitudinal study for $\ell_0 = 10{,}000{,}000$ lives extending perhaps 100 years or more is ridiculously impractical. Furthermore, even if it were done, the model would probably not accurately reflect current mortality patterns due to changes in medicine, care, prevalent disease etc.. The various q_k are instead estimated from a cross-sectional study extending over a several year period. A person enters the study at some age $x_0 > 0$ and is observed either until death or the end of the study. For such an individual one does not observe a value of X, the random lifetime of a newborn, rather, one observes a truncated and censored form of X. Incomplete data always results in these complications.

As a first step consider the distribution of $Y = X|_{X>x_0}$ (left truncation). By elementary probability $f_X(x|X > x_0) = \dfrac{f_X(x)}{s_X(x_0)}$, $s_X(x|X > x_0) = \dfrac{s_X(x)}{s_X(x_0)}$.

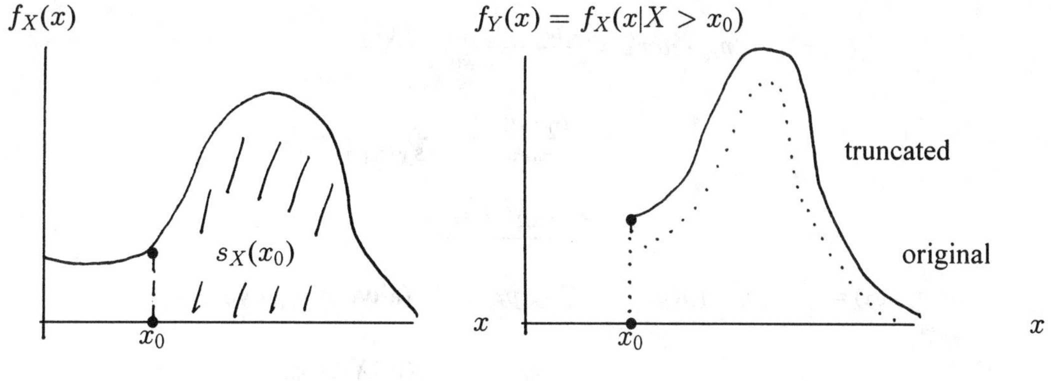

One does not even get to observe Y. Suppose the life entering the study at age x_0 is scheduled to leave the study at age y_0 unless death occurs prior to this age. Then one gets to observe $Z = min(Y,\ y_0)$. Note that $Z = Y$ if $Y < y_0$ (i.e., death occurs during the study) or $Z = y_0$ (the individual is still alive at age y_0 at the end of the study). The variable Y is said to be censored at the right. As a result the density curve for Z looks just like f_Y for the age range (x_0, y_0), but then all probability to the right of y_0 in the Y-distribution is relocated as a point mass at y_0 in the Z-distribution.

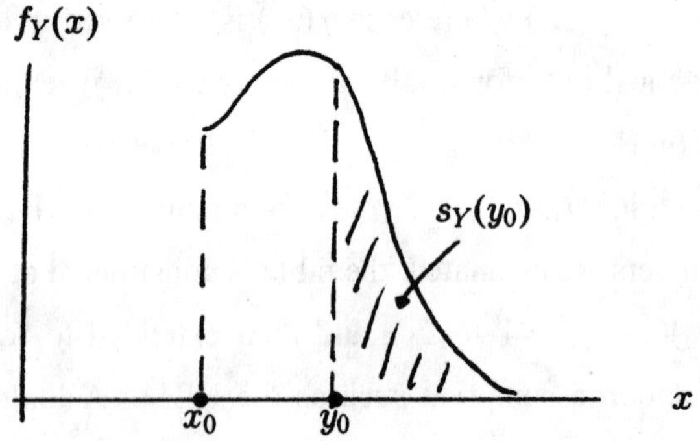

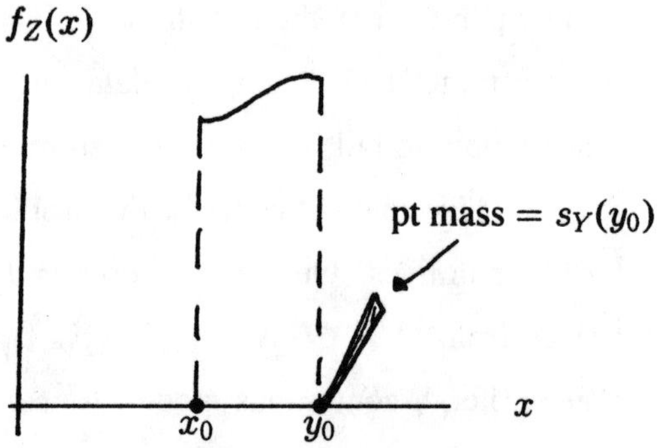

A convenient way to write this Z-density is

$$f_Z(x) = {}_{x-x_0}p_{x_0} \cdot [\mu(x)]^{\delta} \qquad x_0 \le x \le y_0$$

where $\delta = 1$ if the individual dies during the study (i.e., $f_Z(x) = {}_{x-x_0}p_{x_0} \cdot \mu(x)$ and $x_0 \le x \le y_0$), and $\delta = 0$ if she survives to age y_0 at the study's conclusion (i.e., $f_Z(y_0) = {}_{y_0-x_0}p_{x_0} \cdot [\mu(y_0)]^0 = {}_{y_0-x_0}p_{x_0}$).

Notice the consistency of this convenient expression with the pictures above of the Y and Z densities:

$$\underline{\delta = 1;\ Z = x < y_0}$$

$$f_Z(x) = {}_{x-x_0}p_{x_0} \cdot \mu(x) = \frac{{}_{x_0}p_0 \cdot {}_{x-x_0}p_{x_0} \cdot \mu(x)}{{}_{x_0}p_0}$$

$$= \frac{{}_{x}p_0 \cdot \mu(x)}{{}_{x_0}p_0} = \frac{f_X(x)}{s_X(x_0)} = f_Y(x)$$

$$\underline{\delta = 0;\ Z = y_0}$$

$$f_Z(y_0) = {}_{y_0-x_0}p_{x_0} \cdot [\mu(y_0)]^0 = {}_{y_0-x_0}p_{x_0} = Pr(\text{alive at } y_0|\text{alive at } x_0)$$

$$= s_X(y_0|X > x_0) = s_Y(y_0)$$

In general, truncation of X results in a conditional distribution, whereas censoring results in certain chunks of probability being consolidated as point masses thus yielding a mixed distribution (i.e., neither continuous nor discrete).

In the example above we saw a combination of truncation and censoring. Next, we want to look at these issues separately. We begin by considering censoring. There are many study designs based on censoring schemes of one type or another. We continue to use X as the survival model. Generally speaking, a censoring scheme results in some of the X_i in the study be observed exactly. For the rest of the study units we only know that X_i falls in some interval (e.g., $0 < X_i \le x_0^{(i)}$ if $x_0^{(i)}$ is the age the unit would have been at the beginning of the study if it had not failed prior to the study's inception, or that $y_0^{(i)} < X_i$ if $y_0^{(i)}$ is the age the unit reached at the conclusion of the study.)

Suppose we want to study the survival distribution of X, the lifetime of a particular brand of car battery. Many of these were sold from 1990-1994 and the statistical study is to be conducted in the calendar year 1995. The study units consist of the records of 1000 batteries sold during 1990-1994. Suppose that data available on these 1000 units as a result of the study is as follows:

(i) certain batteries failed prior to 1995 at unknown times;

(ii) certain batteries failed during the study at known exact times; and

(iii) the rest of the study units are known to be surviving at the study's conclusion.

Consider one battery in the study sold on July 1, 1991 ($x = 0$ on this date). At the beginning of the study this battery would be age $x_0 = 3.5$ if it were in category (ii) or (iii) above, and would be scheduled to leave observation at age $y_0 = 4.5$ at the conclusion of the study. The data for this unit from the study consists of a pair of random variables:

$$\xi = \begin{cases} -1 & \text{failure prior to the study} \\ 0 & \text{failure during the study} \\ 1 & \text{failure after the study} \end{cases}$$

$$Y = \begin{cases} x_0 = 3.5 & \xi = -1 \\ x & \xi = 0 \\ y_0 = 4.5 & \xi = 1 \end{cases}$$

The corresponding likelihood expression is

$$L = \begin{cases} F_X(x_0) = {}_{x_0}q_0 & \xi = -1 \\ f_X(x) = {}_{x}p_0 \cdot h(x) & \xi = 0 \\ s_X(y_0) = {}_{y_0}p_0 & \xi = 1 \end{cases}$$

The pictures of the X and Y densities below indicate that two chunks of the X-distribution are relocated as point masses in the Y-distribution.

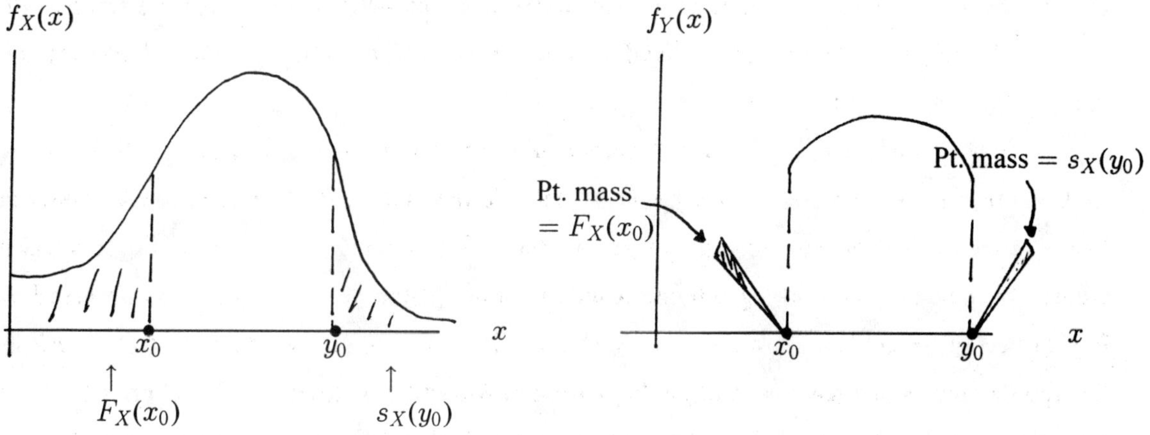

Next let's consider the issue of truncation in the context of the survival model for the lifetime of a battery discussed above. This time let's suppose the 1995 study data consists of only the 1990-1994 sales which failed during 1995. All other batteries are hidden from the investigator. For the battery sold on July 1, 1991 which failed during the 1995 study the data observed is $Y = X|_{3.5<X\leq 4.5}$. The resulting likelihood expression is a conditional density:

$$f_X(x|3.5 < X \leq 4.5) = \frac{f_X(x)}{Pr(3.5 < X \leq 4.5)} = \frac{f_X(x)}{s_X(3.5) - s_X(4.5)},\ 3.5 < x \leq 4.5$$

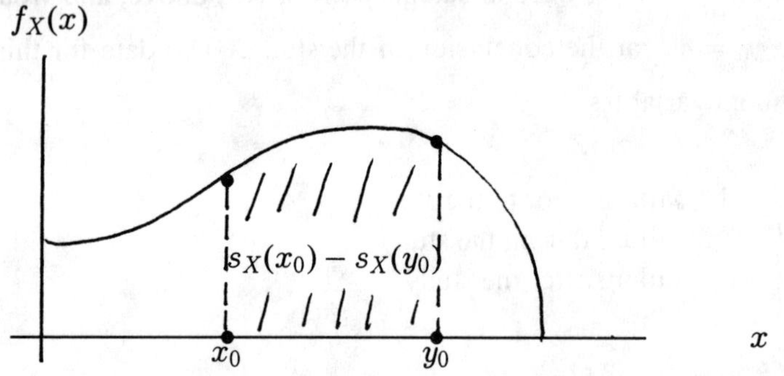

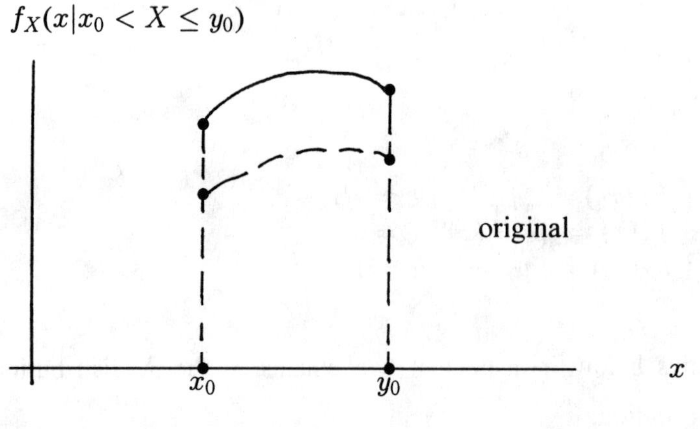

CONDENSED REVIEW NOTES AND ADVANCED TOPICS

Equivalent Functional Descriptions of a Continuous Survival Model

A survival model is specified by the distribution of a positive-valued continuous random variable X. It is the random time from some well-defined point in time (i.e., when $x = 0$) until some random event (called failure) occurs.

(1) $F_X(x) = Pr(X \leq x) =$ Probability that failure occurs by time x. The distribution function F is continuous, increasing, $F(0) = 0$ and $\lim\limits_{x\to\infty} F(x) = 1$

(2) $s_X(x) = Pr(X > x) =$ Probability that failure occurs after time x. The survival function s is continuous, decreasing, $s_X(0) = 1$ and $\lim\limits_{x\to\infty} s_X(x) = 0$.

(3) $f_X(x)$, the probability density function, is not a probability, but $f_X(x)(\Delta x)$ is approximately the probability that failure occurs in $[x, x+\Delta x]$. It is positive, piecewise continuous, and $\int_0^\infty f_X(x)\,dx = 1$

(4) $h_X(x)$, the hazard rate function, is not a probability, but $h_X(x)(\Delta x)$ is approximately the probability that failure occurs in $[x, x+\Delta x]$ given survival to time x. It is piecewise continuous, positive and $\int_0^\infty h_X(x)\,dx = \infty$.

(5) $\ell(x)$ is the expected number of surviving units at time x from a group of ℓ_0 units of time 0. It is continuous, decreasing and $\lim\limits_{x\to\infty} \ell_x = 0$.

(6) $mr\ell(x)$, the mean residual lifetime at time x, is $E[X - x|X > x]$. It is continuous, decreasing and $\lim\limits_{x\to\infty} mr\ell(x) = 0$.

Important Relations

$$F_X(x) = \int_0^x f_X(s)\,ds, \qquad s_X(x) = \int_x^\infty f_X(s)\,ds$$

$$1 = F_X(x) + s_X(x), \quad f_X(x) = F'_X(x) = -s'_X(x)$$

$$h_X(x) = \frac{f_X(x)}{s_X(x)} = -ln(s_X(x))'$$

$$H_X(x) = \int_0^x h_X(s)\,ds \text{ (cumulative hazard function)}$$

$$s_X(x) = exp\left(-\int_0^x h_X(s)\,ds\right) = exp(-H_X(x))$$

$$\ell_x = \ell_0 \cdot s_X(x), \quad s_X(x) = \frac{\ell_x}{\ell_0}$$

$$mr\ell(x) = E[X - x|X > x] \underset{\text{(parts)}}{=} \int_0^\infty \frac{s_X(x+t)\,dt}{s_X(x)} = \int_x^\infty \frac{s_X(s)\,ds}{s_X(x)} = \overset{\circ}{e}_x \quad \text{(actuarial equivalent notation)}$$

$$h_X(x) = \frac{\left(\frac{d\overset{\circ}{e}_x}{dx} + 1\right)}{\overset{\circ}{e}_x}$$

If one is given one of the six functions f, F, s, ℓ, h or $mr\ell$, the other five can be calculated from the above relations. Note: See unit 1 for a calculation of variance of the future lifetime $X - x|_{X>x}$.

Equivalence with Actuarial Survival Model Notation

Think of $x = 0$ as birth, failure as death, and X as the random lifetime of a newborn. Then all the notation and relations of unit 1 can be used in any survival model.

$${}_tp_x = \frac{s_X(x+t)}{s_X(x)} = Pr(X > x+t|X > x)$$

$${}_tq_x = 1 - {}_tp_x = Pr(X \leq x+t|X > x)$$

$${}_{m|n}q_x = Pr(x+m < X \leq x+m+n|X > x) = {}_mp_x \cdot {}_nq_{x+m}$$

$$s_X(x) = {}_xp_0, \; {}_np_x = p_x \cdot p_{x+1} \cdot \dots \cdot p_{x+n-1} \quad (n \text{ integral})$$

Discrete Survival Models

The definitions $F_X(x) = Pr(X \leq x)$ and $s_X(x) = Pr(X > x)$ remain the same, but their graphs are discontinuous step functions. The probability function, $p_X(x)$, is defined by $Pr(X = x)$. Let x_1, x_2, ... be all the possible x-values (in increasing order) with positive probability, and, for convenience, let x_0 be less than x_1; $\sum_{i=1}^{\infty} p_X(x_i) = 1$. the hazard function is defined by

$$h_X(x_j) = Pr(X = x_j|X \geq x_j) = \frac{p_X(x_j)}{p_X(x_j) + p_X(x_{j+1}) + \cdots}$$

$$= 1 - \frac{s_X(x_j)}{s_X(x_{j-1})}$$

$$= \frac{p_X(x_j)}{s_X(x_{j-1})} = \text{probability of failure at time } x_j \text{ given survival at time } x_{j-1}$$

Thus

$$s_X(x) = \frac{s_X(x_1)}{s_X(x_0)} \cdot \frac{s_X(x_2)}{s_X(x_1)} \cdot \dots \cdot \frac{s_X(x_j)}{s_X(x_{j-1})} = [1 - h_X(x_1)][1 - h_X(x_2)] \cdots [1 - h_X(x_j)]$$

for $x_j \leq x < x_{j+1}$.

Regression Models with Covariate Data

$Z_1, Z_2, \ldots, Z_n$ are variables related to X. The idea is to use these variables with regression techniques to study the conditional failure time distributions $X|_{Z_1, \cdots Z_n}$.

1. Accelerated Failure Time Model. $ln(X)$ is regressed on the Z_i according to the model

$$ln(X) = \mu + \sum \gamma_i Z_i + \sigma W$$

W = "error distribution" ($E[W] = 0$, $\sigma_W = 1$)

$$\Rightarrow \quad X|_{Z_1=z_1, \cdots Z_n=z_n} = [e^{\sum \gamma_i z_i}]e^{\mu+\sigma W}$$

$$\begin{cases} e^{\mu+\sigma W} = \text{base-line distribution} = X|_{all\ Z=0} \\ \text{survival function denoted } s_0(x)\text{, hazard function } h_0(x) = -ln(s_0(x))' \end{cases}$$

$$\Rightarrow \quad s(x|Z_1 = z_1, \ldots, Z_n = z_n) = s_0(xe^{-\sum \gamma_i z_i})$$

$$\Rightarrow \quad h(x|Z_1 = z_1, \ldots, Z_n = z_n) = h_0(xe^{-\sum \gamma_i z_i}) \cdot e^{-\sum \gamma_i z_i}$$

The factor $e^{-\sum \gamma_i z_i}$ is an age acceleration factor if it is greater than 1 (i.e., $\sum \gamma_i z_i < 0$), or age degrading factor if it is less than 1 (i.e., $\sum \gamma_i z_i > 0$). If p were the 90th percentile of the baseline distribution then

$$.10 = s_0(p) \quad \Rightarrow \quad s(pe^{\sum \gamma_i z_i}|Z_1 = z_1, \ldots Z_n = z_n) = s_0(pe^{\sum \gamma_i z_i} \cdot e^{-\sum \gamma_i z_i}) = s_0(p) = .10$$

$$\Rightarrow \quad pe^{\sum \gamma_i z_i} \text{ is the } 90^{th} \text{ percentile of } X|_{Z_1=z_1, \ldots Z_n=z_n}.$$

2. Proportional Hazards Model

$$ln(h(x|Z_1 = z_1, \ldots, Z_n = z_n)) = ln(h_0(x)) + \sum \beta_i z_i$$

$$\Rightarrow \quad h(x|Z_1 = z_1, \ldots, Z_n = z_n) = h_0(x)e^{\sum \beta_i z_i}$$

$$\Rightarrow \quad \frac{h(x|Z_1 = a_1, \ldots, Z_n = a_n)}{h(x|Z_1 = b_1, \ldots, Z_n = b_n)} = e^{\sum \beta_i (a_i - b_i)} = k \quad \text{(independent of } x\text{)}$$

$$\Rightarrow \quad s(x|\text{all } Z_i = a_i) = [s(x|\text{all } Z_i = b_i)]^k$$

Censored Random Variables

A statistical study yields incomplete data. For some a, b with $0 \le a < b \le \infty$, the value of X is known precisely only if $a < X \le b$. If the failure occurs before time a or after time b you only know the occurrence, not the exact time. The a, b pair can vary from one study unit to the next and a could be 0 or b could be ∞. The study data consists of

$$\xi = \begin{cases} -1 & X \le a \\ 0 & a < X \le b \\ 1 & b < X \end{cases}, \qquad Y = \begin{cases} a & \xi = -1 \\ X & \xi = 0 \\ b & \xi = 1 \end{cases}$$

and the likelihood expression is

$$L = \begin{cases} F_X(a) = {}_a q_0 & \xi = -1 \\ f_X(x) = {}_x p_0 \cdot h(x) & \xi = 0 \\ s_X(b) = {}_b p_0 & \xi = 1 \end{cases}$$

Truncated Random Variables

The statistical study of X uses data only from failures during the interval $(a, b]$, that is, you get to observe $Y = X|_{a<X\le b}$.

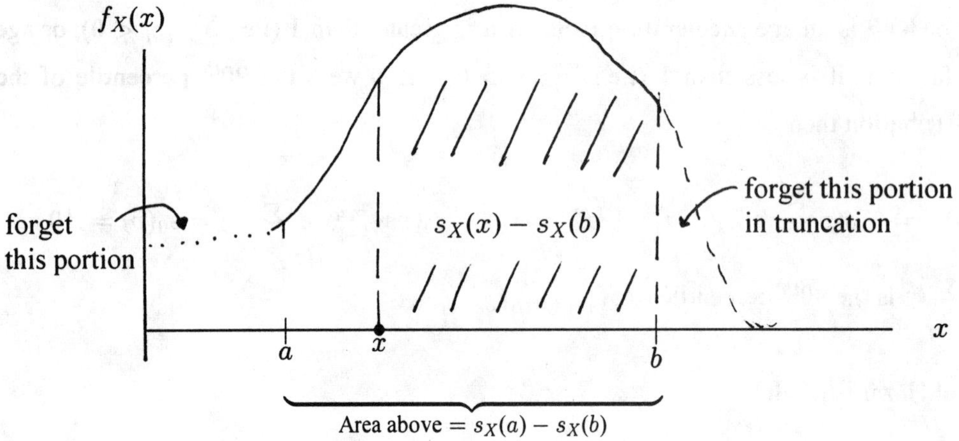

$$s_X(x|a < X \le b) = \frac{s_X(x) - s_X(b)}{s_X(a) - s_X(b)} = \text{fraction of area between } a \text{ and } b \text{ to the right of } x$$

$$\Rightarrow \quad f_X(x|a < X \le b) = -s_X(x|a < X \le b)' \quad (-s' = f \text{ generally}) = \frac{f_X(x)}{s_X(a) - s_X(b)}$$

$$\Rightarrow \quad h_X(x|a < X \le b) = \frac{density}{survival} = \frac{f_X(x)}{s_X(x) - s_X(b)}$$

Note: In the above a could be zero. This is right truncation and $s_X(a)$ becomes $s_X(0) = 1$. One could also have $b = \infty$, left truncation, with the adjustment $s_X(b) = s_X(\infty) = 0$.

CONCEPTUAL REVIEW TEST

1. Contrast the meaning of $f_X(25)(\Delta x)$ with that of $h_X(25)(\Delta x)$.

2. What are the essential properties of F_X, s_X and h_X?

3. How would you compute $Pr(20 < X \leq 30|X > 10)$ from the survival function?

4. In the accelerated failure time model describe the conditional survival function $s(x|Z_1 = z_1, \ldots\ Z_n = z_n)$ in terms of the baseline survival function.

5. If two hazard rates $h(x|Z_1 = a,\ Z_2 = b)$ and $h(x|Z_1 = c,\ Z_2 = d)$ are proportional then what is the relation between the related conditional survival functions.

6. Describe the difference between censoring and truncation.

CONCEPTUAL REVIEW TEST SOLUTIONS

1. $f_X(25)(\Delta x)$ is the unconditional probability of failure during the time interval $[25, 25+\Delta x]$ (computed at $x = 0$ for a "newborn"), whereas $h_X(25)(\Delta x)$ is the conditional probability of failure during the same interval given survival to age 25.

2. F is continuous, increasing with $F(0) = 0$, $F(\infty) = 1$. s is continuous, decreasing with $s(0) = 1$, $s(\infty) = 0$. $h(x)$ is non-negative, (piecewise) continuous and $\int_0^\infty h(x)\,dx = \infty$ so that $s(\infty) = exp(-\int_0^\infty h(x)\,dx) = exp(-\infty) = 0$.

3. From the definition of conditional probability

$$Pr(20 < X \leq 30|X > 10) = \frac{Pr(\{20 < X \leq 30\} \cap \{X > 10\})}{Pr(X > 10)} = \frac{Pr(20 < X \leq 30)}{Pr(X > 10)} = \frac{s(20) - s(30)}{s(10)}$$

4. If $s_0(x)$ is the conditional survival function when all $Z_i = 0$ then $s(x|Z_1 = z_1, \ldots, Z_n = z_n) = s_0(xe^{-\sum \gamma_i z_i})$ where the γ_i are obtained from a regression model of $ln(X)$ on $Z_1, \ldots Z_n$.

5. In general $s_X(x) = exp(-\int_0^x h(s)\,ds)$. So if $h(x|Z_1 = a, Z_2 = b) = k \cdot h(x|Z_1 = c, Z_2 = d)$, it follows from the general relation that $s(x|Z_1 = a, Z_2 = b) = [s(x|Z_1 = c, Z_2 = d)]^k$.

6. With censoring you only know the exact value of X if it falls in $(a, b]$. If failure occurs prior to time a or after time b, you know the occurrence but not the exact time. With truncation you only get to observe the failures that occurred in $(a, b]$.

COMPUTATIONAL REVIEW TEST

1. If $h(x) = \frac{2x}{1+x^2}$ find s, F, f, ℓ_x, and $\overset{\circ}{e}_x$.

2. If X is uniformly distributed on $[0, \omega]$ find s, h, f, ℓ_x and $\overset{\circ}{e}_x$.

3. Suppose a discrete failure time distribution is given by $p(k) = \frac{1}{n}$ for $k = 1, 2, \ldots, n$. Compute $h(k)$ for $k = 1, 2, \ldots, n$.

4. Find the 75th percentile of X in problem 1 above.

5. If $\widetilde{s}(x) = s(1.05x)$ where $s_X(x)$ is as in problem 1, find the 75th percentile of the new survival model and express $\widetilde{h}$ in terms of h.

6. Suppose X is a survival model with $h(x) = \frac{2x}{1+x^2}$ as in problem 1 above.

   (a) An observation on X is censored at the right at time 5. Write the likelihood expression if $X = 1$ or $X > 5$ and evaluate using problem 1.

   (b) An observation on X is truncated at the right at time 5. Write the likelihood expression if $X = 1$ and evaluate.

COMPUTATIONAL REVIEW TEST SOLUTIONS

1. $H(x) = \int_0^x h(s)\,ds = \int_0^x \frac{2s}{1+s^2}ds = ln(1+s^2)\Big|_0^x = ln(1+x^2)$, so
$s_X(x) = exp(-H(x)) = exp(-ln(1+x^2)) = \frac{1}{1+x^2}$. Hence $F(x) = 1 - s_X(x) = \frac{x^2}{1+x^2}$,
$f(x) = F' = -s' = \frac{2x}{[1+x^2]^2}$, $\ell_x = \ell_0 s_X(x) = \frac{\ell_0}{1+x^2}$ (ℓ_0 any number desired), and finally

$$\mathring{e}_x = mr\ell(x) = \int_x^\infty \frac{s(y)\,dy}{s_X(x)}$$

$$= \int_x^\infty \frac{1}{1+y^2}\,dy \Big/ \left(\frac{1}{1+x^2}\right)$$

$$= [tan^{-1}(y)\Big|_x^\infty][1+x^2]$$

$$= \left[\frac{\pi}{2} - tan^{-1}(x)\right][1+x^2]$$

Note: You can check your work by verifying that

$$\frac{2x}{1+x^2} \underset{\text{here}}{\overset{}{=}} h(x) \underset{\text{general}}{\overset{}{=}} \frac{\left[\frac{d\mathring{e}_x}{dx}+1\right]}{\mathring{e}_x}.$$

2. For a uniform distribution $f(x) = \frac{1}{\omega}$ for $0 \le x \le \omega$. Hence $F(x) = \int_0^x f(s)\,ds = \frac{x}{\omega}$,
$s_X(x) = 1 - \frac{x}{\omega}$, $\ell_x = \ell_0 s_X(x) = \omega(1 - \frac{x}{\omega}) = \omega - x$ if $\ell_0 = \omega$, $h(x) = \frac{f(x)}{s_X(x)} = \frac{1}{\omega - x}$

and

$$\mathring{e}_x = \int_x^\omega \frac{s(y)\,dy}{s_X(x)} = \int_x^\omega \frac{\left(1-\frac{y}{\omega}\right)dy}{\left(1-\frac{x}{\omega}\right)}$$

$$= \frac{-\frac{\omega}{2}\left(1-\frac{y}{\omega}\right)^2\Big|_x^\omega}{\left(1-\frac{x}{\omega}\right)}$$

$$= \frac{\frac{\omega}{2}\left(1-\frac{x}{\omega}\right)^2}{\left(1-\frac{x}{\omega}\right)} = \frac{\omega - x}{2}$$

3. $h(k) = \dfrac{p(k)}{p(k) + \cdots + p(n)} = \dfrac{\left(\frac{1}{n}\right)}{\left(\frac{1}{n}\right) + \cdots + \left(\frac{1}{n}\right)} = \dfrac{1}{n-k+1}.$

4. If p is the 75th percentile then $.25 = s(p) = \dfrac{1}{1+p^2}$, $p = \sqrt{3}$.

5. $\tilde{s}(x) = s(1.05x) = .25$ means $1.05x$ is the 75th percentile computed in problem 4; $1.05x = \sqrt{3}$, $x = \dfrac{\sqrt{3}}{1.05}$. Also

$$\tilde{h}(x) = -ln(\tilde{s}(x))' = -ln(s(1.05x))'$$

$$= h(1.05x)\left[\frac{d1.05x}{dx}\right] \qquad \text{(chain rule)}$$

$$= 1.05h(1.05x) = 1.05\left[\frac{2(1.05x)}{1+(1.05x)^2}\right].$$

6. (a) $L = \begin{cases} f(x) & x \leq 5 \\ s(5) & x > 5 \end{cases}$ (general)

$$= \begin{cases} \dfrac{2x}{[1+x^2]^2} & x \leq 5 \\ \dfrac{1}{1+5^2} = s(5) & x > 5 \end{cases} \qquad \text{(problem 1)}$$

So $x = 1$ makes $L = f(1) = \frac{2}{4}$ and $x > 5$ makes $L = s(5) = \frac{1}{26}$.

(b) $f_X(x|X \leq 5) = \dfrac{f_X(x)}{s_X(0) - s_X(5)}$ (general)

$$= \frac{\left[\dfrac{2x}{(1+x^2)^2}\right]}{1 - \frac{1}{1+5^2}} = \frac{26}{25} \cdot \frac{2x}{[1+x^2]^2} \qquad \text{(problem 1)}$$

when $0 < x \leq 5$.

So $x = 1$ makes $L = f_X(1|X \leq 5) = \frac{26}{25} \cdot \frac{2}{4} = \frac{13}{25}$.

UNIT REVIEW QUESTIONS

Some of the following are based on questions from the SOA 160 exam prior to the year 2000 syllabus.

1. You are given:

   (i) A survival model is defined by $h(x) = \frac{1}{3(\omega - x)}$, $0 \leq x < \omega$

   (ii) The median age is 63.

   Calculate $\overset{\circ}{e}_{63}$.

   (A) 4.5 (B) 6.8 (C) 7.9 (D) 9.0 (E) 13.5

2. You are given $h(x) = kx^n$ and the median age is 22. At the median age the hazard rate is 1.26. Calculate n.

   (A) 36 (B) 37 (C) 38 (D) 39 (E) 40

3. A survival distribution is defined by $f_X(x) = \frac{1}{15}$ for $0 \leq x \leq 15$. Calculate $h(7|3 < X \leq 9)$.

   (A) $\frac{1}{2}$ (B) $\frac{1}{3}$ (C) $\frac{1}{4}$ (D) $\frac{1}{6}$ (E) $\frac{2}{15}$

4. Suppose $mr\ell(x) = \frac{3}{4}(80 - x)$ for $0 \leq x \leq 80$. then $s(70) =$

   (A) $\frac{1}{2}$ (B) $\frac{1}{3}$ (C) $\frac{1}{4}$ (D) $\frac{2}{3}$ (E) $\frac{3}{4}$

Use the following information for Questions 5-7.

A 60-month battery is sold with a prorated refund of the purchase price if the battery fails within 60 months. X is the time (in months) until failure of a new battery. Since batteries experience an increasing hazard rate (due to aging), and since none of these batteries is likely to survive beyond 96 months, it is decided that $h(x) = \frac{r}{96 - x}$, $0 \leq x < 96$ is a reasonable model of the hazard function.

5. If the average battery lasts 70 months find r.

   (A) $\frac{14}{70}$ (B) $\frac{18}{70}$ (C) $\frac{22}{70}$ (D) $\frac{26}{70}$ (E) $\frac{30}{70}$

6. Using the r obtained in Question 5 calculate the percentage of batteries expected to fail during the warranty period.

(A) 19% (B) 31% (C) 48% (D) 69% (E) 81%

7. With the r obtained in Question 5 calculate the expected lifetime of a battery known to fail during the warranty period.

(A) 30 months (B) 33 months (C) 36 months (D) 39 months (E) 42 months

Use the following information for Questions 8 and 9.

A pool of mortgages consists of \$10,000,000 in debt amortized over 25 years at $i^{(12)} = 12\%$. The monthly payment for the pool (no prepayment of principal), P, is determined by $10{,}000{,}000 = Pa_{\overline{300}|.01}$. Let B_k be the outstanding balance (principal) of the pool after k months of payments. A randomly chosen dollar of principal from the pool is said to survive at time k (months) if it has not been repaid.

8. If $s(k)$ is the survival function for $k = 0, 1, \ldots, 300$ calculate $s(150)$.

(A) .64 (B) .73 (C) .82 (D) .85 (E) .87

9. If $h(k)$ is the hazard function, calculate $h(150)$ to the nearest thousandth.

(A) .001 (B) .002 (C) .003 (D) .004 (E) .005

Use the following information for Questions 10 and 11.

For waiting time variables X, Y you are given the accelerated aging model $ln(X) = .01Z_1 - .03Z_2 + ln(Y)$ where Y is the baseline distribution (i.e., $X|_{Z_1=0,\, Z_2=0} = Y$). Suppose $h_Y(y) = 2y^2$

10. Find $s_X(2|Z_1 = 1, Z_2 = 3)$.

(A) .0008 (B) .0009 (C) .0010 (D) .0011 (E) .0012

11. Find $h_X(2|Z_1 = 1, Z_2 = 3)$.

(A) 8.1 (B) 8.7 (C) 9.4 (D) 9.8 (E) 10.2

SOLUTIONS TO UNIT REVIEW QUESTIONS

1. $h(x) = \frac{1}{3(\omega - x)}$ is of the type $\frac{p'(x)}{p(x)}c$ where $p(x) = \omega - x$ and $c = -\frac{1}{3}$. In this case $H(x) = \int_0^x \frac{p'(s)}{p(s)} c\, ds = c \cdot ln\left[\frac{p(x)}{p(0)}\right]$ and $s_X(x) = exp(-H(x)) = \left[\frac{p(0)}{p(x)}\right]^c$. Here $s_X(x) = \left[\frac{\omega}{\omega - x}\right]^{-1/3} = \left(1 - \frac{x}{\omega}\right)^{1/3}$. A median age of 63 translates into $s(63) = \left(1 - \frac{63}{\omega}\right)^{1/3} = .50$, resulting in $\omega = 72$. Thus

$$\overset{\circ}{e}_{63} = \int_{63}^{72} \frac{s(y)\,dy}{s(63)} = \int_{63}^{72} \left(1 - \frac{x}{72}\right)^{1/3} dx/(.5) = \left(-\frac{3}{4} \cdot 72\left(1 - \frac{x}{72}\right)^{4/3}\Big|_{63}^{72}\right)(2) = 6.75.$$

ANSWER B

2. $H(x) = \int_0^x h(s)\,ds = \frac{k}{n+1} \cdot x^{n+1}$, so $.5 = s(22) = exp(-H(22)) = exp\left(\frac{-k}{n+1}(22)^{n+1}\right)$. We are also given that $1.26 = h(22) = k(22)^n$. Taking a log of the first equation gives simultaneous equations

$$ln(2) = \frac{k}{n+1}(22)^{n+1}, \text{ and } 1.26 = k(22)^n,$$

which, when divided, results in $\frac{22}{n+1} = \frac{ln(2)}{1.26}$. Thus

$$n = \frac{22(1.26)}{ln(2)} - 1 = 39.99 - 1 = 38.99.$$

ANSWER D

3. $s(x|3 < X \le 9) = \frac{s_X(x) - s(9)}{s(3) - s(9)}$. With $f(x) = \frac{1}{15}$ we obtain $s_X(x) = \int_x^{15} f(t)\,dt = 1 - \frac{x}{15}$; $s(3) = \frac{12}{15}$, $s(9) = \frac{6}{15}$. Thus $s(x|3 < X \le 9) = \frac{s_X(x) - \frac{6}{15}}{\left(\frac{6}{15}\right)}$ and, by differentiation, $f(x|3 < X \le 9) = -s(x|3 < X \le 9)' = \frac{f(x)}{\left(\frac{6}{15}\right)} = \left(\frac{1}{15}\right)\left(\frac{15}{6}\right) = \frac{1}{6}$. Then

$$h(x|3 < X \le 9) = \frac{density}{survival} = \frac{\left(\frac{1}{6}\right)}{\left(s_X(x) - \frac{6}{15}\right)\left(\frac{6}{15}\right)^{-1}}.$$ For $x = 7$ we see that

$$h(7|3 < X \le 9) = \frac{\left(\frac{1}{6}\right)\left(\frac{6}{15}\right)}{\left(\frac{8}{15} - \frac{6}{15}\right)} = \frac{1}{15} \cdot \frac{15}{2} = \frac{1}{2}.$$

ANSWER A

4. In general $h(x) = \left(\frac{dmr\ell(x)}{dx} + 1\right)/mr\ell(x)$. Here, with $mr\ell(x) = \frac{3}{4}(80 - x)$ we obtain $h(x) = \frac{\left(\frac{1}{4}\right)}{\left(\frac{3}{4}\right)(80 - x)} = \frac{\left(\frac{1}{3}\right)}{80 - x}$. As in Question 1 above $h(x) = \frac{p'(x)}{p(x)}c$ with $p(x) = 80 - x$ and $c = -\frac{1}{3}$. Thus $s_X(x) = \left(\frac{p(0)}{p(x)}\right)^c = \left(1 - \frac{x}{80}\right)^{1/3}$; $s(70) = \frac{1}{2}$.

ANSWER A

5. $h(x) = \frac{r}{\omega - x}$ implies $s_X(x) = \left(1 - \frac{x}{\omega}\right)^r$ and $\overset{\circ}{e}_x = \frac{\omega - x}{r + 1}$ (see the examples in the Unit 1 Condensed Review Notes). Thus $70 = E[X] = \overset{\circ}{e}_0 = \frac{96 - 0}{r + 1}$; $r = \frac{26}{70}$. ANSWER D

6. From the above $s_X(x) = \left(1 - \frac{x}{\omega}\right)^r = \left(1 - \frac{x}{96}\right)^{26/70}$, hence $s(60) = \left(\frac{36}{96}\right)^{(26/70)} = .69$. since 69% are expected to survive the warranty period, 31% are expected to fail. ANSWER B

7. The question asks for $E[X|X \le 60]$ (X is truncated at the right). We need to calculate $\int_0^{60} x \cdot f_X(x|X \le 60)dx = \int_0^{60} s_X(x|X \le 60)dx$ (recall from Actuarial Survival Models $\overset{\circ}{e}_x = \int_0^{\omega - x} t \cdot {}_tp_x\mu(x+t)\,dt = \int_0^{\omega - x} {}_tp_x\,dt$ and that ${}_tp_x$ is the survival function of $T(x)$). In the Condensed Review Notes for this unit we saw

$$s_X(x|X \le 60) = \frac{s_X(x) - s(60)}{1 - s(60)}.$$

Thus

$$\int_0^{60} s_X(x|X \le 60)dx = \frac{\int_0^{60} s_X(x)\,dx - 60s(60)}{1 - s(60)}$$

$$\int_0^{60} s_X(x)\,dx = \int_0^{60} \left(1 - \frac{x}{96}\right)^{26/70} dx = -70\left(1 - \frac{x}{96}\right)^{96/70}\Big|_0^{60} = 51.76$$

$$s(60) = .6947$$

$$E[X|X \le 60] = \frac{51.76 - 60(.6947)}{1 - .6947} = 33.03.$$

ANSWER B

8. $s(k)$ is the fraction of unpaid (i.e., "surviving") principal at time k so $s(k) = \frac{B_k}{10{,}000{,}000}$; $s(150) = \frac{Pa_{\overline{150}|.01}}{10{,}000{,}000} = \frac{8{,}164{,}606}{10{,}000{,}000} = .816$.

ANSWER C.

9. The probability function is given by
$p(k) =$ (fraction of 10,000,000 in principal repaid at time k) $= \frac{Pv^{301-k}}{10{,}000{,}000}$, and, for discrete variables, $h(k)$ is given by

$$h(k) = \frac{p(k)}{p(k) + p(k+1) + \cdots}.$$

With $v = \frac{1}{1.01}$ (the monthly discount factor)

$$h(150) = \frac{v^{151}}{v^{151} + \cdots + v^1} = \frac{v^{151}}{a_{\overline{151}|.01}} = \frac{1}{s_{\overline{151}|.01}} = \frac{1}{349.29} = .0029,$$ ANSWER C

Note: Prepayments could be modeled as an increased hazard.

10. From the regression relation $X = Y \cdot e^{.01Z_1 - .03Z_2}$. Thus

$$s_X(x|Z_1 = 1, Z_2 = 3) = Pr(X > x|Z_1 = 1, Z_2 = 3) = Pr(Y \cdot e^{-.08} > x)$$
$$= Pr(Y > xe^{.08}) = s_Y(e^{.08}x)$$

Since $h_Y(y) = 2y^2$, $H_Y(y) = \frac{2}{3}y^3$ and $s_Y(y) = e^{-2y^3/3} = exp\left(-\left(\frac{2}{3}\right)y^3\right)$. Hence $s_X(x|Z_1 = 1, Z_2 = 3) = exp\left[-\left(\frac{2}{3}\right)(e^{.08}x)^3\right] = exp(-.8475x^3)$ and $h_X(x|Z_1{=}1,\ Z_2 = 3) = -\frac{d}{dx}[ln(s_X(x|Z_1 = 1,\ Z_2 = 3))] = -\frac{d}{dx}(-.8475x^3) = 3(.8475)x^2$. (In generic terms the hazard rate is always the negative derivative of the natural log of the survival function.). From the above $s_X(2|Z_1 = 1, Z_2 = 3) = exp(-.8475(2)^3) = .0011$.

ANSWER D

11. $h_X(2|Z_1 = 1, Z_2 = 3) = 3(.8475)(2)^2 = 10.17$. ANSWER E

SECTION II

CONTINGENT PAYMENT MODELS

INTRODUCTORY NOTE

This section of the manual contains six units. For each unit there is a package of five items:

(1) ***Introductory Notes.*** While not as complete as many textbooks, it is designed to cover all the learning objectives set forth in the SOA - Working Group Report on Course 3.

(2) ***Condensed Review Notes and Advanced Topics.*** These notes constitute a list of the major relations with additional comments on more exotic topics. They should be useful as a reference when solving the Unit Review Questions, and as a final checklist of facts you should be familiar with for the exam.

(3) ***Conceptual Review Test.*** This material should be used in conjunction with reading and rereading the Introductory notes.

(4) ***Computational Review Test.*** These questions are more elementary than the Unit Review Questions and emphasize very basic calculations related to the unit reading.

(5) ***Unit Review Questions.*** This is a compilation of past SOA exam questions which still appear to be relevant, and newly created questions to reflect the new learning objectives and syllabus.

UNIT 1: LIFE INSURANCE AND RELATED MODELS

Introduction

The focus in this section of the manual is on models of a series of payments over time where both the timing and amounts of the payments depend on the occurrence of random events, so called contingent payment models. Examples abound:

(i) A life insurance death benefit paid upon the death of a policyholder;

(ii) A series of pension payments received by an annuitant until his death (or by a pair of annuitants until the second death);

(iii) A series of coupon payments plus the par value and call premium at the time a callable bond is called;

(iv) A series of mortgage payments plus the final balance at the time of prepayment of a prepaid mortgage;

(v) A series of coupon payments and maturity value of a bond until default or the time of maturity occurs;

(vi) A warranty refund of part of the purchase price of a battery at the time of failure if it occurs within the warranty period;

(vii) A series of daily charges (varying randomly) for a long as a patient is a nursing home resident.

The framework and principles needed to analyze these situations are virtually identical. The central focus in this section of the manual is on life insurance and annuity models. Some of the other examples will be discussed at appropriate times.

Terminology and Notation of Discrete and Continuous Life Insurance Models

We begin with a survival model for newborn lives (i.e., the probability distribution of X, the random lifetime, or age at death, of a newborn). Suppose one of these lives has reached age x today and has just been issued an insurance contract. Recall that T, the complete future lifetime of (x), is a continuous random variable, whereas K, the curtate future lifetime, defined as $[T]$, is discrete.

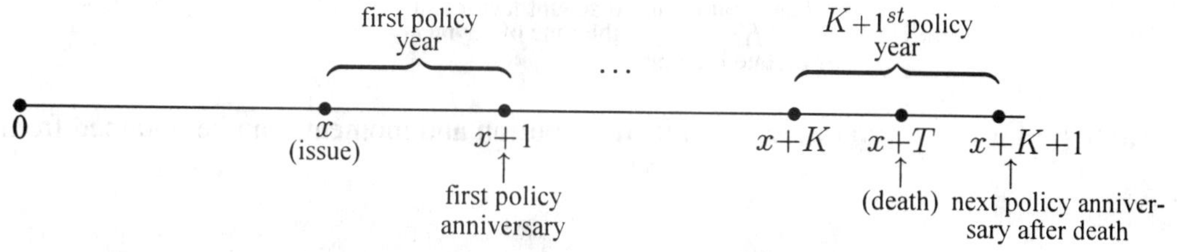

In a continuous life insurance model both the benefit amount and the time of payment are functions of the continuous variable T. The symbol b_T is used to denote the benefit amount as a function of T. In simple cases it has one or two values. In order to study the random present value of this benefit we also need a discount factor from the time of payment. The symbol v_T is used for this purpose. In most cases the payment is assumed to be made at death, that is, T years from issue, so v_T is v^T. The v_T notation is important only in contracts containing an "endowment component." For example, a 30-year pure endowment of \$1000 issued to (x) would pay \$1000 at age x+30 if (x) survives[1] and nothing otherwise. For this contract we would have

$$b_T = \begin{cases} 0 & T < 30 \\ 1000 & T \geq 30 \end{cases}, \quad v_T = \begin{cases} v^T & T < 30 \\ v^{30} & T \geq 30 \end{cases}.$$

The subtle point here is that if $T \geq 30$ the payment is made 30 years after issue, not at age $x+T$ which would require a discount factor of v^T.

The random present value of this continuous insurance model benefit is typically denoted by Z:

<u>Continuous Model</u>

$$\underbrace{Z}_{\substack{\text{random } p.v. \\ \text{of benefit}}} = \underbrace{b_T}_{\substack{\text{benefit amount} \\ \text{if } T \text{ is the future} \\ \text{lifetime of } (x)}} \cdot \underbrace{v_T}_{\substack{\text{discount factor from} \\ \text{the time of payment}}}$$

Note that Z is a function of T. Hence its distribution and moments can be calculated from the density of T. We could also use the relation with T to calculate the Z-density.

In a general discrete life insurance model the benefit amount and the time of payment are functions of $K+1$, a discrete variable corresponding to the policy year during which death occurs. The symbol b_{K+1} is used for the benefit amount and v_{K+1} is used for a discount factor from the time of payment. In most cases[2] the benefit is assumed to be paid $K+1$ years from issue (i.e., on the next policy anniversary following death; very convenient with tabular survival models) so that v_{K+1} is just v^{K+1}. The random present value of this benefit is denoted by

<u>Discrete Model</u>

$$Z = \underbrace{b_{K+1}}_{\substack{\text{benefit amount} \\ \text{if } K \text{ is the} \\ \text{curtate lifetime}}} \cdot \underbrace{v_{K+1}}_{\substack{\text{discount factor from} \\ \text{the time of payment}}}$$

Here Z is a function of the discrete variable K, so its distribution and moments can be obtained from the density of K.

---

1 You may wonder at this point why a survival benefit is considered under the heading *Life Insurance*. It is because the payment is made at the time of failure of a 30-year certain period if it fails before the life.

2 Excluding contracts with an endowment component.

In the following sections we will concentrate on several aspects of the distribution of Z. The expected value of Z is known either as the actuarial present value of the benefit or as the single benefit premium. A single benefit premium is a lump-sum premium received by the insurer at issue which is "on average" the correct amount to charge for the benefit. In Units 1-4 of this section (covering individual life insurance and annuities) the models are very basic. The insurer's outflow is assumed to be just the benefit (commissions, taxes, expenses, dividends, and so on, are not added to the model), whereas the premium inflow consists of net (benefit) premiums (enough to cover benefits) plus, perhaps, a risk charge (compensation for the risk that net premiums will not be enough to pay benefits).

The other aspect to be treated is measuring the risk that the premium is insufficient (i.e., the present value of the benefit exceeds the present value of all premiums). This is an issue of the variability in Z. Hence a lot of effort is expended on the second moment, $E[Z^2]$, and the variance, $Var(Z) = E[Z^2] - (E[Z])^2$.

Much of this unit is devoted to level benefit plans of insurance such as whole life, term, deferred, and endowment insurances. If the amount is a constant b then the present value variable is b times the present value variable for a similar plan with unit benefit amount. Hence we concentrate on unit amount, level-benefit plans.

	Benefit Provided	
Plan Name	Discrete Case	Continuous Case
Whole Life	1 paid in $K+1$ years	1 paid in T years
n-year Term	1 paid in $K+1$ years if $K+1 \leq n$ (zero otherwise)	1 paid in T years if $T \leq n$ (zero otherwise)
n-year Deferred	1 paid in $K+1$ years if $K+1 > n$ (zero otherwise)	1 paid in T years if $T > n$ (zero otherwise)
n-year Endowment	1 paid in $K+1$ years if $K+1 \leq n$, or 1 in n years if $K+1 > n$	1 paid in T years if $T \leq n$, or 1 in n years if $T > n$

See the tables in the following Condensed Review Notes of this manual for a precise description of the present value variables, benefit amount functions, and discount functions for these plans. In the next two sections we will look at the whole life models, both continuous and discrete, in great detail.

The Continuous Whole Life Model

In this section the model concerns a whole life insurance plan paying \$1 at death. Hence $b_T = 1$ and $v_T = v^T$ for all T since the payment is always made T years from the issue at age x. So the random present value variable has the particularly simple form

$$Z = 1 \cdot v^T = e^{-\delta T},\ 0 \le T \le \omega{-}x.$$

From the graph of Z versus T above, we can make

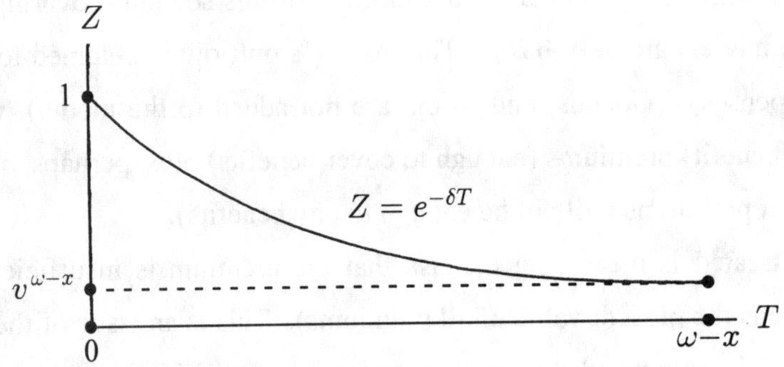

the observations that

(i) Z is a decreasing function of T, and
(ii) the range of possible Z-values is $[v^{\omega-x}, 1]$.

The first question we will consider concerns the adequacy of a single premium P collected by the insurer at issue and invested at an effective annual rate i. It accumulates to $P(1+i)^T = Pe^{\delta T}$ by (x)'s death at age $x+T$. The premium suffices if $Pe^{\delta T} \ge 1$, the benefit amount needed. Multiplying both sides by $e^{-\delta T}$ to bring the comparison back to the time of issue, we see that adequacy of premium corresponds to the present value inequality (random event)

$$P \ge e^{-\delta T} = Z.$$

From the graph below we see that the probability of this random event can be calculated from that of the event $T \ge t_0$, where $e^{-\delta t_0} = P$ (i.e., $t_0 = -ln(P)/\delta$).

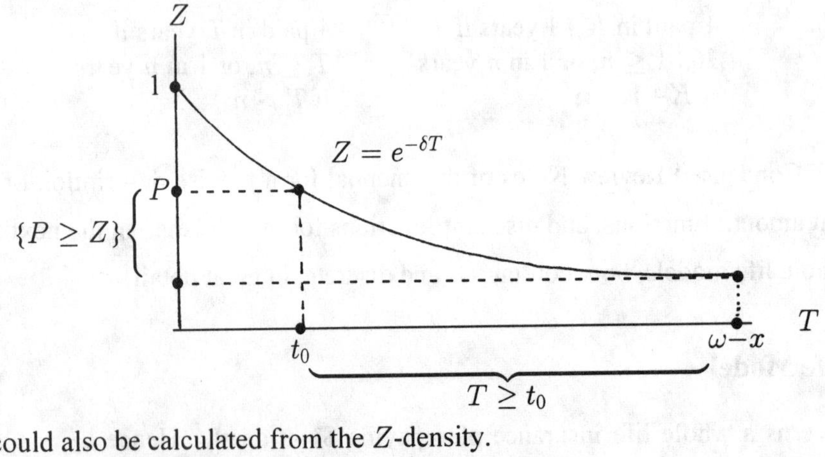

It could also be calculated from the Z-density.

$$Pr(P \text{ is adequate}) = Pr(Z \le P) = Pr(T \ge t_0) = \int_{t_0}^{\omega-x} \underbrace{{}_tp_x\mu(x{+}t)}_{\text{density of } T}\, dt = {}_{t_0}p_x.$$

As P increases, t_0 decreases. As a result, the event $T \geq t_0$ "widens" and the probability grows. The problem is that a higher P provides greater security for the insurer, but a decreasing marketability of the product.

Insurers sink or swim on groups of policyholders, not on individuals. Eventually we will look at the adequacy of aggregate premium for a group of identical policies. The corresponding aggregate present value of benefits is a sum of independent Z-variables like the one above. By the central limit theorem, when the number of policies in the group, n, is reasonably large, the aggregate Z is approximately normal in distribution with mean $n \cdot E[Z]$ and variance $n \cdot Var(Z) = n(E[Z^2] - (E[Z])^2)$. So next we focus on moments of Z.

$E[Z]$ is known as the actuarial present value of the benefit cashflow. In Unit 1 of Section I we briefly discussed the expected present value of a payment P due in n years if an event E occurs. The APV (acronym for actuarial present value) was shown to be $P \cdot v^n \cdot Pr(E)$. In this simple case there is only one possible time of payment. In a more general cashflow of contingent payments at many points in time, the APV is either a sum (discrete case) or integral (continuous case) over all possible times of payment, t, of a product of the payment amount at time t, the discount factor v^t, and the probability of payment at time t. This idea is explained in Appendix 1 to this section of the manual. It is an intuitive method for writing down all the APV formulas.

In our continuous whole life model, $Z = e^{-\delta T}$ is a nice function of T. Hence $E[Z^k]$ can be calculated as the integral of $Z^k = e^{-\delta tk}$ times the density of T, $f_T(t) = {}_tp_x\mu(x+t)$. The first moment $E[Z]$ is denoted $\overline{A}_x$ in standard actuarial notation. "A" is a generic symbol for insurance APV's. The overbar on the "A" indicates payment at death (continuous model) and the other accouterments describe the type of plan. See the Condensed Review Notes of this manual for more detail.

$$\overline{A}_x = E[Z] = \int_0^{\omega-x} \underbrace{e^{-\delta t}}_{\substack{\text{function}\\ \text{of } T}} \cdot \underbrace{{}_tp_x\,\mu(x+t)}_{\text{density of } T}\, dt$$

$$E[Z^2] = \int_0^{\omega-x} (e^{-\delta t})^2 \cdot {}_tp_x\mu(x+t)dt$$

Noting that $(e^{-\delta t})^2 = e^{-(2\delta)t}$, we see that the second moment is the same as the first moment at double the original force of interest. It is thus denoted by ${}^2\overline{A}_x$. This feature is a common trend for the basic level benefit plans where $b_T = 0$ or 1, since $b_T^k = b_T$, and since

$$\begin{cases} v_T^k = (v^n)^k = (e^{-\delta n})^k = e^{-(\delta k)n} = {}^kv_T \\ n = \text{time of payment as a function of } T \\ {}^kv_T = \text{discount factor from the time of payment at } k \text{ times the original force of interest} \end{cases}$$

$$\underbrace{E[Z^k]}_{k^{th}\text{ moment}} = E\left[(b_T v_T)^k\right] = E\left[b_T^k v_T^k\right] = \underbrace{E\left[b_T \cdot {}^k v_T\right]}_{\substack{1^{st}\text{ moment at }k\\ \text{times original force}}}$$

Example 1 Calculate general expressions for $\overline{A}_x$ under de Moivre's law, $\ell_x = \omega - x$ for $0 \le x \le \omega$, and under an assumption of constant force, i.e., $\mu(x) = \mu$ for all $x \ge 0$ (here $\omega = \infty$).

Solution

de Moivre's Law

$\ell_x = \omega - x$ means $\mu(x) = \dfrac{-\ell_x'}{\ell_x} = \dfrac{1}{\omega - x}$. Hence

$$_tp_x\mu(x+t) = \frac{\ell_{x+t}}{\ell_x} \cdot \mu(x+t) = \frac{\omega-(x+t)}{\omega - x} \cdot \frac{1}{\omega-(x+t)} = \frac{1}{\omega - x}$$

for $0 \le t \le \omega - x$. (Thus we see that $_tp_x\mu(x+t)$ is a constant function of t.)

This says that T is uniformly distributed on the interval $[0, \omega - x]$, so

$$\overline{A}_x = \int_0^{\omega-x} e^{-\delta t} \cdot {}_tp_x\mu(x+t)\,dt = \int_0^{\omega-x} e^{-\delta t} \cdot \frac{1}{\omega - x}\,dt$$

$$= \frac{1}{\omega - x}\int_0^{\omega-x} e^{-\delta t}\,dt = \frac{1}{\omega - x} \cdot \underbrace{\frac{1 - e^{-\delta(\omega-x)}}{\delta}}_{\substack{\overline{a}_{\overline{\omega-x|}},\\ \text{the continuous}\\ \text{annuity certain}}}$$

Constant Force

$\mu(x) = \mu$ means $s(x) = e^{-\int_0^x \mu\,ds} = e^{-\mu x}$. Hence $f(x) = -s'(x) = -(-\mu e^{-\mu x}) = \mu e^{-\mu x}$ for $x > 0$. This is the well-known exponential density. It turns out that T has the identical exponential density

$$f_T(t) = {}_tp_x \cdot \mu(x+t) = \frac{s(x+t)}{s(x)} \cdot \mu(x+t) = \frac{e^{-\mu(x+t)}}{e^{-\mu x}} \cdot \mu = \mu e^{-\mu t},$$

so

$$\overline{A}_x = \int_0^{\infty} e^{-\delta t} \cdot {}_tp_x\mu(x+t)\,dt = \int_0^{\infty} e^{-\delta t} \cdot \mu e^{-\mu t}\,dt = \frac{\mu}{\mu + \delta}. \qquad \square$$

The constant force model and de Moivre's law are simple "parametric" survival models and are among the few examples where the integral for $\overline{A}_x$ turns out to be doable by hand. None of these parametric models is suitable for practical use. In Appendix 2 at the end of this section there is a systematic development of results from Units 1 - 4 which are particular to these models.

Example 2 For de Moivre's law with $\omega = 100$, $\delta = .05$, and $x = 30$ find $\overline{A}_{30}$, ${}^2\overline{A}_{30}$, $Var(Z)$, and $E[Z] \pm 2\sigma_Z$, and calculate the probability that the net single premium is adequate to cover the benefit.

Solution $\overline{A}_{30} = \frac{1}{100-30} \cdot \overline{a}_{\overline{100-30}|} = \frac{1}{70} \cdot \frac{1-e^{-70(.05)}}{.05} = .277086$

$${}^2\overline{A}_{30} = \frac{1}{70} \cdot \frac{1-e^{-70(.10)}}{.10} = .142727$$

$$Var(Z) = E[Z^2] - (E[Z])^2 = {}^2\overline{A}_{30} - \left(\overline{A}_{30}\right)^2 = .065950$$

$$\begin{aligned} E[Z] \pm 2\sigma_Z &= .277086 \pm 2\sqrt{.065950} \\ &= [-.236529, .790701] \text{ which is the "likely"}^3 \text{ range for the actual } Z\text{-value} \end{aligned}$$

$$\begin{aligned} Pr(Z \le \overline{A}_{30}) &= Pr(T \ge t_0) = \int_{t_0}^{\omega - x} f_T(t)\,dt \\ &= \int_{t_0}^{70} \frac{1}{70}\,dt = 1 - \frac{t_0}{70} = .6333 \end{aligned}$$

since $t_0 = -\frac{ln(\overline{A}_{30})}{\delta} = 25.6685$ years. □

All of the above results concerning the Z-distribution were obtained from the relation of Z to $T = T(x)$ using the T-density ${}_tp_x\mu(x+t)$. They can also be obtained via the Z-density which carries more information about the pattern of Z-values. In general, if $Z = g(T)$ is a 1-1 function of T, then $f_Z(z) = f_T(g^{-1}(z))\left|\frac{dg^{-1}(z)}{dz}\right|$ over the appropriate range of z-values. For the fully continuous whole life insurance of \$1 model, we have $Z = g(T) = e^{-\delta T}$, a 1-1 decreasing function of T. Since $0 \le T \le \omega - x$ we have $1 = e^{-0} \ge Z \ge e^{-\delta(\omega - x)}$. Furthermore, $T = g^{-1}(Z) = \frac{-ln(Z)}{\delta}$. Thus

$$f_Z(z) = f_T\left(\frac{-ln(z)}{\delta}\right) \cdot \left|\frac{-1}{\delta z}\right| = \frac{f_T\left(\frac{-ln(z)}{\delta}\right)}{(\delta z)}, \quad 1 \ge z \ge e^{-\delta(\omega - x)}.$$

Example 3 For de Moivre's law and the constant force model compute:

(i) the Z-density;

(ii) general expressions for $E[Z]$, $E[Z^2]$; and

(iii) $Pr(Z > \overline{A}_x)$ (i.e., the probability that the single benefit premium is insufficient to cover the benefit.)

---

3 Chebychev says Z falls in this range at least three-quarters of the time. This interval is too wide to be helpful. In aggregate analysis the mean goes up by a factor of n, but the standard deviation grows by $\sqrt{n}$, so the width is controlled.

Solution

(i) de Moivre's law

Since T is uniformly distributed on $[0,\, \omega - x]$, we know $f_T(t) = \frac{1}{\omega - x}$ for $0 \le t \le \omega - x$. Thus

$$f_Z(z) = \frac{f_T\left(\frac{-ln(z)}{\delta}\right)}{(\delta z)} = \frac{1}{\omega - x} \cdot \frac{1}{\delta z}, \quad v^{\omega - x} \le z \le 1$$

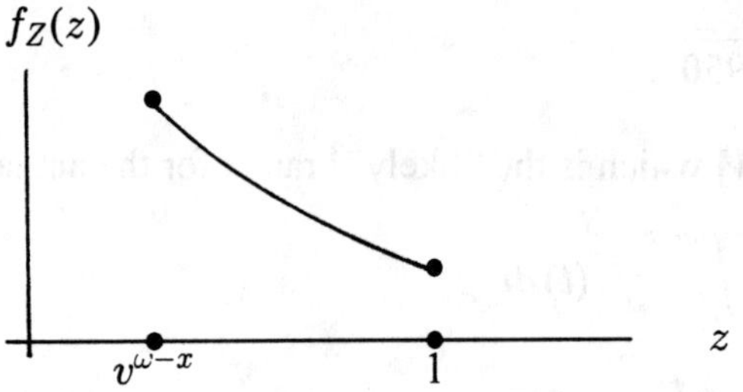

Constant Force

Since T is exponentially distributed on $[0, \infty]$ we know $f_T(t) = \mu e^{-\mu t}$ for $0 \le t \le \infty$. Thus

$$f_Z(z) = \mu \cdot exp\left[\frac{-\mu(-lnz)}{\delta}\right]\frac{1}{\delta z} = \left(\frac{\mu}{\delta}\right) z^{(\mu/\delta)-1}, \quad 0 < z \le 1$$

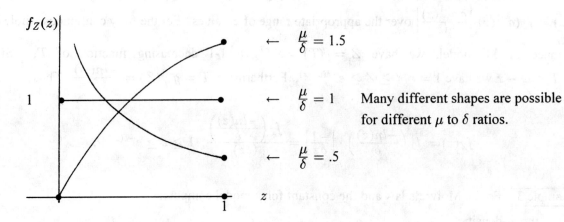

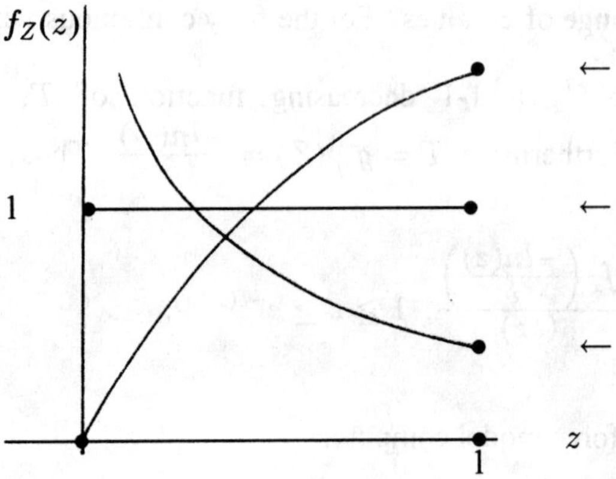

Many different shapes are possible for different μ to δ ratios.

(ii) de Moivre's law

$$E[Z^k] = \int_{v^{\omega-x}}^{1} z^k \cdot \frac{1}{\omega - x} \cdot \frac{1}{\delta z}\, dz = \frac{1}{\delta(\omega - x)} \cdot \frac{z^k}{k}\Big|_{v^{\omega-x}}^{1} = \frac{1}{\omega - x} \cdot \underbrace{\frac{1 - v^{(\omega-x)k}}{k\delta}}_{{}^{k}\bar{a}_{\overline{\omega-x}|}}$$

Constant force

$$E[Z^k] = \int_0^1 z^k \cdot \frac{\mu}{\delta} z^{(\mu/\delta)-1}\, dz = \left(\frac{\mu}{\delta}\right) \cdot \frac{z^{k+(\mu/\delta)}}{k + (\mu/\delta)}\Big|_{z=0}^{1} = \frac{\mu}{\mu + k\delta}$$

(iii) de Moivre's law

$$Pr(Z > \overline{A}_x) = \int_{\overline{A}_x}^{1} f_Z(z)dz = \int_{\overline{A}_x}^{1} \frac{1}{\omega - x} \cdot \frac{1}{\delta z}dz = \frac{1}{\delta(\omega - x)} ln(z)\Big|_{z=\overline{A}_x}^{1} = \frac{-ln(\overline{A}_x)}{\delta(\omega - x)}$$

Note: In Example 1 with $x = 30$, $\omega = 100$ and $\delta = .05$ the above probability is $\frac{-ln(.277086)}{(.05)(70)} = .3667$.

Constant force

$$Pr(Z > \overline{A}_x) = \int_{\mu/(\mu+\delta)}^{1} \left(\frac{\mu}{\delta}\right) z^{(\mu/\delta)-1} dz = 1 - \left(\frac{\mu}{\mu+\delta}\right)^{(\mu/\delta)}$$

Note: With $\delta = .05$, $\mu = \left(\frac{1}{70}\right)$ (comparable to de Moivre above) the probability is $.3493 = 1 - \left(\frac{2}{9}\right)^{(2/7)}$. Notice that in both of these probability calculations we see that the mean of Z is approximately the 63rd or 64th percentile of the Z-distribution. These distributions are skewed to the right.

The Discrete, Whole Life Model

In this section the model concerns a whole life insurance plan paying $1 on the policy anniversary immediately following death,[4] that is, $K+1$ years after the issue at age x. Hence $b_{K+1} = 1$ and $v_{K+1} = v^{K+1}$ since the payment is always made at time $K+1$. The random present value variable is

$$Z = 1 \cdot v^{K+1} = e^{-\delta(K+1)}, K = 0, 1, 2, \ldots, \omega - x - 1$$

for an issue at age x. There are many similarities with the continuous case so we treat this variation more briefly.

All of the following are based on the idea that Z is a function of the discrete variable K with density function $f_K(k) = {}_{k|}q_x = \frac{d_{x+k}}{\ell_x}$. Hence events regarding Z and moments of Z can be handled in terms of the K-distribution. For example, using $Z = v^{K+1}$ and taking logs, an event such as $Z \leq a$ is equivalent to $(K+1)\,ln(v) \leq ln(a)$. Since $ln(v) = -\delta < 0$ we have

$$Z \leq a \Leftrightarrow (K+1)(-\delta) \leq ln(a) \Leftrightarrow K \geq -\frac{ln(a)}{\delta} - 1.$$

4 Very impractical, but ideally suited to calculation with a tabular survival model. Ahead we will see the connection with the more practical continuous model.

In this discrete model the APV of the benefit, $E[Z]$, is denoted by A_x. Again, "A" is a generic APV symbol, and the x-subscript denotes whole life issued to (x). There is no overbar on the "A" because payment is made on the policy anniversary after death. We have

$$A_x = E[Z] = E[v^{K+1}] = \sum_{k=0}^{\omega-x-1} \underbrace{v^{k+1}}_{\text{function of } K} \cdot \underbrace{{}_{k|}q_x}_{K\text{-density}}.$$

This expression is a first principles method of calculation for short-term numerical examples done by hand, or for calculation for a table of values $A_0, A_1, \ldots, A_{\omega-1}$ based on a life table $\ell_0, \ell_1, \ldots, \ell_{\omega-1}$ done by computer. It is easily adapted to a plan of insurance having a variable benefit pattern (see Condensed Review Notes to follow).

Second moment calculations follow the pattern established in the continuous case:

$$\underbrace{E[Z^2]}_{\substack{\text{second}\\\text{moment}}} = E[(v^{K+1})^2] = E\left[\left(e^{-\delta(K+1)}\right)^2\right] = \underbrace{E\left[e^{-(2\delta)(K+1)}\right]}_{\substack{\text{first moment at double}\\\text{the original force;}\\\text{denoted } {}^2A_x}}$$

Example 4 Calculate a general expression for A_x assuming a constant force survival model $\mu_x = \mu$.

Solution We saw in Example 1 that $s(x) = e^{-\mu x}$. Hence

$$f_K(k) = {}_{k|}q_x = {}_kp_x q_{x+k} = \frac{s(x+k)}{s(x)} \cdot (1-p_{x+k}) = \frac{e^{-\mu(x+k)}}{e^{-\mu x}}\left(1 - \frac{e^{-\mu(x+k+1)}}{e^{-\mu(x+k)}}\right) = e^{-\mu k}(1-e^{-\mu}).$$

Hence

$$A_x = E\left[e^{-\delta(K+1)}\right] = \sum_{k=0}^{\infty} e^{-\delta(k+1)} \cdot e^{-\mu k}(1-e^{-\mu})$$

$$= e^{-\delta}(1-e^{-\mu}) \underbrace{\sum_{k=0}^{\infty}\left[e^{-(\delta+\mu)}\right]^k}_{\text{geometric series}}$$

$$= e^{-\delta}(1-e^{-\mu}) \cdot \frac{1}{1-e^{-(\delta+\mu)}}$$

$$= \frac{1-e^{-\mu}}{e^{\delta} - e^{-\mu}} = \frac{q_x}{(1+i)-(1-q_x)} = \frac{q_x}{i+q_x}.$$

$\left(\text{Note the similarity with } \overline{A}_x = \dfrac{\mu}{\mu+\delta}.\right)$ □

Example 5 Assuming an issue at age 90 and an evaluation basis of $i = .06$ and the tabular survival model below, calculate the APV of \$1000 paid on the policy anniversary next following death.

x	90	91	92	93
ℓ_x	100	72	39	0
d_x	28	33	39	—

Solution Here the present value variable is $1000v^{K+1}$, so the APV is $E[1000v^{K+1}] = 1000E[v^{K+1}] = 1000A_{90}$ where

$$A_{90} = \sum_{k=0}^{2} v^{k+1} \cdot \frac{d_{90+k}}{\ell_{90}} = \frac{1}{1.06} \cdot \frac{28}{100} + \frac{1}{1.06^2} \cdot \frac{33}{100} + \frac{1}{1.06^3} \cdot \frac{39}{100} = .885301.$$

Hence the APV is \$885.30. (Interpretation: on average, this amount plus the 6% interest it earns is enough to pay the 1000 benefit when it comes due.) □

The Aggregate Deterministic Analysis of the Discrete Whole Life Model

Assume a tabular survival model giving values $\ell_x, \ell_{x+1}, \ldots, \ell_\omega$. In the aggregate deterministic approach we assume:

(i) perfect cooperation of the populace (i.e., there will be exactly ℓ_{x+k} survivors at age $x+k$ and exactly d_{x+k} deaths between ages $x+k$ and $x+k+1$),

(ii) everyone in the table is issued a discrete life insurance contract paying \$1 on the policy anniversary following death, and

(iii) all issues occur simultaneously.

The diagram below gives the benefit cashflow for the group which is viewed as a certain annuity

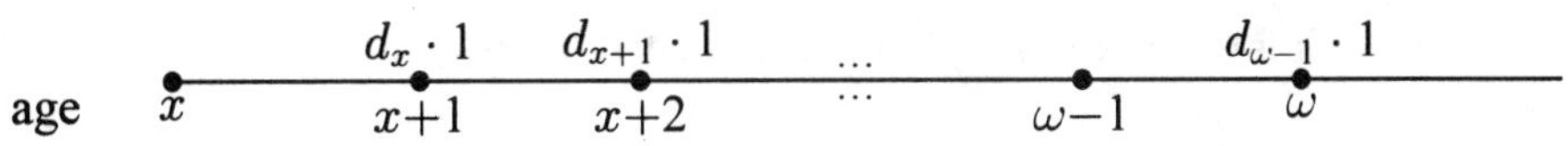

The total present value of benefits is thus

$$d_x \cdot v + d_{x+1} \cdot v^2 + \ldots + d_{\omega-1} \cdot v^{\omega-x}.$$

When this amount is spread over the ℓ_x policy holders we see an average present value of

$$\frac{d_x}{\ell_x} \cdot v + \frac{d_{x+1}}{\ell_x} \cdot v^2 + \cdots + \frac{d_{\omega-1}}{\ell_x} \cdot v^{\omega-x} = \sum_{k=0}^{\omega-x-1} v^{k+1} \cdot {}_{k|}q_x = A_x.$$

Thus $\ell_x A_x$ is the total present value of the aggregate benefit flow. The interpretation here is that a fund of $\ell_x A_x$ at issue is ***exactly*** enough to cover the benefits for the group. (That is, there is no chance that premium is inadequate; no attempt to measure risk which is not in the determinist's vocabulary.) The fund $\ell_x A_x$ grows to $\ell_x A_x(1+i)$ by year end when $d_x \cdot 1$ is withdrawn, leaving a balance of $\ell_x A_x(1+i) - d_x$ to start the second year. Each year the beginning fund earns interest until year end when benefits for the group are withdrawn. Due to the fact that $\ell_x A_x$ is the present value of the withdrawals (i.e., aggregate benefit cashflow) the fund balance will hit zero at age ω with the last death. The insurer exactly breaks even. Remember that the deterministic pattern ℓ_x, ℓ_{x+1}, ... is the same as the expected survival pattern in the random survivorship model.

The Aggregate Risk-theoretical Analysis of the Discrete Whole Life Model

Returning to Example 5 above, lets assume that all 100, ninety year olds in the table purchase \$1 of discrete whole life insurance. In addition to $A_{90} = .885301$, we also need

$$^2A_{90} = \left(\frac{1}{1.06^2}\right) \cdot \frac{28}{100} + \left(\frac{1}{1.06^2}\right)^2 \cdot \frac{33}{100} + \left(\frac{1}{1.06^2}\right)^3 \cdot \frac{39}{100} = .785525$$

$$^2A_{90} - (A_{90})^2 = .001766$$

in order to do a risk theoretical analysis.

Let $Z = v^{k+1}$ be the random present value variable for a 90 year old. Assuming the 100, ninety year olds have independent lifetimes, we denote by $Z_1, \ldots, Z_{100}$ the corresponding 100, independent present value variables which are all distributed like Z. The random present value of all benefits, denoted Z_{Agg}, is accordingly

$$Z_{Agg} = Z_1 + \cdots + Z_{100}.$$

By the Central Limit Theorem it is approximately normal in distribution with

$$\mu(Agg) = E[Z_{Agg}] = 100E[Z] = 100(.885301) = 88.5301$$

$$\sigma_{Agg} = (Var(Z_{Agg}))^{1/2} = (100Var(Z))^{1/2} = (100 \cdot .001766)^{1/2} = .420238$$

Because there is a 50% chance of a normal variable being less than or equal to its mean we have a 50% chance that aggregate net single premium of 88.5301 is adequate. How much more than .885301 would the insurer have to charge each individual so that there would be a 90% chance of adequate premium? This additional amount, r, is a risk charge known as the security loading.

$$.90 = Pr(Z_{Agg} \leq 100(.885301{+}r))$$

$$= Pr\left(\frac{Z_{Agg}-\mu(Agg)}{\sigma_{Agg}} \leq \frac{88.5301 + 100r - \mu(Agg)}{\sigma_{Agg}}\right)$$

$$\approx Pr\left(N(0,1) \leq \frac{100r}{.420238}\right).$$

This means that $\frac{100r}{.420238}$ is the 90th percentile of the standard normal distribution, which is 1.28. As a result $r = .005380$:

$$\underbrace{.890681}_{\substack{\text{total}\\ \text{premium}\\ \text{per policy}}} = \underbrace{.885301}_{\substack{\text{net single}\\ \text{premium}\\ \text{per policy}}} + \underbrace{.005380}_{\substack{\text{security}\\ \text{loading}\\ \text{per policy}}}$$

The Relation of Discrete and Continuous Life Insurance Models

In practice, insurance benefits are paid at death.[5] However, the typical survival model is tabular. Earlier we saw how to calculate an APV in the discrete case from a tabular model. How should this APV be adjusted for a continuous plan paying the same benefit at death rather than at the end of this final policy year?

Under the following conditions there is a very simple relation. Suppose a discrete plan of insurance (no endowment component) pays a death benefit b_{K+1} at time $K{+}1$ if death occurs in the $(K{+}1)^{st}$ policy year. Let $Z = b_{K+1}v^{K+1}$ be the corresponding present value variable. Consider a related continuous model paying b_{K+1} at time T (recall $K \leq T < K{+}1$) and let its present value variable be denoted by $\overline{Z}$. Suppose we have a tabular survival model (i.e., a discrete model) and we extend it to a continuous model via the UDD assumption. Recall that this implies

<u>Discrete Model</u>

$$Z = b_{K+1} \cdot v^{K+1}$$

<u>Related Continuous Model</u>

$$\overline{Z} = b_T \cdot v^T$$

$$\begin{cases} b_T = b_{K+1} \text{ for all } T \text{ in } [K, K{+}1) \\ \text{(i.e., constant over each policy year)} \end{cases}$$

---

5 Within a few business days.

that $T = K + S$ (S = fractional part of final policy year of life) with K and S independent and S uniformly distributed on $[0, 1)$. Thus

$$\underbrace{E[\overline{Z}]}_{\substack{\text{net single}\\ \text{premium in the}\\ \text{continuous model}}} = E[b_T v^T]$$

$$= E\left[b_{K+1} v^{K+S}\right]$$

$$= E\left[\underbrace{b_{K+1} v^{K+1}}_{\text{Function of } K} \cdot \underbrace{v^{S-1}}_{\text{Function of } S}\right]$$

$$= \underbrace{E\left[b_{K+1} v^{K+1}\right]}_{\substack{\text{net single premium}\\ \text{in the discrete model}}} \cdot \underbrace{E\left[v^{S-1}\right]}_{\substack{\text{adjustment factor}\\ \text{equal to } i/\delta}}$$

since

$$E[v^{S-1}] = \int_0^1 \underbrace{v^{s-1}}_{\text{Function of } S} \cdot \underbrace{1}_{S \text{ density}} \, ds = v^{-1} \int_0^1 e^{-\delta s} \, ds$$

$$= e^{\delta} \left[-\frac{1}{\delta} e^{-\delta s} \Big|_{s=0}^{1} \right]$$

$$= e^{\delta} \left(\frac{1 - e^{-\delta}}{\delta} \right) = \frac{e^{\delta} - 1}{\delta} = \frac{1 + i - 1}{\delta} = \frac{i}{\delta}\,.$$

The continuous and discrete whole life models satisfy the conditions above since $b_T = b_{K+1} = 1$ for all T and K and there is no endowment benefit. Hence, if the survival model satisfies the UDD relation then,

$$\overline{A}_x = A_x \cdot \frac{i}{\delta}\,.$$

A Short-term, Non-level Benefit Model

Much of the machinery developed in this unit is geared towards level benefit plans of insurance. In a non-level benefit model one can easily resort to first principles.

Example 6 Consider a discrete insurance model where the survival model is

x	90	91	92	93
ℓ_x	100	72	39	0
d_x	28	33	39	—

and $i = .06$. Assume that $b_1 = 10$, $b_2 = 5$ and $b_3 = 2$. Find $E[Z]$ and $Var(Z)$ for the discrete model present value variable $Z = b_{K+1} v^{K+1}$.

Solution

$$E[Z] = E[b_{K+1} v^{K+1}]$$

$$= \sum_{k=0}^{2} \underbrace{b_{k+1} \cdot v^{k+1}}_{\text{function of } K} \cdot \underbrace{{}_{k|}q_{90}}_{K\text{-density}}$$

$$= (10)\left(\frac{1}{1.06}\right)\left(\frac{28}{100}\right) + (5)\left(\frac{1}{1.06^2}\right)\left(\frac{33}{100}\right) + (2)\left(\frac{1}{1.06^3}\right)\left(\frac{39}{100}\right) = 4.764907$$

$$E[Z^2] = E\left[(b_{K+1} v^{K+1})^2\right]$$

$$= \sum_{k=0}^{2} b_{k+1}^2 \cdot (v^{k+1})^2 \cdot {}_{k|}q_{90}$$

$$= (10^2)\left(\frac{1}{1.06^2}\right)\left(\frac{28}{100}\right) + (5^2)\left(\frac{1}{1.06^4}\right)\left(\frac{33}{100}\right) + (2^2)\left(\frac{1}{1.06^6}\right)\left(\frac{39}{100}\right) = 32.554411$$

$$Var(Z) = 9.850073$$

Note: The second moment is not the same as the first moment at double the force since $b_{K+1}^2 \neq b_{K+1}$. One has $b_{K+1}^2 = b_{K+1}$ only when b_{K+1} is either 0 or 1.

Warranty of a Battery

The essential feature of life insurance models is that a payment is made at the time of a failure event. In this section we discuss the cost of a manufacturers warranty on a car battery using the same ideas employed in life insurance. Suppose a particular brand of 5-year battery wholesales for $\$P$ and retails at $\$P(1+r)$ (r the rate of mark-up). The warranty provides a prorated refund of the retail price at the time of battery failure, if it occurs within 5 years of sale. What percentage of the wholesale price is needed to cover the warranty?

The answer to this question ultimately depends on both the probability distribution of the time until battery failure variable, X, and the interest rate used to calculate present values. The manufacturer might actually establish a fund from a percentage of each wholesale price earned and use i as something close to the rate of earning of this fund. He might also just leave the money in the business and use an internal rate of return.

At any rate lets suppose that $i = .06$ and discuss the survival model. As batteries age the hazard rate, $h(x)$, should increase. From a small scale study of similar past battery sales and considering current improvements in design and manufacturing, the manufacturer decides that the two-parameter hazard model, $h(x) = \frac{r}{\omega - x}$, $0 \leq r < \omega$, is appropriate.

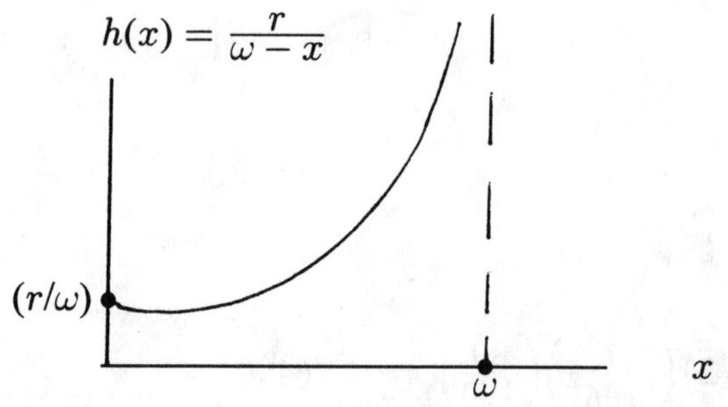

Since no battery is likely to survive beyond 10 years he chooses $\omega = 10$. The battery is expected to survive 7 years so the r value is determined from $7 = E[X] = \mathring{e}_0 = \frac{\omega - 0}{r+1} = \frac{10}{r+1}$; $r = \frac{3}{7}$. When $h(x) = \frac{r}{\omega - x}$ we saw in Unit 1 of Section I of this manual that $f_X(x) = \frac{r}{\omega}\left(1 - \frac{x}{\omega}\right)^{r-1} = \frac{3}{70}\left(1 - \frac{x}{10}\right)^{-(4/7)}$, $0 \le x \le 10$. Now that we have our evaluation basis ("mortality" and interest) we are prepared to calculate the cost.

The warranty will cause a payment $b_X = \left(\frac{5-X}{5}\right)(1+r)P$ to occur at time X if $X \le 5$. The random present value of this contingent payment is $Z = b_X \cdot v^X = \left(\frac{5-X}{5}\right)(1+r)P \cdot 1.06^{-X}$ if $X \le 5$, and is zero otherwise. To assess the cost of this warranty it might be decided to use the APV, $E[Z]$, or to choose some percentile of the Z-distribution, say the 75th. Both possibilities are considered next.

The actuarial present value is calculated as

$$E[Z] = \int_0^5 \underbrace{\left(\frac{5-x}{5}\right)(1+r)P(1.06)^{-x}}_{\text{function of } X} \cdot \underbrace{\frac{3}{70}\left(1 - \frac{x}{10}\right)^{-(4/7)}}_{X\text{-density}} dx$$

$$= \frac{(1+r)P}{5} \underbrace{\int_0^5 (5-x)(1.06)^{-x} f_X(x)dx}_{\text{Same as } \overline{DA}^{\,1}_{0:\overline{5}|} \text{ in life insurance notation}}$$

While is pretty difficult to evaluate this final integral by hand using the fundamental theorem of calculus, an approximate value of $.1086(1+r)P$ was readily obtained with a TI-85 calculator. $\frac{100E[Z]}{P}$ represents the percentage of the wholesale price needed to cover the APV of the warranty.

Now $Z = b_X \cdot v^X$ is a rather complicated function of X so obtaining its density in closed form is rather unlikely. Z is a 1-1, decreasing function of X (for $X \le 5$) since both $(5 - X)$ and 1.06^{-X} are decreasing, but finding a closed form expression for X in terms of Z (the inverse function) is impossible. Nevertheless, since it is a decreasing relationship, $z_{.75}$, the 75th percentile of Z, is $b_{x_{.25}} \cdot v^{x_{.25}}$, where $x_{.25}$ is the 25th percentile of X. From the above

$$.25 = F_X(x_{.25}) \quad \Rightarrow \quad .75 = s_X(x_{.25})$$

$$.75 = \left(1 - \tfrac{x_{.25}}{\omega}\right)^r = \left(1 - \tfrac{x_{.25}}{10}\right)^{3/7}$$

$\Rightarrow \quad x_{.25} = 4.889$ years (Note: it is necessary for this to be < 5 to find the 75th percentile)

$$\Rightarrow \quad z_{.75} = \left[\frac{5-4.889}{5}\right](1+r)P \cdot 1.06^{-4.889} = .0166(1+r)P.$$

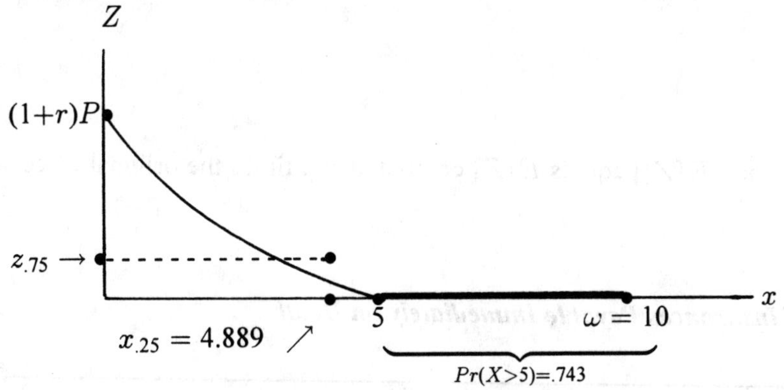

Note: The Z-distribution is mixed with a point mass of .743 at $Z = 0$.

CONDENSED REVIEW NOTES AND ADVANCED TOPICS

Continuous Models — Insurances Payable at Death

Z = random present value at issue of the benefit $= b_T \cdot v_T$

where: b_T = benefit paid if T years is the future lifetime

v_T = discount factor from the time the benefit is paid if T years is the future lifetime

$E[Z]$ = net single benefit premium (single benefit premium) for the contract

= actuarial present value of the benefit

$$= \int_{t=0}^{\omega-x} (b_t v_t)\,{}_tp_x\,\mu(x+t)\,dt$$

$$Var(Z) = E[Z^2] - \left(E[Z]\right)^2$$

Theorem: If $b_T = 0$ or 1 for all T then $E[Z^j]$ equals $E[Z]$ computed at j times the original force of interest.

Summary of Insurances Payable Immediately on Death

Name	Benefit Function b_t	Discount Function v_T	Present Value Function Z	N.S.P.	2nd Moment
Whole life	1	v^T	v^T	$\overline{A}_x$	${}^2\overline{A}_x$
n-year term	$\begin{cases} 1 & T \le n \\ 0 & T > n \end{cases}$	v^T	$\begin{cases} v^T & T \le n \\ 0 & T > n \end{cases}$	$\overline{A}^{\,1}_{x:\overline{n}\|}$	${}^2\overline{A}^{\,1}_{x:\overline{n}\|}$
n-year pure endowment	$\begin{cases} 0 & T < n \\ 1 & T \ge n \end{cases}$	v^n	$\begin{cases} 0 & T < n \\ v^n & T \ge n \end{cases}$	$A_{x:\overset{\,1}{\overline{n}\|}}$	${}^2A_{x:\overset{\,1}{\overline{n}\|}}$
n-year endowment	1	$\begin{cases} v^T & T \le n \\ v^n & T > n \end{cases}$	$\begin{cases} v^T & T \le n \\ v^n & T > n \end{cases}$	$\overline{A}_{x:\overline{n}\|}$	${}^2\overline{A}_{x:\overline{n}\|}$
n-year deferred	$\begin{cases} 0 & T \le n \\ 1 & T > n \end{cases}$	v^T	$\begin{cases} 0 & T \le n \\ v^T & T > n \end{cases}$	${}_{n\|}\overline{A}_x$	${}_{n\|}{}^2\overline{A}_x$
annually increasing	$[T+1]$	v^T	$[T+1]v^T$	$I\overline{A}_x$	first principles
continuously increasing	T	v^T	$T \cdot v^T$	$\overline{I}\overline{A}_x$	first principles
annually decreasing n-year term	$\begin{cases} n-[T] & T \le n \\ 0 & T > n \end{cases}$	v^T	$\begin{cases} (n-[T])v^T & T \le n \\ 0 & T > n \end{cases}$	$(D\overline{A})^1_{x:\overline{n}\|}$	first principles

Discrete Models - Insurance Payable at the End of the Policy Year of Death

Z = random present value at issue of the benefit $= b_{K+1} \cdot v_{K+1}$

where: b_{K+1} = amount of benefit if death occurs in policy year $K+1$

v_{K+1} = discount factor from time the benefit is paid if death occurs in policy year $K+1$.

$E[Z]$ = net single premium for contract = actuarial present value of benefit $= \sum_{k=0}^{\omega-x-1} (b_{k+1}v_{k+1})_k|q_x$

$Var(Z) = E[Z^2] - (E[Z])^2$

Theorem: If $b_{K+1} = 0$ or 1 for all K then $E[Z^j]$ equals $E[Z]$ computed at j times the original force of interest.

Summary of Discrete Insurance Models

Name	Benefit Function b_{K+1}	Discount Function v_{K+1}	Present Value Function Z	N.S.P.	2^{nd}Moment
Whole life	1	v^{K+1}	v^{K+1}	A_x	${}^2A_x$
n-year term	$\begin{cases} 1 & K=0,1,\ldots,n-1 \\ 0 & K=n,n+1 \end{cases}$	v^{K+1}	$\begin{cases} v^{K+1} & K=0,1,\ldots,n-1 \\ 0 & K=n,n+1,\ldots \end{cases}$	$A^1_{x:\overline{n}\|}$	${}^2A^1_{x:\overline{n}\|}$
n-year endowment	1	$\begin{cases} v^{K+1} & K=0,1,\ldots,n-1 \\ v^n & K=n,n+1 \end{cases}$	$\begin{cases} v^{K+1} & K=0,1,\ldots,n-1 \\ v^n & K=n,n+1,\ldots \end{cases}$	$A_{x:\overline{n}\|}$	${}^2A_{x:\overline{n}\|}$
n-year deferred	$\begin{cases} 0 & K=0,1,\ldots,n-1 \\ 1 & K=n,n+1 \end{cases}$	v^{K+1}	$\begin{cases} 0 & K=0,1,\ldots,n-1 \\ v^{K+1} & K=n,n+1,\ldots \end{cases}$	${}_n\|A_x$	${}^2{}_n\|A_x$
increasing	$K+1$	v^{K+1}	$[K+1]v^{K+1}$	IA_x	first principles
decreasing n-year term	$\begin{cases} n-K & K=0,1,\ldots,n-1 \\ 0 & K=n,n+1 \end{cases}$	v^{K+1}	$\begin{cases} (n-K)v^{K+1} & K=0,1,\ldots,n-1 \\ 0 & K=n,n+1,\ldots \end{cases}$	$(DA)^1_{x:\overline{n}\|}$	first principles

Aggregate Deterministic Analysis of Whole Life

Suppose ℓ_x lives age x purchase \$1 of whole life. Then $A_x = \sum_{k=0}^{\omega-x-1} v^{k+1} \cdot {}_k|q_x = \sum_{k=0}^{\omega-x-1} v^{k+1}\frac{d_{x+k}}{\ell_x}$, thus $\ell_x A_x$ = aggregate net premium $= \sum_{k=0}^{\omega-x-1} v^{k+1} d_{x+k}$ = aggregate present value of benefits if exactly d_{x+k} deaths occur between ages $x+k$, $x+k+1$.

The aggregate fund earns interest and death benefits are paid out from it. The deterministic fund balance after k years of operation (i.e., expected balance) is $\ell_{x+k}A_{x+k}$. Thus (Actual Fund)$_k - \ell_{x+k} \cdot A_{x+k}$ = aggregate gain (+) or loss (−) due to deviations in interest and mortality from that used in the model.

UDD Relations Between Discrete and Continuous Models

$T = K + S$, K and S independent, $S \sim U(0,1)$ if UDD is assumed.

Theorem: Under the UDD, if $v_T = {}^*v^T$ and b_T is a function of K^{**} then $E[b_T v_T] = E[b_{K+1}v_{K+1}]\frac{i}{\delta}$.

* Not true for contracts with an endowment component

** b_T is piece wise flat; $b_T = b_{K+1}$ for all $T \in (K, K+1]$

Examples: (UDD assumed) (1) $\bar{A}_x = \frac{i}{\delta}\, A_x$, $\bar{A}^{\,1}_{x:\overline{n|}} = \frac{i}{\delta} A^{\,1}_{x:\overline{n|}}$

$$\bar{A}_{x:\overline{n|}} = \bar{A}^{\,1}_{x:\overline{n|}} + A_{x:\overline{n|}}^{\;\;\;1} = \frac{i}{\delta}A^{\,1}_{x:\overline{n|}} + A_{x:\overline{n|}}^{\;\;\;1}$$

(2) Annually increasing:

$$b_T = \begin{cases} 1 & T \in (0, 1] \\ 2 & T \in (1, 2] \\ \cdots & \\ K & T \in (K-1, K] \\ \cdots & \end{cases} = \text{is a function of } K;\quad (I\bar{A})_x = \frac{i}{\delta}(IA)_x$$

(3) Continuously Increasing: $b_T = T$ is *not* a function of K.

$$(\bar{I}\bar{A})_x = E[Tv^T] = E[(K+1 + S-1)v^{K+1} \cdot v^{S-1}]$$

$$= E[(K+1)\, v^{K+1}]E[v^{S-1}] + E[v^{K+1}]E[(S-1)v^{S-1}]$$

$$= (IA)_x \cdot \frac{i}{\delta} + A_x \cdot E[(S-1)\, v^{S-1}] \quad \text{where}$$

$$E[(S-1)\, v^{S-1}] = \int_{s=0}^{1} (s-1)\, v^{s-1} \cdot 1 \cdot ds \qquad \big(S \sim U(0, 1);\; f_S(s) = 1\big)$$

$$= v^{-1}\int_0^1 (s-1)e^{-\delta s}\, ds$$

$$= (1+i)\left[\frac{-(s-1)}{\delta}\, e^{-\delta s} - \frac{1}{\delta^2}\, e^{-\delta s}\Big|_{s=0}^{1}\right]$$

$$= (1+i)\left[-\frac{v}{\delta^2} - \frac{1}{\delta} + \frac{1}{\delta^2}\right]$$

$$= (1+i)\left[\frac{d}{\delta^2} - \frac{1}{\delta}\right] = \frac{i}{\delta^2} - \frac{1+i}{\delta}$$

$$= \frac{i}{\delta}\left[\frac{1}{\delta} - \frac{1+i}{i}\right] = \frac{i}{\delta}\left[\frac{1}{\delta} - \frac{1}{d}\right]$$

Thus $(\bar{I}\bar{A})_x = \frac{i}{\delta}(IA)_x + \frac{i}{\delta}\left[\frac{1}{\delta} - \frac{1}{d}\right] A_x$

Recursion Relations

$$A_x = v \cdot {}_{0|}q_x + v^2 \cdot {}_{1|}q_x + \cdots = v \cdot q_x + vp_x \cdot (vq_{x+1} + v^2 \cdot {}_{1|}q_{x+1} + \cdots)$$

$$= vq_x + vp_x \cdot A_{x+1}$$

$$\overline{A}_x = \overline{A}^{\,1}_{x:\overline{t|}} + {}_{t|}\overline{A}_x = \overline{A}^{\,1}_{x:\overline{t|}} + v^t \cdot {}_tp_x \cdot \overline{A}_{x+t}$$

Density Functions

1. Whole Life Insurance of \$1/Benefits at Death

$$Z = v^T = e^{-\delta T} \quad 0 \le T \le \omega - x$$

$$f_Z(z) = f_T(-lnz/\delta)/(\delta z) \qquad e^{-\delta(\omega - x)} = v^{\omega - x} \le z \le 1$$

a. de Moivres Law

Using $T \sim U(0, \omega - x)$ (T uniformly distributed), and $f_T(t) = \frac{1}{\omega - x}$ for $0 \le t \le \omega - x$ with the above gives $f_Z(z) = \frac{1}{(\omega - x)\delta z}$ for $v^{\omega - x} \le z \le 1$

b. Constant Force

Using $T \sim \xi(\mu)$ (T exponentially distributed) and $f_T(t) = \mu e^{-\mu t}$ for $0 \le t < \infty$ with the above gives $f_Z(z) = \left(\frac{\mu}{\delta}\right)[z]^{(\mu/\delta)-1}$ for $0 < z \le 1$

Note: These densities offer alternate ways to calculate probabilities involving Z or moments of Z that had been done in terms of the T-density. For example:

$$E[Z^k] = \int_{v^{\omega - x}}^{1} z^k f_Z(z)dz = \int_0^{\omega - x} (e^{-\delta t})^k \, {}_tp_x \mu(x+t)dt \text{ where } Z \text{ is for whole life of \$1.}$$

2. Other Basic \$1 Insurances/Benefits at Deaths

(a) n year term insurance

$$Z = \begin{cases} v^T & 0 \le T \le n \\ 0 & n < T \le \omega - x \end{cases}$$

$$f_Z(z) = \begin{cases} f_T(-lnz/\delta)/(\delta z) & v^n \le z \le 1 \quad \text{(cont. part)} \\ {}_np_x & z = 0 \quad \text{(point mass, disc. part)} \end{cases}$$

(b) n-year deferred insurance

$$Z = \begin{cases} 0 & 0 \le T \le n \\ v^T & n < T \le \omega - x \end{cases}$$

$$f_Z(z) = \begin{cases} f_T(-ln z/\delta)/(\delta z) & v^{\omega-x} \le z \le v^n & \text{(cont. part)} \\ {}_nq_x & z = 0 & \text{(point mass, disc. part)} \end{cases}$$

(c) endowment insurance

$$Z = \begin{cases} v^T & 0 \le T \le n \\ v^n & n < T \le \omega - x \end{cases}$$

$$f_Z(z) = \begin{cases} f_T(-ln z/\delta)/(\delta z) & v^n < z \le 1 & \text{(cont. part)} \\ {}_np_x & v^n = z & \text{(point mass, disc. part)} \end{cases}$$

Note: Only the whole life density of Z is easy. It follows from a generic relation of f_Y to f_X when $Y = g(X)$ is a 1-1 transformation; namely, $f_Y(y) = f_X(g^{-1}(y))\left|\frac{dg^{-1}(y)}{dy}\right|$.

Here, with $Z = e^{-\delta T} = g(T)$, $T = g^{-1}(Z) = -ln(Z)/\delta$ and $\left|\frac{dg^{-1}(y)}{dy}\right| = \frac{1}{\delta y}$.

Calculation of Discrete Insurances
From Tables of A_x Values and ℓ_x Values

1. Basic \$1 Insurances

$${}_{n|}A_x = v^n\, {}_np_x A_{x+n},\quad {}_np_x = \ell_{x+n}/\ell_x$$

$$A^{1}_{x:\overline{n|}} = A_x - {}_{n|}A_x = A_x - v^n\, {}_np_x A_{x+n}$$

$$A_{x:\overline{n|}} = A^{1}_{x:\overline{n|}} + A_{x:\overline{n|}}^{\ \ 1} \quad \text{(use above)}$$

Notation: $v^n\, {}_np_x = {}_nE_x$

2. Non-level Insurances

(a) Example: Suppose (40) has 20,000 units of coverage to age 60, 10,000 units between 60 and 70, reducing to 5000 units after age 70. View the NSP as
$20{,}000\, A_{40} - 10{,}000\, {}_{20|}A_{40} - 5000\, {}_{30|}A_{40}$ and calculate the deferred insurances as above.

(b) General variable discrete insurance

$$NSP = \sum_{k=0}^{\omega-x-1} \underbrace{b_{k+1}}_{\text{amount}} \cdot \underbrace{v^{k+1}}_{\text{discount}} \cdot \underbrace{{}_{k|}q_x}_{\text{probability}}$$

A Short Term Numerical Example of Aggregate Analysis From Both the Deterministic and Risk Theoretical Points of View

1. Deterministic: assume all $\ell_{90} = 64$ lives in the table purchase a \$1000, discrete, whole life insurance and mortality in the group is exactly as the table predicts.

x	ℓ_x	d_x
90	64	44
91	20	20
92	0	

$i = .25$

$$1000A_{90} = 1000\left[1 \cdot \frac{1}{1.25} \cdot \frac{44}{64} + 1 \cdot \frac{1}{1.25^2} \cdot \frac{20}{64}\right] = 750$$

Deterministic Aggregate Cashflow

	90	91	92
Benefits		44(1000)	20(1000)
Premium	48,000 = 64(750)		

Spreadsheet Analysis

Year	Beginning Fund	Premium	Interest	Benefits	Ending Fund
1	0	48,000	12,000	44,000	16,000
2	16,000	0	4,000	20,000	0

Point: you exactly break even charging the NSP

2. Risk Theoretical: $Z_1, \ldots, Z_{64}$ are independent and identically distributed like $Z = v^{k+1}$ where $K = K(90)$ is as above. $Z_{Agg} = Z_1 + \cdots + Z_{64}$ is the aggregate present value of benefits. It is approximately normal in distribution with

$$\mu(Agg) = E[Z_{Agg}] = 64E[Z] = 64(750) = 48{,}000$$

$$\sigma^2_{Agg} = Var(Z_{Agg}) = 64Var(Z) = (64)(1000)^2({}^2A_{90} - A_{90}{}^2) = 352{,}000$$

since $^2A_{90} = \frac{1}{1.25^2} \cdot \frac{44}{64} + \frac{1}{1.25^4} \cdot \frac{20}{64} = .568.$

The 50th percentile of Z_{Agg} is $\mu(Agg) = 48{,}000$. So if each life is charged $48{,}000/64 = 750$, the NSP, $.50 = Pr(Z \leq 48{,}000)$, that is, there is a 50% chance that premium covers benefits. The 95th percentile of Z_{Agg} is $\mu(Agg) + 1.645\sigma_{Agg} = 48{,}976$. So if each life is charged $48{,}976/64 = 765.25 = 750 + 15.25$, the NSP plus a risk charge, $.95 = Pr(Z \leq 48{,}976)$, that is, there is a 95% chance that premium covers benefits.

CONCEPTUAL REVIEW TEST

1. Assuming $i = .05$, write an expression for the present value of the benefit to (25) specified by the following insurances if death occurs at age 55.7:

   (a) 1000 of whole life payable at death;

   (b) 1000 of whole life payable on the policy anniversary next following death;

   (c) 1000 of 30-year term insurance with benefits at death;

   (d) 1000 of 25-year endowment insurance with death benefits payable at death.

2. If (x) is issued a whole life contract paying a \$1 benefit at the time of his death and $\delta = .05$, express the random present value of the benefit, Z, in terms of the random future lifetime of (x), T. Draw the graph of Z versus T.

3. For Z and T as in Question 2, what event in terms of T is equivalent to $Z \leq \frac{1}{2}$? Express Z in terms of T and solve for an equivalent inequality. Justify with the graph in Question 2.

4. If $Z = e^{-\delta T}$ is the present value of benefit variable for \$1 of whole life insurance issued to (x), use the fact that Z is a function of T to express the expected present value of benefit, $\bar{A}_x$, as an integral. What is the interpretation of $\bar{A}_x$?

5. If \$325 is invested at age x at a force of interest $\delta = .05$, will there be enough money to pay \$1000 upon the death of (x) if he dies at age $x+20$? age $x+30$?

6. Assume (x) is (25), $\omega = 100$ and $\delta = .05$. Write an expression for the random present value of benefit variable for the following insurances:

   (i) \$1000 payable at death if (x) dies prior to age 60 (i.e., 35-year term insurance),
   (ii) \$1000 payable at death if (x) dies prior to age 60, reducing to \$500 if death is after age 60.

7. Suppose an insurance is issued to (25) providing \$1000 on the policy anniversary next following death if death occurs prior to age 65, or \$1000 at age 65 if he is surviving. Express the present value of benefit variable, Z, in terms of the curtate future lifetime of (25), K. Assume $i = .05$.

   Express $Pr(PV = 1000/1.05^{40})$ in life table symbols.

8. In Question 7 use the fact that $E[g(K)] = \sum g(k) \cdot f_K(k)$ and the fact that $f_K(k)$ can be written in terms of life table values, to write a summation for the actuarial (i.e., expected) present value of the benefit or net single premium in terms of interest and life table symbols. Assume $\omega = 100$.

9. Explain the relation $\ell_x \cdot A_x = \sum_{k=0}^{\omega-x-1} v^{k+1} \cdot d_{x+k}$ in a deterministic framework for a group of ℓ_x individuals age x purchasing \$1 of whole life insurance for a single premium of $\$A_x$ paid at issue.

10. Suppose 100 individuals aged 25 purchase \$1000 of whole life insurance with benefits payable at death. If Z_i is the present value of benefit variable for the ith individual, then $Z_{Agg} = Z_1 + \cdots + Z_{100}$ is the aggregate random present value of benefits paid by the insurer. Write an expression for the expected value and variance of Z_{Agg} in terms of $\overline{A}_{25}$ and ${}^2\overline{A}_{25}$.

11. Use the relation between T, the complete future lifetime of (x), K, the curtate lifetime of (x), and S, the fractional part of the final policy year of life to relate the present value of benefit for \$1 of whole life payable at death to the analogous variable if payable on the policy anniversary following death.

12. Explain why $\overline{A}_x$ is slightly bigger than A_x.

CONCEPTUAL REVIEW TEST ANSWERS

1. (a) $\dfrac{1000}{1.05^{30.7}}$ since $T = 55.7 - 25 = 30.7$

   (b) $\dfrac{1000}{1.05^{31}}$ since $K = 30$ (i.e., death during 31st policy year)

   (c) 0, death occurred after coverage expired

   (d) $\dfrac{1000}{1.05^{25}}$ since the 1000 is paid as an endowment benefit at age 50, 25 years from issue.

2. $Z = e^{-\delta T} = e^{-.05T}$ for $0 \leq T \leq \omega - x$

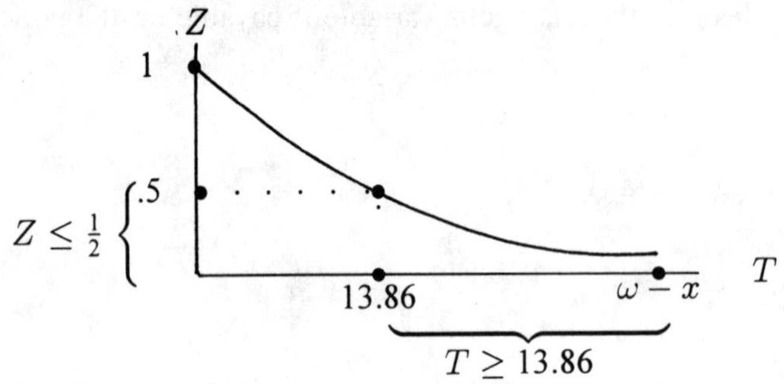

3. $Z \leq \frac{1}{2} \;\Leftrightarrow\; e^{-.05T} \leq \frac{1}{2} \;\Leftrightarrow\; -.05T \leq -ln\,2 \;\Leftrightarrow\; T \geq \frac{ln\,2}{.05} = 13.86$ (years).

4. In general, if $Y = g(X)$ is a function of the random variable X, then $E[Y] = \int g(x)\, f_X(x)\, dx$. Thus since $Z = e^{-\delta T}$ and $f_T(t) = {}_tp_x \cdot \mu(x+t)$ for $0 \leq t \leq \omega - x$, we have $\overline{A}_x = E[Z] = \int_0^{\omega - x} e^{-\delta t} \cdot {}_tp_x \cdot \mu(x+t)dt$. "On average" $\overline{A}_x$ is the right amount of money to invest at issue so as to have enough money to pay \$1 in T-years. Sometimes it is less than enough and other times more than enough.

5. In 20 years \$325 grows to \$883.44 = $325 \cdot e^{20(.05)}$, which is not sufficient. In 30 years it grows to \$1456.55 = $325 \cdot {}^{30(.05)}$, which is more than sufficient. For any given amount A invested at issue, there is a time $t_A = \dfrac{ln\,(1000/A)}{.05}$ such that A is insufficient to pay \$1000 if (x) dies before age $x + t_A$ and is sufficient otherwise.

6. (i) $Z = \begin{cases} 1000\, e^{-.05T} & 0 \leq T \leq 35 \\ 0 & 35 < T \leq 75 \end{cases}$ (ii) $Z = \begin{cases} 1000\, e^{-.05T} & 0 \leq T \leq 35 \\ 500\, e^{-.05T} & 3 < T \leq 75 \end{cases}$,

   a combination of \$1000 of 35-year term insurance plus \$500 of 35-year deferred insurance.

7. (a) $Z = \begin{cases} 1000/1.05^{K+1} & K = 0, 1, \ldots, 39 \\ 1000/1.05^{40} & K = 40, 41, 42, \ldots \end{cases}$

(b) $\left\{PV = \frac{1000}{1.05^{40}}\right\} = \left\{K = 39, 40, \ldots\right\}$. Thus $Pr = {}_{39}p_{25} = \frac{\ell_{64}}{\ell_{25}}$

8. $APV = \sum_{k=0}^{39}\left(\frac{1000}{1.05^{k+1}}\right)f_K(k) + \sum_{k=40}^{74}\left(\frac{1000}{1.05^{40}}\right)f_K(k)$ where $f_K(k) = {}_{k|}q_{25} = \frac{d_{25+k}}{\ell_{25}}$ and the second sum simplifies to $\left(\frac{1000}{1.05^{40}}\right)\frac{d_{65}+\cdots+d_{99}}{\ell_{25}} = \left(\frac{1000}{1.05^{40}}\right)\frac{\ell_{65}}{\ell_{25}} = \left(\frac{1000}{1.05^{40}}\right){}_{40}p_{25}$.

9. $\ell_x \cdot A_x$ is the total pool of money available to the insurer at issue. Assuming exactly d_{x+k} deaths occur between ages $x+k$ and $x+k+1$, the insurer must pay $d_{x+k} \cdot \$1$ at a time $k+1$ years in the future, which has present value $d_{x+k} \cdot v^{k+1}$. Thus the relation says the pool available is exactly equal the present value of benefits paid out to the entire group.

10. $E[Z_{Agg}] = 100 \cdot E[Z] = 100[1000 \cdot \overline{A}_{25}]$

$Var(Z_{Agg}) = 100 \cdot V(Z) = 100 \cdot 1000^2({}^2\overline{A}_{25} - \overline{A}_{25}{}^2)$

where $Z = 1000 \cdot v^T$, $\overline{A}_{25} = E[v^T]$ and ${}^2\overline{A}_{25} = E[(v^T)^2]$.

11. $T = K + S = K + 1 + S - 1$, thus $v^T = v^{K+S} = v^{K+1+S-1} = v^{K+1} \cdot v^{S-1}$.

12. With $\overline{A}_x$ the benefit is always paid between 0 and 1 years earlier than with A_x. If the benefit is paid slightly earlier, its present value is slightly higher. Since this relation holds for all values of T, the same relation holds for expected values.

COMPUTATIONAL REVIEW TEST

1. Using the fact that $\int_0^\infty t^n \cdot e^{-\beta t}\,dt = \frac{n!}{\beta^{n+1}}$ for any positive integer n, calculate $\overline{A}_{25} = E[Z]$ and $Var(Z)$ where $Z = e^{-\delta T}$ is the present value of benefit variable for \$1 of whole life to (25) payable at death. Assume $\delta = .05$ and that the p.d.f. of T, the future lifetime of (25), is given by $f(t) = \frac{1}{100} \cdot t \cdot e^{-.10t}$ for $t > 0$. Remember that $E[Z^2]$ is the same as $E[Z]$ at twice the force of interest and that $E[Z] = \int e^{-\delta t} \cdot f_T(t)\,dt$.

2. Suppose the benefit in Problem 1 is \$1000 instead of \$1, and $Z_1 = 1000 \cdot e^{-\delta T} = 1000 \cdot Z$ is the present value of benefit variable. What is the relation between $E[Z_1]$, $Var(Z_1)$, σ_{Z_1} and the corresponding items for Z?

3. If $Z = e^{-\delta T}$ is the present value of benefit variable for \$1 of whole life to (x), and $\overline{A}_x = .250$, $Var(Z) = .0144$, let Z_{Agg} be the aggregate present value of benefit variable corresponding to 100 independent lives aged x. Express $Pr(23 \le Z_{Agg} \le 28)$ in terms of Φ, the standard normal distribution function, using the central limit theorem to approximate the distribution of Z_{Agg}.

4. In Question 3, what single premium should the insurer charge to each of the 100 lives aged x in order to have a fund at issue having a 95% chance of covering the benefits, that is, find a single premium P such that it is 95% certain that 100P, aggregate premium, exceeds Z_{Agg}, aggregate present value of benefits. Use the central limit theorem and note that the answer should be slightly higher than .25, the net single premium. Note: $.95 = Pr(N(0,1) \le 1.645)$.

For Questions 5-8 you are given the following for a table of life insurance values and mortality

(i) $i = .06$

(ii) $A_{25} = .0816496$, $A_{65} = .4397965$

(iii) $\ell_{25} = 95{,}650.15$, $\ell_{65} = 75{,}339.63$

$\ell_{66} = 73{,}733.37$, $\ell_{67} = 72{,}016.33$

5. Calculate the following net single premiums assuming death benefits are payable at the end of the policy year during which death occurs:

   (i) \$1000 of whole life to (25)

   (ii) \$1000 of 40-year endowment insurance of (25).

6. Under the uniform distribution of deaths assumption calculate the NSP's in Question 5 assuming death benefits are payable at death.

7. In Question 5(i) express the probability that the net single premium, \$81.65, will be sufficient to pay the benefit in terms of K, the curtate future lifetime of (25).

8. Calculate the probability in 7.

COMPUTATIONAL REVIEW TEST SOLUTIONS

1. $\overline{A}_{25} = E[Z] = \int_0^\infty \frac{e^{-.05t} \cdot t \cdot e^{-.10t}}{100} dt = .01 \cdot \int_0^\infty t \cdot e^{-.15t} dt = (.01) \cdot \frac{1!}{(.15)^2} = \frac{.01}{.0225} = .4\overline{4} = \frac{4}{9}.$

$E[Z^2] = \int_0^\infty e^{-.10t} \cdot t \cdot e^{-.10t}/100\, dt = .01 \cdot \int_0^\infty t \cdot e^{-.20t} dt = (.01) \cdot \frac{1!}{(.20)^2} = \frac{.01}{.04} = .25 = \frac{1}{4}$

$Var(Z) = E[Z^2] - (E[Z])^2 = \frac{1}{4} - \left(\frac{4}{9}\right)^2 = \frac{17}{324} = .0525$

We have relied on the fact that $E[g(T)] = \int_0^\infty g(t) \cdot f_T(t) dt.$

2. $E[Z_1] = 1000E[Z] = 444.44$, $Var(Z_1) = Var(1000Z) = 1000^2 \cdot Var(Z) = 1{,}000{,}000(.0525)$, and $\sigma_{Z_1} = \left(Var(Z_1)\right)^{1/2} = \left(1000^2 \cdot Var(Z)\right)^{1/2} = 1000 \cdot (Var\ Z)^{1/2} = 1000 \cdot \sigma_Z$. Thus both expected value and standard deviation are multiplied by 1000, whereas variance goes up by a factor of 1000^2.

3. $E[Z_{Agg}] = 100 \cdot E[Z] = 25$, $Var(Z_{Agg}) = 100 \cdot Var(Z) = 100 \cdot (.0144) = 1.44$, hence $\sigma_{Agg} = \sqrt{1.44} = 1.2$. Thus

$$Pr(23 \le Z_{Agg} \le 28) = Pr\left(\frac{23-25}{1.2} \le \frac{Z_{Agg}-25}{1.2} \le \frac{28-25}{1.2}\right)$$

$$\approx Pr\left(\frac{-2}{1.2} \le N(0,1) \le \frac{3}{1.2}\right) = \Phi(2.5) - \Phi(-1.6\overline{6}).$$

4. $$.95 = Pr(Z_{Agg} \le 100P) = Pr\left(\frac{Z_{Agg}-25}{1.2} \le \frac{100P-25}{1.2}\right) \approx Pr\left(N(0,1) \le \frac{100P-25}{1.2}\right)$$

$.95 = Pr(N(0,1) \le 1.645)$. Thus $1.645 = \frac{100P-25}{1.2}$,

or $P = \frac{25 + (1.2)(1.645)}{100} = \underset{\text{(net prem.)}}{.2500} + \underset{\text{(security margin)}}{.0197}.$

5. (i) $1000A_{25} = 81.65$ (directly in the table)

(ii) $1000A_{25:\overline{40|}} = 1000[\underbrace{A_{25} - v^{40}\,{}_{40}p_{25}A_{65}}_{\text{term insurance}} + \underbrace{v^{40}\,{}_{40}p_{25}}_{\text{pure endowment}}] = 124.55$ based on

$A_{25} = .0816496$, $A_{65} = .4397965$, $\ell_{25} = 95{,}650.15$ and $\ell_{65} = 75{,}339.63$ from the table.

6. $1000\overline{A}_{25} = 1000 \cdot \frac{i}{\delta} \cdot A_{25} = \frac{i}{\delta} \cdot (81.65) = \frac{.06}{ln(1.06)} \cdot (81.65) = 84.08$

$1000\overline{A}_{25:\overline{40|}} = 1000\left(\overline{A}^{\,1}_{25:\overline{40|}} + A_{25:\overline{40|}}^{\quad\ 1}\right) = 1000\left(\frac{i}{\delta}\, A^{\,1}_{25:\overline{40|}} + A_{25:\overline{40|}}^{\quad\ 1}\right)$

$= \frac{.06}{ln\,1.06}(47.97) + 76.58 = 49.40 + 76.58 = \$125.98$

7. $Pr(\text{NSP is sufficient}) = Pr(81.65 \geq 1000v^{K+1})$ where $v = \frac{1}{1.06}$. This inequality is equivalent to $ln(.08165) \geq ln(v) \cdot (K+1)$ where $ln(v) = -ln(1.06) = -\delta$. Thus the probability is the same as $Pr\left(\frac{-ln(.08165)}{ln\,1.06} \leq K+1\right)$, or equivalently, $Pr(41.996 \leq K)$. Since K is a whole number, this is the same as $Pr(42 \leq K)$.

8. $Pr(42 \leq K) = {}_{42}p_{25} = \frac{\ell_{67}}{\ell_{25}} = \frac{72{,}016.33}{95{,}650.15} = .753$

UNIT REVIEW QUESTIONS

1. There are 100 club members age x who each contribute an amount N to a fund. The fund earns interest at 10%. The probability is 0.95 that sufficient funds will be on hand to pay a 1000 death benefit to each member. You are given the following values calculated at $i = 10\%$:

   (i) $\overline{A}_x = 0.06$ (ii) ${}^2\overline{A}_x = 0.01$

   Calculate N. (Assume the future lifetimes are independent and that a normal distribution may be used. If Z is a standard normal variable, then $Pr(Z < 1.645) = 0.95$.)

   (A) 60 (B) 68 (C) 73 (D) 82 (E) 99

2. A 25-year mortgage is to be repaid with continuous payments at a rate of 1 per annum. An insurance policy is designed to pay the outstanding principal on the mortgage immediately upon death of the mortgagor. The mortgage interest rate is the same as that used in calculating the premium for the policy. The mortgagor is age 35 at the date of issue of the insurance policy (which coincides with the date the mortgage loan was made). You are given:

   (i) $i = .05$
   (ii) $A^1_{35:\overline{25|}} = .0616$
   (iii) ${}_{25}p_{35} = .8692$
   (iv) The UDD is assumed to hold.

   Then the NSP for this insurance is closest to

   (A) .46 (B) .48 (C) .50 (D) .52 (E) .54

3. A 2-year term insurance policy issued to (x) pays a death benefit of 1 at the end of the year of death. Given the following values, calculate q_{x+1}.

   (i) $q_x = .50$
   (ii) $i = 0$
   (iii) $Var(Z) = .1771$, where Z is the random variable representing the present value of future benefits.

   (A) .51 (B) .52 (C) .53 (D) .54 (E) .55

4. Let Z be the present value variable for \$1 of whole life insurance with benefits payable at death and issued on (40). If $\ell_x = 110 - x$ for $0 \le x \le 110$ and $\delta = .05$. Then $f_Z(.8)$ is closest to

   (A) .24 (B) .27 (C) .30 (D) .33 (E) .36

5. A 2-year term insurance is issued to (30). Benefits are payable at the end of the year of death. The death benefit for policy year t is b_t. You are given the following:

$$q_{30} = 0.1, \qquad b_2 = 10.0 - b_1, \qquad 0 \le b_1, \qquad b_2 \le 10\,, \qquad q_{31} = 0.6, \qquad i = 0$$

Find the value of b_1 which minimizes $Var(Z)$. (Answer to nearest 0.1)

(A) 0.0 (B) 5.0 (C) 6.8 (D) 8.6 (E) 10.0

6. A mortality table (T^*) having a 2-year select period is constructed from an ultimate table(T) by setting

$$q^*_{[x]} = q^*_{[x]+1} = vq_x \qquad q^*_{x+k} = q_{x+k},\ k \ge 2$$

where the q_x and q^*_x values refer to Tables T and T^*, respectively. Assume deaths are uniformly distributed throughout each year. Determine $\overline{A}^*_{[x]}$ at interest rate $i > 0$.

(A) $\overline{a}_{\overline{1}|}\ [vq_x + v^2 q_x - v^3 q_x^2 + v(1-vq_x)^2\ A_{x+2}]$

(B) $\overline{a}_{\overline{1}|}\ [vq_x + v^2 q_x - v^3 q_x^2 + v^2(1-vq_x)^2\ A_{x+2}]$

(C) $\overline{a}_{\overline{1}|}\ [vq_x +\ v^3 q_x^2 + v^3 q_x^2\ A_{x+2}]$

(D) $\overline{a}_{\overline{1}|}\ [vq_x + v^2 q_x + vA_{x+2}]$

(E) $\overline{a}_{\overline{1}|}\ [vq_x + v^2 q_x\ + v^2\ A_{x+2}]$

7. Calculate A_{77}, given that $A_{76} = .800$, $vp_{76} = .9$,and $i = .03$.

(A) .805 (B) .810 (C) .815 (D) .820 (E) .825

8. An insurance is issued to (x) that pays 1000 at the end of n years if (x) is alive, or returns the single premium π at the moment of death if (x) dies during the first n years. The variance of the present value random variable at issue can be written as

$$(1000)^2({}^2A_{x:\overline{n}|}^{\ \ 1}) + \pi^2({}^2\overline{A}_{x:\overline{n}|}^{1}) - (1000)^2(A_{x:\overline{n}|}^{\ \ 1})^2 - \pi^2(\overline{A}_{x:\overline{n}|}^{1})^2 + K.$$

Determine K.

(A) $-2000\pi A_{x:\overline{n}|}^{\ \ 1}\overline{A}_{x:\overline{n}|}^{1}$ (B) $-1000\pi A_{x:\overline{n}|}^{\ \ 1}\ \overline{A}_{x:\overline{n}|}^{1}$ (C) 0 (D) $1000\pi A_{x:\overline{n}|}^{\ \ 1}\ \overline{A}_{x:\overline{n}|}^{1}$ (E) $2000\pi A_{x:\overline{n}|}^{\ \ 1}\ \overline{A}_{x:\overline{n}|}^{1}$

9. Let Z denote the present value random variable for a 1-year insurance to (x) which pays a benefit of b at the end of the year if (x) dies during the year, and a benefit of e at the end of the year if (x) is still alive. Determine an expression for $Var(Z)$.

(A) $p_x q_x\, v^2(b{+}e)^2$ (B) $p_x q_x\, v^2(b{-}e)^2$ (C) $p_x q_x\, v^2(b^2{+}e^2)$ (D) $v^2(b^2 q_x + e^2 p_x)$ (E) $v^2(b^2 p_x + e^2 q_x)$

10. A whole life insurance of 50 is issued to (x). The benefit is payable at the moment of death. The p.d.f of the future lifetime, T, for (x) is

$$f(t) = \begin{cases} t/5000 & 0 \leq t \leq 100 \\ 0 & \text{elsewhere} \end{cases}$$

The force of interest is .10. Calculate the net single premium

(A) $1 - 11e^{-10}$ (B) $1 - 9e^{-10}$ (C) $1 + 9e^{-10}$ (D) $1 + 10e^{-10}$ (E) $1 + 11e^{-10}$

11. Let Z be the present value variable for \$1 of 20 year deferred whole life insurance with benefits payable at death and issued on (40). Z has a mixed distribution. If $\ell_x = 110 - x$ for $0 \leq x \leq 110$ and $\delta = .05$ then the discrete part of Z is a

(A) Point mass of v^{70} at $z = 1$

(B) Point mass of v^{70} at $z = \frac{5}{7}$

(C) Point mass of v^{70} at $z = \frac{2}{7}$

(D) Point mass of $\frac{2}{7}$ at $z = 0$

(E) Point mass of $\frac{2}{6}$ at $z = 0$

12. You are given:

(i) $i = 0.02$
(ii) $p_{50} = 0.98$
(iii) $A_{51} - A_{50} = 0.004$
(iv) ${}^2A_{51} - {}^2A_{50} = 0.005$

Let Z be the random variable representing the present value of a whole life insurance of 1 with death benefit payable at the end of the year of death. Calculate $Var(Z)$ for $x = 51$.

(A) 0.055 (B) 0.060 (C) 0.065 (D) 0.260 (E) 0.265

13. You are given that deaths are uniformly distributed over each year of age. Express $\dfrac{(I\bar{A})_x - (\bar{I}\bar{A})_x}{\bar{A}_x}$ in terms of interest functions.

(A) $\frac{i - \delta}{\delta^2}$ (B) $\frac{1+i}{\delta}$ (C) $\frac{i}{\delta}\left(\frac{i}{\delta} - 1\right)$ (D) $\frac{1}{d} - \frac{1}{\delta}$ (E) $\frac{1+i}{\delta} - \frac{i}{\delta^2}$

14. Z is the present-value random variable for a special increasing whole life insurance with benefits payable at the moment of death of (50). You are given:

(i) $b_t = 1 + .1t$
(ii) $v_t = (1 + .1t)^{-2}$
(iii) ${}_tp_{50}\,\mu(50+t) = .02 \qquad 0 \leq t < 50$

Calculate $Var(Z)$

(A) .01 (B) .02 (C) .03 (D) .04 (E) .05

15. An increasing whole life insurance pays $k+1$ at the end of year $k+1$ if (80) dies in year $k+1$, $k = 0, 1, 2, \ldots$ You are given:

(i) $v = .925$ (ii) The net single premium for this insurance is 4 if $q_{80} = .10$.

P is the net single premium for this insurance if $q_{80} = .20$ and q_x is unchanged for all other ages.

Calculate P.

(A) 3.40 (B) 3.66 (C) 3.75 (D) 3.87 (E) 3.94

16. Z_1 is the present-value random variable for an n-year term insurance of 1 on the life of (x). Z_2 is the present-value random variable for an n-year endowment insurance of 1 on the life of (x). You are given:

(i) $v^n = .20$
(ii) ${}_np_x = .50$
(iii) $E[Z_1] = .23$
(iv) $Var(Z_1) = .08$
(v) Death benefits are payable at the moment of death.

Calculate $Var(Z_2)$.

(A) .034 (B) .044 (C) .054 (D) .064 (E) .074

17. You are given:

(i) X is the present-value random variable for a 25-year term insurance of 7 on (35).
(ii) Y is the present-value random variable for a 25-year deferred, 10-year term insurance of 4 on the same life.
(iii) $E[X] = 2.80$ and $E[Y] = .12$
(iv) $Var(X) = 5.76$ and $Var(Y) = .10$

Calculate $Var(X+Y)$.

(A) 4.75 (B) 5.19 (C) 5.51 (D) 5.86 (E) 6.14

18. Which of the following are true?

I. $(DA)^1_{x:\overline{10}|} = \sum_{k=0}^{9}(10-k)\,{}_{k|}A^1_{x:\overline{1}|}$

II. $A_x = vq_x + v^2p_xq_{x+1} + v^3\,{}_2p_xA_{x+2}$

III. $(\bar{I}\bar{A})_x = \frac{i}{\delta}(IA)_x$ under the assumption of uniform distribution of deaths.

(A) I and II only (B) I and III only (C) II and III only (D) I, II and III
(E) The correct answer is not given by (A), (B), (C) or (D).

19. A special n-year endowment insurance on (x) pays a pure endowment of 1000 at the end of n years and pays only the net single premium at the end of the year of death if death occurs during the n-year period. The net single premium for this insurance is 600.

The net single premium for an n-year endowment insurance of 1000 with death benefits payable at the end of the year of death of (x) is 800.

Calculate the net single premium for an n-year pure endowment of 1000 on (x).

(A) 100 (B) 200 (C) 300 (D) 400 (E) 500

20. A whole life insurance provides a death benefit at the moment of death equal to 1 plus a return of the net single premium with interest at $\delta = .08$. The net single premium for this insurance is calculated using $\mu = .04$ and force of interest 2δ. Calculate the net single premium.

(A) .24 (B) .30 (C) .36 (D) .42 (E) .48

21. You are given:

(i) Deaths are uniformly distributed over each year of age.
(ii) $i = .05$
(iii) $q_{35} = .01$
(iv) $\bar{A}_{36} = .185$

Calculate A_{35}.

(A) .1797 (B) .1815 (C) .1840 (D) .1864 (E) .1883

22. Z is the present-value random variable for a special whole life insurance with death benefits payable at the moment of death of (x).

You are given for $t \geq 0$:

(i) $b_t = e^{.05t}$
(ii) $\delta_t = .06$
(iii) $\mu(x+t) = .01$

Calculate $Var(Z)$.

(A) .037 (B) .057 (C) .063 (D) .083 (E) .097

23. Z is the random present value variable for a 5-year endowment insurance of 1000 on (60). You are given

(i) $A_{60:\overline{5|}} = .7896$
(ii) ${}^2A_{65} = .2836$, ${}^2A_{60} = .2196$, ${}^2A_{\overset{\,1}{60:\overline{5|}}} = .5649$

Calculate $Var(Z)$.

(A) 476 (B) 588 (C) 624 (D) 826 (E) 881

24. You are given:

(i) Deaths are uniformly distributed over each year of age.
(ii) $i = .10$
(iii) $q_x = .05$
(iv) $q_{x+1} = .08$

Calculate $\bar{A}^{1}_{x:\overline{2|}}$.

(A) .103 (B) .108 (C) .111 (D) .114 (E) .119

25. A whole life insurance provides a death benefit at the moment of death equal to 1 plus a return of the net single premium with interest at $\delta = .04$.

The net single premium for this insurance is calculated using $\mu = .04$ and force of interest 2δ.

Calculate the net single premium.

(A) .25 (B) .50 (C) .67 (D) .75 (E) 1.00

26. You are given:

(i) $u(x) = \frac{d}{\delta} q_x + v p_x u(x+1), \qquad x = 0, 1, 2, \ldots$
(ii) $u(80) = 1$
(iii) Deaths uniformly distributed within each year of age.

Which of the following expressions is equal to $u(40)$?

(A) $\bar{A}_{40:\overline{40|}}$ (B) $A_{40:\overline{40|}}$ (C) $A^{1}_{40:\overline{40|}}$ (D) $\bar{A}^{1}_{40:\overline{40|}}$

(E) The correct answer is not given by A, B, C or D

27. You are given:

(i) $A^{1}_{35:\overline{1|}} = .9434$
(ii) $A_{35} = .1300$
(iii) $p_{35} = .9964$
(iv) $(IA)_{35} = 3.7100$

Calculate $(IA)_{36}$.

(A) 3.81 (B) 3.88 (C) 3.94 (D) 4.01 (E) 4.08

28. For a modified ten-year pure endowment of 1000 on (35), you are given:

(i) $A_{35:\overline{10|}} = .57$
(ii) This modified pure endowment includes a death benefit payable at the end of the year of death.
(iii) Z_1 is the present value random variable if the death benefit is $1000\,{}_{10}E_{35}$.
(iv) Z_2 is the present value random variable if the death benefit is $750\,{}_{10}E_{35}$.
(v) Z_3 is the present value random variable if the death benefit is $500\,{}_{10}E_{35}$.
(vi) $\dfrac{E[Z_1]}{E[Z_2]} = 1.005$

Calculate $E[Z_3]$.

(A) 550 (B) 555 (C) 560 (D) 565 (E) 570

29. You are given:

(i) $q_x = .10$
(ii) $q_{x+1} = .20$
(iii) $i = .12$
(iv) Deaths are uniformly distributed over each year of age.

Calculate ${}^2\bar{A}^{\,1}_{x:\overline{2|}}$.

(A) .206 (B) .209 (C) .218 (D) .224 (E) .232

30. A special 35-year endowment insurance of 1000 is issued on (30). You are given:

(i) (30) has two children ages 3 and 6 at issue.
(ii) The death benefit is 3000 if both children are less than 11 years old at the moment of death of (30).
(iii) The death benefit is 2000 if only one child is less than 11 years old at the moment of death of (30).
(iv) The death benefit is payable at the moment of death.
(v) Assume that both children will survive to age 11.
(vi) $\mu_{30+t} = .04 \qquad t \geq 0$
(vii) $\delta = .06$
(viii) ${}_{35}E_{30} = .0302$

Calculate the net single premium for this insurance.

(A) 638 (B) 766 (C) 777 (D) 796 (E) 807

31. A special 3-year endowment insurance is issued on (60).

The death benefit is 100 during policy year 1 and 200 thereafter. Death benefits are payable at the moment of death.

The pure endowment benefit is 200.

You are given:
(i) Mortality follows de Moivre's law with $\omega = 70$.
(ii) $i = 0$

Calculate the variance of this insurance.

(A) 0 (B) 900 (C) 3,600 (D) 6,500 (E) 15,700

Use the following information for Questions 32 -34.

Z denotes the present value random variable for a 10-year insurance issued to (30). It is calculated assuming $i = .06$. The policy pays the following benefits:

(i) If (30) dies in year 1, a death benefit of 1 payable at the end of the year;
(ii) If (30) dies in year 2, 3, 4, ..., 10, a death benefit, payable at the end of the year, equal to 1.06 times the previous year's death benefit; and
(iii) 1 at the end of year 10 if (30) is still alive.

Assume mortality follows de Moivre's law with $\omega = 100$.

---

32. $E[Z]$ is closest to which of the following?

(A) .61 (B) .65 (C) .69 (D) .73 (E) .77

33. What is the probability that Z equals 1.06^{-1}?

(A) 1/70 (B) 1/30 (C) 10/70 (D) 10/30 (E) 9/70

34. $Var(Z)$ is closest to which of the following ?

(A) .009 (B) .010 (C) .014 (D) .018 (E) .134

Use the following information for Questions 35 - 38.

An engineering firm installs a tunnel-surrounded steam pipe system on the campus of Enormous State U. and guarantees it for 10 years against a major failure. In the event of failure during this period the contract calls for a 2 million dollar payment to the University. Let X denote the time after installation until a major failure occurs in the system. You are given:

(i) $\delta = .05$;

(ii) The conditional probability of failure in $[x, x+\Delta x]$ given survival at time x (for small (Δx)) is proportional to $\frac{\Delta x}{(60-x)}$;

(iii) The expected life of the system is 20 years.

Let Z denote the random present value of the possible guarantee payment.

35. The survival function for X is given by

(A) $\left(1-\frac{x}{20}\right)^3$ (B) $\left(1-\frac{x}{20}\right)^2$ (C) $\left(1-\frac{x}{20}\right)$ (D) $\left(1-\frac{x}{60}\right)^3$ (E) $\left(1-\frac{x}{60}\right)^2$

36. What is the probability that Z is zero?

(A) $\frac{24}{36}$ (B) $\frac{25}{36}$ (C) $\frac{26}{36}$ (D) $\frac{27}{36}$ (E) $\frac{28}{36}$

37. The actuarial present value of the guarantee is closest to

(A) 235,000 (B) 297,000 (C) 382,000 (D) 485,000 (E) 501,000

38. The 81st percentile of Z is closest to

(A) 1.3 million (B) 1.4 million (C) 1.5 million (D) 1.6 million (E) 1.7 million

SOLUTIONS TO UNIT REVIEW QUESTION

1. $.95 = Pr(\text{Funds are sufficient}) = Pr(100N > \text{Aggregate Present Value Benefits})$.
If Z_{Agg} is the aggregate present value then $E[Z_{Agg}] = 100 \cdot 1000\overline{A}_x = 6000$ and $Var(Z_{Agg}) = 100 \cdot 1000^2 \cdot [{}^2\overline{A}_x - \overline{A}_x{}^2]$. Hence $\sigma_{Z_{Agg}} = 10 \cdot 1000(.01 - .06^2)^{1/2} = 800$.

So $.95 = Pr\left(\frac{100N - 6000}{800} > \frac{Z_{Agg} - E[Z_{Agg}]}{\sigma_{Z_{Agg}}}\right) \approx Pr\left(\frac{100N - 6000}{800} > N(0,1)\right)$.

Since 1.645 is the 95 percentile of $N(0,1)$ we must have $1.645 = \frac{100N - 6000}{800}$ or $N = 73.16$.

ANSWER C

2. If death occurs t years from issue the outstanding balance is $\overline{a}_{\overline{25-t}|}$. Thus the NSP for this insurance is

$$\begin{aligned}
E[\overline{a}_{\overline{25-T}|} \cdot v^T] &= \int_0^{25} \frac{1 - v^{25-t}}{\delta} \cdot v^t \cdot {}_tp_{35} \cdot \mu(35+t)\,dt \\
&= \frac{1}{\delta}\int_0^{25} v^t \cdot {}_tp_{35} \cdot \mu(35+t)dt - \frac{v^{25}}{\delta}\int_0^{25} {}_tp_{35}\mu(35+t)\,dt \\
&= \frac{1}{\delta} \cdot \overline{A}^{1}_{35:\overline{25}|} - \frac{v^{25}}{\delta} \cdot {}_{25}q_{35} \\
&= \frac{1}{\delta} \cdot \overline{A}^{1}_{35:\overline{25}|} - \frac{v^{25}(1 - {}_{25}p_{35})}{\delta} \\
&= \frac{1}{\delta}\left(\frac{i}{\delta} A^{1}_{35:\overline{25}|}\right) - \frac{v^{25}(1 - {}_{25}p_{35})}{\delta} \\
&= 1.2939 - .7917 = .5022,
\end{aligned}$$

ANSWER C

3. Z is a discrete random variable having value either 1 or 0:
$f_Z(1) = {}_2q_x = q_x + {}_1|q_x = q_x + p_x \cdot q_{x+1} = \frac{1}{2} + \frac{1}{2} \cdot q_{x+1}$,
$f_Z(0) = {}_2p_x = 1 - {}_2q_x = \frac{1}{2} - \frac{1}{2}q_{x+1}$. Z is in fact a Bernoulli variable. Thus
$.1771 = Var(Z) = p \cdot q = \left(\frac{1}{2} + \frac{1}{2}q_{x+1}\right)\left(\frac{1}{2} - \frac{1}{2}q_{x+1}\right) = \frac{1}{4}\left(1 - q^2_{x+1}\right)$; hence
$1 - .7084 = q^2_{x+1}$, $q_{x+1} = .54$.

ANSWER D

4. In general $f_Z(z) = \frac{f_T(-lnz/\delta)}{(\delta z)}$. Here $T \sim U(0, 70)$ (de Moivre's law with $\omega = 110$) and $\delta = .05$ so $f_T(t) = \frac{1}{70}$ and

$$f_Z(.8) = \left(\frac{1}{70}\right)/(.05)(.8) = .357.$$

ANSWER E

5. Let Z be the random present value of benefit. Since $i = 0$ we have

$Z = z$	$f_Z(z)$	
b_1	${}_0\vert q_{30} = .1$	dies during 2-year period of coverage
$10 - b_1$	${}_1\vert q_{30} = (.9)(.6)$	
0	${}_2p_{30} = (.9)(.4)$	dies after coverage ceases

$$Var(Z) = E[Z^2] - \left(E[Z]\right)^2 = \left(b_1^2(.1) + (10-b_1)^2(.54)\right) - \left(b_1(.1) + (10-b_1)(.54)\right)^2$$

$$0 = \frac{d\,Var(Z)}{b_1} = 2b_1(.1) - 2(10 - b_1)(.54) - 2\left(b_1(.1) + (10-b_1)(.54)\right)(-.44)$$

$\Rightarrow$ $.8928\, b_1 = 6.048$ or $b_1 = 6.77$, ANSWER C

Note: Min is at the critical point since $Var(Z) = b_1^2\,(.4464) + \cdots$ is concave up.

6. Under the UDD assumption

$$\begin{aligned}
\overline{A}^*_{[x]} &= \tfrac{i}{\delta} A^*_{[x]} \\
&= \bar{s}_{\overline{1}|} \cdot \left(v \cdot q^*_{[x]} + v^2 \cdot {}_1|q^*_{[x]} + v^2 \cdot {}_2p^*_{[x]} \cdot A_{x+2}\right) \quad \text{(see recursive relations)} \\
&= \bar{s}_{\overline{1}|} \cdot \left(v \cdot (vq_x) + v^2 \cdot (1-q^*_{[x]}) \cdot (q^*_{[x]+1}) + v^2 \cdot (1-q^*_{[x]})(1-q^*_{[x]+1})\, A_{x+2}\right) \\
&= \bar{s}_{\overline{1}|}\left(v^2 q_x + v^2(1-vq_x)(vq_x) + v^2(1-vq_x)^2 A_{x+2}\right) \\
&= v\bar{s}_{\overline{1}|}\left(vq_x + v^2 q_x - v^3 q_x^2 + v(1-vq_x)^2\, A_{x+2}\right)
\end{aligned}$$

ANSWER A

7. $A_{76} = vq_{76} + vp_{76} \cdot A_{77}$. Since $v = \frac{1}{1.03}$ we obtain $p_{76} = .9(1.03) = .927$, $q_{76} = .073$. Thus $.8 = A_{76} = \frac{.073}{1.03} + \frac{.927}{1.03} \cdot A_{77}$, which implies $A_{77} = .810$. ANSWER B

8. If Z is the random present value of benefit then

$$E[Z] = \underset{\text{(return prem.)}}{\pi \overline{A}^{\,1}_{x:\overline{n}|}} + \underset{\text{(survival)}}{1000\, A_{x:\overline{n}|}^{\;\;\;\;1}}, \quad E[Z^2] = \pi^2 \cdot {}^2\overline{A}^{\,1}_{x:\overline{n}|} + 1000^2 \cdot {}^2A_{x:\overline{n}|}^{\;\;\;\;1}.$$

$$Var(Z) = E[Z^2] - \left(E[Z]\right)^2 = \pi^2 \cdot {}^2\overline{A}^{\,1}_{x:\overline{n}|} + 1000^2 \cdot {}^2A_{x:\overline{n}|}^{\;\;\;\;1} - \left(\pi\overline{A}^{\,1}_{x:\overline{n}|} + 1000A_{x:\overline{n}|}^{\;\;\;\;1}\right)^2.$$

Expanding out the squared term and scanning the answers yields $-K$ as the mixed term, $2\left(\pi\overline{A}^{\,1}_{x:\overline{n}|}\right)\left(1000A_{x:\overline{n}|}^{\;\;\;\;1}\right)$. ANSWER A

9.

Z	$f_Z(z)$
vb	q_x
ve	p_x

Notice that $Z = vb + (ve - vb)Y$ where Y is the Bernoulli variable with $f_Y(0) = q_x$, $f_Y(1) = p_x$. Thus $Var(Z) = Var\Big(vb + v(e-b)Y\Big) = v^2(e-b)^2\, Var(Y) = v^2(b-e)^2 p_x q_x$. ANSWER B

10.

$$\begin{aligned} 50\,\overline{A}_x = E\big[50e^{-\delta T}\big] &= 50\int_{t=0}^{100} e^{-.10t}\, f_T(t)\,dt \\ &= 50\int_{t=0}^{100} e^{-.10t}\cdot\frac{t}{5000}\,dt \\ &= \frac{50}{5000}\left(\frac{-\,t\,e^{-.10t}}{.10} - \frac{e^{-.10t}}{(.10)^2}\bigg|_{t=0}^{100}\right) \\ &= .01\left(\frac{-\,100\,e^{-10}}{.10} - \frac{e^{-10}}{.01} + 0 + \frac{1}{.01}\right) \\ &= 1 - 10\,e^{-10} - e^{-10} \;=\; 1 - 11e^{-10}, \end{aligned}$$

ANSWER A

11. From the graph of

$$Z = \begin{cases} 0 & 0 \le T \le 20 \\ v^T & 20 < T \le 70 \end{cases}$$

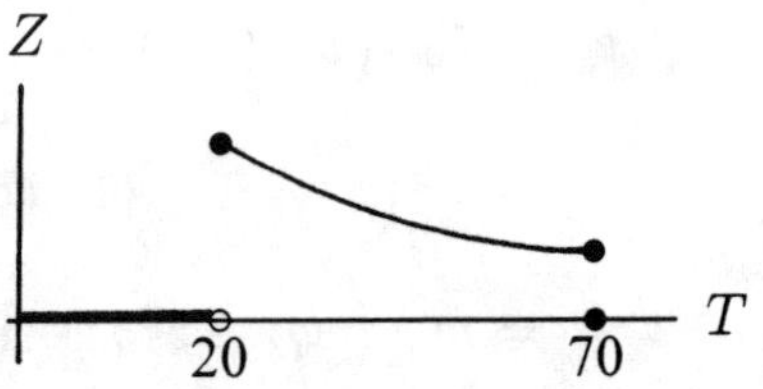

we see that $Pr(Z = 0) = Pr(T \le 20) = \int_0^{20} \frac{1}{70}dt = \frac{2}{7}$

(de Moivre's law; $f_T(t) = \frac{1}{\omega - x} = \frac{1}{110-40}$) is a point mass, and for $T > 20$ we see Z is a continuous decreasing function of T. The only point mass of probability, that is, where Z is a constant function of T, is $\frac{2}{7}$ at $z = 0$. ANSWER D

12. Recall the recursive relation $A_x = v\cdot q_x + v\cdot p_x\cdot A_{x+1}$. Doubling the force of interest results in squaring the discount factor, hence we also have ${}^2A_x = v^2\cdot q_x + v^2\cdot p_x\cdot {}^2A_{x+1}$. As a result

$$\begin{aligned} .004 &= A_{51} - A_{50} \\ &= A_{51} - (vq_{50} + vp_{50}A_{51}) \\ &= A_{51} - (.019608 + .960784\,A_{51}), \end{aligned}$$

so $A_{51} = .602004$. Using the analogous relation at double the force yields ${}^2A_{51} = .417252$, so $Var(Z) = {}^2A_{51} - {A_{51}}^2 \;=\; .054843$, ANSWER A

13. If T is the random future lifetime, then under the UDD $T = K + S$ where K and S are independent and $S \sim U(0,1)$. So

$$\begin{aligned}(I\overline{A})_x - (\overline{I}\overline{A})_x &= E\left[(K+1)\,v^T\right] - E\left[T \cdot v^T\right] \\ &= E\left[(K+1-T)\,v^T\right] \\ &= E\left[(1-S)\,v^{K+1+S-1}\right] \\ &= E\left[(1-S)\,v^{S-1}\right] E\left[v^{K+1}\right] \\ &= \int_0^1 (1-s)\,v^{s-1}\,ds \cdot A_x \\ &= (1+i)\left[\tfrac{1}{\delta} - \tfrac{d}{\delta^2}\right] \tfrac{\delta}{i}\,\overline{A}_x \\ &= \tfrac{1}{d}\left[1 - \tfrac{d}{\delta}\right]\overline{A}_x = \left[\tfrac{1}{d} - \tfrac{1}{\delta}\right]\overline{A}_x,\end{aligned}$$

ANSWER D

14. From first principles, using $f_T(t) = .02$,

$$\begin{aligned}E[Z] = E\left[(1+.1T)(1+.1T)^{-2}\right] &= E\left[(1+.1T)^{-1}\right] \\ &= \int_0^{50} \frac{1}{1+.1t} \cdot f_T(t)\,dt \\ &= \int_0^{50} \frac{.02}{1+.1t}\,dt \\ &= \frac{1}{50}\,\frac{ln(1+.1t)}{.1}\bigg|_0^{50} \\ &= \tfrac{1}{5}\,ln(6) = .358, \text{ and}\end{aligned}$$

$$\begin{aligned}E[Z^2] &= E\left[\left((1+.1T)^{-1}\right)^2\right] \\ &= \int_0^{50} \frac{1}{(1+.1t)^2} \cdot f_T(t)\,dt \\ &= \frac{1}{50}\,\frac{-1}{.1(1+.1t)}\bigg|_0^{50} \\ &= \tfrac{1}{5}\left(1 - \tfrac{1}{6}\right) = \tfrac{1}{6}.\end{aligned}$$

Then

$Var(Z) = \frac{1}{6} - (.358)^2 = .038$, which is closest to

ANSWER D

15. Breaking the coverage into year 1 and 1-year deferred leads to

$4 = (IA)_{80} = vq_{80} + vp_{80} \cdot APV_{81}(\text{future benefits}) = .925\left(.1 + .9(APV_{81})\right)$,

or $APV_{81}(\text{future benefits}) = 4.69369$. So if $q'_{80} = .2$ one has

$(IA)'_{80} = vq'_{80} + vp'_{80}(4.69369) = .925\left(.2 + .8(4.69369)\right) = 3.65833$,

ANSWER B

16. Since Z_2 is the present value for endowment insurance

$$\begin{aligned} Var(Z_2) &= {}^2\overline{A}_{x:\overline{n}|} - \left(\overline{A}_{x:\overline{n}|}\right)^2 \\ &= \left({}^2\overline{A}^{\,1}_{x:\overline{n}|} + {}^2A_{x:\overline{n}|}^{\;\;\,1}\right) - \left(\overline{A}^{\,1}_{x:\overline{n}|} + \overline{A}_{x:\overline{n}|}^{\;\;\,1}\right)^2. \end{aligned}$$

Similarly, $.08 = Var(Z_1) = {}^2\overline{A}^{\,1}_{x:\overline{n}|} - \overline{A}^{\,1\;\,2}_{x:\overline{n}|} = {}^2\overline{A}^{\,1}_{x:\overline{n}|} - (.23)^2$.

So ${}^2\overline{A}^{\,1}_{x:\overline{n}|} = .08 + (.23)^2 = .1329$. Substituting into the above

$$\begin{aligned} Var(Z_2) &= (.1329 + v^{2n} \cdot {}_np_x) - (.23 + v^n \cdot {}_np_x)^2 \\ &= \left(.1329 + (.2)^2(.5)\right) - \left(.23 + (.2)(.5)\right)^2 \\ &= .044, \end{aligned}$$

ANSWER B

17. From the descriptions

$$X = \begin{cases} 7v^t & 0 < t \le 25 \\ 0 & \text{otherwise} \end{cases} \quad \text{and} \quad Y = \begin{cases} 4v^t & 25 < t \le 35 \\ 0 & \text{otherwise} \end{cases}$$

so it is clear that $XY = 0$ and $E[XY] = 0$. Hence

$$\begin{aligned} Var(X{+}Y) &= Var(X) + Var(Y) + 2 \cdot Cov(X,Y) \\ &= 5.76 + .10 + 2(E[XY] - E[X] \cdot E[Y]) \\ &= 5.86 + 2(0 - (2.80)(.12)) = 5.188, \end{aligned}$$

ANSWER B

18. I. The summation can be written out as $10A^{\,1}_{x:\overline{1}|} + 9({}_1|A^{\,1}_{x:\overline{1}|}) + \ldots + 1({}_9|A^{\,1}_{x:\overline{1}|})$, which would provide benefits of 10, 9, … , 1 respectively in years 1, 2, … , 10. This is exactly the same benefit pattern provided by an NSP of $(DA)^{\,1}_{x:\overline{10}|}$ so the NSP's are equal. True.

II. In general $A_x = A^{\,1}_{x:\overline{2}|} + {}_2|A_x = (v \cdot q_x + v^2 \cdot {}_1|q_x) + v^2 \cdot {}_2p_x \cdot A_{x+2}$. The ${}_1|q_x$ term can be written as $p_x \cdot q_{x+1}$, however the right side of the alleged equation contains v^3 in the third term where is should have had v^2. False.

III. Under UDD it follows that $(\overline{I}\overline{A})_x = \frac{i}{\delta}(IA)_x + \frac{i}{\delta}\left[\frac{1}{\delta} - \frac{1}{d}\right]A_x$,

(See the Condensed Review Notes in this Unit), so III is also false,

ANSWER E

19. From the descriptions

$$600 = 600A^{1}_{x:\overline{n}|} + 1000A_{x:\overline{n}|}^{\;\;\,1}$$

$$800 = 1000A^{1}_{x:\overline{n}|} + 1000A_{x:\overline{n}|}^{\;\;\,1}.$$

These two equations in two unknowns solve easily for

$$A^{1}_{x:\overline{n}|} = .5,\ A_{x:\overline{n}|}^{\;\;\,1} = .3.$$

Thus $1000A_{x:\overline{n}|}^{\;\;\,1} = 300$, ANSWER C

20. The present value variable for the return of premium is $Z = \underbrace{(NSP \cdot e^{.08T})}_{\text{Amount}} \underbrace{(e^{-.16T})}_{\substack{v \text{ when} \\ \delta = .16}}$,

which is $NSP \cdot e^{-.08T}$. Since $\mu = .04$ we know that the T-density is $.04e^{-.04T}$, hence

$$\begin{aligned} E[Z] &= NSP \cdot E[e^{-.08T}] \\ &= NSP \cdot \int_0^{\infty} e^{-.08t}(.04e^{-.04t})\,dt = NSP\left(\tfrac{.04}{.12}\right) = \tfrac{NSP}{3}. \end{aligned}$$

With constant force it is also known that

$$\overline{A}_x = \frac{\textit{force of mortality}}{\textit{force of mortality} + \textit{force of interest}} = \frac{.04}{.04 + .16} = \frac{1}{5}.$$

The basic equation for NSP is

$$NSP = \underbrace{\overline{A}_x}_{\text{1 at death}} + \underbrace{NSP/3}_{\substack{\text{return of prem.} \\ \text{plus interest}}},$$

which means $NSP = \frac{3}{2}\left(\frac{1}{5}\right) = .30$, ANSWER B

21. The data given suggests using the standard recursive relation

$$A_{35} = A^{1}_{35:\overline{1}|} + {}_{1|}A_{35} = vq_{35} + (vp_{35})A_{36}$$

and the UDD relation $\overline{A}_{36} = \frac{i}{\delta}A_{36}$ to convert the continuous NSP to a discrete one:

$$A_{36} = \tfrac{\delta}{i}\overline{A}_{36} = \left(\tfrac{.04879}{.05}\right)(.185) = .180523$$

$$A_{35} = \tfrac{.01}{1.05} + \left(\tfrac{.99}{1.05}\right)(.180523) = .1797.$$

ANSWER A

22. $Z = b_t v^t = (e^{.05t})(e^{-.06t}) = e^{-.01t}$ is the present value of benefit variable and $f_T(t) = .01e^{-01t}$ is the density function of T (constant force $\Rightarrow$ exponential density):

$$E[Z] = \int_0^\infty (b_t v^t) f_T(t)dt = \int_0^\infty .01e^{-.02t}dt = \tfrac{.01}{.02} = \tfrac{1}{2}$$

$$E[Z^2] = \int_0^\infty (b_t v^t)^2 f_T(t)dt = \int_0^\infty .01e^{-.03t}dt = \tfrac{.01}{.03} = \tfrac{1}{3}$$

$$Var(Z) = \tfrac{1}{3} - \left(\tfrac{1}{2}\right)^2 = \tfrac{1}{12} = .08\overline{3}.$$

ANSWER D

23. The standard relation for this variance is $Var(Z) = \left[({}^2A_{60:\overline{5}|} - A_{60:\overline{5}|}{}^2).\right] 1000^2$ We are given $A_{60:\overline{5}|}$ so we need the second moment ${}^2A_{60:\overline{5}|}$. Taking the relation $A_{60:\overline{5}|} = A^1_{60:\overline{5}|} + A_{60:\overline{5}|}^{\ \ \ 1}$ and consistently doubling the force gives ${}^2A_{60:\overline{5}|} = {}^2A^1_{60:\overline{5}|} + {}^2A_{60:\overline{5}|}^{\ \ \ 1}$: we are given ${}^2A_{60:\overline{5}|}^{\ \ \ 1}$. Now focus on the term insurance second moment:

$$A^1_{60:\overline{5}|} = A_{60} - A_{60:\overline{5}|}^{\ \ \ 1} \cdot A_{65}$$

$$\Rightarrow \quad {}^2A^1_{60:\overline{5}|} = {}^2A_{60} - {}^2A_{60:\overline{5}|}^{\ \ \ 1} \cdot {}^2A_{65} = (.2196) - (.5649)(.2836) = .0594$$

$$\Rightarrow \quad {}^2A_{60:\overline{5}|} = {}^2A^1_{60:\overline{5}|} + {}^2A_{60:\overline{5}|}^{\ \ \ 1} = .0594 + .5649 = .6243$$

$$\Rightarrow \quad Var(Z) = (.6243 - .7896^2)1000^2 = 826.2,$$ ANSWER D.

24. Under the UDD $\overline{A}^1_{x:\overline{2}|} = \left(\frac{i}{\delta}\right) A^1_{x:\overline{2}|}$ and

$$A^1_{x:\overline{2}|} = 1 \cdot v \cdot q_x + 1 \cdot v^2 \cdot {}_{1|}q_x = \left(\frac{.05}{1.1}\right) + \frac{(.95)(.08)}{1.1^2} = .1083.$$

$$\overline{A}^1_{x:\overline{2}|} = \left[\frac{.10}{ln(1.1)}\right](.1083) = .114$$

ANSWER D.

25. The random present value of benefit variable is $Z = b_T \cdot v_T$ where $b_T = 1 + (e^{.04T})P$, $v_T = e^{-.08T}$ and P is the net single premium. With $\mu = .04$ we know $f_T(t) = .04e^{-.04t}$ for $t > 0$. Thus

$$\begin{aligned} P = E[Z] &= E[(1{+}Pe^{.04T})(e^{-.08T})] \\ &= \int_0^\infty (1 + Pe^{.04t})(e^{-.08t})(.04e^{-.04t})dt \\ &= .04\left(\int_0^\infty e^{-.12t}dt + P\int_0^\infty e^{-.08t}dt\right) \\ &= .04\left(\tfrac{1}{.12} + P\tfrac{1}{.08}\right). \end{aligned}$$

This gives $.5P = \left(\frac{1}{3}\right)$ or $P = \frac{2}{3}$,

ANSWER C

26. A rather unorthodox question asking you to guess what a recursion formula is calculating. You are given $u(80) = 1$ and a backward recursion, so try $u(79)$:

$$u(79) = \frac{d}{\delta} q_{79} + vp_{79} \cdot 1 \qquad \text{(from (i) with } x = 79\text{)}$$

$$= \frac{i}{\delta} vq_{79} + vp_{79}$$

$$= \frac{i}{\delta} A^{1}_{79:\overline{1|}} + A_{79:\overline{1|}}^{\;\;\;\;1} \underset{\text{UDD}}{=} \bar{A}_{79:\overline{1|}}$$

This makes ANSWER A the only reasonable guess that would continue this pattern. A proof would be based on mathematical induction.

27.

Benefit			1	2	...
Pattern		1	1	1	...
Age	35	36	37	38	...

This diagram splitting the benefit pattern purchased with IA_{35} suggests the relation $IA_{35} = A_{35} + vp_{35} IA_{36}$. You are given $IA_{35} = 3.71$, $A_{35} = .13$, $p_{35} = .9964$ and $.9434 = A_{35:\overline{1|}} = vq_{35} + vp_{35} = v$. Substituting these four values into the above equation results in $IA_{36} = 3.808$.

ANSWER A.

28. From (iii) and (iv) it follows that

$$E[Z_1] = (1000\,{}_{10}E_{35}) A^{1}_{35:\overline{10|}} + 1000\,{}_{10}E_{35}$$

$$E[Z_2] = (750\,{}_{10}E_{35}) A^{1}_{35:\overline{10|}} + 1000\,{}_{10}E_{35}.$$

Notice that ${}_{10}E_{35}$ can be factored out of the right sides. Using (vi) and dividing the above equations results in $1.005 = \frac{E[Z_1]}{E[Z_2]} = \frac{1000A^{1}_{35:\overline{10|}} + 1000}{750A^{1}_{35:\overline{10|}} + 1000}$, or $A^{1}_{35:\overline{10|}} = .02030$. Thus $A_{35:\overline{10|}}^{\;\;\;\;\;1} = {}_{10}E_{35} = A_{35:\overline{10|}} - A^{1}_{35:\overline{10|}} = .57 - .02030 = .54970$. Finally

$$E[Z_3] = 500\,{}_{10}E_{35} A^{1}_{35:\overline{10|}} + 1000\,{}_{10}E_{35}$$

$$= (10.15)(.54970) + 549.70 = 555.28$$

ANSWER B

29. In general we have $\overline{A}^{\,1}_{x:\overline{2}|} \underset{\text{UDD}}{=} \left(\frac{i}{\delta}\right) A^{1}_{x:\overline{2}|} = \left(\frac{i}{\delta}\right)(1 \cdot v \cdot q_x + 1 \cdot v^2 \cdot {}_{1|}q_x)$. To obtain ${}^2\overline{A}^{\,1}_{x:\overline{2}|}$ we need to consistently double the force in the above equation using $v^2 = e^{-2\delta}$, $(1+i)^2 = e^{2\delta}$ (i.e., $1+2i+i^2 = e^{2\delta} \quad \Rightarrow \quad {}^2i = 2i + i^2$):

$$
\begin{aligned}
{}^2\overline{A}^{\,1}_{x:\overline{2}|} &= \left(\frac{2i+i^2}{2\delta}\right)[1 \cdot v^2 \cdot q_x + 1 \cdot (v^2)^2 \cdot {}_{1|}q_x] \\
&= \left[\frac{.2544}{2 \cdot ln(1.12)}\right]\left[\frac{(.1)}{(1.12)^2} + \frac{(.9)(.2)}{(1.12)^4}\right] \\
&= .2179
\end{aligned}
$$

ANSWER C

30. The benefit pattern in this problem is like a series of steps. With a problem of this type a good way to proceed is to begin with a whole life insurance of the initial face value and then move to the steps adding or subtracting a deferred insurance to adjust the benefit from this age onward. Preliminaries for this solution:

$$\overline{A}_x = \frac{\mu}{\mu+\delta} = .4 \text{ at any age } x \geq 30 \quad \text{(constant force)}$$

$$v^n \, {}_np_x = e^{-n\delta} \cdot e^{-n\mu} = e^{-(\mu+\delta)n} = e^{-.10n}$$

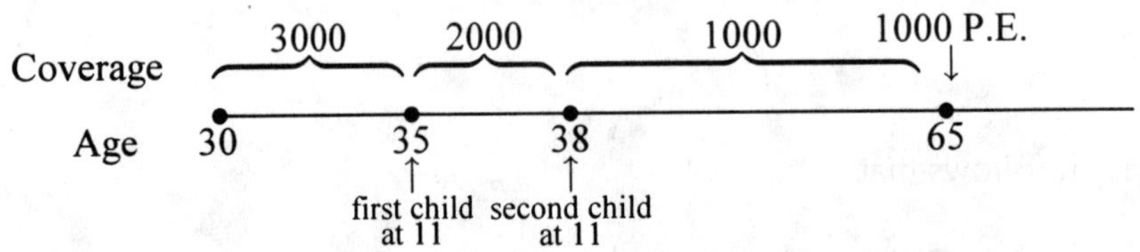

$$
\begin{aligned}
APV_{30}(\text{Benefits}) &= 3000\overline{A}_{30} - v^5 \cdot {}_5p_{30} \cdot 1000\overline{A}_{35} - v^8 \cdot {}_8p_{30} \cdot 1000\overline{A}_{38} \\
&\qquad - v^{35} \cdot {}_{35}p_{30} \cdot 1000\overline{A}_{65} + 1000v^{35} \cdot {}_{35}p_{30} \\
&= 1000\left(\frac{\mu}{\mu+\delta}\right)[3 - e^{-.10(5)} - e^{-.10(8)} - e^{-.10(35)}] + 1000e^{-.10(35)} = 795.78.
\end{aligned}
$$

ANSWER D

31. As a first step, the random present value variable Z is given by

$$Z = \begin{cases} 100v^T & 0 < T \leq 1 \\ 200v^T & 1 < T \leq 3 \\ 200v^3 & 3 < T \end{cases}.$$

Using $i = 0$ makes Z look like a discrete random variable with just 2 values:

Z	Event	Probability
100	$T \leq 1$	q_{60}
200	$T > 1$	p_{60}

For $x = 60$ and $\omega = 70$ in de Moivres law we have $\ell_x = 70 - x$, $q_{60} = 1 - \frac{\ell_{61}}{\ell_{60}} = 1 - \frac{9}{10} = .10$. It follows easily that $Var(Z) = 37{,}000 - (190)^2 = 900$.

ANSWER B

32 - 34

According to the description in (i)-(iii) the benefit, b_{K+1}, is given by 1.06^K for $K = 0, 1, \ldots, 9$ or 1 for $K \geq 10$. Thus

$$Z = \begin{cases} b_{K+1} \cdot v^{K+1} = 1.06^K / 1.06^{K+1} = 1/1.06 & K = 0, 1, \ldots, 9 \\ 1 \cdot v^{10} & K \geq 10 \end{cases}.$$

From de Moivre's law ($\ell_x = 100 - x$) we see that
$Pr(Z = 1.06^{-1}) = Pr(K = 0, 1, \ldots 9) = {}_{10}q_{30} = 10/70$ and $Pr(Z = v^{10}) = 60/70$.

So Question 33 has ANSWER C.

$E[Z]$ is calculated as

$$\left(\frac{1}{1.06}\right) Pr(K < 10) + \left(\frac{1}{1.06^{10}}\right) Pr(K \geq 10) = \left(\frac{1}{1.06}\right)\left(\frac{10}{70}\right) + \left(\frac{1}{1.06^{10}}\right)\left(\frac{60}{70}\right) = .6134.$$

Question 32 has ANSWER A.

$$E[Z^2] = \left(\frac{1}{1.06}\right)^2 \left(\frac{10}{70}\right) + \left(\frac{1}{1.06^{10}}\right)^2 \left(\frac{60}{70}\right) = .3944, \text{ hence } Var(Z) = .3944 - .6134^2 = .0182.$$

Question 34 has ANSWER D.

35 - 38.

Item (ii) says $h(x) = \frac{r}{60 - x}$. This model was discussed extensively in the Condensed Review Notes of Unit 1 of Section I of this manual: $s(x) = \left(1 - \frac{x}{60}\right)^r$, $\mathring{e}_x = \frac{60-x}{r+1}$. From (iii) we see $20 = \mathring{e}_0 = \frac{60}{r+1}$; $r = 2$. Hence $s(x) = \left(1 - \frac{x}{60}\right)^2$ and $f(x) = \frac{1}{30}\left(1 - \frac{x}{60}\right) = -s'(x)$.

Question 35 has ANSWER E.

The random present value of the guarantee payment is

$$Z = \begin{cases} (2{,}000{,}000)e^{-.05X} & X \leq 10 \\ 0 & X > 10 \end{cases},$$

so $Pr(Z = 0) = Pr(X > 10) = s(10) = \left(1 - \frac{10}{60}\right)^2 = \frac{25}{36}$.

Question 36 has ANSWER B.

Viewing Z as a function of X we calculate the APV, $E[Z]$, as the integral of Z times the X-density:

$$E[Z] = \int_0^{10} 2{,}000{,}000e^{-.05x} \cdot \tfrac{1}{30}\left(1 - \tfrac{x}{60}\right)dx$$

$$= (66{,}666.67)\left[\int_0^{10} e^{-.05x}dx - \tfrac{1}{60}\int_0^{10} x \cdot e^{-.05x}dx\right]$$

$$= (66{,}666.67)\left[\frac{1-e^{-.50}}{.05} + \tfrac{1}{60}((20x+400)e^{-.05x})\Big|_0^{10}\right]$$

$$= 484{,}535.14$$

Question 37 has ANSWER D.

The graph of Z versus X looks like

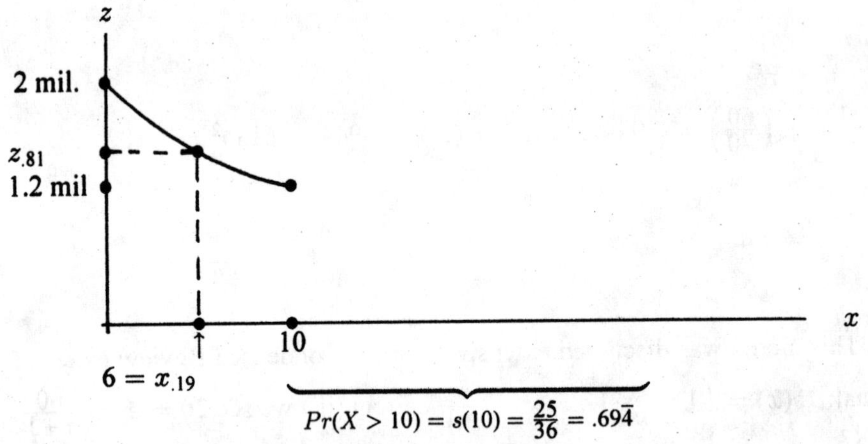

Since $.81 > .69\overline{4}$ we see that the 81st percentile of Z corresponds to the 19th percentile of X:

$$.19 = F_X(x_{.19}) = 1 - s_X(x_{.19}) \quad \Rightarrow \quad .81 = s_X(x_{.19}) = \left(1 - \tfrac{x_{.19}}{60}\right)^2 \quad \Rightarrow \quad x_{.19} = 6.$$

Thus $z_{.81}$ is $z = 2{,}000{,}000e^{-.05x_{.19}} = 1{,}481{,}636$.

Question 38 has ANSWER C.

UNIT 2: LIFE ANNUITIES AND RELATED MODELS

Introduction To Annuity Models

A life annuity is a series of payments made by or to an individual at regular time intervals and which are contingent on his survival. The two most prominent examples are the series of insurance premiums paid by an insured, and a retirement annuity received by an annuitant. As with life insurance there are both continuous and discrete models.

In a continuous life annuity to (x) a payment is received by (x) at each instant of some time interval that he is surviving. We will use P_t for the annual rate of payment at time t. P_t is zero when no payment is possible and $P_t > 0$ during time intervals where payments are possible. If (x) is surviving at time t the amount paid during the infinitesimal time interval $[t, t+dt]$ is $P_t \cdot dt$ (i.e., a fraction, dt, of the annual rate at time t). The unit concentrates most heavily on level annuities so that $P_t = P$ for times at which payments are possible and $P_t = 0$ otherwise.

Corresponding to this general, continuous life annuity paying at annual rate P_t at time t is the random present value of annuity payments, which is usually denoted by a Y:

$$Y = \begin{cases} \text{random present value at age } x \text{ of the totality of annuity} \\ \text{payments by or to } (x) \text{ over his } T \text{ years of future life.} \end{cases}$$

$$= \int_0^T \underbrace{\underbrace{v^t}_{\substack{\text{discount}\\ \text{factor}}} \cdot \underbrace{P_t\,dt}_{\substack{\text{amount received}\\ \text{in } [t,\,t+dt]}}}_{\substack{\text{present value of the portion of}\\ \text{payment received in } [t,\,t+dt]}} \qquad \text{(a function of } T\text{)}$$

For example, with a continuous whole life annuity of \$1/yr to (x) we would have $P_t = 1$ for $0 \le t \le \omega - x$

$$Y = \int_0^T v^t \cdot 1\,dt = \int_0^T e^{-\delta t}\,dt = \frac{1 - e^{-\delta T}}{\delta} = \bar{a}_{\overline{T|}}\,.$$

This is intuitively correct since (x) receives $\$T$ paid uniformly and continuously over his T future years. If the annuity is a continuous, n-year temporary life annuity of \$1/ year to (x) then

$$P_t = \begin{cases} 1 & 0 \le t \le n \\ 0 & n < t \le \omega - x \end{cases}$$

and

$$Y = \begin{cases} \int_0^T v^t \cdot 1 dt = \bar{a}_{\overline{T|}} & T \le n \\ \int_0^n v^t \cdot 1 dt + \int_n^T v^t \cdot 0\,dt = \bar{a}_{\overline{n|}} & T > n \end{cases}.$$

In a discrete life annuity to (x) a series of payments $P_0, P_1, P_2, \cdots, P_K$ is made at ages x, $x+1$, $\ldots, x+K$ (i.e., for as long as (x) survives, at one-year intervals: some P_t could be zero). The random present value at age x of all payments made is thus

$$Y = \sum_{k=0}^{K} P_k \cdot v^k = P_0 + P_1 \cdot v^1 + \cdots + P_K \cdot v^K .$$

Ahead we will analyze the basic (i.e., $P_K = 1$) whole life annuity due to (x). In this case

$$Y = \sum_{k=0}^{K} 1 \cdot v^k = \ddot{a}_{\overline{K+1|}}$$

which is intuitively correct since \$1 is received at the start of each year for $K+1$ years.

Much of this unit is devoted to level life annuities paying \$1 annually. If the annual rate were P/yr then the present value is P times the present value variable for a similar annuity of \$1/yr. See the Condensed Review Notes for a description of these annuities and the corresponding Y-variables.

The Continuous, Whole Life Annuity Model

This treatment will parallel that of the continuous, whole life insurance model of Unit 1 and, in fact, you will see an important connection between the annuity and the life insurance. In this section we consider a continuous life annuity of \$1/yr. paid to (x). Since \$$T$ is paid uniformly and continuously over the T-years of future lifetime, the random present value variable is:

$$Y = \bar{a}_{\overline{T|}} = \frac{1 - v^T}{\delta}, 0 \leq T \leq \omega - x,$$

which is a function of the continuous variable T.

From the graph of Y versus T below we see:

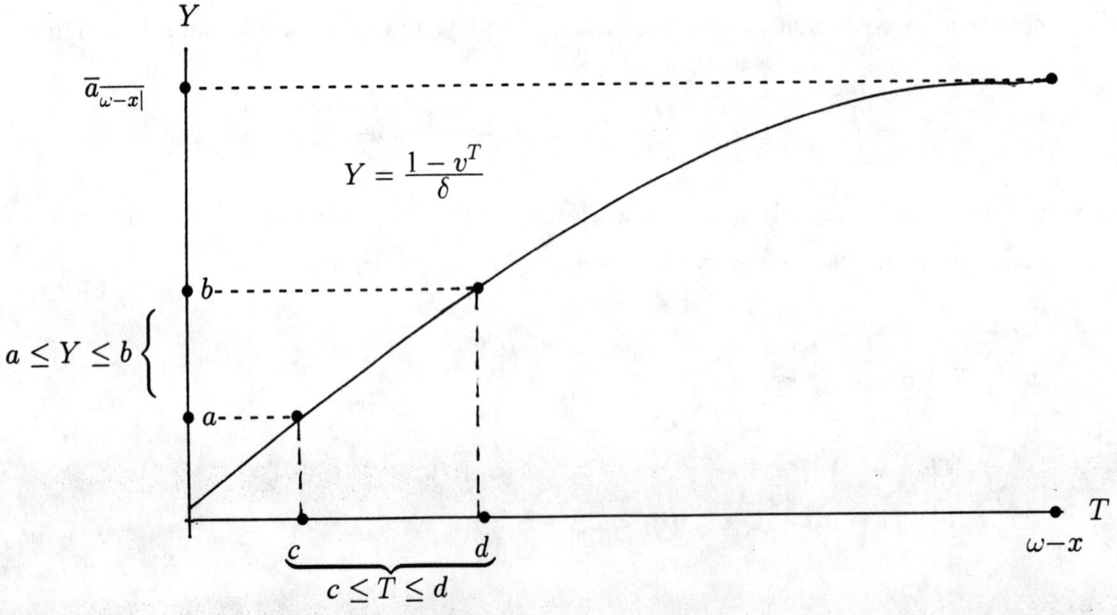

that Y is an increasing function of T and that events of the type $a \le Y \le b$ have the same probability as events like $c \le T \le d$ (i.e., equivalent inequalities) where a y-value is converted to a t-value via the inverse function of $y = \dfrac{1-v^t}{\delta}$:

$$y = \frac{1-v^t}{\delta} \quad \Leftrightarrow \quad t = -\frac{ln(1-\delta y)}{\delta}.$$

What is the probability that \$10 invested today at a force δ will be sufficient to pay \$1/yr. continuously for as long as (x) survives? The fund grows continuously at force δ and shrinks continuously at \$1/yr. to pay (x) his annuity. The question concerns whether the fund hits a zero balance before (x)'s demise. This question of sufficiency is equivalent to the present value inequality

$$\underbrace{10}_{\substack{\text{present value}\\ \text{of fund}}} \ge \underbrace{\bar{a}_{\overline{T|}}}_{\substack{\text{present value}\\ \text{of annuity}}} = Y.$$

Equivalently $T \le -\dfrac{ln(1-10\delta)}{\delta} = t_0$, so the probability of sufficiency can be calculated from the T-density as

$$_{t_0}q_x = \int_{t=0}^{t_0} {}_tp_x\mu(x+t)\,dt.$$

The expected or actuarial present value of the annuity payments, $E[Y]$, is denoted by $\bar{a}_x$ in standard actuarial notation. The a is a generic annuity APV symbol, the overbar denotes continuous payment, and other accouterments denote the type of annuity. Since Y is a function of T

$$\bar{a}_x = E[Y] = E\left[\bar{a}_{\overline{T|}}\right] = \int_{t=0}^{\omega-x} \underbrace{\bar{a}_{\overline{t|}}}_{\text{function of } T} \cdot \underbrace{{}_tp_x\mu(x+t)}_{T\text{-density}}\,dt.$$

As it turns out there is a slightly better integral for evaluation of the APV. The above formula is known as the "aggregate payment technique" since $\bar{a}_{\overline{t|}}$ is the present value of all \$$t$ received by (x). An integration by parts with

$$\left.\begin{aligned} u &= \frac{1-v^t}{\delta} = \bar{a}_{\overline{t|}} \\ dv &= {}_tp_x\mu(x+t)\,dt \end{aligned}\right\} \Rightarrow \quad \begin{aligned} du &= -\frac{1}{\delta}\left(\frac{de^{-\delta t}}{dt}\right) = e^{-\delta t}\,dt = v^t\,dt \\ v &= -{}_tp_x \quad \text{(see Chapter 3)} \end{aligned}$$

results in

$$\bar{a}_x = E[Y] = \int_{t=0}^{\omega-x} v^t \cdot {}_tp_x\,dt,$$

which is known as the *current payment* method. This is a more intuitive expression since it it the integral over all possible instants of payment, t, of a product of the amount paid in $[t, t+dt]$ (i.e., $\$dt$), the discount factor from time t (i.e., v^t), and the probability that (x) is surviving at this instant (i.e., ${}_tp_x$: the probability that the payment is made).

With annuity variables like Y the second moment is never the same as a first moment at twice the force of interest:

$$\begin{aligned}
\text{Second moment} = E[Y^2] &= E\left[\left(\frac{1-v^T}{\delta}\right)^2\right] \\
&= E\left[\frac{1-2v^T+v^{2T}}{\delta^2}\right] \\
&= E\left[\frac{(2-2v^T)-(1-v^{2T})}{\delta^2}\right] \\
&= E\left[\frac{2}{\delta}\cdot\frac{1-v^T}{\delta} - \frac{2}{\delta}\cdot\frac{1-v^{2T}}{2\delta}\right] \\
&= \frac{2}{\delta}\Bigg(\underbrace{E\left[\frac{1-v^T}{\delta}\right]}_{\text{first moment at original force}} - \underbrace{E\left[\frac{1-v^{2T}}{2\delta}\right]}_{\text{first moment at double the original force}}\Bigg) \\
&= \frac{2}{\delta}\left(\bar{a}_x - {}^2\bar{a}_x\right).
\end{aligned}$$

An alternate approach is possible via the relation of the continuous life annuity here to the continuous whole life insurance model of Unit 1 where $Z = v^T = e^{-\delta T}$. Notice that

$$Y = \bar{a}_{\overline{T|}} = \frac{1-v^T}{\delta} = \frac{1-Z}{\delta}.$$

This relation is exploited to give a third method of calculating $\bar{a}_x$ and an expression for $Var(Y)$ in terms of $Var(Z) = {}^2\bar{A}_x - (\bar{A}_x)^2$. Observe that Y is a linear function of Z, hence

(i) $\bar{a}_x = E[Y] = \left[\frac{1-Z}{\delta}\right] = \frac{1-\bar{A}_x}{\delta}$

(equivalently, $1 = \delta\bar{a}_x + \bar{A}_x$; there are many analogs of this annuity/insurance APV relation) and

(ii) $$\begin{aligned} Var(Y) = Var\left(\frac{1-Z}{\delta}\right) &= \left(\frac{1}{\delta}\right)^2 Var(1-Z) \\ &= \frac{1}{\delta^2}(-1)^2\, Var(Z) = \frac{1}{\delta^2}\left({}^2\bar{A}_x - (\bar{A}_x)^2\right). \end{aligned}$$

Example 1 Find general expressions for $\overline{a}_x$ for the de Moivre and constant force parametric survival models.

Solution We already have $\overline{A}_x = \frac{1}{\omega - x}\, \overline{a}_{\overline{\omega-x|}}$ for de Moivre and $\overline{A}_x = \frac{\mu}{\mu+\delta}$ for constant force, so it is easiest to use the annuity/insurance relation to obtain

$$\overline{a}_x = \frac{1-\overline{A}_x}{\delta} = \frac{(\omega-x) - \overline{a}_{\overline{\omega-x|}}}{(\omega-x)\delta} = \frac{\overline{D}\overline{a}_{\overline{\omega-x|}}}{(\omega-x)} \text{ (de Moivre)},$$

or

$$\overline{a}_x = \frac{1-\overline{A}_x}{\delta} = \frac{1-\mu/(\mu+\delta)}{\delta}$$

$$= \frac{\delta/(\mu+\delta)}{\delta} = \frac{1}{\mu+\delta} \text{ (constant force).}$$

□

Example 2 Suppose $(x) = (30)$ and mortality follows de Moivre's law with $\omega = 100$. Assume $i = .06$. A deposit of $\overline{a}_{30}$ is made into a savings account at age 30 and (30) continuously withdraws \$1/yearly until death. What is the probability that the account has a positive balance at (30)'s death?

Solution The event is the same as $\overline{a}_{30} > Y = \frac{1-v^T}{\delta}$ which is equivalent to $T < -\frac{ln(1-\delta\overline{a}_{30})}{\delta}$ by the above. From Example 1

$$\overline{a}_{30} = \frac{70 - \overline{a}_{\overline{70|}}}{70\delta} = 13.025494$$

so $t_0 = -\frac{ln(1-\delta\overline{a}_{30})}{\delta} = 24.419213$ years. Since T is uniformly distributed on $[0, 70]$ it follows that

$$Pr(\overline{a}_{30} > Y) = Pr(T < 24.419213) = \int_0^{24.419213} \frac{1}{70}\, dt = .348846.$$

Note: Compare the probability of the annuity APV being adequate which we just computed to the probability of an insurance APV being adequate which was computed in Example 2 of Unit 1. The annuity has less than a 50% chance and the insurance has greater than a 50% chance. This is because the Y density is typically skewed to the left whereas the Z density is skewed to the right.

□

All of the above results concerning the Y-distribution were obtained from the relation of Y to $T = T(x)$ using the T-density ${}_tp_x\mu(x+t)$. They can also be obtained from the Y-density which carries more information about the pattern of Y values. Since $Y = \overline{a}_{\overline{T|}} = \frac{1-v^T}{\delta}$ is an increasing (therefore

1-1) function of T we know from general principles that $f_Y(y) = f_T(g^{-1}(y))\left|\frac{dg^{-1}(y)}{dy}\right|$ where $g^{-1}(y) = \frac{-ln(1-\delta y)}{\delta}$ is the inverse function of $y = g(t) = \frac{(1-v^t)}{\delta}$. Since $0 \le T \le \omega - x$ we have $\bar{a}_{\overline{0}|} = 0 \le Y \le \bar{a}_{\overline{\omega-x}|}$. Furthermore,

$$f_Y(y) = \frac{f_T\left(\frac{-ln(1-\delta y)}{\delta}\right)}{(1-\delta y)}$$

$$f_T(t) = {}_tp_x\mu(x+t), \quad 0 \le y \le \bar{a}_{\overline{\omega-x}|}.$$

Example 3 For de Moivre's law and the constant force model compute:

(i) The Y-density;

(ii) General formulas for $Var(Y)$; and

(iii) $Pr(Y > \bar{a}_x)$.

Solution

(i) de Moivre's law

Since T is uniformly distributed on $[0, \omega-x]$ we know $f_T(t) = \frac{1}{\omega - x}$ for $0 \le t \le \omega - x$. Thus

$$f_Y(y) = \frac{f_T\left(\frac{-ln(1-\delta y)}{\delta}\right)}{(1-\delta y)} = \frac{1}{\omega - x}\cdot\frac{1}{1-\delta y}, \quad 0 \le y \le \bar{a}_{\overline{\omega-x}|}$$

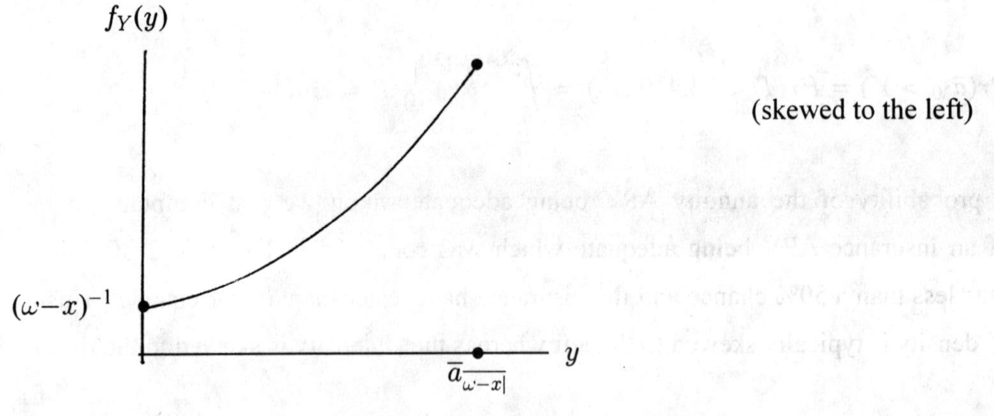

Constant Force

Since T is exponentially distributed on $[0, \infty)$ we know $f_T(t) = \mu e^{-\mu t}$ for $t \geq 0$. Thus

$$f_Y(y) = \mu \cdot \frac{exp\left(\frac{\mu\, ln(1-\delta y)}{\delta}\right)}{(1-\delta y)} = \mu[1-\delta y]^{(\mu/\delta)-1}, \quad 0 \leq y \leq \overline{a}_{\overline{\infty}|} = \tfrac{1}{\delta}$$

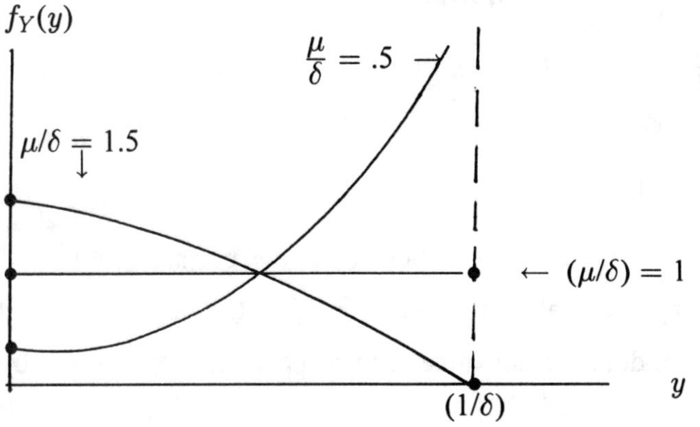

Shape varies according to (μ/δ)

(ii) Integrating $y^k \cdot f_Y(y)$ directly is quite difficult, so use $Y = \frac{1-Z}{\delta}$ where Z is the variable described in Unit 1 for $1 of whole life insurance at death:

$Y = \overline{a}_{\overline{T}|} = \frac{1-v^T}{\delta}$, $Z = v^T$. Then

$$Var(Y) = Var\left(\frac{1-Z}{\delta}\right) = \left(\frac{1}{\delta}\right)^2 Var(1-Z) = \left(\frac{1}{\delta}\right)^2 Var(-Z)$$

$$= \frac{(-1)^2}{\delta^2} Var(Z) = \frac{1}{\delta^2}[{}^2\overline{A}_x - \overline{A}_x^2]$$

de Moivres law

$$\overline{A}_x = \left(\frac{1}{\omega - x}\right)\overline{a}_{\overline{\omega-x}|}, \quad {}^2\overline{A}_x = \left(\frac{1}{\omega - x}\right){}^2\overline{a}_{\overline{\omega-x}|}$$

Constant force

$$\overline{A}_x = \frac{\mu}{\mu+\delta}, \quad {}^2\overline{A}_x = \frac{\mu}{\mu+2\delta}$$

(iii) Obtaining $Pr(Y > \overline{a}_x)$ by integrating the Y-density is rather tedious. Consider $Y = \frac{1-Z}{\delta}$ (as above): $Y > \overline{a}_x \quad \Leftrightarrow \quad \frac{1-Z}{\delta} > \overline{a}_x \quad \Leftrightarrow \quad Z < 1 - \delta\overline{a}_x \quad \Leftrightarrow \quad Z < \overline{A}_x$.

Thus $Pr(Y > \overline{a}_x) = Pr(Z < \overline{A}_x) = Pr(Z \leq \overline{A}_x)$ (continuous variable fact). Thus $Pr(Y > \overline{a}_x) = Pr(Z \leq \overline{A}_x) = 1 - Pr(Z > \overline{A}_x)$, which was obtained in Unit 1 Example 3:

$$Pr(Y > \overline{a}_x) = \begin{cases} 1 + \dfrac{ln(\overline{A}_x)}{\delta(\omega - x)} & \text{de Moivre} \\ \left(\dfrac{\mu}{\mu+\delta}\right)^{(\mu/\delta)} & \text{Constant force} \end{cases}.$$

The Discrete, Life Annuity Due Model

Suppose (x) is to receive \$1 at ages x, $x+1$, ..., $x+K$ where K is her curtate lifetime. This is the payout in a basic, life annuity due to (x). A total of \$$(K+1)$ is paid at the beginnings of the $(K+1)$ policy years that (x) survives. Thus the random present value of these payments, Y, is given by

$$Y = 1 + v + v^2 + \cdots + v^K = \ddot{a}_{\overline{K+1|}}, \qquad K = 0, 1, 2, \ldots, \omega{-}x{-}1,$$

a function of the discrete variable K, having density function

$$f_K(k) = {}_{k|}q_x = {}_kp_x \cdot q_{x+k} = {}_kp_x(1{-}p_{x+k}) = {}_kp_x - {}_{k+1}p_x = \frac{d_{x+k}}{\ell_x}$$

(all of these forms have a use).

Suppose $\$B$ is deposited in a fund earning an effective annual rate i. What is the probability that (x) will be able to withdraw \$1 at the beginning of each year for the rest of her life? This event is equivalent to the present value inequality $B \geq Y = \ddot{a}_{\overline{K+1|}}$. Writing $\ddot{a}_{\overline{K+1|}} = \frac{1-v^{K+1}}{d}$ and solving for K results in an equivalent inequality

$$K \leq -\frac{ln(1{-}Bd)}{\delta} - 1.$$

For example, if $B = 10$ and $i = .06$, the inequality above becomes $K \leq 13.3266$. Since K is an integer this is the same as $K \leq 13$, which has probability

$$Pr(K \leq 13) = Pr(T < 14) = {}_{14}q_x.$$

The expected or actuarial present value of the annuity payments, $E[Y]$, is denoted by $\ddot{a}_x$ in standard actuarial notation. Since $Y = \ddot{a}_{\overline{K+1}|}$ is a function of K it follows that

$$\ddot{a}_x = E[Y] = E\left[\ddot{a}_{\overline{K+1}|}\right] = \sum_{k=0}^{\omega-x-1} \underbrace{\ddot{a}_{\overline{k+1}|}}_{\text{function of } K} \cdot \underbrace{{}_{k|}q_x}_{K\text{-density}}.$$

As in the continuous model in section 2, this expression is known as the "aggregate payment formula" due to the fact that $\ddot{a}_{\overline{K+1}|}$ is the present value of all payments received by (x). Using a summation by parts or substituting

$$\ddot{a}_{\overline{k+1}|} = \frac{1 - v^{k+1}}{d}, \qquad {}_{k|}q_x = {}_kp_x - {}_{k+1}p_x$$

and rearranging, one can obtain the "current payment formula"

$$\ddot{a}_x = \sum_{k=0}^{\omega-x-1} 1 \cdot v^k \cdot {}_kp_x,$$

which expresses the APV as the sum over all possible times of payment, k, of a product of three factors: amount due at time k,1; the discount factor, v^k; and the probability of payment at time k, ${}_kp_x$. (This idea common to all APV's is explained in Appendix 1 located at the end of the Contingent Payment Model section of this manual).

Second moments are not the same as first moments at double the force of interest, so variance of Y is gotten from the relation of the annuity with the discrete whole life insurance model in Unit 1:

Basic Life Annuity Due	Basic Whole Life Insurance
$Y = \underbrace{\ddot{a}_{\overline{K+1}|} = \frac{1-v^{K+1}}{d}}_{\text{random present value of annuity payments}}$	$Z = \underbrace{v^{K+1}}_{\text{random present value of 1 on policy anniversary following death}}$

Relation: $Y = \dfrac{1-Z}{d}$

Taking expected values of this relation and using standard actuarial notation we have

$$\ddot{a}_x = \frac{1 - A_x}{d}$$

as a third possible method of getting an $\ddot{a}_x$-value. Taking variances and using linearity of the Y to Z relation

$$Var(Y) = \frac{1}{d^2}\,Var(Z) = \frac{1}{d^2}({}^2A_x - (A_x)^2)\,.$$

Example 4 A basic life annuity due of \$1 per year is paid to (90) where

x	90	91	92	93
ℓ_x	100	72	39	0

is the survival model and $i = .06$. If Y is the random present value variable, find the distribution of Y, $E[Y] = \ddot{a}_{90}$, and $Var(Y)$.

Solution $Y = \ddot{a}_{\overline{K+1}|}$ for $K = 0,1,2$ and $f_K(k) = \dfrac{d_{90+k}}{\ell_{90}}$. The distribution of Y is summarized below:

$Y = \ddot{a}_{\overline{K+1}\|}$ value	Probability	K-event
$\ddot{a}_{\overline{1}\|} = 1$	$\frac{d_{90}}{\ell_{90}} = \frac{28}{100}$	$K = 0$
$\ddot{a}_{\overline{2}\|} = 1.943396$	$\frac{d_{91}}{\ell_{90}} = \frac{33}{100}$	$K = 1$
$\ddot{a}_{\overline{3}\|} = 2.833393$	$\frac{d_{92}}{\ell_{90}} = \frac{39}{100}$	$K = 2$

From first principles

$$E[Y] = \sum_{y\text{-values}} \text{value} \cdot \text{probability} = (1)(.28) + (1.943396)(.33) + (2.833393)(.39) = 2.026344$$

$$E[Y^2] = \sum_{y\text{-values}} \text{value}^2 \cdot \text{probability} = 4.657305$$

Hence $Var(Y) = E[Y^2] - (E[Y])^2 = .551235$.

Possible alternate methods of calculation:

(i) the current payment method:

$$\begin{aligned}\ddot{a}_{90} &= \sum_{k=0}^{\omega-x-1} 1 \cdot v^k \cdot {}_kp_{90} \\ &= 1 \cdot \left(\frac{1}{1.06}\right)^0 \cdot \frac{100}{100} + 1 \cdot \left(\frac{1}{1.06}\right)^1 \frac{72}{100} + 1 \cdot \left(\frac{1}{1.06}\right)^2 \cdot \frac{39}{100} \\ &= 2.026344, \text{ and}\end{aligned}$$

(ii) the relation with whole life insurance to 90 (in Example 5 of Unit 1 we found $A_{90} = .885301$ for this same model and shortly thereafter calculated ${}^2A_{90} = .785525$, ${}^2A_{90} - (A_{90})^2 = .001766$)

$$\ddot{a}_{90} = \frac{1 - A_{90}}{d} = \frac{1 - .885301}{(6/106)} = 2.026349 \text{ (slight rounding error)}$$

$$Var(Y) = \frac{1}{d^2}\left({}^2A_{90} - (A_{90})^2\right) = \left(\frac{106}{6}\right)^2 (.001766) = .551188 \text{ (slight rounding error).}$$

Aggregate Analysis of the Life Annuity Due

Suppose all ℓ_x lives at age x in a table receive a life annuity due of \$1 per year. In the deterministic view the aggregate payout

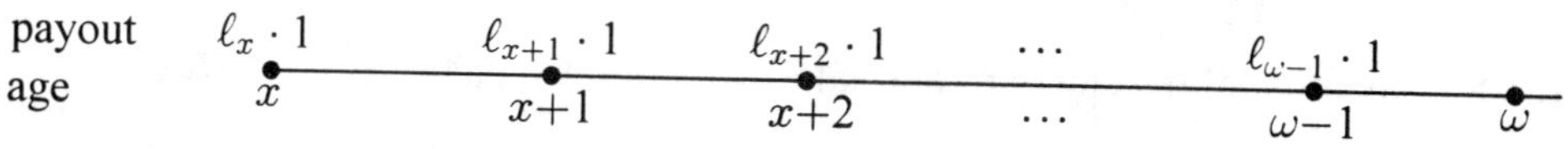

is a certain annuity having total present value

$$\ell_x \cdot v^0 + \ell_{x+1} \cdot v^1 + \cdots + \ell_{\omega-1} \cdot v^{\omega-x-1}.$$

The present value per member of the group is

$$\frac{\sum_{k=0}^{\omega-x-1} \ell_{x+k} \cdot v^k}{\ell_x} = \underbrace{\sum_{k=0}^{\omega-x-1} {}_kp_x \cdot v^k}_{\substack{\text{current payment} \\ \text{formula for } \ddot{a}_x}} = \ddot{a}_x\,.$$

Rearranging this equation it can be seen that $\ell_x \ddot{a}_x$ is the present value of the aggregate payout. Hence a deposit at time 0 of this amount into a fund earning an effective annual rate i is exactly enough to fund the annuities.

Example 5 Consider the 90 year olds in Example 4. How much should be deposited at time $t = 0$ so that there is a 95% chance that all annuity payments for the 100 nanoes[6] can be withdrawn.

[6] nano - a 90 year old.

Solution The aggregate present value of payout to the 100 nanoes, Y_{Agg}, is a sum of 100 independent variables like the Y of Example 4:

$$\mu(Agg) = E[Y_{Agg}] = 100E[Y] = 100(2.026344) = 202.6344$$

$$\sigma^2_{Agg} = Var(Y_{Agg}) = 100Var(Y) = 100(.551235) = 55.1235$$

$$\sigma_{Agg} = 7.424520.$$

By the Central Limit Theorem Y_{Agg} is approximately normal. If B is the needed deposit then

$$.95 = Pr\,(Y_{Agg} \le B) = Pr\left(\frac{Y_{Agg} - \mu(Agg)}{\sigma_{Agg}} \le \frac{B - \mu(Agg)}{\sigma_{Agg}}\right) \approx Pr\left(N(0{,}1) \le \frac{B - \mu(Agg)}{\sigma_{Agg}}\right).$$

Since 1.645 is the 95th percentile of the standard normal distribution we have:

$$1.645 = \frac{B - \mu(Agg)}{\sigma_{Agg}},$$

or $B = \mu(Agg) + 1.645\sigma_{Agg} = 214.8477$. This is approximately 6% greater than the aggregate APV of $202.6344 = 100\ddot{a}_{90}$.

The mth-ly Life Annuity Due

Here we are concerned with a \$1/year annuity to (x) for as long as he lives with \$ $1/m$ being paid at the beginning of each mth that (x) survives. A first principles expression for the APV, denoted $\ddot{a}_x^{(m)}$, is fairly easy to write down:

$$\ddot{a}_x^{(m)} = \sum_{\substack{\text{times of}\\ \text{payment}}} \text{(amount)(discount)(probability)}$$

$$= \frac{1}{m} \cdot v^0 \cdot {}_0p_x + \frac{1}{m} \cdot v^{1/m} \cdot {}_{1/m}p_x + \cdots .$$

If one has a tabular survival model and x is a whole number age, then values such as

$${}_{1/m}p_x = \frac{\ell_{x+1/m}}{\ell_x}$$

must be obtained by some interpolation scheme. Typically the UDD assumption is employed. With this method there is a particularly simple relation between the mth-ly annuity APV $\ddot{a}_x^{(m)}$ and the annual annuity APV $\ddot{a}_x$:

$$\ddot{a}_x^{(m)} = \alpha(m)\ddot{a}_x - \beta(m)$$

where the age-independent constants $\alpha(m)$ and $\beta(m)$ are given by

$$\alpha(m) = \frac{id}{i^{(m)}d^{(m)}}\,,\ \beta(m) = \frac{i - i^{(m)}}{i^{(m)}d^{(m)}}.$$

The following is a brief outline of how this relation arises from the UDD assumption.

Recall the annuity/insurance relation $1 = d\ddot{a}_x + A_x$. There is an analogous one, $1 = d^{(m)}\ddot{a}_x^{(m)} + A_x^{(m)}$, where $A_x^{(m)}$ is the APV of a discrete whole life model paying \$1 at the end of the mth of the policy year during which the death occurs. There is also a simple relation of $A_x^{(m)}$ to A_x under the UDD Assumption. Suppose these m^{th}-*ly* insurance plans are issued to all ℓ_x x-year olds. For each m deaths in a policy year the insurer would pay out \$1 at the end of each mth since one death would occur each mth. The equivalent year end amount is

$$ms_{\overline{1}|}^{(m)} = m \cdot \frac{(1+i)^1 - 1}{i^{(m)}} = m \cdot \frac{i}{i^{(m)}}.$$

So for each \$1 paid out during the year under the mth-*ly* plan, the equivalent year-end payout is $\frac{i}{i^{(m)}}$ (slightly bigger than 1). The relation between APV's should be $A_x^{(m)} = \frac{i}{i^{(m)}} A_x$ if UDD is assumed. This relation is substituted into:

$$d^{(m)}\ddot{a}_x^{(m)} + A_x^{(m)} = 1$$

which is solved simultaneously with $d\ddot{a}_x + A_x = 1$ for $\ddot{a}_x^{(m)}$, resulting in

$$\ddot{a}_x^{(m)} = \underbrace{\frac{id}{i^{(m)}d^{(m)}}}_{\substack{\text{defined as}\\ \alpha(m)}} \ddot{a}_x - \underbrace{\frac{(i-i^{(m)})}{i^{(m)}d^{(m)}}}_{\substack{\text{defined as}\\ \beta(m)}}.$$

Example 6 Assuming the UDD find $\ddot{a}_{90}^{(2)}$ for the evaluation basis (i.e., mortality and interest assumptions) of Example 4.

Solution

$$\alpha(2) = \frac{id}{i^{(2)}d^{(2)}} = \frac{(.06)(.056604)}{(.059126)(.057428)} = 1.000212$$

$$\beta(2) = \frac{i - i^{(2)}}{i^{(2)}d^{(2)}} = .257391$$

$$\ddot{a}_{90}^{(2)} = \alpha(2)\ddot{a}_{90} - \beta(2) = (1.000212)(2.026344) - .257391 = 1.76938$$

An alternate, first principles calculation is

$$\ddot{a}_{90}^{(2)} = \frac{1}{2} \cdot v^0 \cdot {}_0p_{90} + \frac{1}{2} \cdot v^{1/2} \cdot {}_{1/2}\,p_{90} + \cdots + \frac{1}{2} \cdot v^{5/2} \cdot {}_{5/2}\,p_{90}$$

where the "$\frac{1}{2}$-year rates" are obtained by the UDD as

$${}_{1/2}p_{90} = \frac{\ell_{90.5}}{\ell_{90}} = \frac{\frac{1}{2}\ell_{90} + \frac{1}{2}\ell_{91}}{\ell_{90}} = \frac{\ell_{90} - \frac{1}{2}d_{90}}{\ell_{90}} = \frac{100 - \frac{1}{2}(28)}{100} = .86,$$

and so on.

Bond Models Including the Contingencies of Default and Call

Consider the 10-year, annual coupon bond whose cash flow is given in the diagram below.

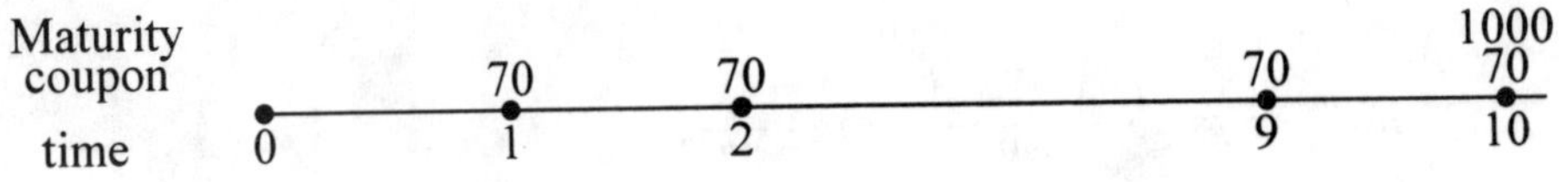

In interest theory the cashflow is viewed as a certain annuity and one studies the price versus yield relationship:

$$P = 70a_{\overline{10}|i} + \frac{1000}{(1+i)^{10}} = g(i)$$

i = effective annual yield rate

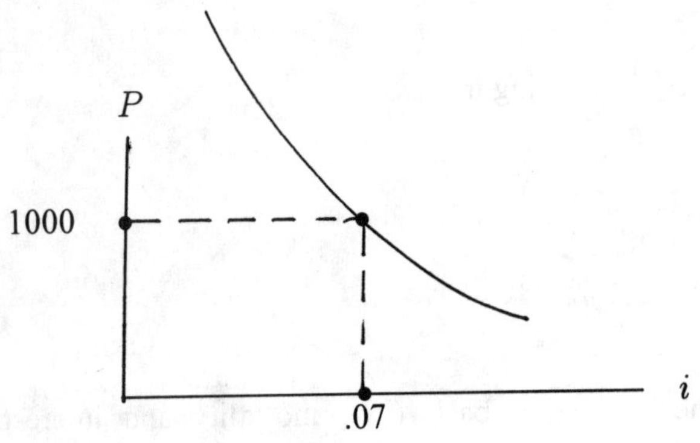

Now we would like to expand this model to include the risk (contingency) of default by the bond issuer. The additional feature is a survival model for the time until default variable, T. $T = 0$ corresponds to the issue of the bond and we assume all the bond cashflow ceases after time T if any of the cashflow is still remaining. The bond is said to fail ("die") at time T and to be surviving at time t if $T > t$. To model the idea that there is a small risk of default during the 10-year period, we could choose a distribution for T such that $Pr(T > 10)$ is relatively close to 1. (The $f_T(t)$ values for $t > 10$ are irrelevant. Only $f_T(t)$ values for $t \le 10$ and $s_T(10)$ really matters.) Since the bond cashflow continues as long as the bond survives (the risk of default), we can view it as a "life" annuity and employ actuarial notation:

$${}_n p_0 = Pr(T > n) = Pr(\text{default occurs after } n \text{ years})$$

The random present value of the bond cashflow, Y, is given by

$$Y = \begin{cases} 70a_{\overline{[T]}|i} & T < 10 \\ 70a_{\overline{10}|i} + \dfrac{1000}{(1+i)^{10}} & T \ge 10 \end{cases}$$

where $[T]$ is the greatest integer in T. This setup implies the following convention: if $T = 1, 2, \ldots, 9$ or 10 the payments due at time T are made and default occurs an instant later. We envision a continuous model for T so $Pr(T = 1, 2, \ldots, 9, \text{ or } 10) = 0$. The actuarial present value of Y could be calculated by the aggregate payment method using the Y formula above, or, via the more convenient current payment method, as

$$Price = APV(Y) = \sum_{n=1}^{10} \underbrace{70}_{\text{amount}} \cdot \underbrace{(1+i)^{-n}}_{\text{discount}} \cdot \underbrace{{}_n p_0}_{\text{probability}} + 1000 \cdot (1+i)^{-10} \cdot {}_{10}p_0 = \text{some function of } i$$

With these generalities established we consider next the distribution of T. Studies abound on the default rates of various types of bonds. One could simply employ empirical data to estimate the probabilities ${}_1p_0, {}_2p_0, \ldots, {}_{10}p_0$ needed above. As a simple parametric alternative suppose we consider T to have a constant hazard rate $h(t) = h$. Recall that $h(t)dt$ would represent the conditional probability of default in the interval $[t, t+dt]$ given that the bond has not defaulted by time t. This might not be too unrealistic for a single bond, and it might be quite appropriate for a bond fund (pool of thousands of bonds). We explore this idea next.

Now if $h(t) = h$ is constant we know that ${}_n p_0 = exp(-\int_0^n h(t)dt) = e^{-nh}$. Suppose we choose h to satisfy our belief that our bond has a 2% chance of default within its 10-year history:

$$.98 = Pr(T > 10) = e^{-10h}, \; h = \frac{-ln(.98)}{10} = .00202.$$

Now, using the current payment method,

$$Price = APV = \sum_{n=0}^{10} 70 \cdot (1+i)^{-n} \cdot e^{-hn} + 1000 \cdot (1+i)^{-10} \cdot e^{-10h},$$

which can be rearranged as

$$Price = APV = \sum_{n=1}^{10} 70 \cdot (1+j)^{-n} + 1000 \cdot (1+j)^{-n},$$

where $(1+j)^{-n} = (1+i)^{-n} \cdot e^{-nh} = [(1+i)e^h]^{-n}$, that is, $j = (1+i)e^h - 1$. (This final form of the price formula above looks like the annuity-certain bond model where j is the "apparent" yield rate. This means that a calculator with annuity keys can be employed to value the bond cashflow.)

Example 7 In the model above where $h(x) = h$ and $.98 = e^{-10h}$, calculate:

(i) Price if $i = .06$; and

(ii) The value of i if $Price = 980$.

Solution

(i) $1+j = (1+i)e^h = 1.06214$, so $Price = 70a_{\overline{10}|.06214} + 1000(1.06214)^{-10} = 1057.24$.

(ii) $980 = 70a_{\overline{10}|j} + 1000(1+j)^{-10}$

results in $j = 7.2886\%$ using the annuity keys of the BA-35 calculator. So $(1+j) = (1+i)e^h$ results in $i = 7.0720\%$. The "apparent" yield rate $j = 7.2886\%$ masks the "actual" yield $i = 7.0720\%$, with the drop due to the model of the risk of default.

Now we turn our attention to a simple model of a callable bond. Suppose the same 10-year, annual coupon bond with which we began the default risk model can be called at time 6 or time 8 for 1020 and 1010 respectively. In this discussion we disregard the risk of default and model only the risk that the bond be called. Here we are concerned with a time until call variable, K, which is discrete with possible values $K = 6$, 8 or 10. Choosing $Pr(K = 10)$ near 1 means there is a small risk of call (i.e., at $K = 6$ or 8).

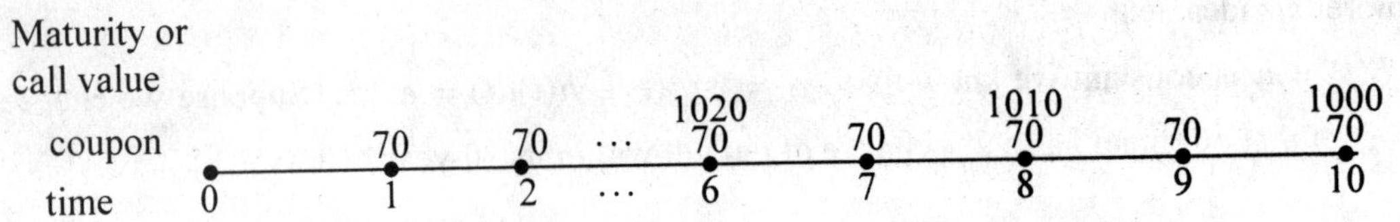

The coupon payments are contingent on surviving "call" at the time they come due (like a "life" annuity), whereas the maturity or call value occurs at the time of failure (like a "life" insurance). The random present value of the bond cashflow, Y, is given by

$$Y = \begin{cases} 70a_{\overline{6}|i} + 1020(1+i)^{-6} & K = 6 \\ 70a_{\overline{8}|i} + 1010(1+i)^{-8} & K = 8 \\ 70a_{\overline{10}|i} + 1000(1+i)^{-10} & K = 10 \end{cases}.$$

Here it is simpler to compute the APV (i.e. Price) via the aggregate payment method as

$$Price = APV = [70a_{\overline{6}|i} + 1020(1+i)^{-6}]Pr(K=6)$$
$$+ [70a_{\overline{8}|i} + 1010(1+i)^{-8}]Pr(K=8)$$
$$+ [70a_{\overline{10}|i} + 1000(1+i)^{-10}]Pr(K=10)$$

Example 8 Suppose there is a 15% chance of call after 6 years and a 25% chance of call after 8 years.

(i) Calculate the Price for $i = 6$, 7 or 8% and compare with the corresponding prices if call wa impossible.

(ii) Estimate i if the price is 1010.

Solution We are given that $Pr(K=6) = .15$, $Pr(K=8) = .25$. Hence $Pr(K=10) = .60$.

(i)

$i\%$	Callable Price	Price Without Call
6	1070.74	1073.60
7	1003.45	1000.00
8	941.68	932.90

e.g., $1070.74 = (1063.27)(.15) + (1068.37)(.25) + (1073.60(.60)$

$$1073.60 = 70a_{\overline{10}|.06} + \frac{1000}{1.06^{10}}$$

(ii) The yield rate equation is a polynomial equation of degree 10 that would require an iterative solution. It cannot be solved with the BA-35. From the table above we see that a callable price of 1010 must occur somewhere between $i = 6\%$ and 7%. A good guess for i based on linear interpolation is:

$$i \approx .06 + \left[\frac{1070.74 - 1010}{1070.74 - 1003.45}\right].01 = .0690.$$

Plugging $i = .0690$ in the price equation gives a price of 1009.93, which is pretty close to the 1010 we began with. Thus $i \approx .0690$ is pretty accurate. If more accuracy is desired another linear interpolation could be done between the 2 yield/price points (6.9%, 1009.93) and (6.8%, 1016.45).

Mortgage Models Including the Contingency of Prepayment

For the following consider an n period loan of L to be amortized by level payments, P, at the ends of the next n periods. If i is the effective rate of interest per period then $L = Pa_{\overline{n}|i}$. The balance of the loan an instant after the kth payment, Bal_k, is computed prospectively as $Pa_{\overline{n-k}|i}$. To this situation we now wish to add the risk (contingency) of prepayment of the entire remaining balance of the loan at an instant after a payment. This means we need a probability (survival) model for a time until prepayment variable, K, where $Pr(K > n)$ represents the probability the loan will not be prepaid. The price (market value) of this loan note at a yield rate of j per period depends on when and if the loan is prepaid. It is a random variable, Y, which is a function of K:

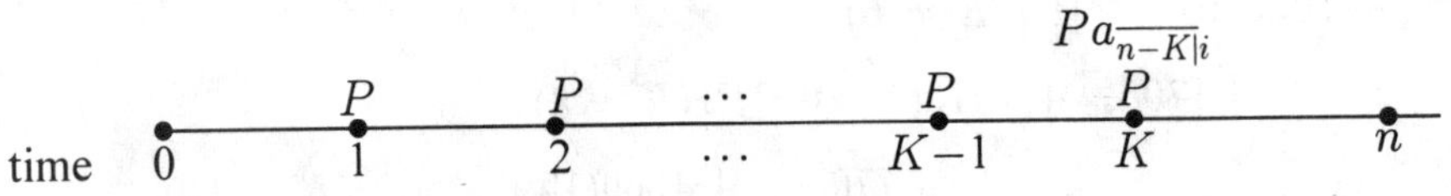

$$Y = \begin{cases} P[a_{\overline{K}|j} + a_{\overline{n-K}|i}(1+j)^{-K}] & K = 1, 2, \ldots, n-1 \\ P[a_{\overline{n}|j}] & K \geq n \end{cases}$$

Understanding the distribution of Y is essential in analyzing the effect of the prepayment contingency on the market value of the loan note. This technique could also be used on a securitized pool of prepayable mortgages. In this regard several models for K have been proposed. We discuss these models next and then conclude with a small scale numerical example.

The distribution of K drives the distribution of Y (i.e., Y is a function of K). It is convenient here to employ actuarial survival model notation, viewing issue of the loan as "birth" and prepayment as "death." So $s_K(k) = Pr(K > k) = {}_kp_0$ is the probability that the loan has not been prepaid by time k, and $f_K(k) = {}_{k-1|}q_0 = {}_{k-1}p_0 \cdot q_{k-1} = Pr(K = k)$ is the unconditional probability of prepayment at time k. In contrast, q_{k-1} is the conditional probability of prepayment at time k, given that the loan has not been prepaid by time $k-1$. (In a discrete survival model this is the hazard rate at time k. See Unit 2 of Section I of this manual.) Both the CPR (Constant Prepayment Rate) and PSA (Public Securities Association) prepayment models specify the probabilities $q_0, q_1, \ldots$. In these models a period is one month, the usual payment interval on mortgages.

<u>CPR Model</u>

$q = q_0, q_1, \ldots, \qquad p = 1 - q$

$1 - CPR = (1 - q)^{12}$ (CPR represents an annual "mortality" rate)

$f_K(k) = {}_{k-1|}q_0 = p_0 p_1 \cdots p_{k-2} \cdot q_{k-1} = p^{k-1} \cdot q = (1-q)^{k-1} q$
(geometric distribution)

<u>PSA Model</u>

$(1 - q_k)^{12} = (1 - .002(k+1)), \quad k = 0, 1, \ldots, 29$

$q_{29} = q_{30} = q_{31} = \cdots$ (constant thereafter)

Using the CPR model for the distribution of K lets return to the random variable Y, which is the present value of the loan cashflow at a yield rate j. Y represents the market price of the note to earn a yield rate j. It varies (randomly) with the time of prepayment. $E[Y]$, the actuarial present value of the loan cashflow, is "on average" the correct price to earn the yield j:

$$Price = E[Y] = \sum_{k=1}^{\infty} y(k)Pr(K = k) = \sum_{k=1}^{n-1} P(a_{\overline{k}|j} + a_{\overline{n-k}|i}(1+j)^{-k})p^{k-1}q + \sum_{k=n}^{\infty}(Pa_{\overline{n}|j})p^{k-1}q$$

$$= \sum_{k=1}^{n-1} P(a_{\overline{k}|j} + a_{\overline{n-k}|i}(1+j)^{-k})p^{k-1}q + (Pa_{\overline{n}|j})p^{n-1}$$

$$(p^{n-1} = p^{n-1}q + p^{n-2}q + \cdots)$$

Note: If $j = i$ then $Y = L = Pa_{\overline{n}|i}$ with probability 1!

Example 9 If $n = 3$, $P = 1$ and $i = .01$ compute:

(i) $L = Pa_{\overline{n}|i}$;

(ii) The distribution of Y using the CPR model with $q = .2$ and $j = .015$ (i.e., $1 - CPR = .8^{12}$, $CPR = 1 - .8^{12}$); and

(iii) $E[Y]$, $Var(Y)$ and the relative risk $\sigma_Y / E[Y]$.

Solution

(i) $L = a_{\overline{3}|.01} = 2.940985$

(ii)

Probability	K	Y-value
.2	1	$a_{\overline{1}|.015} + a_{\overline{2}|.01}/1.015 = 2.926498$
$.16 = (.8)(.2)$	2	$a_{\overline{2}|.015} + a_{\overline{1}|.01}/1.015^2 = 2.916347$
$.64 = (.8)^2$	≥ 3	$a_{\overline{3}|.015} = 2.912200$

(iii) $E[Y] = 2.915817$ (lower than the book value of the loan $L = 2.940985$, but higher than the market value at $j = .015$ with no prepayment, $a_{\overline{3}|.015} = 2.912200$)

$E[Y^2] = 8.502022$

$Var(Y) = .000031$

$\frac{\sigma_Y}{E[Y]} = .002$ (small relative risk)

Other features of this model worth studying include the random cashflow at time k, C_k, and the random balance at time k an instant after the cashflow at time k, B_k:

$$B_k = \begin{cases} 0 & K \leq k \\ Pa_{\overline{n-k}|i} & K > k \end{cases} \quad \text{(function of } K\text{)}$$

$$C_k = \underbrace{B_{k-1} - B_k}_{\text{principal}} + \underbrace{B_{k-1} \cdot i}_{\text{interest}} \quad \text{(function of } K\text{)}$$

$$\left.\begin{aligned} E[B_k] &= Pa_{\overline{n-k}|i}Pr(K > k) \quad \text{(general)} \\ &= Pa_{\overline{n-k}|i}(1-q)^k \quad \text{(CPR)} \end{aligned}\right\} \text{Expected Balance}$$

$$\left.\begin{aligned} E[C_k] &= (1+i)E[B_{k-1}] - E[B_k] \quad \text{(general)} \\ &= P(1-q)^{k-1} + Pa_{\overline{n-k}|i}q(1-q)^{k-1} \quad \text{(CPR)} \end{aligned}\right\} \text{Expected Cashflow}$$

CONDENSED REVIEW NOTES AND ADVANCED TOPICS

Basic Continuous Life Annuities

Whole Life: \$1/yr. paid continuously while (x) survives (i.e., for T yrs.)

$$Y = \text{random present value of payments} = \bar{a}_{\overline{T}|} = \frac{1-v^T}{\delta}$$

$$\bar{a}_x = APV(Y) = E[Y] = \underbrace{\int_0^{\omega-x} \frac{1-v^t}{\delta}\, {}_tp_x \mu(x+t)dt}_{\text{(aggregate payment)}} = \underbrace{\int_0^{\omega-x} v^t\, {}_tp_x\, dt}_{\text{(current payment)}}$$

Z = random present value of basic continuous whole life $= v^T$

$$Y = \frac{1-v^T}{\delta} = \frac{1-Z}{\delta} \quad \Rightarrow \quad 1 = \delta Y + Z,$$

$$1 = \delta\bar{a}_x + \bar{A}_x,\ Var(Y) = Var\left(\frac{1-Z}{\delta}\right) = \frac{1}{\delta^2}\left({}^2\bar{A}_x - \bar{A}_x{}^2\right)$$

n-year temporary: \$1/yr. paid continuously during the next n years while (x) survives (i.e., for $min(T, n)$ years)

$$Y = \text{random present value of payments} = \begin{cases} \bar{a}_{\overline{T}|} = \dfrac{1-v^T}{\delta} & T \le n \\ \bar{a}_{\overline{n}|} = \dfrac{1-v^n}{\delta} & T > n \end{cases}$$

$$\bar{a}_{x:\overline{n}|} = APV(Y) = E[Y] = \int_{t=0}^{n} \frac{1-v^t}{\delta}\, {}_tp_x\, \mu(x+t)\, dt + \int_{t=n}^{\omega-x} \bar{a}_{\overline{n}|}\, {}_tp_x \mu(x+t)\, dt$$

$$= \int_{t=0}^{n} \frac{1-v^t}{\delta}\, {}_tp_x \mu(x+t)\, dt + \bar{a}_{\overline{n}|} \cdot {}_np_x \text{ (aggregate payment)}$$

$$= \int_{t=0}^{n} v^t\, {}_tp_x\, dt \quad \text{(current payment)}$$

$$Z = \text{random p.v. of basic endowment insurance} = \begin{cases} v^T & T \le n \\ v^n & T > n \end{cases}$$

$$Y = \frac{1-Z}{\delta} \quad \Rightarrow \quad 1 = \delta Y + Z, \quad 1 = \delta \bar{a}_{x:\overline{n}|} + \bar{A}_{x:\overline{n}|}$$

$$Var(Y) = Var\left(\frac{1-Z}{\delta}\right) = \frac{1}{\delta^2}\left({}^2\bar{A}_{x:\overline{n}|} - \bar{A}_{x:\overline{n}|}{}^2\right)$$

n-year deferred: $1yr. paid continuously beginning n-yrs from today for as long as (x) survives

$$Y = \text{random present value of payments} = \begin{cases} 0 & T \le n \\ \bar{a}_{\overline{T|}} - \bar{a}_{\overline{n|}} & T > n \end{cases}$$

$$_{n|}\bar{a}_x = APV(Y) = E[Y] = \int_{t=0}^{n} 0\,dt + \int_{t=n}^{\omega-x} \left(\bar{a}_{\overline{t|}} - \bar{a}_{\overline{n|}}\right) {}_tp_x\mu(x+t)\,dt \quad \textbf{(aggregate payment)}$$

$$= \int_{t=n}^{\omega-x} v^t\,{}_tp_x\,dt \quad \text{(current payment)}$$

$$E[Y^2] = \int_{t=n}^{\omega-x} \left(\bar{a}_{\overline{t|}} - \bar{a}_{\overline{n|}}\right)^2 {}_tp_x\mu(x+t)\,dt \qquad \left(\bar{a}_{\overline{t|}} - \bar{a}_{\overline{n|}} = v^n \cdot \frac{1-v^{t-n}}{\delta}\right)$$

$$= v^{2n} \int_{t=n}^{\omega-x} \left(\frac{1-v^{t-n}}{\delta}\right)^2 {}_np_x \cdot {}_{t-n}p_{x+n} \cdot \mu(x+n+t-n)\,dt$$

$$= v^{2n} \cdot {}_np_x \int_{s=0}^{\omega-(x+n)} \left(\frac{1-v^s}{\delta}\right)^2 {}_sp_{x+n}\mu(x+n+s)\,ds \qquad (s = t-n)$$

$$= v^{2n} \cdot {}_np_x \cdot \frac{2}{\delta}\left(\bar{a}_{x+n} - {}^2\bar{a}_{x+n}\right)$$

n-year certain and life: $1/yr paid continuously with the first n years certain and the rest life contingent

$$Y = \text{random present value of payments} = \begin{cases} \bar{a}_{\overline{n|}} & 0 \le T \le n \\ \bar{a}_{\overline{T|}} & n < T \end{cases}$$

$$= \bar{a}_{\overline{n|}} + \begin{cases} 0 \\ \bar{a}_{\overline{T|}} - \bar{a}_{\overline{n|}} \end{cases} = a_{\overline{n|}} + Y_1$$

where Y_1 is the random present value variable for the n year deferred life annuity.

$\bar{a}_{\overline{\overline{x:n|}}} = APV(Y) = \bar{a}_{\overline{n|}} + {}_{n|}\bar{a}_x$ ($\overline{\overline{x:n|}}$ is a last survivor notation explained in Unit 5)

$Var(Y) = Var(\bar{a}_{\overline{n|}} + Y_1) = Var(Y_1)$ (see above)

Relations

$$\bar{a}_x = \bar{a}_{x:\overline{n|}} + {}_{n|}\bar{a}_x$$

$$_{n|}\bar{a}_x = v^n \cdot {}_np_x \cdot \bar{a}_{x+n}$$

Basic Discrete Life Annuities

Single Payment: $1 paid n years from now if (x) is surviving $\Big(n$-year pure endowment to $(x)\Big)$

$$Y = \text{random present value of payment} = \begin{cases} 0 & T \le n \\ v^n & T > n \end{cases} = v^n \cdot B(n=1, p={}_np_x) \text{ (binomial distribution)}$$

$$A_{x:\overline{n}|}^{\;\;1} = APV(Y) = E[Y] = v^n \cdot 1 \cdot p = v^n \cdot 1 \cdot {}_np_x$$

$$Var(Y) = v^{2n}\, Var\Big(B(n=1, p={}_np_x)\Big) = v^{2n} \cdot {}_np_x \cdot {}_nq_x$$

${}_nE_x = A_{x:\overline{n}|}^{\;\;1}$ = discount factor for n years survival and interest

$\dfrac{1}{{}_nE_x}$ = n-year accumulation factor for interest and survivorship

$$A_{x:\overline{n}|}^{\;\;1} = v^n\; {}_np_x \qquad \Rightarrow \qquad \Big(\ell_x \cdot A_{x:\overline{n}|}^{\;\;1}\Big)(1+i)^n = \ell_{x+n}$$

Deterministic Interpretation: If each of the ℓ_x lives pays $\$A_{x:\overline{n}|}^{\;\;1}$ into a fund earning interest at rate i, there will be $1 per survivor in the fund after n-years.

Whole Life ("*due*"): $1 paid at ages x, $x+1$, ... , $x+K$ where K is the random curtate lifetime of (x)

$$Y = \text{random present value of payments} = \ddot{a}_{\overline{K+1}|} = \frac{1-v^{K+1}}{d}$$

$$\ddot{a}_x = APV(Y) = E[Y] = \sum_{k=0}^{\omega-x-1} \frac{1-v^{k+1}}{d} \cdot {}_{k|}q_x = \sum_{k=0}^{\omega-x-1} v^k \cdot {}_kp_x$$

(aggregate payment) (current payment)

$$Z = \text{random present value of basic discrete whole life} = v^{K+1}$$

$$Y = \frac{1-v^{K+1}}{d} = \frac{1-Z}{d} \qquad \Rightarrow \qquad 1 = dY + Z,$$

$$1 = d\ddot{a}_x + A_x, \quad Var(Y) = Var\Big(\frac{1-Z}{d}\Big) = \frac{1}{d^2}\Big({}^2A_x - A_x^{\,2}\Big)$$

("*immediate*"): $Y = a_{\overline{K}|} = \ddot{a}_{\overline{K+1}|} - 1$

$$a_x = E[Y] = \ddot{a}_x - 1,$$

$$Var(Y) = Var(\ddot{a}_{\overline{K+1}|}) = \frac{1}{d^2}\Big({}^2A_x - A_x^{\,2}\Big)$$

n-year temporary: \$1 paid at ages x, $x+1, \ldots$, $x + min(K, n-1)$

$$Y = \text{random present value of payments} = \begin{cases} \ddot{a}_{\overline{K+1}|} & K = 0, 1, \ldots, n-1 \\ \ddot{a}_{\overline{n}|} & K = n, n+1, \ldots \end{cases}$$

$$\ddot{a}_{x:\overline{n}|} = APV(Y) = E[Y] = \sum_{k=0}^{n-1} v^k \cdot {}_k p_x \quad \text{(current payment)}$$

$$Z = \begin{array}{c}\text{random present value of basic} \\ \text{discrete endowment ins.}\end{array} = \begin{cases} v^{K+1} & K = 0, \ldots, n-1 \\ v^n & K = n, n+1, \ldots \end{cases}$$

$$Y = \frac{1-Z}{d} \Rightarrow 1 = dY + Z,\ 1 = d\ddot{a}_{x:\overline{n}|} + A_{x:\overline{n}|},\ Var(Y) = \frac{1}{d^2}\left({}^2A_{x:\overline{n}|} - A_{x:\overline{n}|}{}^2\right)$$

n-year deferred: \$1 paid at ages $x+n$, $x+n+1, \ldots$ if (x) is surviving

$$Y = \text{random present value of payments} = \begin{cases} 0 & K = 0, 1, \ldots, n-1 \\ \ddot{a}_{\overline{K+1}|} - \ddot{a}_{\overline{n}|} & K = n, n+1, \ldots \end{cases}$$

$${}_{n|}\ddot{a}_x = APV(Y) = E[Y] = \sum_{k=n}^{\omega-x-1} v^k \cdot {}_k p_x \quad \text{(current payment)}$$

$$E[Y^2] = \sum_{k=n}^{\omega-x-1} \left(\ddot{a}_{\overline{k+1}|} - \ddot{a}_{\overline{n}|}\right)^2 \cdot {}_{k|}q_x$$

Relations

$$\ddot{a}_x = \ddot{a}_{x:\overline{n}|} + {}_{n|}\ddot{a}_x$$

$${}_{n|}\ddot{a}_x = v^n \cdot {}_n p_x \cdot \ddot{a}_{x+n}$$

m^th-ly Annuities

$$\ddot{a}_x^{(m)} = APV\left(\frac{\$1}{m} \text{ paid at ages } x, x+\frac{1}{m}, \ldots \text{ while } (x) \text{ survives}\right)$$

$$= \frac{1}{m} + \frac{1}{m} \cdot v^{1/m} \cdot {}_{1/m} p_x + \cdots \quad \text{(current payment)}$$

Relations with annual annuities:

due: $$1 = d\ddot{a}_x + A_x\text{: } 1 = d^{(m)}\ddot{a}_x^{(m)} + A_x^{(m)} \underset{\text{UDD}}{=} d^{(m)}\ddot{a}_x^{(m)} + \frac{i}{i^{(m)}} A_x$$

$$\Rightarrow \ddot{a}_x^{(m)} \underset{\text{UDD}}{=} \underbrace{\frac{id}{i^{(m)}d^{(m)}}}_{\alpha(m)} \ddot{a}_x - \underbrace{\frac{i - i^{(m)}}{i^{(m)}d^{(m)}}}_{\beta(m)} = \alpha(m)\ddot{a}_x - \beta(m)$$

$$\ddot{a}_{x:\overline{n}|}^{(m)} \underset{\text{UDD}}{=} \ddot{a}_x^{(m)} - {}_{n|}\ddot{a}_x^{(m)} = \left(\alpha(m)\ddot{a}_x - \beta(m)\right) - {}_nE_x\left(\alpha(m)\ddot{a}_{x+n} - \beta(m)\right)$$

$$\underset{\text{UDD}}{=} \alpha(m)\ddot{a}_{x:\overline{n}|} - \beta(m)\,(1 - {}_nE_x)$$

$${}_{n|}\ddot{a}_x^{(m)} \underset{\text{UDD}}{=} \alpha(m)\,{}_{n|}\ddot{a}_x - \beta(m)\,{}_nE_x$$

immediate: $a_x^{(m)} = \ddot{a}_x^{(m)} - \frac{1}{m}$

$$\underset{\text{UDD}}{=} \alpha(m)\ddot{a}_x - \left(\beta(m)+\frac{1}{m}\right)$$

$$\left[\begin{aligned}\gamma(m) &= \alpha(m) - \beta(m) - \frac{1}{m} \\ &= \frac{d^{(m)} - d}{i^{(m)}d^{(m)}}\end{aligned}\right]$$

$$\underset{\text{UDD}}{=} \alpha(m)a_x + \underbrace{\left(\alpha(m) - \beta(m) - \frac{1}{m}\right)}_{\gamma(m)}$$

Doubling The Force

	Original Force	Double Force
Force	δ	2δ
Rate of Interest	i	$2i + i^2$
Rate of Discount	d	$2d - d^2$
Discount Factor	v	v^2
m^{th}-ly Rate of Interest	$i^{(m)}$	$2i^{(m)} + \frac{i^{(m)2}}{m}$

Applications

$$1 = \delta\,\bar{a}_x + \bar{A}_x \quad\Rightarrow\quad 1 = (2\delta)\,{}^2\bar{a}_x + {}^2\bar{A}_x$$

$$1 = d\ddot{a}_x + A_x \quad\Rightarrow\quad 1 = (2d - d^2)\,{}^2\ddot{a}_x + {}^2A_x$$

$$A_x^{(m)} \underset{\text{UDD}}{=} \frac{i}{i^{(m)}} A_x \Rightarrow {}^2A_x^{(m)} \underset{\text{UDD}}{=} \left[\frac{2i + i^2}{2i^{(m)} + \frac{i^{(m)2}}{m}}\right] {}^2A_x$$

Alternate 2nd Moment and Variance Calculations

Continuous Whole Life

$$Y^2 = \bar{a}_{\overline{T|}}^2 = \left(\frac{1 - v^T}{\delta}\right)^2$$

$$= \frac{2}{\delta}\cdot\frac{1-v^T}{\delta} - \frac{2}{\delta}\cdot\frac{1-v^{2T}}{2\delta}$$

$$= \frac{2}{\delta}\left[\bar{a}_{\overline{T|}} - {}^2\bar{a}_{\overline{T|}}\right]$$

$$E[Y^2] = \frac{2}{\delta}\left[\bar{a}_x - {}^2\bar{a}_x\right]$$

$$Var(Y) = \frac{2}{\delta}\left[\bar{a}_x - {}^2\bar{a}_x\right] - (\bar{a}_x)^2$$

Discrete Whole Life

$$Y^2 = \ddot{a}_{\overline{K+1|}}^2 = \left(\frac{1 - v^{K+1}}{d}\right)^2$$

$$= \frac{2}{d}\cdot\frac{1-v^{K+1}}{d} - \frac{2d-d^2}{d^2}\cdot\frac{1-v^{2(K+1)}}{2d-d^2}$$

$$= \frac{2}{d}\,\ddot{a}_{\overline{K+1|}} - \frac{2-d}{d}\cdot{}^2\ddot{a}_{\overline{K+1|}}$$

$$E[Y^2] = \frac{2}{d}\left[\ddot{a}_x - \left(1-\frac{d}{2}\right)\cdot{}^2\ddot{a}_x\right]$$

$$Var(Y) = \frac{2}{d}\left[\ddot{a}_x - \left(1-\frac{d}{2}\right)\cdot{}^2\ddot{a}_x\right] - (\ddot{a}_x)^2$$

Density Function for the Continuous Whole Life Annuity

$Y = \bar{a}_{\overline{T|}}$ = random p.v. of 1/yr paid continuously for as long as (x) survives

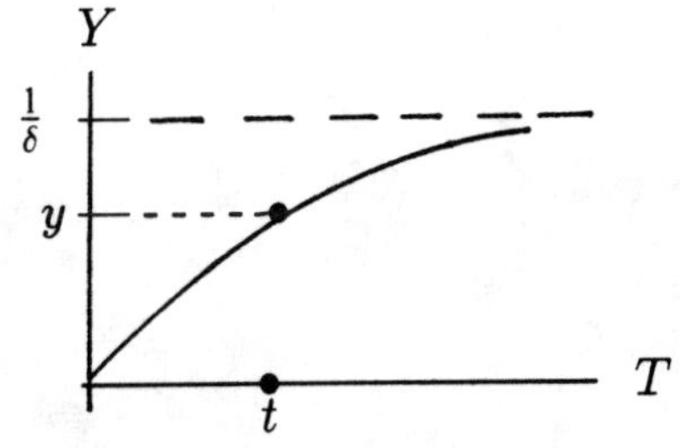

$$y = \frac{1 - v^t}{\delta} \quad \Rightarrow \quad t = -ln(1 - \delta y)/\delta$$

$$F_Y(y) = Pr(Y \leq y) = Pr(T \leq t) = F_T(-ln(1-\delta y)/\delta)$$

$$f_Y(y) = F'_Y(y) = f_T(-ln(1-\delta y)/\delta)/(1-\delta y)$$

Special Cases

1. de Moivre's Law

$$\ell_x = \omega - x, \ T \sim U(0, \omega), \ f_T(t) = \frac{1}{\omega - x} \quad 0 \leq t \leq \omega - x$$

$$f_Y(y) = \frac{1}{(\omega-x)(1-\delta y)} \quad 0 \leq y \leq \bar{a}_{\overline{\omega-x|}}$$

2. Constant Force

$$T \sim \xi(\mu), \ f_T(t) = \mu e^{-\mu t} \quad 0 \leq t < \infty$$

$$f_Y(y) = \mu(1 - \delta y)^{(\mu/\delta)-1} \quad 0 \leq y < \bar{a}_{\overline{\infty|}} = \frac{1}{\delta}$$

Calculation of Annuities From Tables of $\ddot{a}_x$ Values

$${}_{n|}\ddot{a}_x = v^n \, {}_np_x \ddot{a}_{x+n}$$

$$\ddot{a}_{x:\overline{n|}} = \ddot{a}_x - v^n \, {}_np_x \ddot{a}_{x+n}$$

$$\ddot{a}_x^{(m)} \underset{\text{UDD}}{\equiv} \alpha(m)\ddot{a}_x - \beta(m)$$

$$\bar{a}_x \underset{\text{UDD}}{\equiv} \alpha(\infty)\ddot{a}_x - \beta(\infty)$$

CONCEPTUAL REVIEW TEST

1. Assuming $i = .05$, write an expression for the present value of payments to (25) specified by the following life annuities if death occurs at age 55.7:

   (a) \$1000/year paid continuously for life;
   (b) \$1000/year life annuity due;
   (c) 20-year temporary life annuity due of 1000/year; and
   (d) 20-year deferred life annuity due of 1000/year.

2. If (x) is to receive a continuous life annuity of \$1/year, let Y be the random present value of benefit variable.

   (a) Express Y as a function of T, the future lifetime of (x), and draw its graph.
   (b) Using the fact that Y is a function of T, express the actuarial present value, $\overline{a}_x$, as an integral (aggregate payment method). What is the interpretation of $\overline{a}_x$?
   (c) Use the graph in (a) to relate the event $Y \leq y_0$ to some event $T \leq t_0$, where t_0 is a function of y_0 and δ.
   (d) What is the relation between Y and Z, the random present value of benefit for \$1 of whole life to (x) payable on death?
   (e) Use the relations in (d) to express $\overline{a}_x$ in terms of $\overline{A}_x$ and $Var(Y)$ in terms of insurance values.

3. Let $Y = \ddot{a}_{\overline{K+1}|}$ be the random present value of a life annuity due to (x) of \$1/year. The aggregate payment expression for the actuarial present value, $\ddot{a}_x = \sum_{k=0}^{\omega-x-1} \ddot{a}_{\overline{k+1}|} \cdot f_K(k)$ where $f_K(k) = {}_{k|}q_x = \frac{d_{x+k}}{\ell_x}$, is obtained from the fact that Y is a function of K. Write the current payment expression for $\ddot{a}_x$ and use this relation to give an aggregate deterministic interpretation of a fund equal $\$\ell_x \cdot \ddot{a}_x$.

4. If K is the curtate lifetime of (30), write an expression for Y in terms of K where Y is the present value variable for a 20-year temporary life annuity due to (30). Write both the aggregate and current payment expressions for the actuarial present value $\ddot{a}_{30:\overline{20}|}$.

5. Relate the Y in Question 4 to a present value variable Z corresponding to an endowment insurance to (30). Use this to relate $\ddot{a}_{30:\overline{20}|}$ and $Var(Y)$ to insurance values.

6. What is the difference between $\overline{a}_{25}$ and $\overline{a}_{\overline{25}|}$? If $\omega = 100$ explain why $\overline{a}_{25} < \overline{a}_{\overline{75}|}$.

CONCEPTUAL REVIEW TEST SOLUTIONS

1. (a) $1000\,\bar{a}_{\overline{30.7}|.05}$ since $30.7 = T$
   (b) $1000\,\ddot{a}_{\overline{31}|.05}$ since (25) is alive at the start of 31 years
   (c) $1000\,\ddot{a}_{\overline{20}|.05}$ since death occurs more than 20 years later
   (d) $1000\left(\ddot{a}_{\overline{31}|.05} - \ddot{a}_{\overline{20}|.05}\right)$ since (25) is alive for the beginning of 11 years after age 45.

2. (a) $Y = \bar{a}_{\overline{T}|} = \dfrac{1 - v^T}{\delta}$,
   since 1 per year is paid continuously for T years.

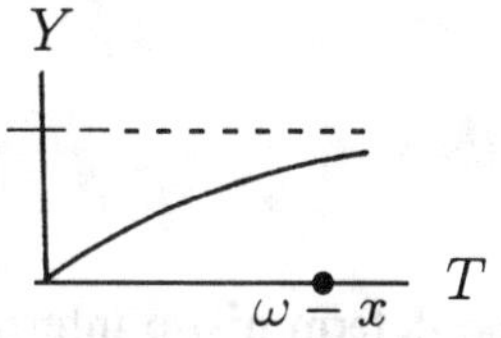

   (b) $\bar{a}_x = E[Y] = E\left[\dfrac{1 - v^T}{\delta}\right] = \displaystyle\int_{t=0}^{\omega - x} \dfrac{1 - v^t}{\delta} \cdot {}_tp_x \cdot \mu(x+t)dt$ since $f(t) = {}_tp_x \cdot \mu(x+t)$. If $\bar{a}_x$ is invested in an account at age x earning continuous interest at rate δ, it is "on average" the amount needed so that \$1 per year can be continuously withdrawn for the rest of life.

   (c)

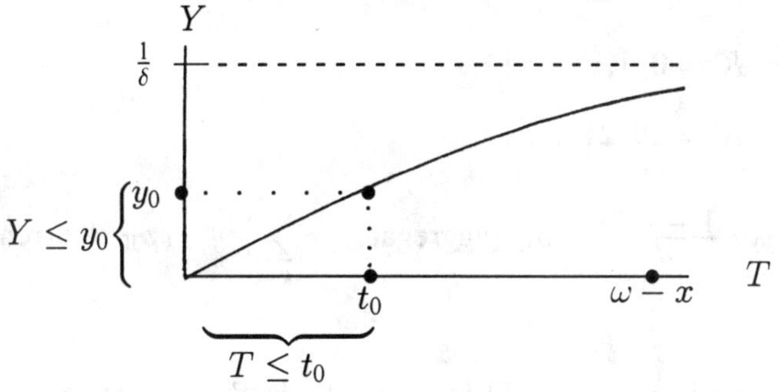

$$y_0 = \bar{a}_{\overline{t_0}|} = \frac{1 - e^{-\delta t_0}}{\delta} \quad \Rightarrow \quad t_0 = \frac{-\,ln(1 - \delta y_0)}{\delta}$$

   (d) Since $Y = \dfrac{1 - e^{-\delta T}}{\delta}$ and $Z = e^{-\delta T}$ we have $Y = \dfrac{1 - Z}{\delta}$.

   (e) $\bar{a}_x = E[Y] = \dfrac{1 - E[Z]}{\delta} = \dfrac{1 - \bar{A}_x}{\delta}$ by linearity of $E[\;\;]$.
   Also $Var(Y) = Var\left(\frac{1}{\delta} - \frac{1}{\delta}Z\right) = Var\left(-\frac{1}{\delta}Z\right)$ since $Var(a + X) = Var(X)$,
   and $Var\left(-\frac{1}{\delta}Z\right) = \left(-\frac{1}{\delta}\right)^2 Var(Z) = \frac{1}{\delta^2}\left({}^2\bar{A}_x - \bar{A}_x{}^2\right)$.

3. The current payment expression is $\ddot{a}_x = \sum_{k=0}^{\omega-x-1} v^k \cdot {}_kp_x$. It can be obtained by summation by parts from the aggregate payment expression or by viewing Y as $Y_0+Y_1+Y_2+\cdots$ where Y_k is the random present value of the payment received at age $x+k$ (i.e., $Y_k = 1 \cdot v^k$ if (x) is surviving, or $Y_k = 0 \cdot v^k$ otherwise).

Using linearity of $E[\ ]$ leads to $E[Y] = E[Y_0] + E[Y_1] + \cdots = 1 + v \cdot {}_1p_x + v^2 \cdot {}_2p_x + \cdots$ since $v^0 = 1$, ${}_0p_x = 1$.

$Y_k = Y$	$Pr(Y_k = y)$
0	${}_kq_x$
v^k	${}_kp_x$
$E[Y_k] = 0 \cdot {}_kq_x + v^k \cdot {}_kp_x$	

For the deterministic interpretation substitute ${}_kp_x = \frac{\ell_{x+k}}{\ell_x}$ into the current payment formula and multiply by ℓ_x to obtain $\ell_x\, \ddot{a}_x = \ell_x \cdot 1 + \ell_{x+1} \cdot v + \ell_{x+2} \cdot v^2 + \cdots + \ell_{\omega-1} \cdot v^{\omega-x-1}$. If a fund of $\ell_x \ddot{a}_x$ is available at simultaneous issue, it is exactly enough to pay $\$\ell_x$ immediately, $\$\ell_{x+1}$ one year later, $\$\ell_{x+2}$ two years later, and so on, that is one dollar to each survivor at ages x, $x+1$, $x+2, \ldots$ if exactly ℓ_{x+k} are surviving at age $x+k$ (deterministic view).

4. $$Y = \begin{cases} \ddot{a}_{\overline{K+1|}} = \dfrac{1-v^{K+1}}{d} & K = 0, 1, \ldots, 19 \\ \ddot{a}_{\overline{20|}} = \dfrac{1-v^{20}}{d} & K = 20, 21, \ldots . \end{cases}$$

$$\ddot{a}_{30:\overline{20|}} = \sum_{k=0}^{19} \frac{1-v^{k+1}}{d} \cdot {}_{k|}q_{30} + \frac{1-v^{20}}{d} \cdot {}_{20}p_{30} \text{ (aggregate)} = \sum_{k=0}^{19} v^k \cdot {}_kp_{30} \text{ (current)}$$

5. The Z for a 20-year endowment insurance of \$1 to (30) with death benefits paid at the end of the policy year of death, is given by $Z = \begin{cases} v^{K+1} & K = 0, 1, \ldots, 19 \\ v^{20} & K = 20, 21, \ldots \end{cases}$. Thus

$Y = \frac{1-Z}{d}$, $\ddot{a}_{30:\overline{20|}} = E[Y] = \frac{1-E[Z]}{d} = \frac{1-A_{30:\overline{20|}}}{d}$, and

$Var(Y) = \left(-\frac{1}{d}\right)^2 Var(Z) = \frac{1}{d^2}\left({}^2A_{30:\overline{20|}} - A_{30:\overline{20|}}{}^2\right)$.

6. $\bar{a}_{25}$ is the APV of a continuous annuity of \$1 per year to (25), whereas $\bar{a}_{\overline{25|}} = \frac{1-v^{25}}{\delta}$ is the present value of a continuous, 25-year certain annuity of \$1 per year. If $\omega = 100$, then (25) can receive at most 75 years of continuous payments, thus since $\bar{a}_{25}$ is the average present value of the payments (25) can receive, it is less than the maximum possible present value, $\bar{a}_{\overline{75|}}$.

COMPUTATIONAL REVIEW TEST

1. Suppose $Y = \overline{a}_{\overline{T|}}$ is the random present value variable for a continuous life annuity of \$1/year to (x). Assume $\delta = .05$ and that the future lifetime variable T has p.d.f. given by $f_T(t) = .015e^{-.015t}, t \geq 0$.
   (a) Calculate the APV $\overline{a}_x$ by either the aggregate or current payment method.
   (b) What is the probability that a fund of \$$\overline{a}_x$ at age (x) is sufficient to withdraw \$1/year continuously for as long as (x) lives?
   (c) What is the possible range of values of Y?
   (d) What event in terms of T is equivalent to $5 \leq Y \leq 10$?
   (e) What is $Pr(5 \leq Y \leq 10)$?

2. If $\overline{A}_x = .06$ and ${}^2\overline{A}_x = .01$ and Y is the present value variable for a continuous \$1000/year life annuity to (x), find $E[Y] = 1000\overline{a}_x$ and σ_Y assuming $\delta = .05$.

3. Suppose 100 lives age x are paid \$1000/year continuously while they survive. How big a fund is needed at the time of simultaneous issue in order to be 90% certain of having enough money to pay the life annuities? Assume that the present value variable Y is as in Question 2, and use the central limit theorem on Y_{Agg}, the aggregate present value variable.

For Question 4 - 6 you are given:

(i) $i = .06$

(ii) $\ddot{a}_{25} = 16.22419$ $\ddot{a}_{65} = 9.89693$
$\ell_{25} = 95{,}650.15$ $\ell_{65} = 75{,}339.63$
$\ell_{66} = 73{,}733.37$ $\ell_{67} = 72{,}016.33$
$\ell_{60} = 81{,}880.73$ $\ell_{61} = 80{,}754.01$

4. Calculate the actuarial present value for the following life annuities:
   (a) 1000/year to (25) for life as an annuity due;
   (b) 1000/year to (25) as a 40-year temporary life annuity due:
   (c) 1000/year to (25) as a 40-year deferred life annuity due (hint: use (a) and (b)); and
   (d) 1000/year paid continuously to (25) as a life annuity. Assume UDD and use $1 = \delta\overline{a}_{25} + \overline{A}_{25}$ together with $\overline{A}_{25} = \frac{i}{\delta}A_{25}$.

5. In Questions 4a and 4b what is the probability that the APV is sufficient to make the annuity payments? For part (b) first draw the graph of Y versus K and calculate $\ddot{a}_{\overline{40|}.06}$, the Y value if $K \geq 40$.

6. Suppose (25) is to receive a quarterly payment of \$100 for as long as he lives beginning at age 25. Use the UDD relation of $\ddot{a}_{25}^{(4)}$ to $\ddot{a}_{25}$ to evaluate the APV.

SOLUTIONS TO COMPUTATIONAL REVIEW TEST

1. (a)
$$\bar{a}_x = \int_{t=0}^{\infty} \bar{a}_{\overline{t|}} \cdot f_T(t)dt$$
$$= \int_{t=0}^{\infty} \frac{1-e^{-.05t}}{.05} \cdot .015\, e^{-.015t}dt$$
$$= .3\left[\int_0^{\infty} e^{-.015t}dt - \int_0^{\infty} e^{-.065t}dt\right]$$
$$= .3\left[\frac{1}{.015} - \frac{1}{.065}\right] = 15.3846 \text{ (aggregate)}$$
$$\bar{a}_x = \int_{t=0}^{\infty} v^t \cdot {}_tp_x dt = \int_0^{\infty} e^{-.05t} \cdot e^{-.015t}dt = \frac{1}{.065} = 15.3846 \text{ (current)}$$

(b)
$$Pr(\text{fund is sufficient}) = Pr(15.3846 \geq \text{present value of payments})$$
$$= Pr\left(15.3846 \geq \bar{a}_{\overline{T|}} = \frac{1-e^{-.05T}}{.05}\right)$$
$$= Pr\left(T \leq \frac{-ln(1-(.05)(15.3846))}{.05} = 29.3267\right)$$
$$= \int_{t=0}^{29.3267} .015e^{-.015t}dt = 1 - e^{-(29.3267)(.015)} = .3559.$$

(c) $Y = \bar{a}_{\overline{T|}}$ is an increasing function of T where $0 \leq T < \infty$.

Thus $0 \leq \bar{a}_{\overline{T|}} \leq \bar{a}_{\overline{\infty|}} = \frac{1}{\delta} = \frac{1}{.05} = 20.$

(d) $5 \leq Y \leq 10 \Leftrightarrow 5 \leq \frac{1-e^{-.05T}}{.05} \leq 10 \Leftrightarrow \frac{-ln(.75)}{.05} \leq T \leq \frac{-ln(.50)}{.05} \Leftrightarrow 5.7536 \leq T \leq 13.8629$

(e) $Pr(5 \leq Y \leq 10) = \int_{5.7536}^{13.8629} f_T(t)dt = -e^{-.015t}\Big|_{5.7536}^{13.8629} = .1051$

2. $E[Y] = 1000 \cdot \bar{a}_x = 1000 \cdot \frac{1-\bar{A}_x}{\delta} = (1000)(20)(1-.06) = 18{,}800$

$$\sigma_Y = \sqrt{Var(Y)} = \sqrt{1000^2 \cdot \frac{1}{\delta^2}\left({}^2\bar{A}_x - \bar{A}_x{}^2\right)}$$
$$= 1000 \cdot 20 \cdot (.0100 - .0036)^{1/2} = (1000)(20)(.08) = 1600$$

3. $Y_{Agg} = Y_1 + \cdots + Y_{100}$, so $\mu(Agg) = 100E[Y] = 100(18{,}800) = 1{,}880{,}000$ and $\sigma_{Agg} = \sqrt{100} \cdot \sigma_Y = 10(1600) = 16{,}000$.

$$.90 = Pr(Y_{Agg} \leq F) = Pr\left(\frac{Y_{Agg} - 1{,}880{,}000}{16{,}000} \leq \frac{F - 1{,}880{,}000}{16{,}000}\right)$$
$$\approx Pr\left(N(0,1) \leq \frac{F - 1{,}880{,}000}{16{,}000}\right).$$

Also $.90 = Pr(N(0,1) \leq 1.28)$, hence $F = 1{,}880{,}000 + (1.28)(16{,}000) = 1{,}900{,}480$.

4. (a) $APV = 1000\ddot{a}_{25} = 16{,}224.19$ from $\ddot{a}_{25}$ in the table

(b) $APV = 1000\ddot{a}_{25:\overline{40}|} = 1000(\ddot{a}_{25} - \frac{1}{1.06^{40}}\frac{\ell_{65}}{\ell_{25}}\ddot{a}_{65}) = 15{,}466.30$

(c) $APV = 1000_{40|}\ddot{a}_{25} = 1000(\ddot{a}_{25} - \ddot{a}_{25:\overline{40}|}) = (a) - (b) = 757.89$

(d) $APV = 1000\bar{a}_{25} = 1000\Big(\alpha(\infty)\ddot{a}_{25} - \beta(\infty)\Big) = 15{,}718.93$

$\alpha(\infty) = \frac{id}{\delta^2} = 1.000283$

$\beta(\infty) = .509855$

5. (a)

$$\begin{aligned} Pr(\text{APV is sufficient}) &= Pr(16{,}224.19 \geq 1000\ddot{a}_{\overline{K+1}|}) \\ &= Pr\Big(16.22419 \geq \frac{1 - v^{K+1}}{d}\Big) \\ &= Pr\Big(K \leq \frac{-\,ln(1 - 16.22419\text{d})}{\delta} - 1\Big) \\ &= Pr(K \leq 41.9958) = Pr(K \leq 41) \text{ (since } K \text{ is integral)} \\ &= Pr(T < 42) = {}_{42}q_{25} = 1 - \frac{\ell_{67}}{\ell_{25}} = .2471 \end{aligned}$$

(b) $$Y = \begin{cases} 1000\ddot{a}_{\overline{K+1}|} & K = 0, 1, \ldots, 39 \\ 1000\ddot{a}_{\overline{40}|} = 15{,}949.08 & K = 40, 41 \end{cases}$$

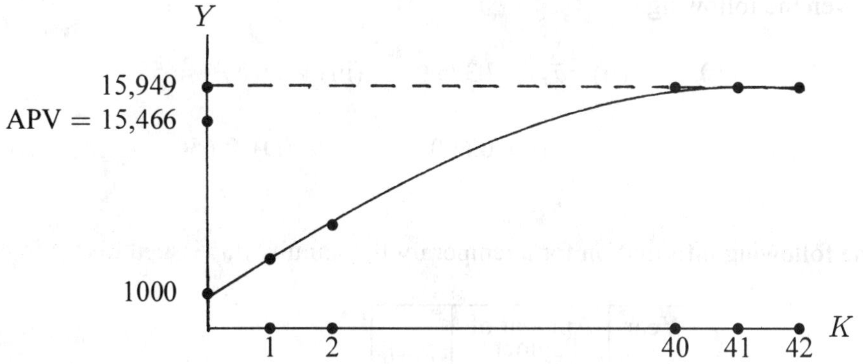

$$Pr(Y \leq 15{,}466) = Pr\Big(\frac{1 - v^{K+1}}{d} \leq 15.466\Big)$$

$$= Pr(K \leq \frac{-\,ln(1 - 15.466d)}{\delta} - 1 = 34.749) = {}_{35}q_{25} = 1 - \frac{\ell_{60}}{\ell_{25}} = .1440$$

6. $APV = 4 \cdot 100 \cdot \ddot{a}^{(4)}_{25} = 400\Big(\alpha(4)\ddot{a}_{25} - \beta(4)\Big) = 6{,}337.70$ since $\alpha(4) = \frac{i \cdot d}{i^{(4)}d^{(4)}} = 1.000265$,

$\beta(4) = \frac{i - i^{(4)}}{i^{(4)}d^{(4)}} = .384239$ and $\ddot{a}_{25} = 16.22419$

UNIT REVIEW QUESTIONS

1. Which of the following are true if deaths are uniformly distributed over each year of age?

I. $\overline{A}_x = \frac{i}{\delta} - \frac{(i-d)\ddot{a}_x}{\delta}$ II. $\overline{A}_{x:\overline{n}|} = \frac{i}{\delta} A_{x:\overline{n}|}$ III. $(\overline{I}\overline{A})_x = \frac{i}{\delta}(IA)_x$

(A) None (B) I only (C) II only (D) III only (E) None of A, B, C, or D

2. A 3-year life annuity due to (x) is defined by the following table:

Year t	Amount of Payment	p_{x+t}
0	1	.80
1	2	.75
2	3	.50

You are given that $v = 0.9$ and that the expected present value of the payments is K. Calculate that probability that the present value of the payments actually made will exceed K.

(A) 0.3 (B) 0.4 (C) 0.5 (D) 0.6 (E) 0.7

3. Determine $\overline{A}_x$, given the following:

(i) $\overline{a}_x = 10$ (ii) ${}^2\overline{a}_x = 7.375$ (iii) $Var(\overline{a}_{\overline{T}|}) = 50$

(A) 0.085 (B) 0.125 (C) 0.600 (D) 0.650 (E) 0.825

4. You are given the following information for a temporary life annuity due issued to (x):

Year t	Amount of Payment	p_{x+t}
0	2	.80
1	3	.75
2	4	.50

Calculate the variance of the random variable which represents the present value of the indicated payments. Assume $v = 0.9$. (Answer to nearest 0.1)

(A) 5.4 (B) 5.5 (C) 5.6 (D) 5.7 (E) 5.8

5. Consider a group of individuals all age x, which is 50% male and 50% female. You are given the following values for each of the subgroups. All values were calculated using $\delta = .10$.

	Male	Female
$\overline{A}_x$	.15	.09
$Var(\overline{a}_{\overline{T}|})$	5.00	4.00

Determine $\overline{a}_x$ and $Var(\overline{a}_{\overline{T}|})$ for an individual chosen at random from the group.

(A) $\overline{a}_x = 7.60$ $\quad Var(\overline{a}_{\overline{T}|}) = 4.50$
(B) $\overline{a}_x = 8.80$ $\quad Var(\overline{a}_{\overline{T}|}) = 4.42$
(C) $\overline{a}_x = 8.80$ $\quad Var(\overline{a}_{\overline{T}|}) = 4.50$
(D) $\overline{a}_x = 8.80$ $\quad Var(\overline{a}_{\overline{T}|}) = 4.59$
(E) There is not enough known information to determine both $\overline{a}_x$ and $Var(\overline{a}_{\overline{T}|})$.

6. You are given the following information:

(i) $\mu(x)$ is the force of mortality at age x on a standard table.

(ii) $\mu^1(x)$ is the force of mortality at age x on a special table.

(iii) δ is the force of interest on a standard basis.

(iv) δ^1 is the force of interest on a special basis.

(v) $\delta = \frac{\delta^1}{3}$

(vi) $\overline{a}_x = \overline{a}^1_x$ for all $x \leq \omega$.

Find $\mu^1(x)$ in terms of $\mu(x)$.

(A) $\frac{\mu(x)}{3}$ (B) $\frac{\mu(x)}{2}$ (C) $\mu(x) - \delta$ (D) $\mu(x) - 2\delta$ (E) $\mu(x) - 3\delta$

7. Y is the present value random variable of a life annuity due of 1 issued to (x). Calculate the variance of Y, given the following values:

(i) $\ddot{a}_x = 10$ (ii) ${}^2\ddot{a}_x = 6$ (iii) $i = 1/24$

(A) 10 (B) 36 (C) 100 (D) 106 (E) 392

8. $\int_0^n \overline{a}_{\overline{t}|} \cdot {}_tp_x \mu(x+t)\, dt = ?$

(A) $\overline{a}_{\overline{n}|} - \overline{a}_{x:\overline{n}|}$ (B) $\int_0^n v^t(1 - {}_tp_x)\, dt$ (C) $\frac{1 + \overline{A}_{x:\overline{n}|}}{d}$ (D) $\frac{\overline{A}^{\,1}_{x:\overline{n}|}}{\delta} - \frac{v^n\, {}_nq_x}{\delta}$

(E) None of A, B, C, or D

9. You are given:

(i) $Var(\bar{a}_{\overline{T|}}) = \frac{100}{9}$ (ii) $\mu(x+t) = k$, for all t (iii) $\delta = 4k$

Calculate k.

(A) .005 (B) .010 (C) .015 (D) .020 (E) .025

10. You are given:

k	$\ddot{a}_{\overline{k|}}$	$_{k-1|}q_x$
1	1.00	.33
2	1.93	.24
3	2.80	.16
4	3.62	.11

Calculate $\ddot{a}_{x:\overline{4|}}$.

(A) 1.6 (B) 1.8 (C) 2.0 (D) 2.2 (E) 2.4

11. T is the random variable for the future lifetime of (x). Determine $Cov\left[\bar{a}_{\overline{T|}},\ v^T\right]$.

(A) $\frac{\bar{A}_x{}^2 - {}^2\bar{A}_x}{\delta}$ (B) $\bar{A}_x{}^2 - {}^2\bar{A}_x$ (C) 0 (D) ${}^2\bar{A}_x - \bar{A}_x{}^2$ (E) $\frac{{}^2\bar{A}_x - \bar{A}_x{}^2}{\delta}$

12. Y is the present-value random variable for a benefit based on (x) such that:

$$Y = \begin{cases} \bar{a}_{\overline{n|}} & 0 \le T(x) \le n \\ \bar{a}_{\overline{T|}} & T(x) > n \end{cases}$$

Determine $E[Y]$.

(A) $\bar{a}_{\overline{x:n|}}$ (B) $\bar{a}_{x:\overline{n|}} + {}_{n|}\bar{a}_x$ (C) $\bar{a}_{\overline{n|}} + {}_{n|}\bar{a}_x$ (D) $\bar{a}_{\overline{n|}} + v^n \cdot \bar{a}_{x+n}$ (E) ${}_nq_x \cdot \bar{a}_{\overline{n|}} + {}_{n|}\bar{a}_{xx}$

13. For a 10-year deferred life annuity-due of 1 per year on (60), you are given:

(i) Mortality follows de Moivre's law with $\omega = 100$.
(ii) $i = 0$

Calculate the probability that the sum of the payments made under the annuity will exceed the actuarial present value, at issue, of the annuity.

(A) .475 (B) .500 (C) .525 (D) .550 (E) .575

14. For (x), you are given:

(i) $\mu(x+t) = \frac{-.024}{ln(.4)}$, for $t \geq 0$

(ii) $\delta = .03$

Calculate the probability that $\bar{a}_{\overline{T(x)}|}$ will exceed 20.

(A) .45 (B) .55 (C) .67 (D) .74 (E) .82

15. Which of the following is true, regardless of the assumption about deaths within each year of age?

I. $\bar{A}_x = \frac{i}{\delta} A_x$

II. $\bar{a}_x = \bar{a}_{x:\overline{1}|} + \delta p_x \bar{a}_{x+1}$

III. $\bar{a}_x = \alpha(\infty)\ddot{a}_x - \beta(\infty)$

IV. $\bar{A}_x = 1 - \delta \bar{a}_x$

(A) None (B) I only (C) II only (D) III only (E) IV only

16. Consider the following present-value random variables, where K is the curtate future lifetime of (x):

$$Y = \ddot{a}_{\overline{K+1}|} \qquad K \geq 0 \qquad\qquad Z = \begin{cases} \ddot{a}_{\overline{K+1}|} & 0 \leq K < n \\ \ddot{a}_{\overline{n}|} & K \geq n \end{cases}$$

You are given:

(i) $i = .06$

(ii) $A_x = .20755$

(iii) $a_{x:\overline{n-1}|} = 6$

Calculate $E[Y] - E[Z]$.

(A) 4 (B) 5 (C) 6 (D) 7 (E) 8

17. For a 3-year temporary life annuity-due on (30), you are given:

(i) $s(x) = 1 - \frac{x}{80}$, $0 \leq x \leq 80$

(ii) $i = .05$

(iii) $Y = \begin{cases} \ddot{a}_{\overline{K+1}|}, & K = 0, 1, 2 \\ \ddot{a}_{\overline{3}|}, & K = 3, 4, 5, \ldots \end{cases}$

Calculate $Var(Y)$.

(A) .08 (B) .29 (C) .36 (D) .60 (E) .93

18. You are given:

(i) $\ddot{a}^{(4)}_{\overline{\infty|}} = 17.287$
(ii) $A_x = .1025$
(iii) Deaths are uniformly distributed over each year of age.

Calculate $\ddot{a}^{(4)}_x$.

(A) 15.48 (B) 15.51 (C) 15.75 (D) 15.82 (E) 15.86

19. For a 5-year deferred whole life annuity-due of 1 on (x), you are given:

(i) $\mu(x+t) = .01,\ t \geq 0$
(ii) $i = .04$
(iii) $\ddot{a}_{x:\overline{5|}} = 4.542$
(iv) The random variable S denotes the sum of the annuity payments.

Calculate $Pr[S > {}_5|\ddot{a}_x]$.

(A) .81 (B) .82 (C) .83 (D) .84 (E) .85

Use the following information for Questions 20-23.

Z is the present-value random variable for a special benefit on (30). This benefit provides the following:

(1) A life income of 1000 per year payable continuously while (30) survives.
(2) An insurance of 5000 payable at the moment of death of (30).

T is the future-lifetime random value for (30).

You are given:

(i) $A_{30} = .14011,\ {}^2A_{30} = .03641$
(ii) $i = .05$
(iii) Deaths are uniformly distributed over each year of age.

20. Which of the following is a correct expression for Z?

(A) $20{,}496 - 15{,}496v^T$
(B) $1000 + 4000v^T$
(C) $20{,}000 - 15{,}000v^T$
(D) $21{,}000 - 16{,}000v^{K+1}$
(E) $20{,}000 - 15{,}000v^{K+1}$

21. Calculate $E[Z]$.

(A) 17,500 (B) 18,000 (C) 18,250 (D) 18,500 (E) 18,750

22. Calculate ${}^2\overline{A}_{30}$.

(A) .03732 (B) .03825 (C) .03862 (D) .03879 (E) .04010

23. Calculate $Var(Z)$.

(A) 4,000,000 (B) 4,100,000 (C) 4,200,000 (D) 4,300,000 (E) 4,400,000

> Use the following information for Questions 24 - 28.
>
> Y is the present value random variable for a 10-year deferred life annuity-due to (40) of 1 per year.
>
> Z_1 is the present value random variable for a whole life insurance of 1 on (40) with benefits at the end of the year of death.
>
> Z_2 is the present value random variable for a 10-year endowment insurance of 1 on (40) with benefits at the end of the year of death.
>
> You are given:
> (i) $i = .05$
> (ii) ${}_{10|}A_{40} = .178809, \ A_{40} = .20799$
> (iii) ${}^2A_{40} = .06741, \ {}^2A_{50} = .12446$
> (iv) $v^{10} \cdot {}_{10}p_{40} = .590041$
> (v) $\ddot{a}_{50} = 14.636060$

24. Express Y as a linear function of Z_1 and Z_2.

(A) $Z_1 + 2Z_2$ (B) $Z_1 - Z_2$ (C) $Z_2 - Z_1$ (D) $21(Z_1 - Z_2)$ (E) $21(Z_2 - Z_1)$

25. Calculate $E[Z_1 Z_2]$.

(A) .13 (B) .14 (C) .15 (D) .16 (E) .17

26. Which of the following is a correct expression for Y^2?

(A) $21(v^{20} - 2v^{10}v^{K+1} + v^{2K+2})$ $K \geq 10$, 0 otherwise
(B) $441(v^{20} - 2v^{10}v^{K+1} + v^{2K+2})$ $K \geq 10$, 0 otherwise
(C) $21(v^{20} + 2v^{10}v^{K+1} + v^{2K+2})$ $K \geq 10$, 0 otherwise
(D) $441(v^{20} + 2v^{10}v^{K+1} + v^{2K+2})$ $K \geq 10$, 0 otherwise
(E) $441(v^{20} + v^{10}v^{K+1} + v^{2K+2})$ $K \geq 10$, 0 otherwise

27. Calculate $E[Y^2]$.

(A) 70 (B) 74 (C) 75 (D) 79 (E) 83

28. Calculate $Var(Y)$.

(A) 7 (B) 8 (C) 9 (D) 10 (E) 11

Use the following information for Questions 29 - 33.

You are given:

(i) $i = .05$
(ii) The UDD is assumed to hold
(iii) ${}_{10|}\bar{A}_{50} = .245134$ ${}_{10|}\bar{a}_{50} = 6.486$
(iv) $\ell_{50} = 8{,}950{,}994$ $\ell_{60} = 8{,}188{,}132$
$\ell_{74} = 5{,}664{,}157$ $\ell_{75} = 5{,}396{,}186$
$\ell_{78} = 4{,}530{,}476$ $\ell_{79} = 4{,}225{,}258$
$\ell_{80} = 3{,}914{,}448$ $\ell_{81} = 3{,}600{,}118$

Z is the random present value variable for a 10-year deferred insurance of 1 on (50) with benefit payable at death.

Y is the random present value variable for a 10-year deferred continuous life annuity of 1 per year to (50).

29. Which is the correct set of graphs for Y and Z versus T?

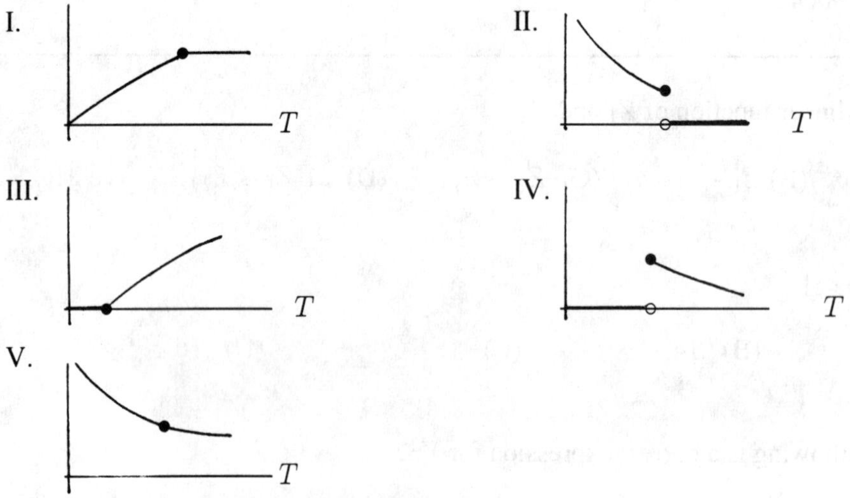

	Z versus T	Y versus T
(A)	II	I
(B)	II	III
(C)	IV	I
(D)	IV	III
(E)	V	III

30. Calculate $Pr(Z > {}_{10|}\bar{A}_{50})$.

(A) .16 (B) .23 (C) .30 (D) .37 (E) .44

31. Calculate the median of Z.

(A) .224 (B) .231 (C) .238 (D) .245 (E) .252

32. Calculate $Pr(Y > {}_{10|}\overline{a}_{50})$.

(A) .56 (B) .61 (C) .66 (D) .71 (E) .76

33. Calculate the median of Y.

(A) 7.20 (B) 7.30 (C) 7.40 (D) 7.50 (E) 7.60

Use the following information for Questions 34 - 36.

Z is the random present value variable of \$1 at the death of (x). Y is the random present value of \$1 per year, continuously to (x) for as long as she lives. You are given that $\mu = .015$, $\delta = .045$.

34. Which of the following is $f_Z(z)$?

(A) $3z^2$, $0 < z \leq 1$

(B) $\frac{1}{3}z^{(1/3)}$, $0 < z \leq 1$

(C) $\left(\frac{1}{3}\right)z^{-(2/3)}$, $0 < z \leq 1$

(D) $\frac{1}{4}z^{-(1/2)}$, $0 < z \leq 1$

(E) $\left(\frac{1}{5}\right)z^{-(4/5)}$, $0 < z \leq 1$

35. Which of the following is $f_Y(y)$?

(A) $.06(1-.06y)^{-1}$ $0 \leq y \leq 20$

(B) $.045(1-.015y)^{-(2/3)}$ $0 \leq y < \infty$

(C) $.015(1-.045y)^{-(2/3)}$ $0 \leq y < \infty$

(D) $.045(1-.015y)^{-(2/3)}$ $0 \leq y \leq \frac{200}{9}$

(E) $.015(1-.045y)^{-(2/3)}$ $0 \leq y \leq \frac{200}{9}$

36. Calculate the median of Y.

(A) 19.25 (B) 19.44 (C) 19.62 (D) 19.80 (E) 19.98

Use the following information for Questions 37 - 39.

A 20-year annual coupon bond pays 60 at the end of each year for the next 20 years and returns the par value of 1000 at maturity. The time until default variable, T, has the exponential density $.01e^{-.01t}$ for $0 \leq t < \infty$.

37. Calculate the probability of default during the 20-year period.

(A) .01 (B) .18 (C) .20 (D) .22 (E) .24

38. Y is the random present value of the bond cashflow at a yield rate of $j = .07$. The price of the bond at a yield of .07 is the actuarial present value of the bond cashflow. The price is closest to which of the following?

(A) 750 (B) 775 (C) 800 (D) 825 (E) 850

39. If the actuarial present value of the bond cashflow is 1000 what rate j is used in discounting the bond cashflow?

(A) .0495 (B) .0515 (C) .0545 (D) .0575 (E) .0600

The following information applies to Questions 40 - 42.

A 15-year loan of \$100,000 is to be amortized by payments at the end of each month for the next 15 years. The rate of interest is $i^{(12)} = .09$. The time (in months) until prepayment variable, K, has a distribution following the CPR model with $CPR = .113615128$. Y is the random present value of the mortgage payments at $i^{(12)} = .12$.

40. If $K = 25$, then calculate Y.

(A) 92,287 (B) 93,329 (C) 94,671 (D) 95,128 (E) 97,143

41. Calculate $Pr(K = k)$.

(A) $.886^{k-1}(.114)$ (B) $.886^{k}(.114)$ (C) $.886(.114)^{k}$ (D) $.9^{k-1}(.1)$ (E) $.99^{k-1}(.01)$

42. Which of the following is a correct expression for $E[Y]$?

(A) $1200.17\sum_{k=1}^{179}(a_{\overline{k}|.01} + a_{\overline{180-k}|.0075}(1.01)^{-k})(.99)^{k-1}(.01) + 12{,}986$

(B) $1200.17\sum_{k=1}^{179}(a_{\overline{k}|.0075} + a_{\overline{180-k}|.0075}(1.01)^{-k})(.99)^{k} + 11{,}384$

(C) $1014.27\sum_{k=1}^{179}(a_{\overline{k}|.0075} + a_{\overline{180-k}|.0075}(1.01)^{-k})(.99)^{k-1}(.01) + 13{,}983$

(D) $10.1427\sum_{k=1}^{179}(a_{\overline{k}|.01} + a_{\overline{180-k}|.0075}(1.01)^{-k})(.99)^{k-1} + 13{,}983$

(E) $1014.27\sum_{k=1}^{179}(a_{\overline{k}|.01} + a_{\overline{180-k}|.0075}(1.01)^{-k})(.99)^{k-1} + 13{,}983$

SOLUTIONS TO UNIT REVIEW QUESTIONS

1. I. $\overline{A}_x = \frac{i}{\delta}A_x = \frac{i}{\delta}(1 - d\ddot{a}_x) = \frac{i}{\delta} - \frac{id}{\delta}\ddot{a}_x$ and $id = i \cdot (1 - v) = i - vi = i - d$. *True*

II. $\overline{A}_{x:\overline{n}|} = \overline{A}^{1}_{x:\overline{n}|} + A_{x:\overline{n}|}^{\;\;\;1} = \frac{i}{\delta}A^{1}_{x:\overline{n}|} + A_{x:\overline{n}|}^{\;\;\;1}$. *False*

III. $(\overline{I}\overline{A})_x = \frac{i}{\delta}(IA)_x + \frac{i}{\delta}\left[\frac{1}{\delta} - \frac{1}{d}\right]A_x$. *False*

II is false since $v_T \neq v^T$ for all T, while III is false since $b_T = T$ is not a function of K. Recall that relations of this type need UDD, $v_T = v^T$ all T, and b_T to be a function of K,

ANSWER B

2. Construct the distribution of the discrete random variable given by the present value of payments. Recall $f_K(k) = {}_{k|}q_x = p_x \cdot p_{x+1} \cdots p_{x+k-1} \cdot q_{x+k}$. If $K = 0$, $PV = 1$ and

${}_{0|}q_x = 1 - p_x = 1 - .8 = .20$. If $K = 1$, $PV = 1 + 2(.9) = 2.8$ and
${}_{1|}q_x = p_x(1 - p_{x+1}) = .8(.25) = .20$. If $K \geq 2$, $PV = 1 + 2(.9) + 3(.9)^2 = 5.23$ and
$Pr(K > 2) = {}_2p_x = .8(.75) = .60$.
$APV = 1(.2) + 2.8(.2) + 5.23(.6) = 3.898$

Thus $\{PV > APV\} = \{K \geq 2\}$ which has probability .6

Event	PV Payments	Prob.
$K = 0$	1	.2
$K = 1$	2.8	.2
$K \geq 2$	5.23	.6

ANSWER D

3. $\overline{A}_x = 1 - \delta\overline{a}_x$, so δ must be computable from the variance information. Recall that if $Y = \overline{a}_{\overline{T}|}$ then $Var(Y) = \frac{2}{\delta}(\overline{a}_x - {}^2\overline{a}_x) - \overline{a}_x^2$: $50 = \frac{2}{\delta}(10 - 7.375) - 10^2 \Rightarrow \delta = .035$. Thus $\overline{A}_x = 1 - \delta\overline{a}_x = 1 - (.035)(10) = 0.65$.

ANSWER D

4. Calculate the distribution of the random p.v. of payments:

Event	Probability	P.V.
$K = 0$	(.2)	2
$K = 1$	(.8)(.25) = .2	$2 + 3(.9) = 4.7$
$K \geq 2$	(.8)(.75) = .6	$2 + 3(.9) + 4(.9)^2 = 7.94$

First Moment $= (.2)\,2 + (.2)(4.7) + (.6)(7.94) = 6.104$
Second Moment $= (.2)\,2^2 + (.2)(4.7)^2 + (.6)(7.94)^2 = 43.044160$
Variance $= 43.044160 - (6.104)^2 = 5.785344$

ANSWER E

5. $\bar{a}_x = E\left[\bar{a}_{\overline{T|}}\middle| Male\right] Pr(Male) + E\left[\bar{a}_{\overline{T|}}\middle| Female\right] Pr(Female)$

$= \bar{a}_x^{Male} \cdot \frac{1}{2} + \bar{a}_x^{Female} \cdot \frac{1}{2} = \frac{1}{2\delta}\left(1 - \bar{A}_x^{Male} + 1 - \bar{A}_x^{Female}\right)$

$= \frac{1}{.2}\left(2 - (.15+.09)\right) = 8.80$

$E\left[\bar{a}_{\overline{T|}}^2\right] = E\left[\bar{a}_{\overline{T|}}^2\middle| Male\right] Pr(Male) + E\left[\bar{a}_{\overline{T|}}^2\middle| Female\right] Pr(Female)$

$= \left(Var(\bar{a}_{\overline{T|}}| Male) + \left(E[\bar{a}_{\overline{T|}}| Male]\right)^2\right)\frac{1}{2} + \left(Var(\bar{a}_{\overline{T|}}| Female) + \left(E[\bar{a}_{\overline{T|}}|Female]\right)^2\right)\frac{1}{2}$

$= 82.03$

$Var(\bar{a}_{\overline{T|}}) = E\left[\bar{a}_{\overline{T|}}^2\right] - E\left[\bar{a}_{\overline{T|}}\right]^2 = 82.03 - 8.80^2 = 4.59$ ANSWER D

Note: Could also be done using $Var(Y) = E[Var(Y|X)] + Var(E[Y|X])$ where $Y = \bar{a}_{\overline{T|}}$ and $X = 0$ for a male or $X = 1$ for a female.

6. Since this holds for all possible force functions consider the case of constant force:

$\bar{a}_x = \int_0^\infty v^t\, {}_tp_x\, dt = \int_0^\infty e^{-\delta t}\, e^{-\mu t}\, dt = \frac{1}{\mu + \delta}$. Thus

$\frac{1}{\mu+\delta} = \bar{a}_x = \bar{a}_x^1 = \frac{1}{\mu^1 + \delta^1} = \frac{1}{\mu^1 + 3\delta}$; $\mu + \delta = \mu^1 + 3\delta$, or $\mu^1 = \mu - 2\delta$.

ANSWER D

7. $Var(Y) = \frac{1}{d^2}\left({}^2A_x - A_x{}^2\right)$. Using $1 = d\ddot{a}_x + A_x$ plus the double-force analogue $1 = (2d - d^2)^2\ddot{a}_x + {}^2A_x$, we obtain $A_x = 1 - d\ddot{a}_x = 1 - \frac{1}{25}(10) = .6\left(i = \frac{1}{n} \Rightarrow d = \frac{1}{n+1}\right)$, and ${}^2A_x = 1 - \left(\frac{2}{25} - \frac{1}{25^2}\right)(6) = .5296$. Thus $Var(Y) = \frac{1}{\left(\frac{1}{25}\right)^2}(.5296 - .6^2) = 106$

ANSWER D

8. $\int_0^n \bar{a}_{\overline{t|}}\, {}_tp_x \mu(x+t)\, dt = \frac{1}{\delta}\int_0^n (1 - v^t)\, {}_tp_x \mu(x+t) dt = \frac{1}{\delta}\left[\, {}_nq_x - \bar{A}^{1}_{x:\overline{n|}}\,\right]$ (NOT D)

$= \frac{1}{\delta}\left[1 - {}_np_x - 1 + \delta\bar{a}_{x:\overline{n|}} + {}_nE_x\right]$

$= \frac{1}{\delta}\left[\delta\bar{a}_{x:\overline{n|}} - {}_np_x(1 - v^n)\right]$

$= \bar{a}_{x:\overline{n|}} - {}_np_x \cdot \bar{a}_{\overline{n|}}$ (NOT A)

$= \frac{1 - \bar{A}_{x:\overline{n|}}}{\delta} - {}_np_x \cdot \bar{a}_{\overline{n|}}$ (NOT C)

Clearly (B) produces $\bar{a}_{\overline{n|}} - \bar{a}_{x:\overline{n|}}$, which can also be eliminated. ANSWER E

9. With a constant force of mortality, $\overline{A}_x = \frac{\mu}{\mu+\delta} = \frac{1}{5}$ and ${}^2\overline{A}_x = \frac{\mu}{\mu+2\delta} = \frac{1}{9}$. Thus

$$\begin{aligned}\frac{100}{9} &= Var(\bar{a}_{\overline{T}|}) = Var\left(\frac{1-v^T}{\delta}\right)\\ &= \frac{1}{\delta^2}\cdot Var(v^T) = \frac{1}{\delta^2}\left({}^2\overline{A}_x - \overline{A}_x{}^2\right)\\ &= \frac{1}{16k^2}\left(\frac{1}{9}-\frac{1}{25}\right) = \frac{16}{16k^2\cdot 9\cdot 25},\end{aligned}$$

or

$$k^2 = \frac{9}{100\cdot 9\cdot 25} = \left(\frac{1}{50}\right)^2,\ k = .02,$$ ANSWER D

10. For completeness we illustrate both the aggregate payment and current payment method.

Aggregate Payment

If $K \geq 3$ then the maximum 4-payments have been made. From the table

$$Pr(K\geq 3) = 1 - Pr(K=0,1,2) = 1-({}_{0|}q_x + {}_{1|}q_x + {}_{2|}q_x) = 1-(.33+.24+.16) = .27.$$

So

$$\begin{aligned}\ddot{a}_{x:\overline{4}|} &= \ddot{a}_{\overline{1}|}\cdot {}_{0|}q_x + \ddot{a}_{\overline{2}|}\cdot {}_{1|}q_x + \ddot{a}_{\overline{3}|}\cdot {}_{2|}q_x + \ddot{a}_{\overline{4}|}\cdot Pr(K\geq 3)\\ &= 1(.33) + 1.93(.24) + 2.80(.16) + 3.62(.27)\\ &= 2.219,\end{aligned}$$ ANSWER D

Current Payment

From $1.93 = \ddot{a}_{\overline{2}|} = 1+v$ it follows that $v = .93$. Also ${}_0p_x = 1$, ${}_1p_x = 1 - {}_{0|}q_x = 1 - .33 = .67$, ${}_2p_x = 1 - {}_2q_x = 1 - {}_{0|}q_x - {}_{1|}q_x = .43$, ${}_3p_x = 1 - {}_3q_x = 1 - (.33+.24+.16) = .27$. Hence

$$\begin{aligned}\ddot{a}_{x:\overline{4}|} &= 1 + v\cdot {}_1p_x + v^2\cdot {}_2p_x + v^3\cdot {}_3p_x\\ &= 1 + (.93)(.67) + (.93)^2(.43) + (.93)^3(.27) = 2.212,\end{aligned}$$ ANSWER D

11. Using $\bar{a}_{\overline{T}|} = \frac{1-v^T}{\delta}$ and properties of covariance

$$\begin{aligned}Cov\left(\bar{a}_{\overline{T}|}, v^T\right) &= Cov\left(\frac{1-v^T}{\delta}, v^T\right)\\ &= \frac{1}{\delta}Cov\left(1-v^T, v^T\right)\\ &= \frac{1}{\delta}\left[Cov\left(1, v^T\right) - Cov\left(v^T, v^T\right)\right]\\ &= \frac{1}{\delta}[0 - Var(v^T)] = -\frac{1}{\delta}\left[{}^2\overline{A}_x - \overline{A}_x{}^2\right],\end{aligned}$$ ANSWER A

12. Since Y is a function of T, its expected value can be computed as the integral of Y times the T-density:

$$E[Y] = \int_0^n \bar{a}_{\overline{n}|} \cdot f_T(t)\, dt + \int_n^{\omega-x} \bar{a}_{\overline{t}|} \cdot f_T(t)\, dt$$

The second integral is close to the integral form for the deferred annuity

$$_{n|}\bar{a}_x = \int_n^{\omega-x} (\bar{a}_{\overline{t}|} - \bar{a}_{\overline{n}|}) \cdot f_T(t)\, dt,$$

which can be rewritten to yield

$$\int_n^{\omega-x} \bar{a}_{\overline{t}|} \cdot f_T(t)\, dt = {}_{n|}\bar{a}_x + \int_n^{\omega-x} \bar{a}_{\overline{n}|} \cdot f_T(t)\, dt$$

$$= {}_{n|}\bar{a}_x + \bar{a}_{\overline{n}|} \cdot \underbrace{Pr(n \le T \le \omega - x)}_{_n p_x}.$$

Substituting this relation into the first equation and noting that

$$\int_0^n \bar{a}_{\overline{n}|} \cdot f_T(t)\, dt = \bar{a}_{\overline{n}|} \cdot {}_n q_x,$$

we see that $E[Y] = \bar{a}_{\overline{n}|} + {}_{n|}\bar{a}_x$, ANSWER C

Note: The benefit described by Y is a continuous life annuity to (x) with the first n years being guaranteed (i.e., not life contingent). If this is recognized then ANSWER C is intuitively clear with no work required.

13. Under de Moivre's law with $\omega = 100$, $\ell_x = \omega - x = 100 - x$. Thus $_tp_{60} = \ell_{60+t}/\ell_{60} = (40-t)/40$. The number of payments in terms of the curtate future lifetime K of (60) is zero if $K \le 9$ and is $K - 9$ if $K \ge 10$. This can be seen since if $K \ge 10$ there are $K+1$ years that (60) begins with no payment received on the first 10 beginnings:

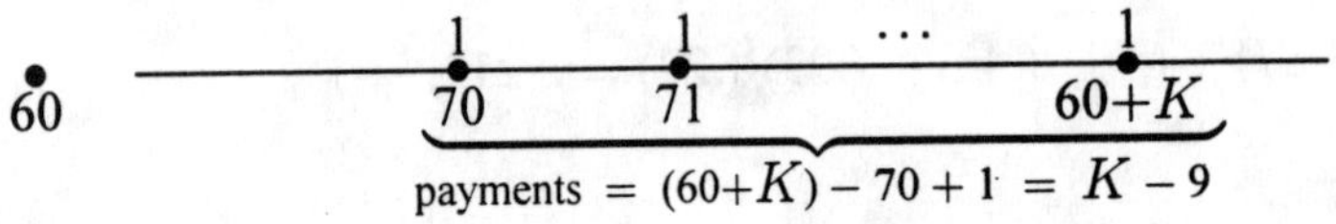

Using the 3-factor approach to the annuity APV (see Appendix 1 of this section of this manual)

$$_{10|}\ddot{a}_{60} = \sum_{k=10}^{40} \underbrace{1}_{\text{amount}} \cdot \underbrace{\frac{40-k}{40}}_{\text{prob.}} \cdot \underbrace{1}_{\substack{\text{discount}\\(i=0)}} = \frac{30+29+\cdots+1}{40} = \frac{(30)(31)}{(2)(40)} = 11.63.$$

Hence

$$Pr(\underbrace{K-9}_{\text{payments}} > \underbrace{11.63}_{APV}) = Pr(\underbrace{K}_{\text{integer}} > 20.63)$$

$$= Pr(K \ge 21) = Pr(T \ge 21) = \frac{\ell_{81}}{\ell_{60}} = \frac{19}{40} = .475,$$

ANSWER A

14. Writing $\overline{a}_{\overline{T(x)}|} = \dfrac{1-v^{T(x)}}{\delta} = \dfrac{1-e^{-\delta T(x)}}{\delta}$, we see that

$20 < \overline{a}_{\overline{T(x)}|} \quad \Leftrightarrow \quad e^{-\delta T(x)} < 1 - 20\delta = 1 - 20(.03) = .40$

$\Leftrightarrow \quad -\delta T(x) < ln(.40) \quad \Leftrightarrow \quad T(x) > -ln(.40)/.03.$

Since we are given constant force of mortality $\mu = -.024/ln(.40)$, we know that the distribution of $T(x)$ is exponential with parameter μ. Hence

$$\begin{aligned} Pr(\overline{a}_{\overline{T(x)}|} > 20) &= Pr(T(x) > -ln(.40)/.03 = a) \\ &= \int_a^\infty f_T(t)dt = \int_a^\infty \mu e^{-\mu t}dt = e^{-\mu a} \\ &= e^{-.8} = .449 \left(\text{note: } \mu a = \frac{.024}{ln(.40)} \cdot \frac{ln(.40)}{.030}\right) \end{aligned}$$

ANSWER A

15. I is a standard UDD relation. II is simply never correct; it should read $\overline{a}_x = \overline{a}_{x:\overline{1}|} + vp_x\overline{a}_{x+1}$. III is another standard UDD relation. (In general, any correct relation involving $\alpha(m)$, $\beta(m)$ must assume the UDD.) IV is generally true with no interpolation assumption needed. ANSWER E

16. From the definitions it follows that $E[Y] = \ddot{a}_x$, $E[Z] = \ddot{a}_{x:\overline{n}|}$. So $E[Y] - E[Z] = {}_{n|}\ddot{a}_x$. The rest of the solution is identity manipulation:

$$\ddot{a}_x = \frac{1-A_x}{d} = \frac{1-.20755}{\left(\frac{6}{106}\right)} = 14$$

$$\ddot{a}_{x:\overline{n}|} = 1 + a_{x:\overline{n-1}|} = 7$$

$$\Rightarrow \quad {}_{n|}\ddot{a}_x = 14 - 7 = 7$$

ANSWER D

17. Y is the random present value variable for a 3-year temporary, annuity-due of \$1/year. From a standard relation $Var(Y) = \dfrac{({}^2A_{30:\overline{3}|} - A_{30:\overline{3}|}^{\;2})}{d^2}$:

$$A_{30:\overline{3}|} = vq_{30} + v^2\,{}_{1|}q_{30} + \underbrace{v^3\,{}_{2|}q_{30} + v^3\,{}_3p_{30}}_{v^3\,{}_2p_{30}}$$

$$= \left(\frac{1}{1.05}\right)\left(\frac{1}{50}\right) + \left(\frac{1}{1.05}\right)^2\left(\frac{1}{50}\right) + \left(\frac{1}{1.05}\right)^3\left(\frac{48}{50}\right) = .8665$$

$${}^2A_{30:\overline{3}|} = v^2q_{30} + v^4\,{}_{1|}q_{30} + v^6\,{}_2p_{30} = .7510$$

$$\Rightarrow \quad Var(Y) = (21)^2[.7510 - .8665^2] = .0825.$$

ANSWER A

18. You are given $17.287 = \ddot{a}^{(4)}_{\overline{\infty}|} = \frac{1}{d^{(4)}}$. Using this along with a standard UDD identity

$$1 = d^{(4)}\ddot{a}^{(4)}_x + A^{(4)}_x \underset{\text{UDD}}{=} d^{(4)}\ddot{a}^{(4)}_x + \left(\frac{i}{i^{(4)}}\right)A_x$$

$$d^{(4)} = \frac{1}{17.287} = .0578,\ i = .06,\ i^{(4)} = .0587$$

$$\Rightarrow \ddot{a}^{(4)}_x = 15.476.$$

ANSWER A

19. With constant force ${}_kp_x = e^{-\mu k}$ and

$$\ddot{a}_x = \sum_{k=0}^{\infty} 1 \cdot v^k \cdot {}_kp_x = \sum_{k=0}^{\infty} e^{-k\delta}e^{-k\mu} = \sum_{k=0}^{\infty}(e^{-(\mu+\delta)})^k = \frac{1}{1-e^{-(\mu+\delta)}}$$
$$= \frac{e^{\delta}}{e^{\delta} - e^{-\mu}} = \frac{1.04}{1.04 - e^{-.01}} = 20.82.$$

So ${}_5|\ddot{a}_x = \ddot{a}_x - \ddot{a}_{x:\overline{5}|} = 20.82 - 4.54 = 16.28$. Thus $Pr(S > 16.28) = Pr(S \geq 17)$. Since this is a 5-year deferred annuity, (x) must survive to age $x + 5 + (17-1) = x + 21$ in order to collect at least 17 payments. The probability sought is ${}_{21}p_x = e^{-21\mu} = .81$. ANSWER A

20 - 23
From the description

$$Z = \underbrace{1000\bar{a}_{\overline{T}|}}_{\text{annuity}} + \underbrace{5000v^T}_{\text{death benefit}} = 1000\left[\frac{1-v^T}{\delta} + 5v^T\right] = 20{,}496 - 15{,}496v^T$$

Question 20 has ANSWER A.

Since $E[v^T] = \overline{A}_{30} = \frac{i}{\delta}A_{30}$ (due to UDD) we have from the given information

$$E[Z] = 20{,}496 - 15{,}496\overline{A}_{30} = 20{,}496 - 15{,}496\underbrace{(1.0248)(.14011)}_{\text{UDD}} = 18{,}271.$$

Question 21 has ANSWER C.

From $Z = 20{,}496 - 15{,}496v^T$ we see $Var(Z) = (15{,}496)^2({}^2\overline{A}_{30} - \overline{A}_{30}{}^2)$ where ${}^2\overline{A}_{30}$ is calculated by doubling the force in the UDD relation $\overline{A}_{30} = \left(\frac{i}{\delta}\right)A_{30}$:

$${}^2\overline{A}_{30} = \left(\frac{{}^2i}{2\delta}\right){}^2A_{30} = \left(\frac{2i+i^2}{2\delta}\right){}^2A_{30} = \left(\frac{.1025}{.09758}\right)(.03641) = .038246$$

$$\Rightarrow Var(Z) = 4{,}233{,}217.$$

So Question 22 has ANSWER B and Question 23 has ANSWER C.

24 - 28

Instead of using Y for every annuity and Z for every insurance it makes sense to use the accouterments of the APV notations with the "$\ddot{a}$" and "A" APV notation. Relations such as $1 = d\ddot{a}_{40} + A_{40}$ are the result of taking expected value of relations like

$$1 = d\ddot{Y}_{40} + Z_{40}$$

$$\ddot{Y}_{40} = \ddot{a}_{\overline{K+1}|}, \qquad Z_{40} = v^{K+1}.$$

Since ${}_{10|}\ddot{a}_{40} = \ddot{a}_{40} - \ddot{a}_{40:\overline{10}|}$ we would have

$$Y = {}_{10|}\ddot{Y}_{40} = \ddot{Y}_{40} - \ddot{Y}_{40:\overline{10}|}.$$

Also $\ddot{a}_{40} = \dfrac{1 - A_{40}}{d}$ and $\ddot{a}_{40:\overline{10}|} = \dfrac{1 - A_{40:\overline{10}|}}{d}$ would have parallel relations

$$\ddot{Y}_{40} = \frac{1 - Z_{40}}{d} \text{ and } \ddot{Y}_{40:\overline{10}|} = \frac{1 - Z_{40:\overline{10}|}}{d}, \text{ respectively.}$$

Thus

$$Y = \ddot{Y}_{40} - \ddot{Y}_{40:\overline{10}|} = \frac{Z_{40:\overline{10}|} - Z_{40}}{d} = 21(Z_2 - Z_1),$$

since $i = .05 = 1/20$ means $d = 1/21$.

Question 24 has ANSWER E.

Next,

$$Z_1 = v^{K+1}, Z_2 = \begin{cases} v^{K+1} & K \le 9 \\ v^{10} & K \ge 10 \end{cases}$$

means

$$Z_1 Z_2 = \begin{cases} (v^2)^{K+1} & K \le 9 \\ v^{10} v^{K+1} & K \ge 10 \end{cases} = \begin{cases} (v^2)^{K+1} \\ 0 \end{cases} + v^{10} \begin{cases} 0 \\ v^{K+1} \end{cases}.$$

Taking expected values $E[Z_1 Z_2] = {}^2A^{\;1}_{40:\overline{10}|} + v^{10} \cdot {}_{10|}A_{40}$.

Now, from the given data

$$v^{10} \cdot {}_{10|}A_{40} = \frac{1}{1.05^{10}}(.178809) = .10977$$

$$\begin{aligned} {}^2A^{\;1}_{40:\overline{10}|} &= {}^2A_{40} - {}_{10|}{}^2A_{40} \\ &= {}^2A_{40} - v^{20}\, {}_{10}p_{40} \cdot {}^2A_{50} \\ &= .06741 - \left(\frac{1}{1.05^{10}} \cdot .590041\right)(.12446) = .02233 \end{aligned}$$

From the above $E[Z_1 Z_2]$ is the sum of these numbers, $.10977 + .02233 = .13210$.

Question 25 has ANSWER A

In general

$$Y = {}_{10|}\ddot{Y}_{40} = \begin{cases} 0 & K \le 9 \\ \ddot{a}_{\overline{K+1|}} - \ddot{a}_{\overline{10|}} & K \ge 10 \end{cases}$$

and $\ddot{a}_{\overline{K+1|}} - \ddot{a}_{\overline{10|}} = (v^{10} - v^{K+1})/d = 21(v^{10} - v^{K+1})$. So

$$Y^2 = 441\begin{cases} 0 & K \le 9 \\ v^{20} - 2v^{10}v^{K+1} + (v^2)^{K+1} & K \ge 10 \end{cases}.$$

Question 26 has ANSWER B.

Taking expected values of the last relation spread out into 3 terms gives

$$E[Y^2] = 441[v^{20} \cdot {}_{10}p_{40} - 2v^{10} \cdot {}_{10|}A_{40} + {}^2{}_{10|}A_{40}]$$

$$= 441\left[\frac{1}{1.05^{10}}(.590041) - \frac{2}{1.05^{10}}(.178809) + .04508\right] = 82.80.$$

Question 27 has ANSWER E.

Since $E[Y] = {}_{10|}\ddot{a}_{40} = v^{10}\, {}_{10}p_{40}\ddot{a}_{50} = 8.635871$ (substituting from given information) we see that

$$Var(Y) = E[Y^2] - (E[Y])^2 = 82.80 - (8.635871)^2 = 8.229.$$

Question 28 has ANSWER B.

29 - 33.
For the given insurance and annuity

$$Z = \begin{cases} 0 & T \le 10 \\ v^T & T > 10 \end{cases} \quad \text{and} \quad Y = \begin{cases} 0 & T \le 10 \\ \bar{a}_{\overline{T|}} - \bar{a}_{\overline{10|}} & T > 10 \end{cases}$$

where $T = T(50)$ is the future lifetime of (50). The graphs look like the following:

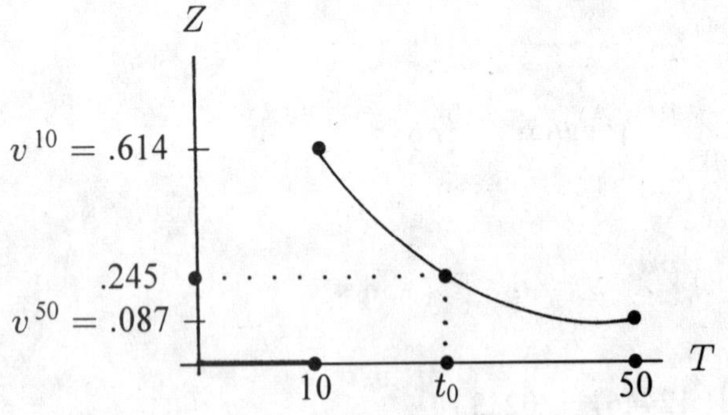

and

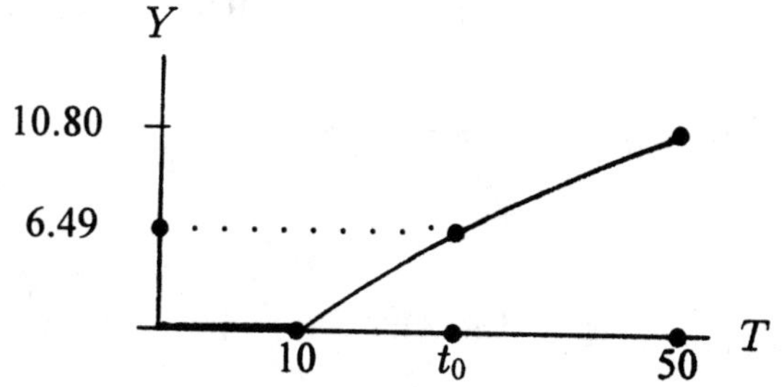

where $\bar{a}_{\overline{50}|} - \bar{a}_{\overline{10}|} = (v^{10} - v^{50})/\delta = 10.7954.$

Question 29 has ANSWER D.

From the graph above of Z versus T, we see that the event $Z > {}_{10|}\bar{A}_{50} = .245134$ is equivalent to the event $10 < T < t_0$, where $.245134 = v^{t_0}$.

This results in $t_0 = -ln(.245134)/\delta = 28.82$. Hence

$$Pr(Z > {}_{10|}\bar{A}_{50}) = Pr(10 < T < 28.82) = \frac{\ell_{60} - \ell_{78.82}}{\ell_{50}} = \frac{\ell_{60} - (\ell_{78} - .82d_{78})}{\ell_{50}} \underset{\text{UDD}}{=} .437.$$

Question 30 has ANSWER E.

The median of Z is a bit tricky due to the graph of Z versus T. It is the value $z_1 = v^{t_1}$ where

$$.50 = Pr(10 < T < t_1) = \frac{\ell_{60} - \ell_{50+t_1}}{\ell_{50}}$$

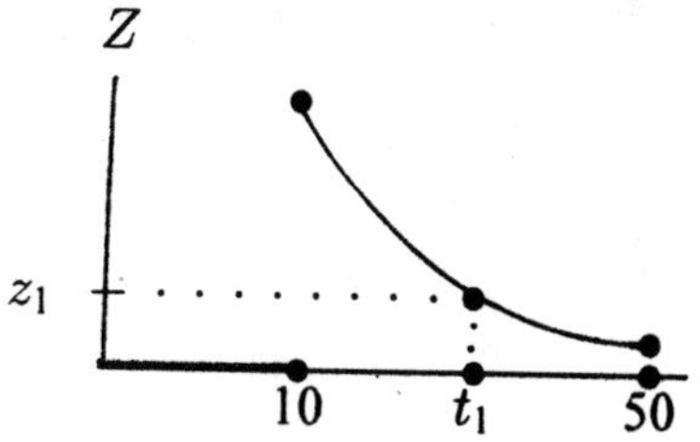

since the picture makes it clear that $Z > z_1$ is equivalent to $10 < T < t_1$. So

$$\ell_{50+t_1} = -\tfrac{1}{2}\ell_{50} + \ell_{60} = 3{,}712{,}635$$

$$\left.\begin{array}{l}\ell_{80} = 3{,}914{,}448 \\ \ell_{81} = 3{,}600{,}118\end{array}\right\} d_{80} = 314{,}330$$

$$\therefore \text{ UDD } \Rightarrow \quad 50 + t_1 = 80 + \frac{3{,}914{,}448 - 3{,}712{,}635}{314{,}330} = 80.642$$

$$\Rightarrow \quad t_1 = 30.642 \quad \Rightarrow \quad z_1 = (1.05)^{-30.642} = .224242.$$

Question 31 has ANSWER A.

From the graph of Y versus T we see that the event $Y > {}_{10|}\bar{a}_{50} = 6.486$ is equivalent to the event $T > t_0$ where

$$6.486 = \bar{a}_{\overline{t_0}|} - \bar{a}_{\overline{10}|} = \frac{v^{10} - v^{t_0}}{\delta}$$

$\therefore\ v^{t_0} = .297458,\ t_0 = 24.85$. Hence

$$Pr(Y > 6.486) = Pr(T > 24.85) = \frac{\ell_{74.85}}{\ell_{50}} = \frac{\ell_{74} - .85d_{74}}{\ell_{50}} = .607 \quad \text{(UDD)}$$

Question 32 has ANSWER B.

The median of Y is straightforward. It is the value $y_1 = \bar{a}_{\overline{t_1}|} - \bar{a}_{\overline{10}|}$ where $.50 = Pr(T < t_1)$,

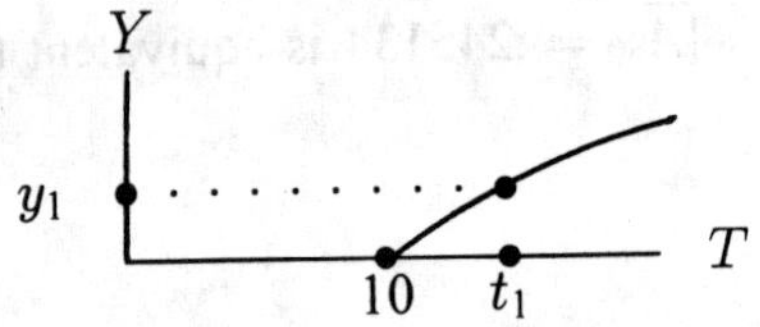

that is, t_1 it the median of T.

$$.50 = Pr(T > t_1) = \frac{\ell_{50+t_1}}{\ell_{50}},\ \ell_{50} = 8{,}950{,}994$$

$\Rightarrow\quad \ell_{50+t_1} = 4{,}475{,}497$

$$\left.\begin{matrix}\ell_{78} = 4{,}530{,}476\\ \ell_{79} = 4{,}225{,}258\end{matrix}\right\} d_{78} = 305{,}218$$

$$\therefore \text{UDD} \Rightarrow \quad 50 + t_1 = 78 + \frac{4{,}530{,}476 - 4{,}475{,}497}{305{,}218} = 78.18$$

$$\Rightarrow y_1 = \bar{a}_{\overline{28.18}|} - \bar{a}_{\overline{10}|} = \frac{v^{10} - v^{28.18}}{\delta} = 7.40.$$

Question 33 has ANSWER C.

34 - 36.

With constant force we saw in Unit 1 of this section that $f_Z(z) = \left(\frac{\mu}{\delta}\right) z^{(\mu/\delta)-1}$ for $v^{\omega - x} \le z \le 1$. Here $\left(\frac{\mu}{\delta}\right) = \left(\frac{1}{3}\right)$ so Question 34 has ANSWER C. Note $v^\infty = 0$.

$Y = \bar{a}_{\overline{T}|} = \frac{1 - v^T}{\delta} = \frac{1 - Z}{\delta}$ so $Z = 1 - \delta Y$. Hence $f_Y(y) = f_Z(1 - \delta y)\left|\frac{\partial z}{\partial y}\right| = f_Z(1 - \delta y) \cdot \delta$. Since $f_Z(z) = \left(\frac{1}{3}\right) z^{(-2/3)}\ 0 < z \le 1$, we must have $f_Y(y) = \frac{1}{3}(1 - .045y)^{(-2/3)}(.045) = .015(1 - .045y)^{-(2/3)}$. Also $Y = \bar{a}_{\overline{T}|}$ so $0 = \bar{a}_{\overline{0}|} \le Y \le \bar{a}_{\overline{\infty}|} = \frac{1}{\delta} = \frac{200}{9}$.

Question 35 has ANSWER E.

From the density expression in Question 35 it easily follows that $s_Y(y) = (1 - .045y)^{(1/3)}$ for $0 \le y \le \frac{1}{.045}$. Solving $s_Y(y_{med}) = .5$ results in $y_{med} = \frac{1 - .5^3}{.045} = 19.44$.

Question 36 has ANSWER B.

37 - 39.
The probability of default is $Pr(T \le 20) = 1 - Pr(T > 20) = 1 - e^{-20(.01)} = .1813$.

Question 37 has ANSWER B.

By the current payment method the actuarial present value is given by

$$\underbrace{\sum_{k=1}^{20} 60 \cdot \left(\tfrac{1}{1.07}\right)^k \cdot Pr(T > k)}_{\text{amount}\cdot\text{discount}\cdot\text{probability}} + 1000\left(\tfrac{1}{1.07}\right)^{20} \cdot Pr(T > 20) = \sum_{k=1}^{20} 60 \cdot \left(\frac{1}{1.07e^{.01}}\right)^k + \frac{1000}{(1.07e^{.01})^{20}}$$

$$= 60a_{\overline{20}|.08075} + \frac{1000}{1.08075^{20}}$$

$$= 797.38.$$

Question 38 has ANSWER C.

Note: The final calculation is possible with the calculator annuity keys.

$1000 = \sum_{k=1}^{20} 60 \cdot \left(\frac{1}{1+j}\right)^k \cdot e^{-.01k} + 1000\left(\frac{1}{1+j}\right)^{20} e^{-.20}$ means $(1+j)e^{.01} = 1.06$ (the coupon rate is also .06) Thus $1+j = 1.06e^{-.01} = 1.0495$.

Question 39 has ANSWER A.

40 - 42.
First we need to determine the monthly payment $P = \frac{100{,}000}{a_{\overline{180}|.0075}} = 1014.27$. If $K = 25$ then $Y = 1014.27a_{\overline{25}|.01} + \frac{1014.27a_{\overline{155}|.0075}}{1.01^{25}} = 94{,}671$.

Question 40 has ANSWER C.

If q is the constantly monthly "mortality" rate $(1 - q)^{12} = 1 - CPR = 1 - .113615128$. This solves for $q = .01$. Thus $Pr(K = k) = {}_{k|}q_0 = p^{k-1}q = .99^{k-1}(.01)$.

Question 41 has ANSWER E.

In general

$$Y = \begin{cases} 1014.27[a_{\overline{k}|.01} + a_{\overline{180-k}|.0075}(1.01)^{-k}] & k = 1, 2, \ldots, 179 \\ 1014.27a_{\overline{180}|.01} & k = 180, 181, \ldots \end{cases}$$

Thus with $Pr(K = k) = .99^{k-1}(.01)$ we have

$$E[Y] = 1014.27\sum_{k=1}^{179}[a_{\overline{k}|.01} + a_{\overline{180-k}|.0075}(1.01)^{-k}](.99)^{k-1}(.01) + 1014.27a_{\overline{180}|.01}(.99)^{179}.$$

In the above we used $Pr(K \geq 180) = p^{179}q + p^{180}q + \cdots = p^{179}$ (geometric series). Also, the final term $1014.27a_{\overline{180}|.01}(.99)^{179} = 13{,}983.31$.

Question 42 has ANSWER D.

UNIT 3: BENEFIT PREMIUMS

Introduction

In the individual life insurance models of Units 1-4 there are two contingent cashflows to balance; the outflow of the insurer (just benefits) and his inflow (premiums sufficient to cover benefits plus, perhaps, a security loading). Unit 1 was concerned with valuing the benefit side of the equation and Unit 2 with the premium side (if premiums were paid annually or semi-annually rather than as a lump sum at issue). In Unit 3 we put the results together to determine net level annual premiums and several variations. There are three categories of models based on assumptions as to when benefits are paid and how frequently premiums are paid:

	Assumptions	
Model Category	Time of Death Benefits	Pattern of Premium Payment
fully discrete	policy anniversary following death	annual, annuity due
semi-continuous	at death	annual, annuity due
fully continuous	at death	continuous life annuity

The fully discrete case gets its name from the fact that both the present value of benefit variable, $Z = v^{K+1}$, and the present value of premium variable, $P \cdot Y = P\ddot{a}_{\overline{K+1}|}$ ($P =$ annual amount), are functions of the discrete variable K. In the semi-continuous case the present value of premium variable is the same, but the present value of benefit variable $Z = v^T$, is a function of the continuous variable T. And, of course, in the fully continuous model both $Z = v^T$ and $P \cdot Y = P\bar{a}_{\overline{T}|}$ are functions of T. Before reading the rest of this material, it might be useful to read Appendix 3 in this section of the manual - a numerical example illustrating the essential ideas of Units 3 and 4.

Fully Discrete Whole Life: The Aggregate Deterministic Approach

We begin with a survival model in the form of a table of values ℓ_x, ℓ_{x+1}, ..., ℓ_ω and a rate of interest i earned by the insurer on investments. We assume that all lives in the table simultaneously purchase a fully discrete whole life plan at age x. They pay annual premiums P at the beginning of each policy year for which they are surviving, and the insurer pays \$1 on the policy anniversary after death to a beneficiary. As determinists we are entitled to full cooperation of the group; there will be exactly d_x,

$d_{x+1}, \ldots$ deaths at ages (last birthday) x, $x+1$, ..., and hence exactly ℓ_{x+1}, $\ell_{x+2}\ldots$ survivors at ages $x+1$, $x+2$, ... Thus the insurer's aggregate cashflow is that in the diagram below:

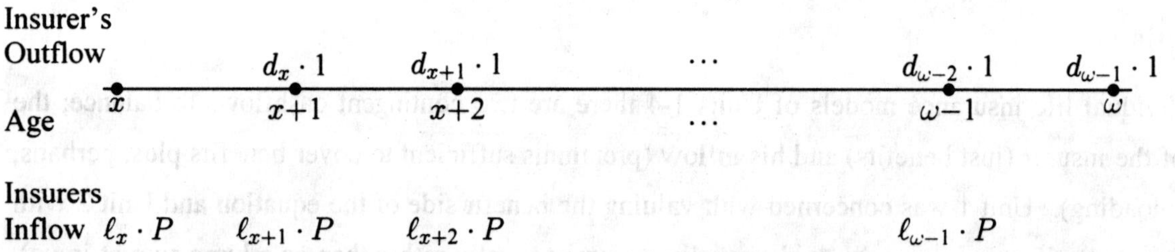

P is called the net level annual premium or annual benefit premium (denoted P_x in standard actuarial notation) if the present value (at rate i) of the insurer's inflow and outflow match:

$$\ell_x \cdot P_x \cdot v^0 + \ell_{x+1} \cdot P_x \cdot v^1 + \cdots + \ell_{\omega-1} \cdot P_x \cdot v^{\omega-x-1} = d_x \cdot 1 \cdot v^1 + d_{x+1} \cdot 1 \cdot v^2 + \cdots + d_{\omega-1} \cdot 1 \cdot v^{\omega-x}$$

Think of the premiums as deposits into an account earning an effective annual rate i, and the benefits as withdrawals. At the start of each year, the premium is deposited. Interest is earned until year end, when benefits are withdrawn. The fact that the present values of deposits and withdrawals match implies that the account balance hits zero at age ω when the final death benefits are paid out. So P_x is such that the insurer will exactly break even in the long run on a group of identical issues: (See example 1 to follow here.)

Lets take a little closer look at the net premium equation above in order to express P_x in terms of familiar quantities. Divide both sides by ℓ_x. Recall that

$$\frac{\ell_{x+k}}{\ell_x} = {}_kp_x, \qquad \frac{d_{x+k}}{\ell_x} = {}_{k|}q_x.$$

Factoring P_x out of the left side gives

$$P_x\underbrace{\left(1 + vp_x + v^2\,{}_2p_x + \ldots\right)}_{\substack{\ddot{a}_x \\ \text{(Unit 2)}}} = \underbrace{\left(v \cdot {}_{0|}q_x + v^2 \cdot {}_{1|}q_x + \ldots\right)}_{\substack{A_x \\ \text{(Unit 1)}}},$$

so

$$P_x = \frac{A_x}{\ddot{a}_x},$$

a typical expression for a net level annual premium in terms of standard actuarial APV symbols.

Example 1 Suppose $i = .06$ and all 100 nanoes in the table below buy \$1000 of fully discrete whole life, paying net level annual premiums $1000P_{90}$ at the beginning of each policy year. Find $1000P_{90}$ to the nearest penny and illustrate the aggregate accounting in a table to show how the insurer breaks even after three years.

x	90	91	92	93
ℓ_x	100	72	39	0
d_x	28	33	39	—

Solution If the benefit were 1 then the net level annual premium is

$$P_{90} = \frac{A_{90}}{\ddot{a}_{90}} = \underset{\text{(common shortcut)}}{\frac{A_{90}}{(1-A_{90})/d}} = \underset{\text{(see Example 5 of Unit 1 notes)}}{\frac{6}{106}\,\frac{.885301}{(1-.885301)}} = .436895.$$

For a \$1000 face value the net level annual premium is $1000P_{90} = 436.90$ (rounded *up* to the nearest penny). The year by year aggregate accounting is given in the table below:

Policy Year	Beginning Fund Balance	New Premium (+)	Annual Interest (+)	Annual Benefits (−)	Ending Balance
1	0	43,690.00	2621.40	28,000	18,311.40
2	18,311.40	31,456.80	2986.09	33,000	19,754.29
3	19,754.29	17,039.10	2207.60	39,000	1.00

In the first row 43,690 is $\ell_{90} \cdot 1000P_{90}$ and 2621.40 is 6% of new premium. Twenty eight deaths occur, reducing the balance by 28,000 to 18,311.40 at year end, which is available to start year 2. In the second row 31,456.80 is $\ell_{91} \cdot 1000P_{90}$ and 2986.09 is 6% of the beginning balance plus new premium, which is invested for the entire year. Thirty three deaths reduce the fund to 19,754.29 at the end of year two. Reason your way through the 3rd year by yourself. Why is there 1 left over at the end of year three? Answer: It is an accumulation of the rounded-up $\frac{1}{2}$ cent "profit" in each premium. This number should theoretically be zero (with no rounding). □

Fully Discrete Whole Life: The Loss Function Approach

Suppose again we have a tabular model of survival, i.e., ℓ_x, ℓ_{x+1}, ..., and a rate of interest i earned by the insurer on invested funds. Here we begin by considering a single issue of \$1 of fully discrete whole life to (x). If P is a level annual premium paid as an annuity due by (x), then the insurer's cashflow is

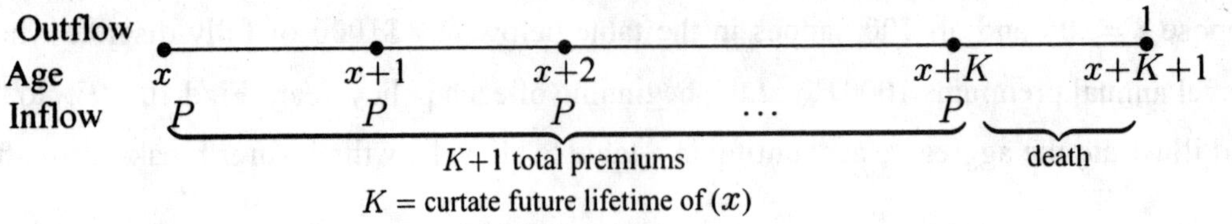

The new concept here is the idea of the insurer's loss function on an individual contract:

$$L = \underbrace{L_K}_{\text{Insurer's Loss}} = \text{Random present value at age } x \text{ of outflow less inflow}$$

$$= \underbrace{1 \cdot v^{K+1}}_{\text{present value of outflow}} - \underbrace{P \cdot \ddot{a}_{\overline{K+1}|}}_{\text{present value of inflow}} \qquad \text{(Form 1)}$$

$$= v^{K+1} - P \cdot \frac{1-v^{K+1}}{d}$$

$$= \left(1 + \frac{P}{d}\right) v^{K+1} - \frac{P}{d} \qquad \text{(Form 2)}$$

A positive value for L indicates the insurer lost money on the contract, whereas a negative value for L indicates the insurer profited (present value of profit $= |L|$). Since v^{K+1} is a decreasing function of K (recall $v < 1$) so is L_K. A typical graph of L verses K is illustrated in the figure below. The loss is non-negative if $K \leq k_0$,

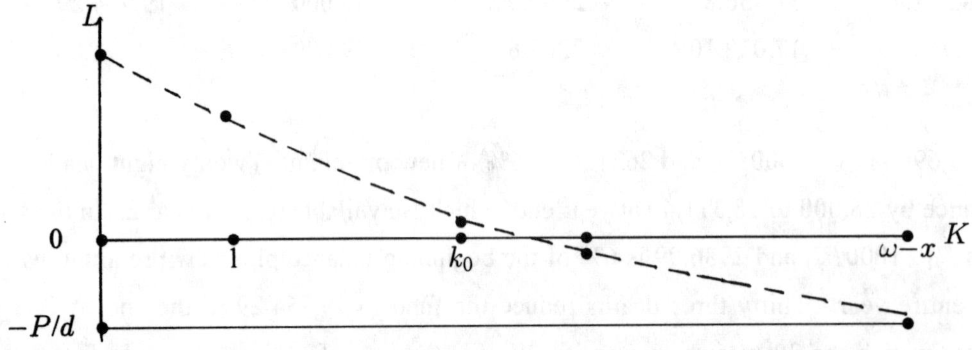

that is, (x) dies "early." On the other hand, if (x) dies "late" ($K \geq k_0+1$) the insurer profits. Because L is a function of the discrete variable K, events in terms of L can be converted to K events for probability calculation. For example, from the graph, $L \geq 0$ is equivalent to $K \leq k_0$. Hence the probability of a non-negative loss is

$$Pr(K \leq k_0) = Pr(T < k_0+1) = {}_{k_0+1}q_x \,.$$

The value of k_0 can be determined as $[k]$ (greatest integer) where $0 = L_k = \left(1+\frac{P}{d}\right) v^{\,k+1} - \frac{P}{d}$, or equivalently by

$$k_0 = \Big[\underbrace{\tfrac{1}{\delta}ln\left(\tfrac{d+P}{P}\right) - 1}_{k}\Big] \qquad \text{(greatest integer)}$$

Recall in the aggregate deterministic analysis the net level annual premium (annual benefit premium) P_x was defined so that the insurer would exactly break even on the group. Here we define it to be the solution $P = P_x$ of the equation $0 = E[L]$:

$$0 = E[L] = E\left[v^{K+1} - P_x\, \ddot{a}_{\overline{K+1|}}\right] \qquad \text{(Form 1 of } L\text{)}$$

$$= E[v^{K+1}] - P_x \cdot E\left[\ddot{a}_{\overline{K+1|}}\right] \;=\; A_x - P_x \cdot \ddot{a}_x$$

$$\Rightarrow \;\; P_x \ddot{a}_x = A_x, \;\; \text{or} \;\; P_x = \frac{A_x}{\ddot{a}_x}$$

The numerical value is the same but the interpretation is slightly different. In the risk theoretic approach (here) the insurer receiving P_x only *expects* to break even on each issue.

Since he only expects to break even there is a possibility (i.e., risk) that he will lose money. We have already measured this probability for a single issue: $Pr(L \geq 0) = {}_{k_0+1}q_x$. Now lets assume all ℓ_x lives in the table are simultaneously issued this contract. What is the probability that the insurer loses on the group? This is a question about the distribution of the insurers aggregate loss function, L_{Agg}, which we view as being a sum of ℓ_x independent individual loss functions like the L above. Invoking the Central Limit Theorem (if ℓ_x is sufficiently large) we can say that L_{Agg} is approximately normal with

$$\mu_{Agg} \;=\; \ell_x \cdot E[L],$$

and

$$\sigma^2_{Agg} \;=\; \ell_x \cdot Var(L).$$

So now we must focus on $Var(L)$. But first notice that when $P = P_x$, $\mu_{Agg} = \ell_x \cdot E[L] = \ell_x \cdot 0 = 0$ so

$$Pr(L_{Agg} \geq 0) \;=\; Pr\left(\frac{L_{Agg} - \mu(Agg)}{\sigma_{Agg}} \;\geq\; \frac{0 - \mu(Agg)}{\sigma_{Agg}} \;=\; \frac{0-0}{\sigma_{Agg}} \;=0\right)$$

$$\approx\; Pr(N(0,1) \geq 0) \;=\; .50.$$

The second form of the loss function,

$$L \;=\; \left(1+\frac{P}{d}\right)v^{K+1} - \frac{P}{d}$$

is convenient for relating $Var(L)$ to insurance values:

$$\begin{aligned} Var(L) &= Var\left(\left(1+\frac{P}{d}\right)v^{K+1} - \frac{P}{d}\right) \\ &= Var\left(\left(1+\frac{P}{d}\right)v^{K+1}\right) \\ &= \left(1+\frac{P}{d}\right)^2 Var(v^{K+1}) \\ &= \left(1+\frac{P}{d}\right)^2 ({}^2A_x - (A_x)^2). \end{aligned}$$

This is a special case of the linearity relation $Var(aX+b) = a^2Var(X)$.

Example 2 Suppose all nanoes in the table below purchase 1 of fully discrete whole life and let $i = .06$.

(i) Find the distribution of L if $P = P_{90}$ is the net level annual premium.

(ii) Find k_0 from this table and verify it from the formula.

(iii) What is the probability of an insurers "loss" on an individual contract.

(iv) Find $Var(L)$ directly from the distribution in (i) as well as by the formula.

(v) How much (i.e., $P = P_{90}+r$, r = risk charge) should each policy holder pay for the insurer to have only a 5% chance of positive loss in the aggregate?

x	90	91	92	93
ℓ_x	100	72	39	0
d_x	28	33	39	—

Solution In our umpteen earlier visits with this example we have seen that

$$A_{90} = .885301 \qquad {}^2A_{90} = .785525 \qquad P_{90} = .436895$$

(i) $$L = v^{K+1} - P_{90}\,\ddot{a}_{\overline{K+1}|} = \left(\frac{1}{1.06}\right)^{K+1} - (.436895)\,\frac{1-(1.06)^{-(K+1)}}{(6/106)}$$

L = loss	K event	Probability
.506501	$K = 0$	$\frac{28}{100}$
.040936	$K = 1$	$\frac{33}{100}$
−398276	$K = 2$	$\frac{39}{100}$

Note: Check $E[L] = 0$ (you will find a small rounding error).

(ii) Losses are positive for $K = 0{,}1$ so $k_0 = 1$;

Formula: $k_0 = \left[\frac{1}{ln(1.06)}\, ln\left(\frac{6/106+.436895}{.436895}\right) - 1\right] = [2.09 - 1] = [1.09] = 1$

(iii) $Pr(L \geq 0) = Pr(K \leq k_0 + 1) = Pr(K = 0 \text{ or } 1) = \frac{28+33}{100} = .61$

(iv) $Var(L) = E[L^2] - 0^2 = \sum_{\text{values}} \text{loss}^2 \cdot \text{probability} = .134248$

Formula: $Var(L) = \left(1+\frac{P}{d}\right)^2 ({}^2A_{90} - A_{90}{}^2) = \underbrace{.134324}_{\substack{\text{slight difference} \\ \text{from rounding}}}$

(v) If $P = P_{90} + r$ is the premium instead of P_{90} we need to recalculate both $E[L]$ and $Var\,(L)$:

(a) $L = v^{K+1} - (P_{90}+r)\ddot{a}_{\overline{K+1|}} \Rightarrow$

$$E[L] = A_{90} - (P_{90}+r)\ddot{a}_{90} = \underbrace{A_{90} - P_{90}\ddot{a}_{90}}_{\substack{\text{zero by defini-} \\ \text{tion of } P_{90}}} - r\,\ddot{a}_{90}$$

$$= -r\ddot{a}_{90} = -r\left[\frac{1 - A_{90}}{d}\right]$$

$$= -\,2.026349r \quad \text{(negative, i.e., an expected profit)}$$

(b)

$$L = \left(1 + \frac{P_{90}+r}{d}\right) v^{K+1} - \frac{P_{90}+r}{d} \Rightarrow$$

$$Var(L) = \left(1 + \frac{P_{90}+r}{d}\right)^2 ({}^2A_{90} - A_{90}{}^2) \Rightarrow$$

$$\sigma_L = \left[1 + \frac{106}{6}(.436895+r)\right](.001767)^{1/2}$$

$$= .366502 + .742660r$$

(c) If L_{Agg} is the new aggregate loss function, it is approximately normal in distribution with mean

$$\mu(Agg) = \underbrace{100}_{\ell_{90}} \cdot E[L] = -202.6349r$$

and standard deviation

$$\sigma_{Agg} = \sqrt{100} \cdot \sigma_L = 3.665018 + 7.426600r.$$

The risk charge r is calculated so that 0 is the 95th percentile of L_{Agg}

(i.e. $.05 = Pr(L_{Agg} > 0)$). Since 1.645 is the 95th percentile of $N(0,1)$,

$$\mu(Agg) + 1.645\sigma_{Agg} = 6.028954 - 190.418143r$$

is the 95th percentile of L_{Agg}. Setting the above expression equal to 0, the 95th percentile, and solving for r gives a risk charge of $r = .031662$. The big picture is

$$\underbrace{.468557}_{\text{total premium}} = \underbrace{.436895}_{\text{net premium}} + \underbrace{.031662}_{\substack{\text{risk charge} \\ \approx 7.25\% \text{ of net}}}$$

□

The Semi-Continuous and Fully Continuous Whole Life Models

In the semi-continuous model the \$1 benefit is paid at death. The annual premium P is paid as an annuity due. So the insurer's loss function on a single issue to (x) is

$$L = \underbrace{1 \cdot v^T}_{\substack{\text{present value}\\ \text{of outflow}}} - \underbrace{P\ddot{a}_{\overline{K+1|}}}_{\substack{\text{present value}\\ \text{of inflow}}} .$$

Here we have a function of both T and K which makes its distribution more complicated. As a result the treatment will focus on the net level annual premium and its relation to the fully discrete model.

For each P we have a different loss function. The unique P such that the expected loss is zero is the net level annual premium (or annual benefit premium), which is denoted by $P(\overline{A}_x)$ in standard actuarial notation. This style of notation is standard with all semi-continuous models. It's expression in terms of insurance and annuity symbols follows the same pattern as the fully discrete premium $P_x = \frac{A_x}{\ddot{a}_x}$.

$$\begin{aligned} 0 &= E[L] = E\left[v^T - P(\overline{A}_x)\ddot{a}_{\overline{K+1|}}\right] \\ &= E[v^T] - P(\overline{A}_x) \cdot E\left[\ddot{a}_{\overline{K+1|}}\right] \\ &= \overline{A}_x - P(\overline{A}_x) \cdot \ddot{a}_x \\ \Rightarrow \quad P(\overline{A}_x) &= \frac{\overline{A}_x}{\ddot{a}_x} . \end{aligned}$$

In the semi-continuous models there is typically a close relation with the fully discrete case if the survival model satisfies the UDD assumption. Recall that in this situation $\overline{A}_x = \left(\frac{i}{\delta}\right) A_x$, so from the above expression

$$P(\overline{A}_x) = \frac{\overline{A}_x}{\ddot{a}_x} \underset{\text{UDD}}{=} \frac{(i/\delta)A_x}{\ddot{a}_x} = \left(\frac{i}{\delta}\right) P_x .$$

The analysis of the fully continuous model is completely parallel to the fully discrete case. Here we have the impractical assumption that the annual amount of premium, P, is paid continuously. The loss function this time is:

$$\begin{aligned} L &= 1 \cdot v^T - P \cdot \overline{a}_{\overline{T|}} && \text{(Form 1)} \\ &= 1 \cdot v^T - P \cdot \frac{1-v^T}{\delta} \\ &= \left(1+\frac{P}{\delta}\right) v^T - \frac{P}{\delta} . && \text{(Form 2)} \end{aligned}$$

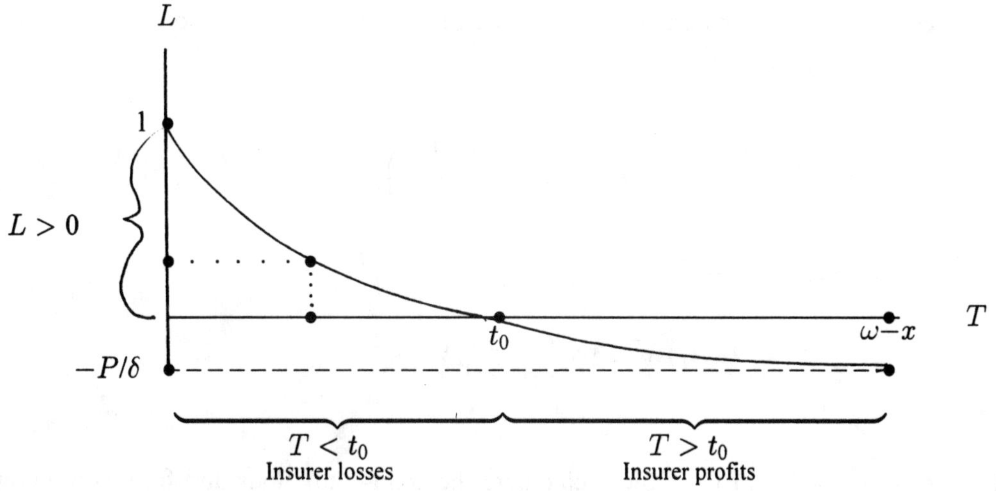

Analogous to the fully discrete case we can calculate the probability of a positive loss as

$$Pr(L > 0) = Pr(T < t_0) = {}_{t_0}q_x$$

where t_0 is found from the inverse function as $t_0 = \frac{1}{\delta} ln\left(\frac{\delta + P}{P}\right)$.

The net level annual premium, denoted by $\overline{P}(\overline{A}_x)$, is calculated from $0 = E[L]$ in the usual way, resulting in

$$\overline{P}(\overline{A}_x) = \frac{\overline{A}_x}{\overline{a}_x}.$$

There is a relation with the fully discrete case under the UDD, but it is more complicated. In addition to $\overline{A}_x = \left(\frac{i}{\delta}\right) A_x$, the UDD implies that $\overline{a}_x = \alpha(\infty)\ddot{a}_x - \beta(\infty)$:

$$\begin{aligned}\overline{P}(\overline{A}_x) &= \frac{\overline{A}_x}{\overline{a}_x} = \frac{i}{\delta}\left[\frac{A_x}{\alpha(\infty)\ddot{a}_x - \beta(\infty)}\right] \\ &= \frac{i}{\delta}\left[\frac{P_x}{\alpha(\infty) - \beta(\infty)\cdot(1/\ddot{a}_x)}\right] \quad \text{(divide top and bottom by } \ddot{a}_x\text{)} \\ &= \frac{i}{\delta}\left[\frac{P_x}{\alpha(\infty) - \beta(\infty)(d+P_x)}\right].\end{aligned}$$

The last step results from dividing the relation $1 = d\ddot{a}_x + A_x$ by $\ddot{a}_x$ to obtain

$$\frac{1}{\ddot{a}_x} = d + P_x.$$

As a final comment here, notice that the variance of the loss function also has a great deal of similarity with that in the fully discrete case:

$$\begin{aligned} Var(L) &= Var\left(\left(1+\frac{\overline{P}(\overline{A}_x)}{\delta}\right)v^T - \frac{\overline{P}(\overline{A}_x)}{\delta}\right) \\ &= \left(1+\frac{\overline{P}(\overline{A}_x)}{\delta}\right)^2 Var(v^T) \\ &= \left(1+\frac{\overline{P}(\overline{A}_x)}{\delta}\right)^2 \left({}^2\overline{A}_x - (\overline{A}_x)^2\right) \end{aligned}$$

Example 3 For the 90-year-olds in Example 1 calculate the semi-continuous and fully continuous net level annual premiums $1000P(\overline{A}_{90})$ and $1000\overline{P}(\overline{A}_{90})$ assuming that the UDD holds.

Solution Recall that we had calculated that the fully discrete premium $1000P_{90}$ was 436.90 (nearest penny). Due to the close relation of this premium to the other two under the UDD assumption

$$1000P(\overline{A}_{90}) = \tfrac{i}{\delta}\,1000P_{90} = \frac{.06}{ln(1.06)}(436.90) = 449.88$$

$$\begin{aligned} 1000\overline{P}(\overline{A}_{90}) &= 1000\,\frac{\overline{A}_{90}}{\overline{a}_{90}} = 1000\left(\tfrac{i}{\delta}\right)\left[\frac{P_{90}}{\alpha(\infty)-\beta(\infty)(P_{90}+d)}\right] \\ &= 600.90 \end{aligned}$$

since

$$\alpha(\infty) = \frac{id}{\delta^2} = 1.000283 \qquad \beta(\infty) = \frac{i-\delta}{\delta^2} = .509855. \qquad \square$$

Example 4 Using the same mortality and interest assumptions as in Example 1 calculate the following for the fully continuous loss function assuming the UDD:

(a) the 20th percentile of the loss function; and

(b) the variance of the loss function.

Solution

(a) Let ℓ be the 20th percentile of L. Using the graph of L versus T and the inverse function we see

$$.20 = Pr(L \le \ell) = P(T \ge t),$$

where

$$\ell = \left(1+\frac{\overline{P}(\overline{A}_{90})}{\delta}\right)v^t - \frac{\overline{P}(\overline{A}_{90})}{\delta}.$$

The first equation says t is the 80th percentile of T, the future lifetime of a 90-year-old. In the table $\ell_{90} = 100$, so we are looking for the amount of time t until the 80th death, which occurs between ages 92 and 93 since $\ell_{92} = 39$ and $\ell_{93} = 0$. Linearly interpolating (i.e., UDD assumption) we see that the number of living at age $92\frac{19}{39}$ is 20 (i.e., the 80th death has just occurred). So $t = 2\frac{19}{39}$ and

$$\ell = \left(1 + \frac{.60090}{ln\,1.06}\right)1.06^{-2\frac{19}{39}} - \frac{.60090}{ln\,(1.06)} = -.5262.$$

There is a 20% chance that $L \leq -.5262$, which can be rephrased to indicate there is a 20% chance of a profit of at least .5262.

(b) We have seen that the loss function's variance is

$$\left(1 + \frac{\overline{P}(\overline{A}_{90})}{\delta}\right)^2 \left({}^2\overline{A}_{90} - (\overline{A}_{90})^2\right)$$

and we have already calculated

$$\overline{P}(\overline{A}_{90}) = .60090, \overline{A}_{90} = \frac{i}{\delta}A_{90} = \left(\frac{.06}{ln\,1.06}\right)(.885301) = .911602.$$

It remains to find ${}^2\overline{A}_{90}$. Mimicking the UDD relation $\overline{A}_{90} = \frac{i}{\delta}A_{90}$ we have

$${}^2\overline{A}_{90} = \frac{2i + i^2}{2\delta} \cdot {}^2A_{90}$$

since $2i + i^2$ is the effective annual rate that goes with a force of 2δ. In Unit 1 of these notes we found ${}^2A_{90} = .785525$. So

$${}^2\overline{A}_{90} = \frac{.1236}{2(.058269)}(.785525) = .833128.$$

Plugging all these numbers into the variance formula results in $Var(L) = .269967$. □

True m^{th}-ly Premiums in the Fully Discrete Whole Life Model

Here we want to examine the relation between the annual premium when it is paid in a lump sum at the beginning of the year versus when the annual premium is paid in equal installments at the beginning of each mth. For the fully discrete model the former annual amount is denoted by P_x, whereas the latter annual amount is denoted $P_x^{(m)}$. Intuitively, there are two reasons that $P_x^{(m)}$ must be larger. First, the insurer loses interest income with m^{th}-ly premiums because they arrive throughout the year rather than as a lump sum at the beginning. This happens every year. Second, in the year of death the insurer will not receive the full $P_x^{(m)}$ unless death occurs in the final m^{th}. Thus there is the potential of lost premium income in the final year. Viewing this as a type of "extra death benefit," we see that $P_x^{(m)}$ must include an "annual premium" for this extra benefit.

Next we will develop the mathematical relation between P_x and $P_x^{(m)}$ then explain the relation in terms of the two ideas above. Since $P_x^{(m)}$ is paid in m^{th}-ly installments we have

$$\underbrace{P_x^{(m)} \cdot \ddot{a}_x^{(m)}}_{\substack{\text{APV of } m^{th}\text{-ly} \\ \text{premiums}}} = \underbrace{A_x}_{\substack{\text{APV of the} \\ \text{benefit}}}$$

Substituting the UDD relation $\ddot{a}_x^{(m)} = \alpha(m)\ddot{a}_x - \beta(m)$ into the above, and solving for the mth-ly premium

$$P_x^{(m)} = \frac{A_x}{\ddot{a}_x^{(m)}} = \frac{A_x}{\alpha(m)\ddot{a}_x - \beta(m)} = \frac{P_x}{\alpha(m) - \beta(m)(d+P_x)}.$$

The last step results from dividing top and bottom by $\ddot{a}_x$ and using $\frac{1}{\ddot{a}_x} = d+P_x$. Crossmultiply in the above relation and solve for $\alpha(m)P_x^{(m)}$:

$$\underbrace{\alpha(m)P_x^{(m)}}_{\substack{\text{Approximately } P_x^{(m)} \\ \text{since } \alpha(m) \approx 1}} = P_x + \underbrace{\beta(m)P_x^{(m)} \cdot d}_{\substack{\text{lost interest due at} \\ \text{the start of the year}}} + \underbrace{\beta(m)P_x^{(m)} \cdot P_x}_{\substack{\text{annual premium for} \\ \text{the lost premium in} \\ \text{the year of death}}}$$

Note:

(i) $\beta(m) \approx \frac{m-1}{2m}$. Now $P_x^{(m)}$ paid in installments at the beginning of each mth is roughly equivalent to $\frac{m+1}{2m}P_x^{(m)}$ at the beginning and $\frac{m-1}{2m}P_x^{(m)}$ at the end. In this approximation all installments in the first half of the year and $\frac{1}{2}$ of midyear premium (if m is even) is moved to the start of the year, and the rest is moved to the end.

(ii) The interest due at the start of the year on the delayed amount $\frac{m-1}{2m}P_x^{(m)}$ is d times this quantity, which is the idea behind the "lost interest" term above.

(iii) The year end amount $\frac{m-1}{2m}P_x^{(m)}$ is lost premium in the year of death. So P_x times this quantity is an annual premium for this extra benefit.

Example 5 Compare $1000P_{90}^{(2)}$ and $1000P_{90}$ for the survival model in Example 1 and using $i = .06$.

Solution We already know $1000P_{90} = 436.90$. Here is an alternate method of calculation of $P_{90}^{(2)}$ based on the identity

$$1 = d^{(2)}\ddot{a}_x^{(2)} + A_x^{(2)}$$

and the UDD relation

$$A_x^{(2)} = \frac{i}{i^{(2)}}\, A_x.$$

$$P_{90}^{(2)} = \frac{A_{90}}{\ddot{a}_{90}^{(2)}} = \frac{A_{90}}{(1-A_{90}^{(2)})/d^{(2)}} = \frac{d^{(2)}A_{90}}{1-\frac{i}{i^{(2)}}A_{90}} = .500343.$$

Hence $1000P_{90}^{(2)} = 500.34$. □

Additional Principles for the Calculation of Premium

Annual Benefit premiums are computed from the equivalence principle:

$APV(\text{premium}) = APV(\text{benefits})$. Here we examine two other principles by which premiums might be set. One idea uses percentiles of the distribution of the loss function and the other employs utility theory. We first consider the method of percentiles.

Consider fully continuous whole life insurance of \$1 to (x) where P is the annual premium amount. The loss function is $L = v^T - P\bar{a}_{\overline{T|}}$. $\overline{P}(\overline{A}_x)$, the level annual benefit premium, was calculated by setting $E[L] = 0$ (i.e., the equivalence principle). Suppose instead we determine P such that the chance of a positive loss is small:

$$\begin{aligned}
\alpha = Pr(L > 0) &= Pr(v^T - P\bar{a}_{\overline{T|}} > 0) \\
&= Pr\left(\left(1+\tfrac{P}{\delta}\right)v^T - \tfrac{P}{\delta} > 0\right) \\
&= Pr\left(v^T > \frac{P}{P+\delta}\right) \\
&= Pr\left(-\delta T > ln\left(\frac{P}{P+\delta}\right)\right) \\
&= Pr\left(T < \tfrac{1}{\delta}ln\left(\tfrac{P+\delta}{P}\right)\right).
\end{aligned}$$

From the above, $\frac{1}{\delta}ln\left(\frac{P+\delta}{P}\right)$ is the $(100\alpha)^{th}$ percentile of the T-distribution, t_α:

$$t_\alpha = \tfrac{1}{\delta}ln\left(\tfrac{P+\delta}{P}\right)$$

$$\Leftrightarrow \qquad P = \frac{\delta}{e^{\delta t_\alpha} - 1} = \frac{1}{\bar{s}_{\overline{t_\alpha|}}} \qquad \text{(at a force of } \delta)$$

Notice that $P\bar{s}_{\overline{t_\alpha|}} = 1$ so that with this annual premium the premiums accumulate exactly to the \$1 benefit if death is in t_α years.

Example 6 Assuming $\mu = .02$ and $\delta = .06$ compare $\overline{P}(\overline{A}_x)$ and the annual premium P such that the probability of a positive loss on a single policy is .25.

Solution With constant force we know $\overline{A}_x = \frac{\mu}{\mu+\delta}$, $\overline{a}_x = \frac{1}{\mu+\delta}$. Hence $\overline{P}(\overline{A}_x) = \mu = .02$. The survival function is $s_T(t) = {}_tp_x = e^{-\mu t} = e^{-.02t}$. The 25th percentile, $t_{.25}$, is determined from the following:

$$.75 = s_T(t_{.25}) = e^{-.02t_{.25}}$$

$$t_{.25} = \frac{-ln(.75)}{.02}.$$

Thus

$$\overline{s}_{\overline{t_{.25}|}} = \frac{e^{\delta t_\alpha} - 1}{\delta} = \frac{e^{.06t_\alpha} - 1}{.06} = \frac{e^{-3ln(.75)} - 1}{.06} = \frac{\left(\frac{4}{3}\right)^3 - 1}{.06} = \frac{37}{27(.06)},$$

$$P = \frac{1}{\overline{s}_{\overline{t_{.25}|}}} = \frac{27(.06)}{37} = .0438 \qquad \square$$

A more reasonable approach using the method of percentiles would be based on the aggregate loss function for a large group of issues rather than on the loss function of a single issue. Suppose we use $\mu = .02$ and $\delta = .06$, as in Example 6, and assume that P is determined so that $.05 = Pr(L_{Agg} > 0)$, where L_{Agg} is the loss function for a group of 100 independent losses like L in the example: $L = v^T - P\overline{a}_{\overline{T|}}$. In other words, 0 is the 95th percentile of the aggregate loss distribution. Using the Central Limit theorem

$$0 = \mu_{Agg} + 1.645\sigma_{Agg} \quad (Pr(N(0;1) > 1.645) = .05),$$

where

$$\mu_{Agg} = 100E[L]$$

$$\sigma_{Agg} = \sqrt{100}\sigma_L.$$

To express μ_{Agg} and σ_{Agg} in terms of P is convenient to set $P = \overline{P}(\overline{A}_x) + r = \mu + r$ where r is a so-called "risk charge." Then

$$E[L] = E[v^T - (\mu+r)\overline{a}_{\overline{T|}}] = -r\overline{a}_x = \frac{-r}{\mu+\delta} = -12.5r,$$

$$\begin{aligned} Var(L) &= \left(1 + \frac{P}{\delta}\right)^2 ({}^2\overline{A}_x - \overline{A}_x^2) \\ &= \left(1 + \frac{\mu+r}{\delta}\right)^2 \left[\frac{\mu}{\mu+2\delta} - \left(\frac{\mu}{\mu+\delta}\right)^2\right] \\ &= \left(\frac{4}{3} + \frac{r}{.06}\right)^2 \left[\frac{2}{14} - \frac{1}{16}\right], \text{ and} \end{aligned}$$

$$\sigma_L = \left(\frac{4}{3} + \frac{r}{.06}\right) \frac{3}{\sqrt{7 \cdot 4}} = \frac{1}{\sqrt{7}}(1 + 12.5r).$$

Finally,

$$\begin{aligned} 0 &= \mu_{Agg} + 1.645\sigma_{Agg} \\ &= 100E[L] + 10\sigma_L \\ &= 100(-12.5r) + 10\left(\frac{1}{\sqrt{7}}\right)(1{+}12.5r), \text{ or} \end{aligned}$$

$r = .0031$. Hence $P = \overline{P}(\overline{A}_x) + r = \mu + r = .0231$.

With discrete models percentiles don't have as clear a meaning. Suppose $i = .05$, $\ell_x = 100 - x$ and we ask: For fully discrete whole life of \$1 to (40), what is the smallest annual premium P so that $Pr(L > 0) \leq .33$? Keep in mind that $L = v^{K+1} - P\ddot{a}_{\overline{K+1}|}$ is a decreasing function of K. First we need to find the 33rd percentile of $T(40)$. With de Moivre's law $T(40)$ is uniformly distributed over the interval $[0, 60]$, so the 33rd percentile is $.33(60) = 19.8$ years. This falls within the 20th policy year. With $P = \frac{1}{\ddot{s}_{\overline{20}|.05}}$ as the annual premium, $L = v^{K+1} - P\ddot{a}_{\overline{K+1}|} = 0$ when $K + 1 = 20$. Since L is a decreasing function of K this means $Pr(L > 0) = Pr(K + 1 \leq 19) = {}_{19}q_{40} = \frac{19}{60} < .33$. Furthermore, if $P < \frac{1}{\ddot{s}_{\overline{20}|.05}}$ then $Pr(L > 0) \geq Pr(K + 1 \leq 20) = \frac{20}{60} = .33\overline{3} > .33$. Hence $P = \frac{1}{\ddot{s}_{\overline{20}|.05}}$ is the smallest possible annual premium so that $Pr(L > 0) < .33$.

Next we turn to a principle arising in utility theory which explains why individuals will pay more than the expected loss to purchase insurance for full coverage of the loss. For wealth level w, $u(w)$, the utility of w, is a function of w measuring the importance of w to the individual. Typically it should be an increasing function (i.e., more money is better). If you wish to model a risk averse (conservative) attitude you might also insist that $u(w)$ is concave down ($u''(w) < 0$). One such parametric utility model is the exponential utility function $u(w) = -e^{-\alpha w}$ where $\alpha > 0$. Now suppose L is an insurer's loss function with the premium unspecified, (i.e., $L = Z - PY$) and suppose $u(w) = -e^{-\alpha w}$ models the insurer's attitude about risk at all levels of wealth. According to the indifference principle, the (indifference) premium is determined from the relation

$$E[u(w)] = E[u(w - L)].$$

The left side is just $u(w)$ at the insurers current wealth w. The right side is the expected utility if the insurer issues the coverage, thus changing his wealth to $w - L$. P shows up in the right side of the equation. If the equation can be solved for P you have found the indifference premium. Since L decreases as P increases one would have $u(w) < E[u(w - L)]$ if L employs a premium bigger than the indifference premium. So the indifference premium represents the minimum amount of premium that will leave the insurer's expected utility undiminished if he issues the coverage. One assumes that a decision maker will always choose an option that increases his expected utility of wealth.

Now let's consider these ideas in a little more detail for fully continuous whole life of \$1 to (x). For a single policy with annual premium amount P, we have $L = v^T - P\bar{a}_{\overline{T|}}$. The indifference equation, $u(w) = E[u(w - L)]$, with $u(w) = -e^{-\alpha w}$, takes the form

$$-e^{-\alpha w} = E[-e^{-\alpha(w-L)}] = E[-e^{-\alpha w} \cdot e^{\alpha L}] = -e^{-\alpha w} M_L(\alpha),$$

where $M_L(\alpha)$ is the moment generating function of L. Canceling the common factors we see that the indifference premium results from solving $M_L(\alpha) = 1$ for the unknown P. In practice, for $L = v^T - P\bar{a}_{\overline{T|}}$, the equation $M_L(\alpha) = 1$ would have to be numerically approximated for P.

Some insight can be obtained by moving from a single policy indifference equation to an indifference equation for a portfolio of n such policies. Use $L_{Agg} = L_1 + \cdots + L_n$ for the aggregate loss function where the L_i are independent and identically distributed like $L = v^T - P\bar{a}_{\overline{T|}}$. The aggregate indifference equation would reduce to solving $M_{L_{Agg}}(\alpha) = 1$ for P. This is still a problem requiring numerical methods but we might avoid that by using Central Limit Theorem. L_{Agg} is approximately normal in distribution so $M_{L\,Agg}(\alpha) \approx exp(\mu_{Agg}\alpha + \sigma^2_{Agg}\alpha^2/2)$.
(Note: the moment generating function of $N(\mu, \sigma^2)$ is $M(t) = e^{\mu t + \sigma^2 t^2/2}$.) Thus, since $e^0 = 1$, the equation $M_{L_{Agg}}(\alpha) = 1$ is approximately the same as $\mu_{Agg}\alpha + \sigma^2_{Agg}\alpha^2/2 = 0$.

Now $\mu_{Agg} = nE[L]$, $\sigma^2_{Agg} = n \cdot Var(L)$ so the above reduces to

$$E[L] + Var(L)\left(\frac{\alpha}{2}\right) = 0$$

after canceling an n and an α. Filling in $E[L] = \bar{A}_x - P\bar{a}_x$, $Var(L) = \left(1 + \frac{P}{\delta}\right)^2 ({}^2\bar{A}_x - \bar{A}_x{}^2)$, we see that the indifference premium is approximately the solution of the quadratic (in P) equation

$$0 = (\bar{A}_x - P\bar{a}_x) + \left(1 + \frac{P}{\delta}\right)^2 ({}^2\bar{A}_x - \bar{A}_x{}^2)\left(\frac{\alpha}{2}\right)$$

Example 7 Assuming $\mu = .02$, $\delta = .06$ (same conditions as in Example 6 and the following discussion) and $\alpha = .05$, find the approximate indifference premium using the Central Limit Theorem.

Solution The quadratic above reduces to

$$0 = \left(\frac{1}{4} - P \cdot 12.5\right) + \left(1 + \frac{P}{.06}\right)^2 \left(\frac{1}{7} - \frac{1}{16}\right)(.025),$$

which solves for $P = .0203$ or $P = 22.26$. The desired result is the smallest $P = .0203$.

In summary, we calculated annual premiums for fully continuous whole life of \$1 to (x) using $\delta = .06$ and $\mu = .02$ in 4 distinct ways:

Example 6: (i) Equivalence Principle: $P = \overline{P}(\overline{A}_x) = \mu = .02$

(ii) Percentiles for a single policy: $P = .0438 \;\Rightarrow\; Pr(L > 0) = .25$

Discussion: after Example 6 (iii) Percentiles for a group of 100 such policies:

$P = .0231 \Rightarrow \; Pr(L_{Agg} > 0) = .05$

Example 7 and preceding: (iv) Indifference principle with a normal approximation and exponential utility:

$P = .0203 \;\Rightarrow\; E[u(w)] = E[u(w - L_{Agg})]$ where $u(w) = -e^{-.05w}$

CONDENSED REVIEW NOTES AND ADVANCED TOPICS

Loss Function

L = random p.v. at issue of excess of outflow over inflow

= random p.v. benefits − random p.v. premium

= $Z - P \cdot Y$ where

Z = random p.v. benefit

Y = random p.v. of annuity of \$1/yr. following premium payment pattern

P = annual amount of premium

Net Annual Premium (Annual Benefit Premium)

The solution P of $E[L] = 0$; $P = \frac{E[Z]}{E[Y]}$

Equivalence Principle: APV (net premiums) = APV (benefits)

$P_{net} \cdot E[Y] = E[Z]$

Types of Models

Model Category	Assumptions: Time of Death Benefit	Assumptions: Pattern of Premium Payment
fully discrete	end of policy year (discrete Z)	annually, at beginning of policy yr. (discrete Y)
semi-continuous	at death (cont. Z)	annually, at beginning of policy yr. (discrete Y)
fully continuous	at death (cont. Z)	continuously (cont. Y)

Fully Continuous Net Annual Premiums

Whole Life: *Loss Function* $L = v^T - P\bar{a}_{\overline{T}|} = \left(1 + \frac{P}{\delta}\right)v^T - \frac{P}{\delta}$

Expected Loss $E[L] = \bar{A}_x - P\bar{a}_x$

Net Annual Premium $\bar{P}(\bar{A}_x) = \frac{\bar{A}_x}{\bar{a}_x} \underset{\text{UDD}}{=} \frac{\frac{i}{\delta}A_x}{\alpha(\infty)\ddot{a}_x - \beta(\infty)}$

where $\alpha(\infty) = \frac{id}{\delta^2}$, $\beta(\infty) = \frac{i-\delta}{\delta^2}$

Variance $Var(L) = \left(1 + \frac{P}{\delta}\right)^2 \left({}^2\bar{A}_x - \bar{A}_x{}^2\right)$

Graph versus T

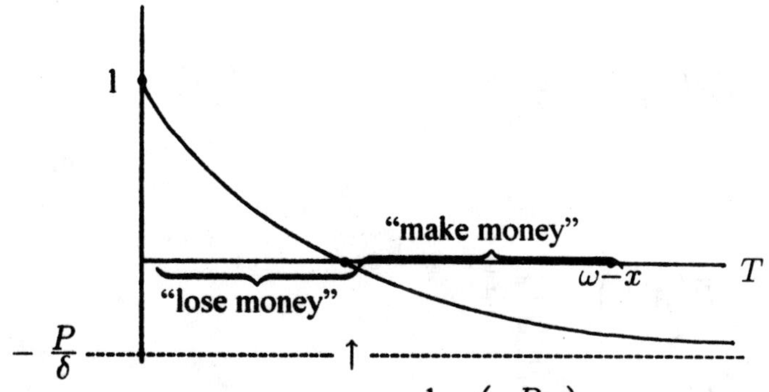

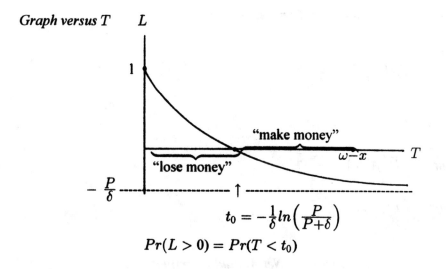

$$t_0 = -\frac{1}{\delta} ln\left(\frac{P}{P+\delta}\right)$$

$$Pr(L > 0) = Pr(T < t_0)$$

n-year Endowment:

Loss Function $\quad L = Z - PY \quad$ where $\quad Z = \begin{cases} v^T & T \le n \\ v^n & T > n \end{cases}$

$$= \left(1 + \frac{P}{\delta}\right) Z - \frac{P}{\delta} \qquad Y = \begin{cases} \bar{a}_{\overline{T}|} & T \le n \\ \bar{a}_{\overline{n}|} & T > n \end{cases}$$

Expected Loss $\quad E[L] = \bar{A}_{x:\overline{n}|} - P\bar{a}_{x:\overline{n}|}$

Net Annual Premium $\quad \bar{P}(\bar{A}_{x:\overline{n}|}) = \dfrac{\bar{A}_{x:\overline{n}|}}{\bar{a}_{x:\overline{n}|}} \overset{=}{\text{UDD}} \dfrac{\frac{i}{\delta} A^1_{x:\overline{n}|} + A_{x:\overline{n}|}^{\ \ 1}}{\alpha(\infty)\ddot{a}_{x:\overline{n}|} - \beta(\infty)(1 - {}_nE_x)}$

Variance $\quad Var(L) = \left(1 + \frac{P}{\delta}\right)^2 \left({}^2\bar{A}_{x:\overline{n}|} - \bar{A}_{x:\overline{n}|}{}^2\right)$

Note: $1 + \dfrac{P}{\delta} = \dfrac{1}{\delta \bar{a}_{x:\overline{n}|}} = \dfrac{1}{1 - \bar{A}_{x:\overline{n}|}}$ if $P = \bar{P}(\bar{A}_{x:\overline{n}|})$

Graph versus T

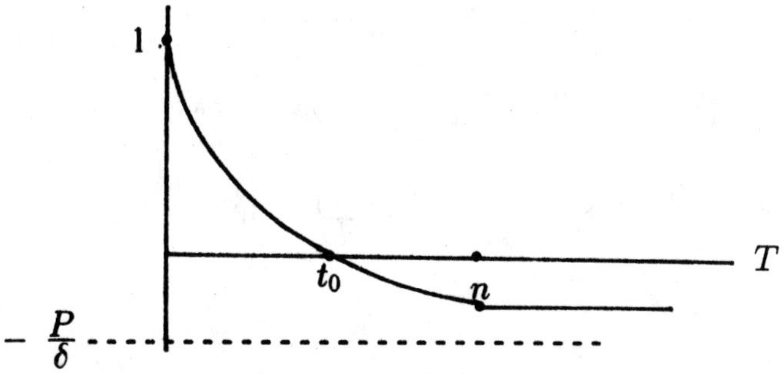

Note: $\bar{A}_x$ is the same as $\bar{A}_{x:\overline{w-x}|}$, so anything that can be done for an endowment insurance also applies to whole life.

Other Fully Continuous Net Premiums

n-yr term: $\overline{P}\left(\overline{A}^{\,1}_{x:\overline{n}|}\right) = \dfrac{\overline{A}^{\,1}_{x:\overline{n}|}}{\overline{a}_{x:\overline{n}|}}$

h-Pay Whole Life: ${}_h\overline{P}(\overline{A}_x) = \dfrac{\overline{A}_x}{\overline{a}_{x:\overline{h}|}}$

n-Yr Pure Endowment $\overline{P}\left(A_{x:\overline{n}|}^{\;\;1}\right) = \dfrac{A_{x:\overline{n}|}^{\;\;1}}{\overline{a}_{x:\overline{n}|}}$

n-Yr Deferred Annuity: $\overline{P}({}_n|\overline{a}_x) = \dfrac{{}_n|\overline{a}_x}{\overline{a}_{x:\overline{n}|}}$

Fully Discrete Net Annual Premiums

Whole Life:

Loss Function $L = v^{K+1} - P\ddot{a}_{\overline{K+1}|} = \left(1 + \frac{P}{d}\right)v^{K+1} - \frac{P}{d}$

Expected Loss $E[L] = A_x - P\ddot{a}_x$

Net Annual Premium $P_x = \dfrac{A_x}{\ddot{a}_x}$

Variance $Var(L) = \left(1 + \frac{P}{d}\right)^2({}^2A_x - A_x{}^2)$

Note: $1 + \frac{P}{d} = \frac{1}{d\ddot{a}_x} = \frac{1}{1 - A_x}$ if $P = P_x$

n-Year Endowment:

Loss Function $L = Z - PY$ where $Z = \begin{cases} v^{K+1} & K < n \\ v^n & K \geq n \end{cases}$

$= \left(1 + \frac{P}{d}\right) Z - \frac{P}{d}$ $\quad Y = \begin{cases} \ddot{a}_{\overline{K+1}|} & K < n \\ \ddot{a}_{\overline{n}|} & K \geq n \end{cases}$

Expected Loss $E[L] = A_{x:\overline{n}|} - P \cdot \ddot{a}_{x:\overline{n}|}$

Net Annual Premium $P_{x:\overline{n}|} = \dfrac{A_{x:\overline{n}|}}{\ddot{a}_{x:\overline{n}|}}$

Variance $Var(L) = \left(1 + \frac{P}{d}\right)^2 \left({}^2A_{x:\overline{n}|} - A_{x:\overline{n}|}{}^2\right)$

Note: $1 + \frac{P}{d} = \frac{1}{d\ddot{a}_{x:\overline{n}|}}$ if $P = P_{x:\overline{n}|}$

Other Fully Discrete Net Premiums

n-yr term: $P^{1}_{x:\overline{n}|} = \dfrac{A^{1}_{x:\overline{n}|}}{\ddot{a}_{x:\overline{n}|}}$

h-Pay Whole Life: ${}_hP_x = \dfrac{A_x}{\ddot{a}_{x:\overline{h}|}}$

n-Yr Deferred Annuity: $P({}_n|\ddot{a}_x) = \dfrac{{}_n|\ddot{a}_x}{\ddot{a}_{x:\overline{n}|}}$

Semi-Continuous Whole Life

Loss Function $L = v^T - P\,\ddot{a}_{\overline{K+1}|} = v^{K+1}v^{S-1} - P\cdot\dfrac{1-v^{K+1}}{d} = \left(v^{S-1}+\dfrac{P}{d}\right)v^{K+1} - \dfrac{P}{d}$

Expected Loss $E[L] = \overline{A}_x - P\ddot{a}_x \underset{\text{UDD}}{=} \dfrac{i}{\delta}A_x - P\ddot{a}_x$

Net Annual Premium $P(\overline{A}_x) = \dfrac{\overline{A}_x}{\ddot{a}_x} \underset{\text{UDD}}{=} \dfrac{\frac{i}{\delta}A_x}{\ddot{a}_x} = \dfrac{i}{\delta}P_x$

Variance $Var(L) = Var\left(\left(v^{S-1}+\dfrac{P}{d}\right)v^{K+1}\right) = 2^{nd}\ mom. - (1^{st}\ mom.)^2$

First Moment $E\left[\left(v^{S-1}+\dfrac{P}{d}\right)v^{K+1}\right] \underset{\text{UDD}}{=} E\left[v^{S-1}+\dfrac{P}{d}\right]E\left[v^{K+1}\right] = \left(\dfrac{i}{\delta}+\dfrac{P}{d}\right)A_x$

Second Moment $E\left[\left(v^{S-1}+\dfrac{P}{d}\right)^2(v^{K+1})^2\right] \underset{\text{UDD}}{=} \underbrace{E\left[\left(v^{S-1}+\dfrac{P}{d}\right)^2\right]}_{\text{carry out square and use linearity}}{}^2A_x$

m^{th}*-ly Premiums for h-Pay Endowment*

Note: Very inclusive type policy since $A_x = A_{x:\overline{\omega-x}|}$ where $h = \omega - x$.

$${}_hP^{(m)}_{x:\overline{n}|} = \text{net annual premium } \left(\tfrac{1}{m}^{th} \text{ paid at beginning of each } m^{th}\right)$$

$$= \frac{A_{x:\overline{n}|}}{\ddot{a}^{(m)}_{x:\overline{h}|}} \underset{\text{UDD}}{=} \frac{A_{x:\overline{n}|}}{\alpha(m)\,\ddot{a}_{x:\overline{h}|} - \beta(m)\,(1-{}_hE_x)}$$

$$= \frac{{}_hP_{x:\overline{n}|}}{\alpha(m) - \beta(m)(1-{}_hE_x)/\ddot{a}_{x:\overline{h}|}}$$

(divide top and bottom by $\ddot{a}_{x:\overline{n}|}$)

$(1 = d\ddot{a}_{x:\overline{h}|} + A^{1}_{x:\overline{h}|} + {}_hE_x)$

$$= \frac{{}_hP_{x:\overline{n}|}}{\alpha(m) - \beta(m)\left(d + P^{1}_{x:\overline{h}|}\right)}$$

$$\therefore\ \alpha(m)\,{}_hP^{(m)}_{x:\overline{n}|} = {}_hP_{x:\overline{n}|} + \beta(m)\cdot{}_hP^{(m)}_{x:\overline{n}|}\left(d + P^{1}_{x:\overline{h}|}\right)$$

Explanation: m^{th}-ly premiums have to be larger than corresponding annual premiums for *two reasons* – *lost interest income* on delayed premium and *lost premium* in year of death. Recall $\alpha(m) \approx 1$ and $\beta(m) \approx \frac{m-1}{2m}$ ("traditional approximations"). Thus $\frac{\text{annual premium}}{m}$ at the beginning of each mth is roughly equivalent to $\frac{m+1}{2m} \cdot$ *annual prem.* at the beginning of the year and $\frac{m-1}{2m} \cdot$ *annual premium* $\approx \beta(m)\ {}_hP^{(m)}_{x:\overline{n}|}$ at the end. The term $\beta(m) \cdot {}_hP^{(m)}_{x:\overline{n}|} \cdot d$ represents lost interest income due to the delay in premium. In the year of death, $\beta(m)_h P^{(m)}_{x:\overline{n}|}$ at the end is approximately the lost premium. This can only be lost during the first h-years and is like an extra death benefit. It is covered by charging $\left(\beta(m)_h P^{(m)}_{x:\overline{n}|}\right) P^{1}_{x:\overline{h}|}$ — an annual premium for h-years of term coverage at face amount equal "lost premium."

Analogous Relations Under UDD

$$\alpha(m) \cdot {}_hP^{(m)}_x = {}_hP_x + \beta(m) \cdot {}_hP^{(m)}_x \left(d + P^{1}_{x:\overline{h}|}\right)$$

$$\alpha(m) \cdot {}_hP^{(m)}\left(\overline{A}_{x:\overline{n}|}\right) = {}_hP\left(\overline{A}_{x:\overline{n}|}\right) + \beta(m) \cdot {}_hP^{(m)}\left(\overline{A}_{x:\overline{n}|}\right)\left(d + P^{1}_{x:\overline{h}|}\right)$$

Fully Discrete Whole Life of \$1 to (x)
Accumulation Benefits — Return of Premium
(if death occurs in first n-years)

Without Interest: Net annual premium P determined from

$$P\ddot{a}_x = APV_{prem} = APV_{death\ benefit} + APV_{premium\ refund} = A_x + P(IA)^{1}_{x:\overline{n}|}$$

The premium refund is $(K+1)P$ if $K+1 \le n$

With Interest: Net annual premium P determined from

$$P\ddot{a}_x = APV_{premium} + APV_{benefits} = \underbrace{A_x}_{\text{(death)}} + \underbrace{P\left[\ddot{a}_{x:\overline{n}|} - \ddot{a}_{\overline{n}|} \cdot {}_nP_x\right]}_{\substack{\text{(premiums \& interest)} \\ \text{see below}}}$$

The premium refund is $P\ddot{s}_{\overline{K+1}|}$ if $K+1 \le n$.

Event	PV Premium Refund $= Y_1$	Probability
$K = 0$	$(P\ddot{s}_{\overline{1}\rceil})v = P\ddot{a}_{\overline{1}\rceil}$	${}_{0\vert}q_x$
$K = 1$	$P\ddot{s}_{\overline{2}\rceil})v^2 = P\ddot{a}_{\overline{2}\rceil}$	${}_{1\vert}q_x$
$\vdots$		$\vdots$
$K = n-1$	$(P\ddot{s}_{\overline{n}\rceil})v^n = P\ddot{a}_{\overline{n}\rceil}$	${}_{n-1\vert}q_x$
$K \geq n$	0	${}_n p_x$

This discrete distribution is related to the P.V. random variable of an n-year temporary annuity for annual amount P, namely

$$Y = \begin{cases} P\ddot{a}_{\overline{K+1}\rceil} & K < n \\ P\ddot{a}_{\overline{n}\rceil} & K \geq n \end{cases}.$$

Note: $Y = Y_1 + P\ddot{a}_{\overline{n}\rceil} \cdot I$ where $I = \begin{cases} 0 & K < n \\ 1 & K \geq n \end{cases}.$

Thus $P\ddot{a}_{x:\overline{n}\rceil} = E[Y] = E[Y_1] + (P\ddot{a}_{\overline{n}\rceil})\, E[I],\ E[I] = {}_n p_x.$

So $E[Y_1] = P\ddot{a}_{x:\overline{n}\rceil} - P\ddot{a}_{\overline{n}\rceil} \cdot {}_n p_x = P\left[\ddot{a}_{x:\overline{n}\rceil} - \ddot{a}_{\overline{n}\rceil} \cdot {}_n p_x\right].$

CONCEPTUAL REVIEW TEST

1. Suppose (25) purchases \$1000 of whole life payable at death with annual premiums of \$7/year payable continuously. If δ=.05, what is the insurer's loss if death occurs at age 47.6? 80?

2. Suppose (x) pays \$P/year continuously for a whole life policy paying \$1 at death, and let L be the insurer's loss function.

   (a) Express L as a function of v^T.

   (b) L is a decreasing function of T. Find t_0 such that the insurer loses money if $T \leq t_0$ and makes money (i.e., $L < 0$) if $T > t_0$.

   (c) Express the expected loss in terms of standard actuarial NSP symbols.

   (d) Write the equation defining the net level annual premium and solve for it.

   (e) Express the variance of the loss function in terms of insurance values.

3. Write standard actuarial P symbols for the following net level annual premiums and express them as a ratio of "A, $\ddot{a}$" values:

   (a) (Fully Discrete) \$1 of 10-pay, 20-year endowment insurance to (30).

   (b) (Semi-Continuous) \$1000 of 20-pay whole life to (35) with premiums payable semiannually.

4. Give the relation between the premium in 3(b) and the corresponding net level premium paid annually. Explain the relation in terms of "lost interest income" and "lost premium income."

5. What is the deterministic interpretation of the fully discrete, net level annual premium P_x?

   Contrast this with the probabilistic interpretation in terms of a loss function.

   Begin with $P_x\ddot{a}_x = A_x$, write A_x, $\ddot{a}_x$ as summations and multiply by ℓ_x.

CONCEPTUAL REVIEW TEST ANSWERS

1. If death is at age 47.6 then $T = 22.6$ and the loss is $1000e^{-22.6(.05)} - 7 \cdot \bar{a}_{\overline{22.6}|} = \left(1000 + \frac{7}{\delta}\right)e^{-22.6(.05)} - \frac{7}{\delta} = 228.26$. For death at age 80 the corresponding loss is $\left(1000 + \frac{7}{\delta}\right) e^{-55(.05)} - \frac{7}{\delta} = -67.12$ (a profit).

2. (a) $L = PV(\text{benefit}) - PV(\text{premium}) = v^T - P\bar{a}_{\overline{T}|} = v^T - P \cdot \frac{1-v^T}{\delta} = \left(1+\frac{P}{\delta}\right)v^T - \frac{P}{\delta}$.

   (b) $0 = L \Rightarrow \quad v^{t_0} = \frac{P}{\delta+P} \Rightarrow t_0 \cdot ln\,(v) = ln\left(\frac{P}{\delta+P}\right) \Rightarrow t_0 = \frac{1}{\delta}ln\left(\frac{\delta+P}{P}\right)$ since $-\delta = ln\,(v)$.

   (c) $E\left[v^T - P\bar{a}_{\overline{T}|}\right] = \bar{A}_x - P\bar{a}_x$, which can be rewritten as either $1 - (\delta+P)\bar{a}_x$ or as $\left(1+\frac{P}{\delta}\right)\bar{A}_x - \frac{P}{\delta}$ by using the identity $1 = \delta\bar{a}_x + \bar{A}_x$.

   (d) $0 = E\,[L] = \bar{A}_x - P\bar{a}_x \Rightarrow P = \bar{P}(\bar{A}_x) = \frac{\bar{A}_x}{\bar{a}_x}$.

   (e) Use the form $L = \left(1+\frac{P}{\delta}\right)v^T - \frac{P}{\delta}$ plus the fact $Var(aX+b) = a^2Var(X)$ to obtain $Var(L) = \left(1+\frac{P}{\delta}\right)^2 Var(v^T)$ where $Var(v^T) = {}^2\bar{A}_x - \bar{A}_x{}^2$.

3. (a) ${}_{10}P_{30:\overline{20}|} = \frac{A_{30:\overline{20}|}}{\ddot{a}_{30:\overline{10}|}}$ (b) $1000 \cdot {}_{20}P^{(2)}(\bar{A}_{35}) = 1000 \cdot \frac{\bar{A}_{35}}{\ddot{a}^{(2)}_{35:\overline{20}|}}$

4. $\alpha(2) \cdot {}_{20}P^{(2)}(\bar{A}_{35}) = {}_{20}P(\bar{A}_{35}) + \beta(2) \cdot {}_{20}P^{(2)}(\bar{A}_{35})\left(d+P^{1}_{35:\overline{20}|}\right)$ where $\beta(2) \cdot {}_{20}P^{(2)}(\bar{A}_{35}) \cdot d$ represents lost interest income due to half of the semiannual premium being delayed until midyear, and $\beta(2) \cdot {}_{20}P^{(2)}(\bar{A}_{35}) \cdot P^{1}_{35:\overline{20}|}$ is the net annual premium for 20 years of term insurance at a face value of $\beta(2) \cdot {}_{20}P^{(2)}(\bar{A}_{35})$, which represents lost premium income in the policy year of death. Recall that $\alpha(m) \approx 1$ and $\beta(m) \approx \frac{m-1}{2m}$ so that semiannual premiums $\frac{1}{2} \cdot {}_{20}P^{(2)}(\bar{A}_{35})$ paid at times $t = 0$ and $\frac{1}{2}$ are roughly equivalent to $\frac{3}{4} \cdot {}_{20}P^{(2)}(\bar{A}_{35})$ at $t = 0$ and $\frac{1}{4} \cdot {}_{20}P^{(2)}(\bar{A}_{35})$ at $t = 1$. Interest income is lost on the latter in each of the premium paying years, and this premium amount is lost in the policy year of death if death occurs within 20 years.

5. Substituting $\ddot{a}_x = \sum_{k=0}^{\omega-x-1} v^k \cdot {}_kp_x = \sum_{k=0}^{\omega-x-1} v^k \cdot \frac{\ell_{x+k}}{\ell_x}$, and $A_x = \sum_{k=0}^{\omega-x-1} v^{k+1} \cdot {}_{k|}q_x = \sum_{k=0}^{\omega-x-1} v^{k+1} \cdot \frac{d_{x+k}}{\ell_x}$ into $P_x\ddot{a}_x = A_x$ and multiplying by ℓ_x gives the relation (*) $\sum_{k=0}^{\omega-x-1} v^k \cdot \ell_{x+k} \cdot P_x = \sum_{k=0}^{\omega-x-1} v^{k+1} \cdot d_{x+k} \cdot 1$. For the determinist there are exactly ℓ_{x+k} survivors at age $x+k$ paying an aggregate premium $\ell_{x+k} \cdot P_x$ having present value $v^k \cdot \ell_{x+k} \cdot P_x$, and d_{x+k} deaths between ages $x+k$ and $x+k+1$ resulting in aggregate death benefits of $d_{x+k} \cdot 1$ having present value $v^{k+1} \cdot d_{x+k} \cdot 1$. Thus (*) says the present value of premiums is exactly equal the present value of benefits. These two streams of money are viewed as certain annuities. For the probabilist, the premium P_x is such that the insurer *expects* to break even, that is $E\,[L] = A_x - P_x\ddot{a}_x = 0$. For some (x) the insurer loses money ("small" T), for others he profits ("large T"), and on average he breaks even.

COMPUTATIONAL REVIEW TEST

1. Suppose $L = 1000v^T - 10\bar{a}_{\overline{T|}}$ is the loss function for a fully continuous whole life insurance to (x), whose future lifetime T has the density function $f_T(t) = \frac{2t}{2500}$ for $0 \leq t \leq 50$. Assume $\delta = .05$.

   (a) Does the insurer expect to "profit" or "lose?" Hint: $\int_0^{50} e^{-.05t} \cdot t\, dt = 285.08$

   (b) What is the t_0 such that the insurer "breaks even" if $T = t_0$?

   (c) What is the probability that the insurer suffers a loss?

   (d) What annual premium should the insurer charge so that he will make a profit with 50% probability? That is, find P such that $Pr(L < 0) = .5$ where

   $L = 1000v^T - P\bar{a}_{\overline{T|}} = (1000+20P)e^{-.05T} - 20P$. First find the 50th percentile of T.

2. Assume $\delta = .05$, $\bar{A}_x = .06$, ${}^2\bar{A}_x = .0040$. A group of 100 lives age x purchase fully continuous whole life policies of face value \$1000 for annual premiums of \$3.50. Let L_{Agg} be the aggregate loss function $\sum_{i=1}^{100} L_i$ where each L_i is distributed like $L = 1000e^{-.05T} - 3.5\bar{a}_{\overline{T|}}$.

   (a) What is the expected aggregate loss?

   (b) Find the variance of L_{Agg}.

   (c) Apply the central limit theorem to L_{Agg} and the fact that $.95 = Pr(-1.96 \leq N(0,1) \leq 1.96)$ to find a 95% prediction interval for L_{Agg} (i.e., an interval I such that $.95 = Pr(L_{Agg} \in I)$).

3. Assuming a semicontinuous model, find the net level annual premium for 1000 of whole life to (35) with premiums paid semiannually. You are given:

   (i) $\ddot{a}_{35} = 15.39262$;
   (ii) $i = .06$;
   (iii) the UDD assumption

COMPUTATIONAL REVIEW TEST SOLUTIONS

1. (a) $L = \left(1000 + \frac{10}{.05}\right)v^T - \frac{10}{.05} = 1200\,e^{-.05T} - 200$, so

$E[L] = \frac{2400}{2500}\int_0^{50} e^{-.05t}\cdot t\,dt - 200 = \frac{24}{25}(285.08) - 200 = 73.67$; the insurer expects to lose.

(b) $0 = L = 1200\cdot e^{-.05t_0} - 200 \Rightarrow t_0 = \frac{-\,ln(2/12)}{.05} = 35.83$

(c) $Pr(L \geq 0) = Pr(T \leq t_0) = \int_0^{35.83}\frac{2t}{2500}dt = .51$

(d) Since L is a decreasing function of T, the 50th percentile of T corresponds to the 50th percentile of L. Now $.5 = Pr(T \leq t_m) = \int_0^{t_m}\frac{2t}{2500}dt \Rightarrow t_m = 35.355$. Thus we want a P such that the loss function is zero when $T = t_m$: $0 = (1000{+}20P)\,e^{-.05t_m} - 20P$ $\Rightarrow P = 10.29$.

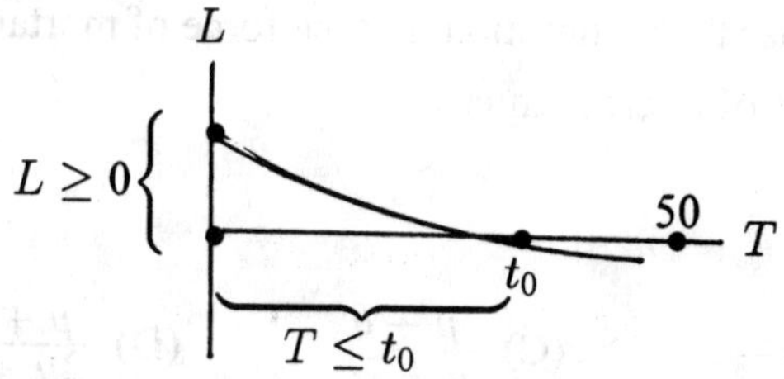

2. (a) $E[L_{Agg}] = 100E[L]$

$$= 100\left[\left(1000 + \frac{3.50}{.05}\right)E[v^T] - \frac{3.50}{.05}\right] = 100[1070(.06) - 70] = -\,580$$

(b) $Var(L_{Agg}) = 100\,Var(L) = 100\cdot\left(1000 + \frac{3.50}{.05}\right)^2\cdot({}^2\overline{A}_x - \overline{A}_x{}^2) = 45{,}796$, $\sigma_{Agg} = 214$

(c) Since $\frac{L_{Agg} - \mu(Agg)}{\sigma_{Agg}}$ is approximately standard normal,

$.95 \approx Pr\left(-1.96 \leq \frac{L_{Agg} - (-580)}{214} \leq 1.96\right)$, or equivalently

$.95 \approx Pr(-999 \leq L_{Agg} \leq -160)$.

3. $1000P^{(2)}(\overline{A}_{35}) = 1000\,\frac{\overline{A}_{35}}{\ddot{a}_{35}^{(2)}} = \frac{1000\cdot(\frac{i}{\delta})\,A_{35}}{\alpha(2)\ddot{a}_{35} - \beta(2)} = 8.75^*$

(Compare with $1000\cdot P(\overline{A}_{35}) = 8.61$)

*paid in two installments of 8.75/2 each policy year.

UNIT REVIEW QUESTIONS

1. A level premium whole life insurance of 1, payable at the end of the year of death, is issued to (x). A premium of G is due at the beginning of each year, provided (x) survives. You are given the following:
(i) L = the insurer's loss when $G = P_x$.
(ii) L^* = the insurer's loss when G is chosen such that $E[L^*] = -0.20$.
(iii) $Var(L) = 0.30$.

Calculate $Var(L^*)$.

(A) 0.192 (B) 0.240 (C) 0.300 (D) 0.360 (E) 0.432

2. A fully continuous whole life insurance of 1 is issued to (x). You are given the following:

$L = v^T - \overline{P}(\overline{A}_x)\bar{a}_{\overline{T|}}$ under the assumption that the force of mortality $\mu(x)$ equals μ for all x, and the force of interest equals δ.

Calculate $Var(L)$.

(A) $\frac{\mu}{\mu+2\delta}$ (B) $\frac{\mu}{\mu+\delta}$ (C) $\frac{\mu+\delta}{\mu+2\delta}$ (D) $\frac{\mu+2\delta}{2\mu+2\delta}$ (E) $\frac{2\mu+\delta}{2\mu+2\delta}$

3. An insured buys a whole life insurance policy with an initial death benefit of 1. The interest rate is 4%. The insured's net premiums and death benefit are scheduled to increase each year at a compound rate of 4%. The death benefit is payable at the end of the year of death. Calculate the net premium payable at the beginning of the first policy year.

(A) $\frac{v^2}{1+e_x}$ (B) $\frac{v}{1+e_x}$ (C) $\frac{1}{1+e_x}$ (D) $\frac{1+i}{1+e_x}$ (E) $\frac{(1+i)^2}{1+e_x}$

4. You are given the following information: $A_x = .19$ $\quad {}^2A_x = .064$ $\quad d = .057$ $\quad \pi_x = .019$

π_x is the gross annual premium the insurer charges per \$1 of whole life coverage. What is the minimum number of policies the insurer must issue to people aged x so that the probability of a positive total loss on the policies issued is less than or equal to .05? (You may assume different policies are independent risks, and use the fact that for the standard normal random variable Z, $Pr(Z \le 1.645) = .95$.)

(A) 21 (B) 22 (C) 23 (D) 24 (E) 25

5. A whole life policy issued to (x) has a net single premium of $\overline{A}_x = .4$ at $\delta = .06$, and $Var(L) = .25$ where L is the insurer's loss associated with the net annual premium $\overline{P}(\overline{A}_x)$. The insurer charges a gross annual premium of .05, payable continuously, and this results in a new loss function L'. Calculate $Var(L')$.

(A) .2500 (B) .2650 (C) .2750 (D) .2925 (E) .3025

6. A fully discrete level annual premium 10-year insurance to (30) pays 1 at the end of the year of death. If the insured is alive at the end of the 10-year period, all premiums are returned (without interest). The annual premium is determined by the equivalence principle. You are given:

(i) $A_{30:\overline{10|}} = .60$

(ii) $A_{\overset{\;\;1}{30}:\overline{10|}} = .47$

(iii) $d = .05$

Calculate the annual premium.

(A) .031 (B) .035 (C) .039 (D) .041 (E) .045

7. A deferred annuity is issued to (55) for an annual income of 10,000 commencing at age 65. Net annual premiums are to be paid during the deferred period. The death benefit during the premium paying period is the return of the net annual premiums without interest.

You are given:

(i) $\ddot{a}_{55:\overline{10|}} = 8$

(ii) $\ddot{a}_{55} = 12$

(iii) $IA^{1}_{55:\overline{10|}} = 2.5$

The death benefit is payable at the end of the year of death. Calculate the net annual premium.

(A) 5,400 (B) 6,675 (C) 7,273 (D) 11,129 (E) 14,546

8. L is the loss random variable for a fully-discrete, 2-year term insurance of 1 issued to (x). The net level annual premium is calculated using the equivalence principle. You are given:

(i) $q_x = .10$ (ii) $q_{x+1} = .20$ (iii) $v = .90$

Calculate $Var(L)$.

(A) .119 (B) .143 (C) .160 (D) .187 (E) .202

9. A fully-continuous level annual premium insurance issued to (x) pays a benefit $b_t = (1+i)^t$ at death. The premium is determined by the equivalence principle using interest rate i. L is the loss-at-issue random variable for this insurance. Determine an expression for L.

(A) $\dfrac{v^T - \overline{A}_x}{1 + \overline{A}_x}$ (B) $(v^T - \overline{A}_x)(1 - \overline{A}_x)$ (C) $v^T - \overline{A}_x$

(D) $(v^T - \overline{A}_x)(1 + \overline{A}_x)$ (E) $\dfrac{v^T - \overline{A}_x}{1 - \overline{A}_x}$

10. You are given:

(i) Deaths are uniformly distributed over each year of age
(ii) $i = .04$ and $\delta = .0392$
(iii) ${}_nE_x = .600$
(iv) $\overline{A}_{x:\overline{n}|} = .804$

Calculate $1000P(\overline{A}_{x:\overline{n}|})$.

(A) 153 (B) 155 (C) 157 (D) 159 (E) 161

11. L_1 is the loss-at-issue random variable for a fully continuous whole life insurance of 1 on the life of (x) with a net level annual premium determined by the equivalence principle.

You are given: (i) $\overline{a}_x = 5.0$ (ii) $\delta = .080$ (iii) $Var(L_1) = .5625$

L_2 is the loss-at-issue random variable for this insurance with a premium which is 4/3 times the net level annual premium. Calculate the sum of the expected value of L_2 and the standard deviation of L_2.

(A) .30 (B) .40 (C) .60 (D) .70 (E) .90

12. For a special fully discrete whole life insurance of 1000 issued on the life of (75), increasing premiums, π_k, are payable at time k, for $k = 0, 1, 2, \ldots$ You are given:

(i) $\pi_k = \pi_0(1+i)^k$
(ii) Mortality follows de Moivre's law with $\omega = 105$.
(iii) $i = .05$
(iv) Premiums are calculated in accordance with the equivalence principle.

Calculate π_0.

(A) 33.1 (B) 39.7 (C) 44.3 (D) 51.2 (E) 56.4

13. For a 10-year term insurance of 10,000 with death benefits payable at the end of the year of death of (30), you are given:

(i) $A^{\,1}_{30:\overline{10}|} = .015$ (ii) $\ddot{a}_{30:\overline{10}|} = 8$ (iii) ${}_{10}E_{30} = .604$ (iv) $i = .05$
(v) Deaths are uniformly distributed over each year of age.
(vi) Level true fractional premiums are determined in accordance with the equivalence principle.

Calculate the additional annual premium for this insurance if premiums are paid in monthly rather than semi-annual installments.

(A) .05 (B) .10 (C) .15 (D) .20 (E) .25

14. A fully discrete whole life insurance with annual premiums payable for 10 years is issued on (30).

You are given:

(i) The death benefit is equal to 1000 plus the refund of the net level annual premiums paid without interest.
(ii) Premiums are calculated in accordance with the equivalence principle.

Determine the net annual premium for this insurance.

(A) $\dfrac{1000A_{30}}{\ddot{a}_{30:\overline{10}|} + 10 \cdot {}_{10|}A_{30}}$ (B) $\dfrac{1000A_{30}}{\ddot{a}_{30:\overline{10}|} - 10 \cdot {}_{10|}A_{30}}$ (C) $\dfrac{1000A_{30}}{\ddot{a}_{30:\overline{10}|} - (IA)^{\,1}_{30:\overline{10}|}}$

(D) $\dfrac{1000A_{30}}{\ddot{a}_{30:\overline{10}|} - (IA)^{\,1}_{30:\overline{10}|} + 10 \cdot {}_{10|}A_{30}}$ (E) $\dfrac{1000A_{30}}{\ddot{a}_{30:\overline{10}|} - (IA)^{\,1}_{30:\overline{10}|} - 10 \cdot {}_{10|}A_{30}}$

15. L is the loss-at-issue random variable for a fully discrete whole life insurance of 1 on (49).

You are given:

(i) $A_{49} = .29224$, ${}^2A_{49} = .11723$
(ii) $i = .05$
(iii) $Var(L) = .10$

Calculate $E[L]$.

(A) -1.22 (B) $-.60$ (C) $-.25$ (D) $-.15$ (E) $.00$

16. L is the loss-at-issue random variable for a fully discrete whole life insurance of 1 on (x). The annual premium charged for this insurance is .044. You are given:

(i) $A_x = .40$
(ii) $\ddot{a}_x = 10$
(iii) $Var(L) = .12$

An insurer has a portfolio of 100 such insurances on 100 independent lives. Eighty of these insurances have death benefits of 4 and 20 have death benefits of 1. Assume that the total loss for this portfolio is distributed normally.

Calculate the probability that the present value of the gain for this portfolio is greater than 22.

(A) .01 (B) .07 (C) .10 (D) .16 (E) .25

17. L is the loss-at-issue random variable for a fully continuous whole life insurance of 2 on (x). This insurance has a total level annual premium rate of .09. You are given:

(i) $\mu(x+t) = .04$ for $t \geq 0$ (ii) $\delta = .06$

Calculate $Var(L)$.

(A) .02 (B) .09 (C) .32 (D) .56 (E) 1.10

18. The random variable ${}_0L$ is the prospective loss at issue for a fully continuous whole life insurance of 1 on (40). You are given:

(i) $\delta = .02$
(ii) Mortality follows de Moivre's law with $\ell_x = 100 - x, 0 \leq x \leq 100$.
(iii) ${}^2\overline{A}_{40} = .379$
(iv) Premiums are determined by the equivalence principle.

Calculate $Var({}_0L)$.

(A) .040 (B) .095 (C) .150 (D) .184 (E) .228

19. For a fully continuous whole life insurance of 1 on (x), you are given:

(i) Z is the present-value random variable at issue of the death benefit.
(ii) L is the loss-at-issue random variable.
(iii) Premiums are determined using the equivalence principle
(iv) $\dfrac{Var(Z)}{Var(L)} = .36$
(v) $\bar{a}_x = 10$

Calculate $\overline{P}(\overline{A}_x)$.

(A) .03 (B) .04 (C) .05 (D) .06 (E) .07

20. You are an actuary reviewing a tentative pricing calculation for a fully discrete whole life insurance of 1000 on (60). The tentative benefit premium seems surprisingly high. You discover that an incorrect value for q_{60} was used. You are given:

(i) $i = .06$
(ii) The incorrect value $q_{60} = .10$ was used.
(iii) Based on that incorrect value, $1000A_{60} = 405.54$.
(iv) The correct value is $q_{60} = .01$.
(v) For all other ages, the correct mortality rates were used.
(vi) L^* denotes the insurer's loss-at-issue random variable, assuming the tentative benefit premium is not corrected.

Calculate $E[L^*]$.

(A) −110 (B) −105 (C) −100 (D) −95 (E) −90

21. For a fully discrete whole life insurance of 10,000 on (30), you are given:

(i) π denotes an annual premium
(ii) $L(\pi)$ denotes the loss-at-issue random variable for this insurance
(iii) $\ell_{30} = 9{,}501{,}382$, $\ell_{77} = 4{,}828{,}285$, $\ell_{78} = 4{,}530{,}476$
(iv) $i = .06$

Calculate the lowest premium π' such that the probability is less than .5 that the loss $L(\pi')$ is positive.

(A) 34.6 (B) 36.6 (C) 36.8 (D) 39.0 (E) 39.1

22. A special fully discrete insurance on (25) with level premiums to age 65 provides the following benefits:

- A pure endowment of 150,000 payable at age 65.
- The return of the gross annual premiums accumulated with interest to the end of the year of death if the insured dies before age 65.

You are given:

(i) $i = .06$
(ii) $\ddot{s}_{\overline{40|}} = 164.05$
(iii) ${}_{40}p_{25} = .800$
(iv) $P_{25:\overline{40|}} = .008$
(v) The gross annual premium is equal to 1.2 times the net level premium.

Calculate the net level premium.

(A) 584 (B) 668 (C) 727 (D) 812 (E) 955

23. You are given:

(i) ${}_{k|}q_x = \dfrac{.90^{k+1}}{9}$, $k = 0, 1, 2, \ldots$
(ii) $i = .08$
(iii) The force of mortality, μ, is constant.

Calculate $1000(\overline{P}(\overline{A}_x) - P_x)$.

(A) 11.34 (B) 11.94 (C) 12.77 (D) 13.17 (E) 13.76

24. For a special decreasing term insurance on the life of (x), you are given:

(i) Z is the present value random variable:

$$Z = \begin{cases} v^{K+1} - \dfrac{\ddot{a}_{\overline{K+1}|}}{\ddot{s}_{\overline{5}|}} & K < 5 \\ 0 & K \geq 5 \end{cases}$$

(ii) $i = .05$

(iii) $P_{x:\overline{5}|} = .19$

Calculate the net level annual premium for this insurance.

(A) .010 (B) .012 (C) .014 (D) .016 (E) .018

25. A 25-year mortgage of 100,000 issued to (40) is to be repaid with equal annual payments at the end of each year. A 25-year term insurance has a death benefit which will pay off the mortgage at the end of the year of death including the payment then due. You are given:

(i) $i = .05$

(ii) $\ddot{a}_{40:\overline{25}|} = 14$

(iii) ${}_{25}q_{40} = .20$

Calculate the net annual premium for this term insurance.

(A) 405 (B) 414 (C) 435 (D) 528 (E) 694

Use the following information for Questions 26 - 30.

For a fully discrete whole life insurance on (x), you are given:

(i) $d = .05$ (ii) $A_x = .40$ (iii) ${}^2A_x = .20$

(iv) The annual premium is .05 times the amount of insurance.

(v) L is the loss function at issue if the face amount is 1.

(vi) A company has 145 policies of this type where 135 have face amount 1 and 10 have face amount 3.

26. This question consists of an assertion and a reason:

Assertion: $E[L] < 0$

Reason: The premium exceeds the premium determined by the equivalence principle.

Which of the following is correct?

(A) Both statements are correct, and the reason *is* a correct explanation.
(B) Both statements are correct, but the reason is *not* a correct explanation.
(C) The assertion is true, but the reason is false.
(D) The assertion is false, but the reason is true.
(D) Both statements are false.

27. Calculate $E[L]$.

(A) $-.20$ (B) $-.10$ (C) $.00$ (D) $.10$ (E) $.20$

28. Calculate $Var(L)$.

(A) .12 (B) .14 (C) .16 (D) .18 (E) .20

29. Determine the expected value and variance of the present value at issue of the losses on the 145 policies.

	$E[Loss]$	$Var(Loss)$
(A)	−37	26
(B)	−33	26
(C)	−33	36
(D)	0	26
(E)	0	36

30. Use the normal approximation to determine the probability that the present value at issue of the insurer's total gain on these policies will exceed 45.

(A) .01 (B) .02 (C) .03 (D) .05 (E) .10

Use the following information for Question 31-34.

π is the annual premium for a semicontinuous whole life insurance of 1 with death benefits payable at the moment of death of (45).

$L(\pi)$ is the loss-at-issue random variable for one such policy.

You are given:

(i) $A_{45} = .25191$, $\ddot{a}_{45} = 15.709843$, $\ell_{45} = 9{,}164{,}070$, $\ell_{77} = 4{,}828{,}285$, $\ell_{78} = 4{,}530{,}476$
(ii) $i = .05$
(iii) Deaths are uniformly distributed over each year of age.

31. Calculate π_a, the net level annual premium determined in accordance with the equivalence principle.

(A) .0155 (B) .0158 (C) .0161 (D) .0164 (E) .0167

32. Calculate the median of $T(45)$, the future lifetime of (45).

(A) 31.83 (B) 32.00 (C) 32.50 (D) 32.63 (E) 32.83

33. Express the median of $L(\pi)$ in terms of π.

(A) $.2015 - \pi(16.5928)$
(B) $.2015 - \pi(16.8027)$
(C) $.1998 - \pi(16.8027)$
(D) $.1998 - \pi(16.5928)$
(E) $.1998 - \pi(16.0025)$

34. Calculate π_b, the annual premium such that the median of $L(\pi_b)$ is $-.10$.

(A) .0173 (B) .0176 (C) .0179 (D) .0182 (E) .0185

Use the following information for Questions 35 - 38.

$L(\pi)$ is the loss-at-issue random variable for a fully-discrete whole life insurance of 1000 with level annual premiums π issued to (25). You are given:

(i) Mortality follows de Moivre's law with $\omega = 100$.
(ii) $i = .05$

35. $1000A_{25}$ is closest to

(A) 250 (B) 260 (C) 270 (D) 280 (E) 300

36. Calculate the premium, π_a, such that the distribution of $L(\pi_a)$ has mean zero.

(A) 15.71 (B) 15.96 (C) 16.21 (D) 16.46 (E) 16.71

37. Calculate the lowest premium, π_b, such that the probability is less than .25 that the loss, $L(\pi_b)$, is positive.

(A) 29.80 (B) 31.20 (C) 33.20 (D) 36.10 (E) 39.10

38. $E[L(\pi_b)]$ is closest to

(A) -195 (B) -205 (C) -215 (D) -225 (E) -250

UNIT REVIEW QUESTION SOLUTIONS

1. $L^* = v^{K+1} - G\ddot{a}_{\overline{K+1|}} = \left(1+\frac{G}{d}\right)v^{K+1} - \frac{G}{d} \Rightarrow Var(L^*) = \left(1+\frac{G}{d}\right)^2\left({}^2A_x - A_x{}^2\right)$.
Similarly $L = \left(1+\frac{P_x}{d}\right)v^{K+1} - \frac{P_x}{d} \Rightarrow Var(L) = \left(1+\frac{P_x}{d}\right)^2\left({}^2A_x - A_x{}^2\right)$. Thus
$\frac{Var(L^*)}{Var(L)} = \left(\frac{d+G}{d+P_x}\right)^2$. From $-.2 = E[L^*] = A_x - G\ddot{a}_x = 1 - d\ddot{a}_x - G\ddot{a}_x$ we get
$1.2 = d\ddot{a}_x + G\ddot{a}_x = \ddot{a}_x(d+G) = \frac{d+G}{d+P_x}$ since $\ddot{a}_x = \frac{1}{d+P_x}$. Substituting into the variance quotient gives $(1.2)^2 = \frac{Var(L^*)}{Var(L)} = \frac{Var(L^*)}{.30}$, $Var(L^*) = .432$ ANSWER E
Note: Since $\frac{1}{\ddot{a}_x} = d + P_x$ we have $\frac{d+G}{d+P_x} = (d+G)\ddot{a}_x = 1 - E[L^*]$.
Hence $\frac{Var(L^*)}{Var(L)} = (1 - E[L^*])^2$.

2. With constant force $\mu(x) = \mu$ we have $\overline{A}_x = \frac{\mu}{\mu+\delta}$, $\overline{P}(\overline{A}_x) = \frac{\overline{A}_x}{\overline{a}_x} = \frac{\delta\overline{A}_x}{1-\overline{A}_x} = \mu$.
Thus $L = \left(1 + \frac{\overline{P}(\overline{A}_x)}{\delta}\right)v^T - \frac{\overline{P}(\overline{A}_x)}{\delta}$ implies

$$Var(L) = \left(1 + \frac{\overline{P}(\overline{A}_x)}{\delta}\right)^2\left(\frac{\mu}{\mu+2\delta} - \left(\frac{\mu}{\mu+\delta}\right)^2\right) \quad \left[{}^2\overline{A}_x = \frac{\mu}{\mu+2\delta},\ \overline{A}_x = \frac{\mu}{\mu+\delta}\right]$$

$$= \frac{(\delta+\mu)^2}{\delta^2}\left[\frac{\mu(\mu+\delta)^2 - \mu^2(\mu+2\delta)}{(\mu+2\delta)(\mu+\delta)^2}\right] = \frac{\mu^3 + 2\mu^2\delta + \mu\delta^2 - \mu^3 - 2\mu^2\delta}{\delta^2\,(\mu+2\delta)} = \frac{\mu}{\mu+2\delta}$$

ANSWER A

3. Let P be the first-year net premium. Let $i = .04$, $v = 1.04^{-1}$. Then $P + ((1+i)P)v\,{}_1p_x + ((1+i)^2P)v^2\,{}_2p_x + \cdots = APV(\text{premiums}) = APV(\text{benefits})$ $= 1 \cdot v \cdot {}_{0|}q_x + (1+i)\cdot v^2 \cdot {}_{1|}q_x + \cdots$. The left side simplifies to $P(1+{}_1p_x+\cdots) = P(1+e_x)$ and the right side reduces to $v \cdot ({}_{0|}q_x + {}_{1|}q_x + \cdots) = v \cdot 1$. Thus $P = \frac{v}{1+e_x}$. ANSWER B

4. Loss function: $L = v^{K+1} - \pi\,\ddot{a}_{\overline{K+1|}} = \left(1+\frac{\pi}{d}\right)v^{K+1} - \frac{\pi}{d}$. Thus
$E[L] = (A_x - \pi\,\ddot{a}_x) = A_x - \pi\,\frac{(1-A_x)}{d} = .19 - .019\frac{.81}{.057} = -.08$ and
$Var(L) = \left(1+\frac{\pi}{d}\right)^2({}^2A_x - A_x{}^2) = \left(1+\frac{.019}{.057}\right)^2(.064 - .19^2) = \frac{16}{9}\cdot .0279 = .0496$.
$L_{Agg} =$ agg loss function $= \sum_{i=1}^{n} L_i$, $L_i \sim L$. Hence $E[L_{Agg}] = nE[L] = -.08n$, and
$Var(L_{Agg}) = nVar(L) = n(.0496)$, $\sigma_{L_{Agg}} = \sqrt{n}\,(.2227)$. Hence

$$.05 = Pr(L_{Agg} > 0) = Pr\left(\frac{L_{Agg} - \mu(L_{Agg})}{\sigma_{L_{Agg}}} > \frac{-\mu(L_{Agg})}{\sigma_{L_{Agg}}}\right) \approx Pr\left(N(0,1) > \frac{+.08n}{\sqrt{n}.\,2227}\right).$$

Since $.05 = P\left(N(0,1) > 1.645\right)$ we must have $1.645 = \frac{.08\sqrt{n}}{.2227}$; $n = 20.97$.
Thus $n = 21$ gives $Pr(L_{Agg} > 0) < .05$. ANSWER A

5. $$Var(L) = \frac{{}^2\overline{A}_x - \overline{A}_x{}^2}{(\delta \overline{a}_x)^2}$$

$$\Rightarrow \quad {}^2\overline{A}_x - \overline{A}_x{}^2 = Var(L)\delta^2\overline{a}_x^2 = .25(.06)^2\left(\frac{1-\overline{A}_x}{\delta}\right)^2 = .25(.0036)\left(\frac{1-.4}{.06}\right)^2 = .09.$$

Thus $Var(L') = \left(1+\frac{G}{\delta}\right)^2\left({}^2\overline{A}_x - \overline{A}_x{}^2\right) = \left(1+\frac{.05}{.06}\right)^2(.09) = .3025.$ ANSWER E

6. By the equivalence principle

$$P\ddot{a}_{30:\overline{10|}} = APV \text{ premium} = APV \text{ benefit} = A_{30:\overline{10|}}^{\;\;1} + (10P)A_{30:\overline{10|}}^{1}$$

Thus

$$P = \frac{A_{30:\overline{10|}}^{\;\;1}}{\ddot{a}_{30:\overline{10|}} - 10A_{30:\overline{10|}}^{1}} = \frac{.13}{8-4.7} = .039$$ ANSWER C

7. By the equivalence principle, if P is the net annual premium,

$$APV(\text{premiums}) = APV(\text{benefits}) \text{ implies } P\ddot{a}_{55:\overline{10|}} = \underbrace{10{,}000\,({}_{10|}\ddot{a}_{55})}_{\text{(survivor benefit)}} + \underbrace{P(IA_{55:\overline{10|}}^{1})}_{\text{(death benefit)}}$$

Thus $P = \frac{10{,}000({}_{10|}\ddot{a}_{55})}{\ddot{a}_{55:\overline{10|}} - IA_{55:\overline{10|}}^{1}} = \frac{10{,}000(4)}{8-2.5} = 7{,}273,$ ANSWER C

8. $$P_{x:\overline{2|}}^{1} = \frac{A_{x:\overline{2|}}^{1}}{\ddot{a}_{x:\overline{2|}}} = \frac{(.9)(.1)+(.9)^2(.9)(.2)}{1+(.9)(.9)} = \frac{.23580}{1.81} = .13028.$$

K	Loss_K	Probability
0	$.9 - .13028 = .76972$	.1
1	$.9^2 - .13028\ddot{a}_{\overline{2|}} = .56247$	(.9)(.2)
≥ 2	$-.13028\ddot{a}_{\overline{2|}} = -.24753$	(.9)(.8)

$Var(L) = E[L^2] - \left(E[L]\right)^2 = .16031 - 0^2,$ ANSWER C

Note: For term insurances, variance of the loss function does not follow the pattern with whole life and endowment insurances; $Var(L) \neq \left(1+\frac{P_{x:\overline{2|}}^{1}}{d}\right)^2({}^2A_{x:\overline{2|}}^{1} - A_{x:\overline{2|}}^{1}{}^2)$

9. If P is the level annual premium paid continuously then the loss function L is given by

$$L = b_T \cdot v_T - P\overline{a}_{\overline{T|}} = \text{excess p.v. of benefit over p.v. premium}$$
$$= (1+i)^T \cdot v^T - P\overline{a}_{\overline{T|}} = 1 - P\overline{a}_{\overline{T|}}.$$

The net premium P is such that $E[L] = 1 - P\overline{a}_x$ equals zero, i.e., $P = \frac{1}{\overline{a}_x}$. Thus

$$L = 1 - P\overline{a}_{\overline{T|}} = 1 - \frac{\overline{a}_{\overline{T|}}}{\overline{a}_x} = \frac{\delta\overline{a}_x - (1-v^T)}{\delta\overline{a}_x} = \frac{v^T - (1-\delta\overline{a}_x)}{\delta\overline{a}_x} = \frac{v^T - \overline{A}_x}{1-\overline{A}_x},$$ ANSWER E

10. By definition, $1000P(\overline{A}_{x:\overline{n}|}) = 1000 \cdot \dfrac{\overline{A}_{x:\overline{n}|}}{\ddot{a}_{x:\overline{n}|}} = \dfrac{1000(.804)}{\ddot{a}_{x:\overline{n}|}}$.

Now $\ddot{a}_{x:\overline{n}|} = \dfrac{1-A_{x:\overline{n}|}}{d} = \frac{104}{4}\left(1 - A^{1}_{x:\overline{n}|} - A_{x:\overset{\;\;1}{\overline{n}|}}\right)$.

$A_{x:\overset{\;\;1}{\overline{n}|}}$ is given as ${}_nE_x = .600$ and $A^{1}_{x:\overline{n}|}$ can be coaxed out of the UDD relation

$$\overline{A}_{x:\overline{n}|} = \tfrac{i}{\delta} \cdot A^{1}_{x:\overline{n}|} + A_{x:\overset{\;\;1}{\overline{n}|}}$$

$$.804 = \frac{.04}{.0392} \cdot A^{1}_{x:\overline{n}|} + .600 \Rightarrow A^{1}_{x:\overline{n}|} = .199920.$$

Hence $\ddot{a}_{x:\overline{n}|} = \frac{104}{4}(1 - .199920 - .600) = 5.20208$, and $1000P(\overline{A}_{x:\overline{n}|}) = \dfrac{1000(.804)}{5.20208} = 154.55$,

ANSWER B

11. Note the contrast between the loss functions L_1 and L_2:

$$L_1 = v^T - \overline{P}(\overline{A}_x) \cdot \overline{a}_{\overline{T}|} = \left(1 + \frac{\overline{P}(\overline{A}_x)}{\delta}\right) v^T - \frac{\overline{P}(\overline{A}_x)}{\delta}$$

$$L_2 = v^T - \tfrac{4}{3}\overline{P}(\overline{A}_x)\overline{a}_{\overline{T}|} = \left(1 + \frac{4\overline{P}(\overline{A}_x)}{3\delta}\right) v^T - \frac{4\overline{P}(\overline{A}_x)}{3\delta}.$$

Thus

$$\frac{Var(L_2)}{Var(L_1)} = \frac{\left(1+\frac{4\overline{P}(\overline{A}_x)}{3\delta}\right)^2 Var(v^T)}{\left(1+\frac{\overline{P}(\overline{A}_x)}{\delta}\right)^2 Var(v^T)}.$$

Since $\overline{a}_x = 5.0$ and $\delta = .08$, $\overline{A}_x = 1 - \delta\overline{a}_x = 1 - .4 = .6$ so $\overline{P}(\overline{A}_x) = \frac{\overline{A}_x}{\overline{a}_x} = \frac{.6}{5} = .12$.
Substituting in the above

$$Var(L_2) = Var(L_1) \cdot \frac{\left[1+\frac{(4)(.12)}{3(.08)}\right]^2}{\left(1+\frac{.12}{.08}\right)^2} = (.5625)\left(\frac{30}{25}\right)^2 = .81.$$

Also $E[L_2] = E\left[L_1 - \tfrac{1}{3}\overline{P}(\overline{A}_x)\overline{a}_{\overline{T}|}\right] = E[L_1] - \frac{\overline{P}(\overline{A}_x)}{3}\overline{a}_x = 0 - \frac{.12}{3}(5) = -.2$.
So $E[L_2] + \sqrt{VarL_2} = -.2 + \sqrt{.81} = .7$,

ANSWER D

12. With $x = 75$, $\omega = 105$ and de Moivre's law one can use $\ell_x = 105 - x$.
Thus ${}_{k|}q_{75} = \dfrac{\ell_{75+k} - \ell_{75+k+1}}{\ell_{75}} = \dfrac{1}{30}$ and

$1000A_{75} = 1000\sum_{k=0}^{29} v^{k+1} \cdot {}_{k|}q_{75} = \frac{1000}{30} a_{\overline{30}|.05} = 512.4150$. The APV of premiums is calculated as

$$\pi_0 + \pi_1 \cdot v^1 \cdot {}_1p_{75} + \pi_2 \cdot v^2 \cdot {}_2p_{75} + \cdots + \pi_{29} \cdot v^{29} \cdot {}_{29}p_{75}$$

$$= \pi_0 + \pi_0(1+i)v \cdot {}_1p_{25} + \cdots + \pi_0(1+i)^{29}v^{29} \cdot {}_{29}p_{75}$$

$$= \pi_0(1 + {}_1p_{75} + \cdots + {}_{29}p_{75})$$

$$= \pi_0\left(1 + \frac{29}{30} + \frac{28}{30} + \cdots + \frac{1}{30}\right) = \pi_0\left(\frac{30 \cdot 31}{2 \cdot 30}\right).$$

Hence, by the equivalence principle, $\pi_0 \cdot \frac{31}{2} = 512.4150$, or $\pi_0 = 33.06$,

ANSWER A

13. For true m^{th}-ly premiums under the UDD we have

$$P^{1(m)}_{x:\overline{10}|} = \frac{A^{1}_{x:\overline{10}|}}{\ddot{a}^{(m)}_{x:\overline{10}|}} = \frac{A^{1}_{x:\overline{10}|}}{\alpha(m)\cdot\ddot{a}^{(m)}_{x:\overline{10}|} - \beta(m)(1-{}_{10}E_x)},$$

where $\alpha(2)$, $\beta(2)$, $\alpha(12)$ and $\beta(12)$ are available in the accompanying tables at $i = .05$. Substituting numbers from the problem and data from the tables yields

$$10{,}000P^{1(2)}_{x:\overline{10}|} = \frac{150}{(1.00015)(8)-(.25617)(.396)} = 18.99$$

$$10{,}000P^{1(12)}_{x:\overline{10}|} = \frac{150}{(1.00020)(8)-(.46651)(.396)} = 19.19.$$

The difference is .20, ANSWER D

14. If P is the level annual premium, the APV of the refund benefit is the expected value of

$$Z = \begin{cases} (K+1)P\cdot v^{K+1} & K=0,1,\ldots,9 \\ 10P\cdot v^{K+1} & K=10,11,\ldots, \end{cases}$$

which is $E[Z] = P\cdot(IA)^{1}_{30:\overline{10}|} + 10P\cdot{}_{10|}A_{30}$. The basic equation for P is

$$\begin{aligned} P\cdot\ddot{a}_{30:\overline{10}|} &= APV(\text{premium}) = APV(\text{benefit}) = APV(\text{refund}) + APV(\text{regular death benefit}) \\ &= E[Z] + 1000A_{30} \\ &= P\cdot(IA)^{1}_{30:\overline{10}|} + 10P\cdot{}_{10|}A_{30} + 1000A_{30}. \end{aligned}$$

Solving for P produces ANSWER E. Notice that if the refund feature was only awarded during the premium paying period, then the factor $-10P\cdot{}_{10|}A_{30}$ would be missing from the $E[Z]$ expression and the last equation above, and ANSWER C would then be correct.

15. If P is the amount of annual premium, then the loss function is

$$L = \underbrace{v^{K+1} - P\cdot\ddot{a}_{\overline{K+1}|}}_{\text{Best for } E[L]} = \underbrace{\left(1+\tfrac{P}{d}\right)v^{K+1} - \tfrac{P}{d}}_{\text{Best for } Var(L)}.$$

So

$$E[L] = E[v^{K+1}] - P\cdot E\left[\ddot{a}_{\overline{K+1}|}\right] = A_{49} - P\cdot\ddot{a}_{49}$$

$$Var(L) = \left(1+\tfrac{P}{d}\right)^2({}^2A_{49} - A_{49}{}^2)$$

since $K = K(49)$. Substituting $.10 = Var(L), {}^2A_{49} = .11723$, $A_{49} = .29224$, and $d = \frac{.05}{1.05}$ into the variance expression, you can obtain $P = .036790$. Substituting this value, the A_{49} value above, and $\ddot{a}_{49} = 14.862997$ into the $E[L]$ expression results in

$$E[L] = (.29224) - (.036790)(14.862997) = -.25,$$ ANSWER C

16. The loss function for a \$1 policy, $L = v^{k+1} - (.044)\ddot{a}_{\overline{k+1}|}$, has expected value

$$E[L] = A_x - (.044)\ddot{a}_x = .40 - (.044)(10) = -.04 \quad (\text{ a profit!}).$$

The aggregate loss on the mentioned 100 contracts can be written as

$$L_{Agg} = \sum_{i=1}^{80} 4 \cdot L_i + \sum_{i=81}^{100} 1 \cdot L_i$$

where $L_1, \ldots, L_{100}$ are independent and identically distributed like L.

Hence

$$\mu(Agg) = (80)(4)E[L] + (20)(1)E[L] = -13.60$$
$$\sigma^2_{Agg} = (80)(4)^2 Var(L) + (20)(1)^2 Var(L) = 156$$

and so

$$\begin{aligned} Pr(\text{Present Value Gain} > 22) &= Pr(L_{Agg} < -22) \\ &= Pr\left(\frac{L_{Agg} - \mu(Agg)}{\sigma_{Agg}} < \frac{-22 + 13.60}{\sqrt{156}} = -.673\right) \\ &\approx Pr(N(0,1) < -.673) = Pr(N(0,1) > .673) \\ &= 1 - Pr(N(0,1) < .673) \approx 1 - .75 = .25 \text{ (table)} \end{aligned}$$

ANSWER E

17. The loss function described is $L = 2 \cdot v^T - (.09)\overline{a}_{\overline{T}|}$, which can be rewritten as

$$L = 2 \cdot v^T - (.09)\frac{1 - v^T}{.06} = 3.5v^T - 1.5.$$

As a result,
$Var(L) = Var(3.5v^T - 1.5) = Var(3.5v^T) = 3.5^2\, Var(v^T) = 3.5^2\,({}^2\overline{A}_x - \overline{A}_x{}^2))$. With the assumption of constant force $\overline{A}_x = \dfrac{\mu}{\mu + \delta} = \dfrac{.04}{.04 + .06} = \dfrac{4}{10}$,
${}^2\overline{A}_x = \dfrac{\mu}{\mu + 2\delta} = \dfrac{.04}{.16} = \dfrac{1}{4}$. Finally $Var(X) = (3.5)^2\left(\frac{1}{4} - \left(\frac{4}{10}\right)^2\right) = 1.1025$.

ANSWER E

18. For this fully continuous life insurance $Var(L) = \left(1 + \dfrac{\overline{P}(\overline{A})}{\delta}\right)^2 ({}^2\overline{A}_x - \overline{A}_x{}^2) = \dfrac{({}^2\overline{A}_x - \overline{A}_x{}^2)}{(1 - \overline{A}_x)^2}$.
From de Moivre's law we have seen $\overline{A}_x = \left(\dfrac{1}{\omega - x}\right)\overline{a}_{\overline{\omega - x}|}$, ${}^2\overline{A}_x = \left(\dfrac{1}{\omega - x}\right){}^2\overline{a}_{\overline{\omega - x}|}$. Here $\overline{A}_{40} = \dfrac{1}{60}\overline{a}_{\overline{60}|} = \dfrac{1}{60}\left(\dfrac{1 - e^{-.02(60)}}{.02}\right) = .5823$ and the given ${}^2\overline{A}_{40}$ could have been calculated as $\left(\frac{1}{60}\right)\left(\dfrac{1 - e^{-.04(60)}}{.04}\right)$.

ANSWER E

19. $Var(Z) = ({}^2\overline{A}_x - \overline{A}_x{}^2)$ whereas $Var(L) = \dfrac{({}^2\overline{A}_x - \overline{A}_x{}^2)}{(1-\overline{A}_x)^2}$. So $.36 = \dfrac{Var(Z)}{Var(L)}$ means $.36 = (1-\overline{A}_x)^2$, $\overline{A}_x = .4$. Since $\overline{a}_x = 10$ we see $\overline{P}(\overline{A}_x) = \frac{.4}{10} = .04$. ANSWER B

20. From $L = 1000[v^{K+1} - P_{60}\ddot{a}_{\overline{K+1|}}] = 1000\left[\left(1+\frac{P_{60}}{d}\right)v^{K+1} - \frac{P_{60}}{d}\right]$, $K = K(60)$, it follows that $E[L] = 1000\left[\left(1+\frac{P_{60}}{d}\right)A_{60} - \frac{P_{60}}{d}\right]$. Now $\frac{P_{60}}{d} = \frac{A_{60}}{1-A_{60}} = \frac{.40554}{1-.40554} = .6822$. In computing $E[L^*]$ the $\frac{P_{60}}{d}$ factor is uncorrected, whereas A_{60} is replaced by the corrected A^*_{60} based on $q_{60} = .01$:

$$.40554 = A_{60} = vq_{60} + vp_{60}A_{61} = \left(\frac{1}{1.06}\right)\underbrace{(.10)}_{\text{error}} + \left(\frac{1}{1.06}\right)\underbrace{(.90)}_{\text{error}}A_{61}$$

$$\Rightarrow \quad A_{61} = .36652$$

$$\Rightarrow \quad A^*_{60} = \left(\frac{1}{1.06}\right)\underbrace{(.01)}_{\text{corrected}} + \left(\frac{1}{1.06}\right)\underbrace{(.99)}_{\text{corrected}}(.36652) = .35175$$

$$\Rightarrow \quad E[L^*] = 1000[\underbrace{(1+.6822)}_{\text{uncorrected}}\underbrace{(.35175)}_{\text{corrected}} - \underbrace{.6822}_{\text{uncorrected}}] = -90.48$$

ANSWER E

21. $L(\pi)$ is a decreasing function of $K = K(30)$. With $\ell_{30} = 9{,}501{,}382$ we see that $\ell_{77} < .5\ell_{30} < \ell_{78}$. The median of $K(30)$ is between 47 and 48, which corresponds to the 48th policy year. If π is set to break even if $K+1 = 48$ then $Pr(L(\pi) > 0) = Pr(K+1 \le 47) = 1 - \frac{\ell_{77}}{\ell_{30}} = .492$. If P is the slightest bit smaller you will also have a positive loss if $K+1 = 48$ (i.e., $Pr(L>0) \ge Pr(K+1 \le 48 = .523)$. To break even in policy year 48 you need $\pi\ddot{s}_{\overline{48|}.06} = 1$ (the accumulation of 48 premiums is exactly equal to the benefit needed):

$$\pi = \frac{1}{\ddot{s}_{\overline{48|}.06}} = \frac{1}{271.96}, \quad 10{,}000\pi = 36.77.$$

ANSWER C

22. From the equivalence principle,

$$P\ddot{a}_{25:\overline{40|}} = APV(\text{Premium}) = APV(\text{Pure Endowment}) + APV(\text{Premium Refund})$$

$$= 150{,}000\,{}_{40}E_{25} + \underbrace{1.2P[\ddot{a}_{25:\overline{40|}} - \ddot{a}_{\overline{40|}} \cdot {}_{40}p_{25}]}_{\text{see the last page of the Unit Review Notes}}$$

Substituting

$$\ddot{a}_{25:\overline{40|}} = \frac{1}{d + P_{25:\overline{40|}}} = \frac{1}{[(\frac{.06}{1.06} + .008)]} = 15.47897$$

$$\ddot{a}_{\overline{40|}.06} = 15.949, \quad {}_{40}p_{25} = .80$$

$${}_{40}E_{25} = v^{40} \cdot {}_{40}p_{25} = (1.06)^{-40}(.80) = .0778$$

into the above results in $P = 955.07$. ANSWER E

23. With constant force $\overline{P}(\overline{A}_x) = \frac{\overline{A}_x}{\overline{a}_x} = \frac{\left(\frac{\mu}{\mu+\delta}\right)}{\left(\frac{1}{\mu+\delta}\right)} = \mu$. Also

$$\ddot{a}_x = 1 + vp_x + v^2\,{}_2p_x + \cdots = 1 + e^{-\delta}e^{-\mu} + e^{-2\delta}e^{-2\mu} + \cdots$$
$$= \sum_{k=0}^{\infty}(e^{-(\mu+\delta)})^k = \frac{1}{(1-e^{-(\mu+\delta)})} = \frac{e^{\delta}}{(e^{\delta}-e^{-\mu})}$$
$$= \frac{(1+i)}{[(1+i)-(1-q_x)]} = \frac{(1+i)}{(i+q_x)}.$$

Hence $P_x = \frac{1}{\ddot{a}_x} - d = \frac{i+q_x}{1+i} - \frac{i}{1+i} = \frac{q_x}{1+i}$. From $.9^k(.1) = \frac{.9^{k+1}}{9} = {}_{k|}q_x = {}_kp_x \cdot q_{x+k} = e^{-k\mu}(1-e^{-\mu})$ we see that $.9 = e^{-\mu} = p_x$ and $q_x = .10$. Finally $\overline{P}(\overline{A}_x) = \mu = -ln(p_x) = -ln(.9) = .10536$, $P_x = \frac{q_x}{1+i} = \frac{.10}{1.08} = .09259$, and $1000(\overline{P}(\overline{A}_x) - P_x) = 12.77$. ANSWER C

24. We are seeking $P = \frac{E[Z]}{\ddot{a}_{x:\overline{5}|}}$, the net level annual premium. Z can be rewritten as

$$\begin{cases} v^{K+1} \\ 0 \end{cases} - \left(\frac{1}{\ddot{s}_{\overline{5}|}}\right)\begin{cases} \ddot{a}_{\overline{K+1}|} \\ 0 \end{cases}.$$

Thus $E[Z] = A^{1}_{x:\overline{5}|} - \frac{1}{\ddot{s}_{\overline{5}|}}\underbrace{[\ddot{a}_{x:\overline{5}|} - \ddot{a}_{\overline{5}|}\cdot {}_5p_x]}_{\text{See last page of Unit Review Notes}}$.

Next, notice that $E[Z] = A^{1}_{x:\overline{5}|} + v^5\,{}_5p_x - \frac{\ddot{a}_{x:\overline{5}|}}{\ddot{s}_{\overline{5}|}} = A_{x:\overline{5}|} - \frac{\ddot{a}_{x:\overline{5}|}}{\ddot{s}_{\overline{5}|}}$.

Thus $P = \frac{E[Z]}{\ddot{a}_{x:\overline{5}|}} = P_{x:\overline{5}|} - \frac{1}{\ddot{s}_{\overline{5}|}} = .19 - \frac{1}{5.8019} = .0176$. ANSWER E

25. Each payment is $\frac{100{,}000}{a_{\overline{25}|.05}} = 7095.25$. The APV of these payments is $7095.25\ a_{40:\overline{25}|} = 7095.25(\ddot{a}_{40:\overline{25}|} - 1 + v^{25}\,{}_{25}p_{40}) = 93{,}914.39$. The shortfall in comparison to the loan of 100,000 is 6085.61. This must be made up by the insurance premiums. Thus if P is the level annual premium, $6085.61 = P\cdot\ddot{a}_{40:\overline{25}|} = P(14)$, so $P = 434.69$, ANSWER C

26 - 30.
Here $P_x = \frac{A_x}{\ddot{a}_x} = \frac{dA_x}{1-A_x} = .03\overline{3}$, so $G = .05 > P_x$, and

$$E[L] = A_x - G\ddot{a}_x = A_x - (G-P_x+P_x)\ddot{a}_x$$
$$= (A_x - P_x\ddot{a}_x) + (P_x - G)\ddot{a}_x = 0 + (P_x-G)\ddot{a}_x$$
$$= (.03\overline{3} - .05)(12) = -.20,$$

so Question 26 has ANSWER A and Question 27 has ANSWER A.

Here $Z = v^{K+1}$, $Y = \ddot{a}_{\overline{K+1|}}$ and $L = Z - .05Y$. Hence

$$L = v^{K+1} - .05\,\frac{1-v^{K+1}}{d} = \left(1 + \tfrac{.05}{.05}\right)(v^{K+1}) - \tfrac{.05}{.05} = 2Z - 1.$$

Using $Var(aX + b) = a^2Var(X)$ gives

$$Var(L) = 2^2Var(Z) = 4({}^2A_x - A_x^2) = 4(.2 - .16) = .16.$$

Question 28 has ANSWER C.

If $L_1, \ldots, L_{145}$ are independent and identically distributed as L above (i.e., $E[L_i] = -.20$ and $Var(L_i) \doteq .16$), then the insurer's aggregate loss is

$$L_{Agg} = \sum_{i=1}^{135} L_i + \sum_{i=136}^{145} 3L_i.$$

Thus $\mu(Agg) = 135E[L] + 10(3)E[L] = 165(-.2) = -33$, and
$\sigma^2_{Agg} = 135Var(L) + 10(3^2)Var(L) = 225(.16) = 36.$

By the central limit theorem, L_{Agg} is approximately $N(\mu = -33, \sigma^2 = 36)$, so

$$Pr(\text{Gain} > 45) = Pr(L_{Agg} < -45) \doteq Pr\left(N(0,1) < \frac{-45-(-33)}{\sqrt{36}} = -2\right),$$

which is found to be .023 in the accompanying tables.

Question 29 has ANSWER C and Question 30 has ANSWER B.

31 - 34.
From the description (semi-continuous) we see that the net level annual premium is

$$\pi_a = P(\overline{A}_{45}) = \frac{\overline{A}_{45}}{\ddot{a}_{45}} \underset{\text{UDD}}{=} \frac{i}{\delta}\,\frac{A_{45}}{\ddot{a}_{45}} = 1.0248\left(\frac{.25191}{15.709843}\right) = .016433.$$

Question 31 has ANSWER D.

If m is the median of $T(45)$, then $.5 = Pr(T(45) \le m) = {}_mq_{45} = {}_mp_{45} = \ell_{45+m}/\ell_{45}$. Thus

$$\ell_{45+m} = .5\ell_{45} = .5(9{,}164{,}070) = 4{,}582{,}035.$$

From the given information we see $\ell_{77} = 4{,}828{,}285 > \ell_{45+m} > 4{,}530{,}476 = \ell_{78}$. Linearly interpolating between ℓ_{77} and ℓ_{78} (i.e., UDD is in effect), we find

$$45 + m = 77 + \frac{4{,}828{,}285 - 4{,}582{,}035}{4{,}828{,}285 - 4{,}530{,}476}, \text{ which implies } m = 32.83.$$

Question 32 has ANSWER E.

Since the plan is semi-continuous, $L(\pi) = v^T - \pi \cdot \ddot{a}_{\overline{K+1}|}$, where $T = T(45)$. This is a decreasing function of T, so the median of $L(\pi)$ is the value of $L(\pi)$ at the median of T; $m = 32.83 = T$ implies that $K+1 = 33$, so the median of $L(\pi)$ is $v^{32.83} - \pi \cdot \ddot{a}_{\overline{33}|} = .2015 - \pi(16.8027)$.

Question 33 has ANSWER B.

Setting $.2015 - \pi(16.8027) = -.10$ produces $\pi_b = .0179$.

Question 34 has ANSWER C.

35 - 38.

The loss function is given by $L(\pi) = 1000 \cdot v^{K+1} - \pi \cdot \ddot{a}_{\overline{K+1}|}$ (the excess present value of benefits over the present value of premiums) where K is the curtate future lifetime of (25). Given de Moivre's law we can assume $\ell_x = 100 - x$ and hence

$$Pr(K \leq k) = {}_{k+1}q_{25} = \frac{\ell_{25} - \ell_{25+k+1}}{\ell_{25}} = \frac{75 - (75-k-1)}{75} = \frac{k+1}{75}.$$

If $E\left[L(\pi_a)\right] = 0$ then π_a is the net annual premium $\pi_a = 1000 \cdot \frac{A_{25}}{\ddot{a}_{25}} = 1000 \cdot \frac{dA_{25}}{1 - A_{25}}$.

From de Moivre's law:

$$A_{25} = \sum_{k=0}^{74} v^{k+1} \cdot {}_{k|}q_{25} = \sum_{k=0}^{74} v^{k+1} \cdot \frac{d_{25+k}}{\ell_{25}} = \sum_{k=0}^{74} v^{k+1} \cdot \frac{1}{75} = \frac{1}{75}\, a_{\overline{75}|.05} = \frac{1 - v^{75}}{75(.05)} = .25980.$$

Question 35 has ANSWER B.

Thus

$$\pi_a = 1000 \cdot \frac{(\frac{1}{21})(.25980)}{1 - .25980} = 16.71.$$

Question 36 has ANSWER E.

Remember that losses occur for early deaths (i.e., $L > 0$ means $K \leq k_0$).

Now $.25 > Pr(K \leq k_0) = \frac{1 + k_0}{75}$ means $k_0 \leq 17.75$. So if we pick π_b so as to break even if $K = 18$, that is $0 = 1000 \cdot v^{18+1} - \pi_b \cdot \ddot{a}_{\overline{18+1}|}$, then $Pr(L > 0) = Pr(K \leq 17) < .25$. Multiplying the above equation by $(1+i)^{19}$ and solving for π_b gives $\pi_b = \frac{1000}{\ddot{s}_{\overline{19}|.05}} = 31.19$.

Question 37 has ANSWER B.

The expected loss with the premium in (b) is given by

$$\begin{aligned} E\left[L(\pi_b)\right] &= 1000 \cdot A_{25} - \pi_b \cdot \ddot{a}_{25} \\ &= 1000(.25980) - (31.19)\left(\frac{1 - .25980}{1/21}\right) \\ &= 259.80 - 484.82 = -225.02 \quad \text{(a profit!)} \end{aligned}$$

Question 38 has ANSWER D.

UNIT 4: BENEFIT OR NET PREMIUM RESERVES

Net Level Premium Reserves in the Fully Discrete Whole Life Model: The Aggregate Deterministic View

As a numerical introduction to the idea of reserves, we want to return to our familiar example with the $\ell_x = 100$, 90-year-olds purchasing fully discrete whole life insurance with face value of 1000. (Afterwards we will look at the problem algebraically, and in the next section risk theoretically.) Below we have summarized some of the results already calculated in previous examples with this model.

x	90	91	92	93
ℓ_x	100	72	39	0
d_x	28	33	39	—

$i = .06, \quad A_{90} = .885301, \quad 1000P_{90} = 436.90$ (nearest penny)

AGGREGATE DETERMINISTIC VIEW OF INSURER'S CASHFLOW

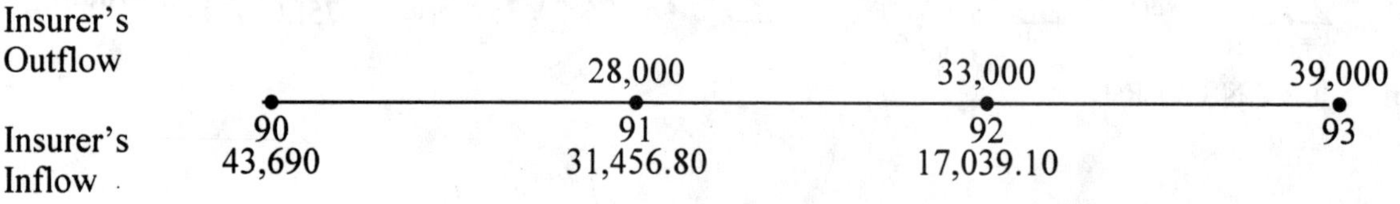

AGGREGATE DETERMINISTIC SPREADSHEET

Policy Year	Beginning Fund Balance	New Premium	Annual Interest	Annual Benefits	Ending Balance
1	0	43,690.00	2,621.40	28,000	18,311.40
2	18,311.40	31,456.80	2,986.09	33,000	19,754.29
3	19,754.29	17,039.10	2,207.60	39,000	1.00
		↑ Inflow in above diagram		↑ Outflow in above diagram	

As we saw before, in the determinist's view net level annual premiums are exactly[1] enough to break even in the long run. This is the first lesson built into this example. Now let's focus on the short run, just the first policy year. At the end of this year there is a fund of 18,311.40 that has accumulated as a result of more premium and interest income than benefit costs. This fund is an asset for the insurer.

---

[1] 1.00 at end of year 3 is due to premium rounding.

In a general accounting framework the assets of a business, at any point in time, can be split into liabilities (totality of obligations) plus equity (that which is left over). In insurance parlance liabilities are referred to as "reserves" and equity as "surplus." So how much of the 18,311.40 asset at time $t = 1$ is surplus and how much is liability? From an intuitive point of view one might guess that surplus is zero, that is, liability exactly matches the asset. The reason is this: If there were some surplus, take it out of the business. Go buy a new BMW. But notice that all of the 18,311.40 is eventually needed for the insurer to break even, because in years two and three, benefits exceed premium. Here is the way to see precisely that the liability at time $t = 1$ matches the asset. If the insurer looks into the future for the remaining $\ell_{91} = 72$ policies in force he sees the following:

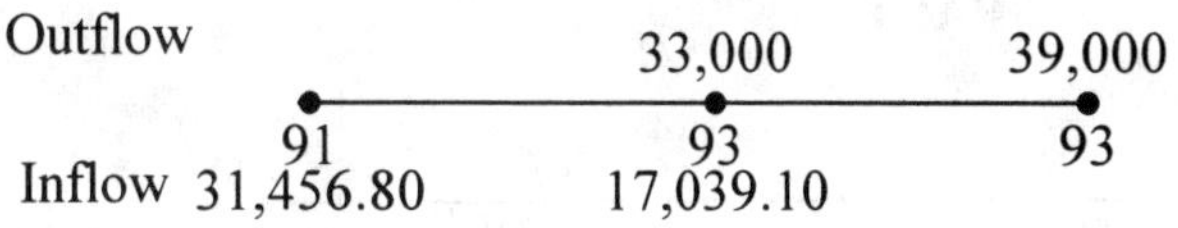

$$\text{Present Value Outflow} = \frac{33{,}000}{1.06} + \frac{39{,}000}{1.06^2} = 65{,}841.94$$

$$\text{Present Value Inflow} = 31{,}456.80 + \frac{17{,}039.10}{1.06} = 47{,}531.42$$

$$\text{Present Value of Future Shortfall} = 65{,}841.94 - 47{,}531.42 = 18{,}310.52$$
(i.e., liability)

Here is the second important lesson in this example. Except for rounding error, this liability exactly matches the asset. This is a general trend in net premium accounting.

The 18,310.51 liability at time $t = 1$ is the aggregate, first-year, net level premium reserve. When it is allocated to the $\ell_{91} = 72$ remaining policies, $254.32 = \frac{18{,}310.51}{72}$ is the first year reserve for an individual policy. In standard actuarial notation we would write

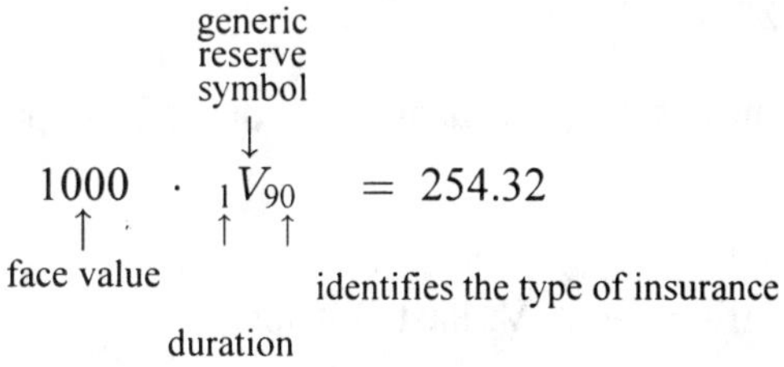

as notation for the reserve at duration one (i.e., the end of the first policy year).

Now let's take a look at a slightly more general problem from an algebraic point of view. All ℓ_x lives at age x purchase a dollar of fully-discrete whole life, paying P_x at the beginning of each policy year. Recall that P_x was such that the present values of the insurer's aggregate inflow and outflow match.

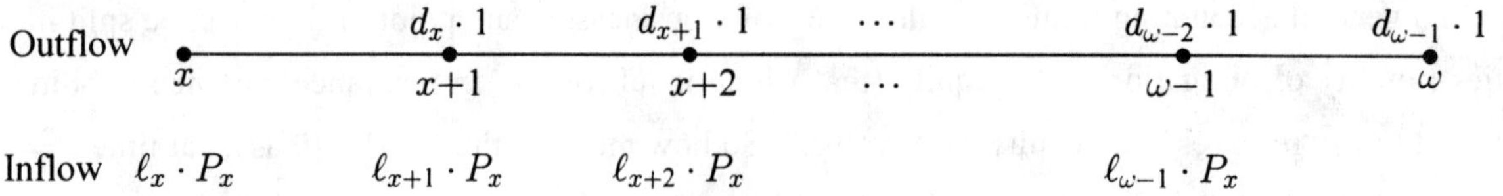

$$\ell_x \cdot P_x + \ell_{x+1} \cdot P_x \cdot v + \cdots + \ell_{\omega-1} \cdot P_x \cdot v^{\omega-x-1} = d_x \cdot 1 \cdot v + d_{x+1} \cdot 1 \cdot v^2 + \cdots + d_{\omega-1} \cdot 1 \cdot v^{\omega-x}$$

Now suppose it is t years later (duration t) and there are ℓ_{x+t} policies remaining in force. Using age $x{+}t$, split the above cashflow diagram into the past and the future.

PAST

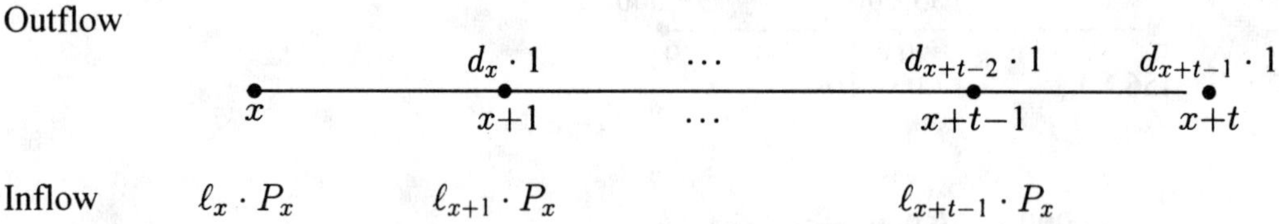

FUTURE

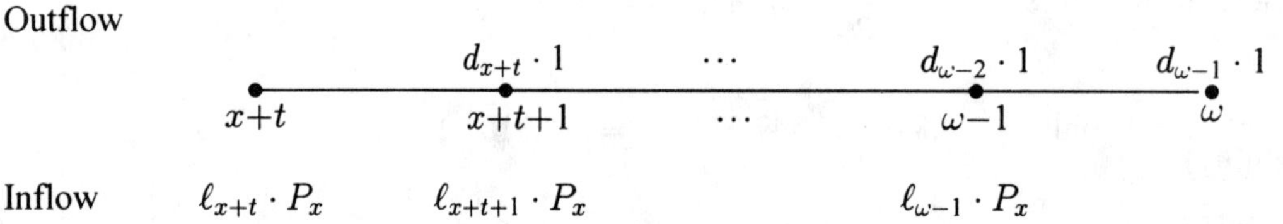

Looking into the future we measure an aggregate liability.

$$\begin{pmatrix}\text{Present value} \\ \text{at age } x{+}t \\ \text{of future shortage}\end{pmatrix} = \text{P.V. Future Outflow} - \text{P.V. Future Inflow}$$
$$= \left(d_{x+t} \cdot 1 \cdot v + \cdots + d_{\omega-1} \cdot 1 \cdot v^{\omega-(x+t)}\right) - \left(\ell_{x+t} \cdot P_x + \ell_{x+t+1} \cdot P_x \cdot v + \cdots + \ell_{\omega-1} \cdot P_x \cdot v^{\omega-(x+t)-1}\right)$$

In the past we can see the buildup of an asset as the accumulation of past premium less past benefit payments.

$$\begin{pmatrix}\text{Accumulated value} \\ \text{at age } x{+}t \\ \text{of past excess}\end{pmatrix} = \text{A.V. Past Inflow} - \text{A.V. Past Outflow}$$
$$= \left(\ell_x \cdot P_x \cdot (1{+}i)^t + \ell_{x+1} \cdot P_x \cdot (1{+}i)^{t-1} + \cdots + \ell_{x+t-1} \cdot P_x \cdot (1{+}i)\right) - \left(d_x \cdot 1 \cdot (1{+}i)^{t-1} + d_{x+1} \cdot 1 \cdot (1{+}i)^{t-2} + \cdots + d_{x+t-1} \cdot 1 \cdot (1{+}i)^0\right)$$

The former is aggregate liability at time t and the latter is aggregate assets at time t. Why do they match? Subtract the two expressions to obtain

(Liability – Assets at time t)

$$= \text{(P.V. Future Outflow – P.V. Future Inflow) – (A.V. Past Inflow – A.V. Past Outflow)}$$

$$= \underbrace{\text{(P.V. Future Outflow + A.V. Past Outflow)}}_{\text{current value at time } t \text{ of the outflow}} - \underbrace{\text{(P.V. Future Inflow + A.V. Past Inflow)}}_{\text{current value at time } t \text{ of the inflow}}.$$

This difference is zero because inflow and outflow had the same value at time 0 due to the definition of P_x, so from interest theory these cashflows must have the same value at any point in time. In particular, at time t, the current values of inflow and outflow must match. So at every duration the insurers books are perfectly balanced.

One other benefit to be gleaned from the preceding is an algebraic form for the reserve in terms of annuity and insurance symbols. At age $x+t$ there are ℓ_{x+t} policies in force, so divide the expression above for the aggregate liability by ℓ_{x+t} to obtain the liability per remaining policy.
(Note: $d_{y+k}/\ell_y = {}_{k|}q_y$, $\ell_{y+k}/\ell_y = {}_kp_y$.)

$$\begin{pmatrix}\text{Liability at age } x+t \\ \text{per remaining policy}\end{pmatrix} = {}_{0|}q_{x+t}\cdot v + {}_{1|}q_{x+t}\cdot v^2 + \cdots + {}_{\omega-(x+t)-1|}q_{x+t}\cdot v^{\omega-x-t}$$
$$- P_x\cdot(1 + {}_1p_{x+t}\cdot v + {}_2p_{x+t}\cdot v^2 + \cdots) = A_{x+t} - P_x\cdot \ddot{a}_{x+t}$$

This is the standard prospective (future-looking) form of the reserve at duration t, which is denoted ${}_tV_x$ in standard actuarial notation. If one divides the accumulated assets at time t by ℓ_{x+t}, one obtains another expression for the reserve,

$${}_tV_x = P_x\cdot \ddot{s}_{x:\overline{t|}} - \frac{1}{{}_tE_x}\cdot A^{\ 1}_{x:\overline{t|}},$$

which is known as the retrospective form since it is calculated at age $x+t$ looking backwards.

Example 1 Use the prospective form of the reserve to check that $1000\cdot {}_1V_{90}$ (the reserve if face value is 1000) is 254.32 as we obtained earlier in this section.

Solution

$$\begin{aligned}
{}_1V_{90} &= A_{91} - P_{90}\cdot \ddot{a}_{91}\\
A_{91} &= {}_{0|}q_{91}\cdot v + {}_{1|}q_{91}\cdot v^2 = \frac{33}{72}\cdot\frac{1}{1.06} + \frac{39}{72}\cdot\frac{1}{1.06^2} = .914471\\
\ddot{a}_{91} &= 1 + {}_1p_{91}\cdot v = 1 + \frac{39}{72}\cdot\frac{1}{1.06} = 1.511006\\
P_{90} &= .436895 \qquad \text{(Unit 3 calculation)}\\
{}_1V_{90} &= .254320
\end{aligned}$$

so

$$1000\cdot {}_1V_{90} = 254.32. \qquad \square$$

Net Level Premium Reserves in the Fully Discrete Whole Life Model: The Risk Theoretical View

As in the first section we first take a numerical look at the problem in the context of the 90-year-olds purchasing 1000 of fully discrete whole life. Suppose that one of these issues has survived to 91. Let's take a look into the future (i.e., from age 91) and consider the insurer's loss function. If death occurs before age 92 the 1000 is paid in one year and one 436.90 premium is received. The loss is $\frac{1000}{1.06} - 436.90 = 506.4962$. Since $\ell_{91} = 72$ and $\ell_{92} = 39$ the probability of this loss is $\frac{33}{72}$. If death occurs between ages 92 and 93 the loss is $\frac{1000}{1.06^2} - 436.90\ddot{a}_{\overline{2|}} = 40.9266$ since the benefit is paid in two years and two premiums are paid. Hence the loss is a discrete random variable with the following distribution:

PROSPECTIVE LOSS FUNCTION AT DURATION ONE

${}_1L$ = Loss	Event	Probability
506.4962	(91) dies before 92	${}_{0|}q_{91} = \frac{33}{72}$
40.9266	(91) dies in [92,93]	${}_{1|}q_{91} = \frac{39}{72}$

Notice that the average loss (i.e., future shortfall of premium with respect to benefit needs) is

$$E[\text{Loss}] = (506.4962)\left(\tfrac{33}{72}\right) + (40.9266)\left(\tfrac{39}{72}\right) = 254.31,$$

which is the same as $1000{}_1V_{90}$ calculated above. The determinist believes the shortfall per policy at age 91 is exactly 254.31, whereas the risk theoretician merely expects a shortfall of this magnitude. She goes on to compute the variance,

$$Var(\text{Loss}) = E[\text{Loss}^2] - (E[\text{Loss}])^2 = 118{,}487.38 - (254.31)^2 = 53{,}813.81,$$

and used the Central Limit Theorem to compute a "likely range" for the aggregate prospective loss, ${}_1L_{Agg}$, corresponding to the 72 remaining policies.

$$\begin{aligned}
E[{}_1L_{Agg}] &= 72 \cdot E[\text{Loss}] = 72(254.31) \approx 18{,}310 \\
Var({}_1L_{Agg}) &= 72 \cdot Var(\text{Loss}) = 72(53{,}813.81) = 3{,}874{,}594 \\
\sigma_{Agg} &= \sqrt{3{,}874{,}594} \approx 1968 \\
.95 &\approx Pr\Big(\underbrace{18{,}310 - 1.96(1968)}_{14{,}453} \le {}_1L_{Agg} \le \underbrace{18{,}310 + 1.96(1968)}_{22{,}167}\Big)
\end{aligned}$$

Notice that $E[{}_1L_{Agg}]$ is the aggregate deterministic liability at duration one (see above).

Now let's move on to an algebraic approach to this problem in a little more general setting. Suppose (x) purchases fully discrete whole life for an annuity-due of net annual premiums P_x. Assume he has survived to age $x+t$ (duration t; t a positive integer). Look at the insurer's prospective loss function using J as a symbol for the curtate future lifetime of $(x+t)$ (to distinguish this from the loss function at issue).

$$\underbrace{{}_tL}_{\substack{\text{prospective loss}\\ \text{function at}\\ \text{duration } t}} = \underbrace{1 \cdot v^{J+1}}_{\substack{\text{present value of}\\ \text{the 1 to be paid}\\ \text{paid in } J+1 \text{ years}}} - \underbrace{P_x \cdot \ddot{a}_{\overline{J+1|}}}_{\substack{\text{present value}\\ \text{of the } J+1\\ \text{future premiums}}}$$

The expected loss, $E[{}_tL]$, is called the tth year, terminal, net level premium reserve and is denoted by ${}_tV_x$. Thus

$${}_tV_x = E[{}_tL] = E[v^{J+1}] - P_x \cdot E[\ddot{a}_{\overline{J+1|}}] = \underbrace{A_{x+t} - P_x \cdot \ddot{a}_{x+t}}_{(J \text{ is future life of } (x+t))} .$$

Notice that we have obtained the same result earlier with the aggregate deterministic analysis. Here we would go on to measure risk by calculating variance of the loss. The following should be a familiar sequence of steps

$${}_tL = v^{J+1} - P_x \cdot \ddot{a}_{\overline{J+1|}} = v^{J+1} - P_x \cdot \frac{1 - v^{J+1}}{d} = \left(1 + \tfrac{P_x}{d}\right) v^{J+1} - \tfrac{P_x}{d}$$

$$\Rightarrow \quad Var({}_tL) = \left(1 + \tfrac{P_x}{d}\right)^2 Var(v^{J+1}) = \left(1 + \tfrac{P_x}{d}\right)^2 ({}^2A_{x+t} - (A_{x+t})^2)$$

(Note: $x+t$ is used since J is the future life of $(x+t)$)

Example 2 Use the variance formula above to verify the result obtained about the variance of the loss at duration 1 for the 1000 issue to (90).

Solution

$$Var({}_1L) = \left(1 + \tfrac{P_{90}}{d}\right)^2 ({}^2A_{91} - (A_{91})^2)$$

$$P_{90} = .43690, \; d = \frac{6}{106}$$

$${}^2A_{91} = \frac{1}{1.06^2} \cdot \frac{33}{72} + \frac{1}{1.06^4} \cdot \frac{39}{72} = .836966$$

$$A_{91} = \frac{1}{1.06} \cdot \frac{33}{72} + \frac{1}{1.06^2} \cdot \frac{39}{72} = .914471$$

$$\Rightarrow \quad Var({}_1L) = .053812$$

$$\Rightarrow \quad Var({}_1L_{Agg}) = 72 \cdot 1000^2 \cdot Var({}_1L) = 3{,}874{,}496 \text{ (small rounding error)}$$

□

Alternate Forms of the Reserve

One of the complicating factors in learning to deal with reserve problems is the many alternate formulas. Here you will see three new ways in addition to the prospective and retrospective forms you saw for fully discrete whole life. Throughout this section the formulas will be restricted to that model.

PROSPECTIVE FORM

${}_tV_x \;=\; A_{x+t} - P_x \cdot \ddot{a}_{x+t}$ measures liability as the APV at age $x{+}t$ of the excess of insurer's future outflow over future inflow.

RETROSPECTIVE FORM

${}_tV_x \;=\; P_x \cdot \ddot{s}_{x:\overline{t}|} \;-\; \frac{1}{{}_tE_x} \cdot A^{\,1}_{x:\overline{t}|}$ shows that the liability at age $x{+}t$ is matched by an asset, namely the accumulation to age $x{+}t$ of the excess of past premium over past benefit costs.

RATIO OF ANNUITIES

${}_tV_x \;=\; 1 - \frac{\ddot{a}_{x+t}}{\ddot{a}_x}$ is useful with the tables of $\ddot{a}_y$ values supplied. This one is obtained from the prospective formula by substituting $A_{x+t} = 1 - d\ddot{a}_{x+t}$ and then replacing $d + P_x$ by $\frac{1}{\ddot{a}_x}$. The last relation follows from dividing $1 \;=\; d\ddot{a}_x + A_x$ by $\ddot{a}_x$.

PREMIUM DIFFERENCE FORM

${}_tV_x \;=\; (P_{x+t} - P_x) \cdot \ddot{a}_{x+t}$ measures the liability by valuing an annuity at age $x{+}t$ of the future shortage, $P_{x+t} - P_x$, of the premium paid in comparison to what is needed at age $x{+}t$ to fully support future benefits. This shortage occurs at the start of each future policy year. This form is obtained from the prospective one by substituting $A_{x+t} = P_{x+t} \cdot \ddot{a}_{x+t}$ and regrouping terms.

THE RECURSIVE METHOD

We have seen in the aggregate deterministic model that assets and liabilities match at each duration. Thus in the $t{+}1^{st}$ row of the spreadsheet we have

$$\underbrace{\ell_{x+t} \cdot {}_tV_x}_{\text{beginning fund}} + \underbrace{\ell_{x+t} \cdot P_x}_{\text{premium income}} + \underbrace{\ell_{x+t} \cdot ({}_tV_x + P_x) \cdot i}_{\text{interest income}} - \underbrace{d_{x+t} \cdot 1}_{\text{benefits}} = \underbrace{\ell_{x+t+1} \cdot {}_{t+1}V_x}_{\text{ending fund}} .$$

Regrouping and dividing by ℓ_{x+t} gives the equivalent form

$$\underbrace{{}_tV_x + P_x}_{\substack{\text{available at}\\ \text{start of year}\\ \text{for each policy}}} \;=\; \underbrace{1 \cdot v \cdot q_{x+t} + {}_{t+1}V \cdot v \cdot p_{x+t}}_{\substack{\text{APV of year-end needs:}\\ \text{1 for deaths and a fund equal}\\ \text{to } {}_{t+1}V_x \text{ for survivors}}} .$$

The other formulas have the limitation that they only have analogies for level benefit/level premium plans of insurance. The recursive method is easily adaptable to non-level benefits and premiums as well as to the case where a different i is credited each year. The latter is a common feature of the more modern, interest-sensitive products of the 1980's.

Reserves with True m^{th}-*ly* Premiums

Here we assume (x) purchases fully discrete whole life of face value 1, but pays $P_x^{(m)}$ annually in m^{th}-ly installments. To distinguish this case the reserve notation follows the net premium notation and is written ${}_tV_x^{(m)}$. Prospectively

$$ {}_tV_x^{(m)} = \underbrace{A_{x+t}}_{\substack{\text{APV of}\\ \text{future benefit}}} - \underbrace{P_x^{(m)} \cdot \ddot{a}_{x+t}^{(m)}}_{\substack{\text{APV of } m^{th}\text{-}ly\\ \text{annuity of future}\\ \text{premium}}} . $$

This should be intuitive enough.

Under the UDD assumption there is a relation with the reserve ${}_tV_x$ based on annual premiums. Substituting the UDD relation $\ddot{a}_x^{(m)} = \alpha(m) \cdot \ddot{a}_x - \beta(m)$ and rearranging terms leads to

$$ {}_tV_x^{(m)} = \left(1 + \beta(m) \cdot P_x^{(m)}\right) {}_tV_x. $$

Recall that $\beta(m) \cdot P_x^{(m)}$ was the "lost premium" in the year of death. We described it as being an "extra" death benefit. So the insurer must hold an extra reserve, $\beta(m)P_x^{(m)} \cdot {}_tV_x$, for this face amount.

Examples of Other Type Reserves

SEMI-CONTINUOUS ENDOWMENT INSURANCE

Suppose a 20-year endowment insurance of 1, issued to (45), pays benefits at death. Premiums are assumed to be annual as an annuity-due. What is the 5th year reserve?

Notation: ${}_5V(\bar{A}_{45:\overline{20|}})$

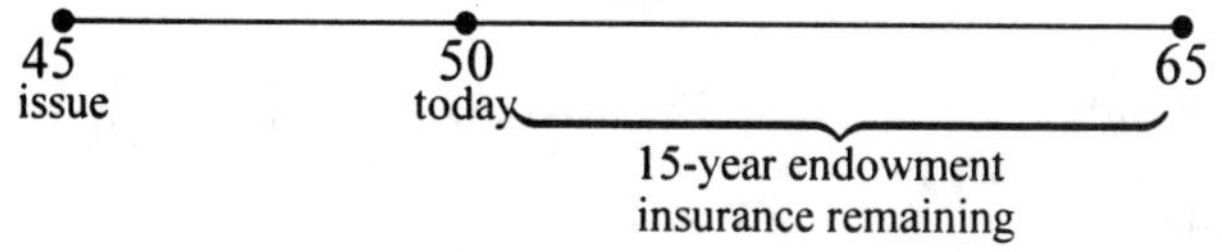

$$ {}_5V(\bar{A}_{45:\overline{20|}}) = \underbrace{\bar{A}_{50:\overline{15|}}}_{\substack{\text{APV at 50 of}\\ \text{remaining}\\ \text{possible benefits}}} - \underbrace{P(\bar{A}_{45:\overline{20|}}) \cdot \ddot{a}_{50:\overline{15|}}}_{\substack{\text{APV of remaining}\\ \text{future premiums}}} $$

LIMITED PAYMENT VARIATION

Suppose we have the same plan as above except that premiums are limited to the first ten policy years. Now what is the 5th year reserve?

Notation: ${}^{10}_{5}V(\bar{A}_{45:\overline{20|}})$ (the 10 is for limited premiums)

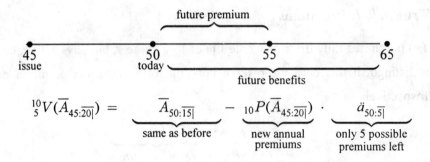

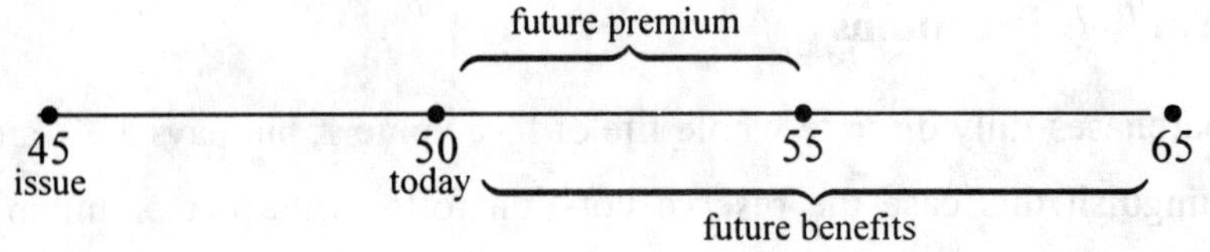

$${}^{10}_{5}V(\bar{A}_{45:\overline{20|}}) = \underbrace{\bar{A}_{50:\overline{15|}}}_{\text{same as before}} - \underbrace{{}_{10}P(\bar{A}_{45:\overline{20|}})}_{\text{new annual premiums}} \cdot \underbrace{\ddot{a}_{50:\overline{5|}}}_{\text{only 5 possible premiums left}}$$

If we ask for a reserve such as ${}^{10}_{15}V(\bar{A}_{45:\overline{20|}})$, which is at duration 15, the answer is simpler. The individual is now 60 with 5 years of future coverage and no further premium to be paid. So the reserve is simply $\bar{A}_{60:\overline{5|}}$.

NOTE: Appendix 3 of this manual is a short-term numerical example of the major ideas in Units 3 and 4 of this section of this manual.

Reserves With Other Contingent Payment Models

We return briefly to the battery warranty model discussed at the end of Unit 1. In that example, a 5-year battery was assumed to wholesale for $\$P$ and retail for $\$(1+r)P$. The warranty was assumed to provide a prorated refund of the retail price at the time of failure, X, if it occurred within 5 years. The random present value variable, $Z = b_X \cdot v^X$, was given by

$$Z = \begin{cases} \left(\frac{5-X}{5}\right)(1+r)P \cdot (1.06)^{-X} & X \le 5 \\ 0 & X > 5 \end{cases},$$

and was evaluated under the assumption that $i = .06$ and $f_X(x) = \frac{3}{7}\left(1 - \frac{x}{10}\right)^{-(4/7)}$, $0 \le x \le 10$. We saw that $E[Z] = .1086(1+r)P$.

One could view this situation as a single premium ($E[Z] = .1086(1+r)P$), 5-year, decreasing benefit ($b_X = \left(\frac{5-x}{5}\right)(1+r)P$), term "life" insurance. As such, you would be interested in the reserve, ${}_xV$, at any duration x, $0 \le x \le 5$;

$${}_xV = APV(\text{future warranty payments after age } x) - APV(\text{future premiums after age } x).$$

The second term is zero since we view $E[Z]$ as a single premium. So suppose we have a battery still surviving at age $x = 2$. How do we calculate ${}_2V$?

First we need to consider $T = X - 2|_{X>2}$, the future time until failure after age 2 for a battery surviving at age 2. Using standard actuarial ideas

$$f_T(t) = {}_tp_2 h(2+t) = \frac{s_X(2+t)}{s_X(2)} \cdot h(2+t) \qquad 0 \le t \le 10-2$$

where $s_X(x) = \left(1 - \frac{x}{10}\right)^{3/7}$, $h(x) = \frac{\left(\frac{3}{7}\right)}{10-x}$. Substituting these expressions into the $f_T(t)$ formula gives

$$f_T(t) = \frac{\left(1-\frac{t}{8}\right)^{3/7}\left(\frac{3}{7}\right)}{8-t} = \left(\frac{3}{56}\right)\left(1-\frac{t}{8}\right)^{-4/7}, \quad 0 \le t \le 8.$$

The prospective loss function at duration 2 is

$${}_2L = b_{2+T} \cdot v^T = \left(\frac{3-T}{5}\right)(1+r)P \cdot (1.06)^{-T}$$

for $0 \le T \le 3$ and is zero if $T > 3$. (Notice that no random present value of future premium is subtracted off since this is a single-premium model.) Finally,

$${}_2V = E[{}_2L] = \int_0^3 \left(\frac{3-t}{5}\right)(1+r)P \cdot (1.06)^{-t} \cdot \left(\frac{3}{56}\right)\left(1-\frac{t}{8}\right)^{-4/7} dt = (1+r)P(.0493).$$

(Numerical integration)

So for each battery surviving at age 2 the manufacturer faces a future liability whose actuarial present value is $(.0493)(1+r)P$. He should have funds set aside to match this liability.

CONDENSED REVIEW NOTES AND ADVANCED TOPICS

$$U = T - t|_{T>t} = X - (t+x)|_{X>t+x} = \text{future lifetime of } (x+t)$$

$$J = [U] = \text{curtate future lifetime of } (x+t)$$

Loss Function

For a policy issued to (x) and still in force t years later, the *prospective loss function* at duration t is

$$\begin{aligned} {}_tL &= \text{random p.v. of future benefits} - \text{random p.v. of future premium} \\ &= \text{random future shortfall (liability)} \end{aligned}$$

Whole Life

$$\begin{cases} {}_tL = v^U - \overline{P}(\overline{A}_x)\overline{a}_{\overline{U}|} & \text{(fully continuous)} \\ {}_tL = v^{J+1} - P_x\ddot{a}_{\overline{J+1}|} & \text{(discrete)} \end{cases}$$

n-Year Endowment Insurance

$${}_tL = \begin{cases} v^U - \overline{P}(\overline{A}_{x:\overline{n}|})\,\overline{a}_{\overline{U}|} & U \le n-t \\ v^{n-t} - \overline{P}(\overline{A}_{x:\overline{n}|})\,\overline{a}_{\overline{n-t}|} & U > n-t \end{cases} \quad \text{(fully continuous)}$$

$${}_tL = \begin{cases} v^{J+1} - P_{x:\overline{n}|}\,\ddot{a}_{\overline{J+1}|} & J \le n-t-1 \\ v^{n-t} - P_{x:\overline{n}|}\,\ddot{a}_{\overline{n-t}|} & J \ge n-t \end{cases} \quad \text{(discrete)}$$

Benefit (Net Premium) Reserves

${}_tV = E[{}_tL] = t^{th}$ *year terminal, net level premium reserve*

Whole Life

$$\begin{cases} {}_t\overline{V}(\overline{A}_x) = \overline{A}_{x+t} - \overline{P}(\overline{A}_x)\overline{a}_{x+t} & \text{(fully continuous)} \\ {}_tV_x = A_{x+t} - P_x\ddot{a}_{x+t} & \text{(discrete)} \end{cases}$$

n-Year Endowment Insurance

$$\begin{cases} {}_t\overline{V}(\overline{A}_{x:\overline{n}|}) = \overline{A}_{x+t:\overline{n-t}|} - \overline{P}(\overline{A}_{x:\overline{n}|})\overline{a}_{x+t:\overline{n-t}|} & \text{(fully continuous)} \\ {}_tV_{x:\overline{n}|} = A_{x+t:\overline{n-t}|} - P_{x:\overline{n}|}\ddot{a}_{x+t:\overline{n-t}|} & \text{(discrete)} \end{cases}$$

Variance of Loss Function

Whole Life

$$\begin{cases} Var({}_tL) = \left(1+\dfrac{\overline{P}(\overline{A}_x)}{\delta}\right)^2 \left({}^2\overline{A}_{x+t} - \overline{A}_{x+t}{}^2\right) & \text{(fully continuous)} \\ Var({}_tL) = \left(1+\frac{P_x}{d}\right)^2 \left({}^2A_{x+t} - A_{x+t}{}^2\right) & \text{(discrete)} \end{cases}$$

n-Year Endowment Insurance

$$\begin{cases} Var({}_tL) = \left(1+\dfrac{\overline{P}(\overline{A}_{x:\overline{n}|})}{\delta}\right)^2 \left({}^2\overline{A}_{x+t:\overline{n-t}|} - \overline{A}_{x+t:\overline{n-t}|}{}^2\right) & \text{(fully continuous)} \\ Var({}_tL) = \left(1+\frac{P_{x:\overline{n}|}}{d}\right)^2 \left({}^2A_{x+t:\overline{n-t}|} - A_{x+t:\overline{n-t}|}{}^2\right) & \text{(discrete)} \end{cases}$$

Retrospective Formulas

Given by accumulated past premium less accumulated cost of past benefits

$${}_t\overline{V}(\overline{A}_x) = \overline{P}(\overline{A}_x)\overline{s}_{x:\overline{t}|} - \frac{1}{{}_tE_x}\overline{A}^{\,1}_{x:\overline{t}|}$$

$${}_tV_x = P_x\,\ddot{s}_{x:\overline{t}|} - \frac{1}{{}_tE_x}A^{\,1}_{x:\overline{t}|}$$

$${}_t\overline{V}(\overline{A}_{x:\overline{n}|}) = \overline{P}(\overline{A}_{x:\overline{n}|})\overline{s}_{x:\overline{t}|} - \frac{1}{{}_tE_x}\overline{A}^{\,1}_{x:\overline{t}|}$$

Note: ${}_tk_x = A^{\,1}_{x:\overline{t}|}/{}_tE_x$ and ${}_t\overline{k}_x = \overline{A}^{\,1}_{x:\overline{t}|}/{}_tE_x$ are occasionally used to shorten expressions.

Alternate Reserve Formulae

(*n-Yr Endowment Insurance*)

Fully Continuous

$${}_t\overline{V}(\overline{A}_{x:\overline{n}|}) = 1 - \frac{\overline{a}_{x+t:\overline{n-t}|}}{\overline{a}_{x:\overline{n}|}} = \frac{\overline{A}_{x+t:\overline{n-t}|} - \overline{A}_{x:\overline{n}|}}{1 - \overline{A}_{x:\overline{n}|}} = \frac{\overline{P}(\overline{A}_{x+t:\overline{n-t}|}) - \overline{P}(\overline{A}_{x:\overline{n}|})}{\overline{P}(\overline{A}_{x+t:\overline{n-t}|}) + \delta}$$

Fully Discrete

$${}_tV_{x:\overline{n}|} = 1 - \frac{\ddot{a}_{x+t:\overline{n-t}|}}{\ddot{a}_{x:\overline{n}|}} = \frac{A_{x+t:\overline{n-t}|} - A_{x:\overline{n}|}}{1 - A_{x:\overline{n}|}} = \frac{P_{x+t:\overline{n-t}|} - P_{x:\overline{n}|}}{P_{x+t:\overline{n-t}|} + d}$$

Limited Payment Plans

(h-Pay, Fully Discrete, n-Year Endowment Insurance)

Type of Formula	Relation of t to h	${}^{h}_{t}V_{x:\overline{n}|}$
prospective	$t < h$	$A_{x+t:\overline{n-t}|} - {}_hP_{x:\overline{n}|} \cdot \ddot{a}_{x+t:\overline{h-t}|}$
prospective	$t \geq h$	$A_{x+t:\overline{n-t}|}$
retrospective	$t < h$	${}_hP_{x:\overline{n}|}\ddot{s}_{x:\overline{t}|} - \frac{1}{{}_tE_x} \cdot A^1_{x:\overline{t}|}$
retrospective	$t \geq h$	${}_hP_{x:\overline{n}|}\ddot{s}_{x:\overline{h}|}\left(\frac{1}{{}_{t-h}E_{x+h}}\right) - \frac{1}{{}_tE_x} \cdot A^1_{x:\overline{t}|}$

Reserves on a Semi-Continuous Basis

(h-Pay; n-Year Endowment Insurance; Prospectively; $t < h$)

$$
\begin{aligned}
{}^{h}_{t}V(\overline{A}_{x:\overline{n}|}) &= \overline{A}_{x+t:\overline{n-t}|} - {}_hP\left(\overline{A}_{x:\overline{n}|}\right)\ddot{a}_{x+t:\overline{h-t}|} \\
&\underset{\text{UDD}}{=} \frac{i}{\delta}A^1_{x+t:\overline{n-t}|} + A_{x+t:\overline{n-t}|}^{\ \ \ \ \ \ \ \ 1} - \left(\frac{i}{\delta}\,{}_hP^1_{x:\overline{n}|} + {}_hP_{x:\overline{n}|}^{\ \ \ \ 1}\right)\ddot{a}_{x+t:\overline{h-t}|} \\
&= \frac{i}{\delta}\,{}^{h}_{t}V^1_{x:\overline{n}|} + {}^{h}_{t}V_{x:\overline{n}|}^{\ \ \ \ 1}
\end{aligned}
$$

True Fractional Premium Reserves (UDD)

Fully Discrete Whole Life

$$
\begin{aligned}
\alpha(m)P_x^{(m)} &= P_x + \beta(m)P_x^{(m)}(d+P_x) \\
{}_tV_x^{(m)} - {}_tV_x &= \left(A_{x+t} - P_x^{(m)}\ddot{a}_{x+t}^{(m)}\right) - \left(A_{x+t} - P_x\ddot{a}_{x+t}\right) \\
&= P_x\ddot{a}_{x+t} - P_x^{(m)}\ddot{a}_{x+t}^{(m)} \\
&= P_x^{(m)}\left(\frac{P_x}{P_x^{(m)}} \cdot \ddot{a}_{x+t} - \ddot{a}_{x+t}^{(m)}\right) \\
&= P_x^{(m)}\left([\alpha(m) - \beta(m)(d+P_x)]\,\ddot{a}_{x+t} - \left(\alpha(m)\ddot{a}_{x+t} - \beta(m)\right)\right) \\
&= \beta(m)\,P_x^{(m)}\left(1 - [d+P_x]\,\ddot{a}_{x+t}\right) = \beta(m)\,P_x^{(m)}\left(1 - \frac{\ddot{a}_{x+t}}{\ddot{a}_x}\right) \\
&= \beta(m)\,P_x^{(m)} \cdot {}_tV_x \quad \text{(extra reserve for "lost premium"), or} \\
{}_tV_x^{(m)} &= \left(1+\beta(m)\,P_x^{(m)}\right){}_tV_x
\end{aligned}
$$

Analogous Relations

$$(t < h) \quad {}^{h}_{t}V_x^{(m)} = {}^{h}_{t}V_x + \beta(m)_h P_x^{(m)} \cdot {}_tV^{1}_{x:\overline{h|}} \quad \text{(lost premium is possible in first } h \text{ years)}$$

$$(t \geq h) \quad {}^{h}_{t}V_x^{(m)} = {}^{h}_{t}V_x = A_{x+t}$$

$$t < h \quad {}^{h}_{t}V^{(m)}(\overline{A}_{x:\overline{n|}}) = {}^{h}_{t}V(\overline{A}_{x:\overline{n|}}) + \beta(m)_h P^{(m)}(\overline{A}_{x:\overline{n|}}) \cdot {}_tV^{1}_{x:\overline{h|}}$$

$$t < h \quad {}^{h}_{t}\overline{V}(\overline{A}_{x:\overline{n|}}) = {}^{h}_{t}V(\overline{A}_{x:\overline{n|}}) + \beta(\infty)_h \overline{P}(\overline{A}_{x:\overline{n|}}) \cdot {}_tV^{1}_{x:\overline{h|}} \quad \text{(let } m \to \infty \text{ in preceding relation)}$$

Reserves at Fractional Durations $t+s$, $s \in (0,1)$

Approximate Method

$${}_{t+s}V \approx (1-s)\,{}_tV + s \cdot {}_{t+1}V + \text{“unearned premium”}$$

(linear interpolation between terminal reserves) + “unearned premium”

$${}_{t+s}V_x \approx (1-s)\,{}_tV_x + s \cdot {}_{t+1}V_x + (1-s)P_x$$

$${}_{t+1/3}V_x^{(2)} \approx \left(\tfrac{2}{3}\right){}_tV_x^{(2)} + \left(\tfrac{1}{3}\right){}_{t+1}V_x^{(2)} + \left(\tfrac{1}{2} - \tfrac{1}{3}\right)P_x^{(2)}$$

Exact Method

$${}_{t+s}V + APV\text{ (premium in }[t+s, t+1]) = APV\text{ (all requirements at }t+1)$$

$${}_{t+s}V_x + 0 = \underbrace{v^{1-s} \cdot {}_{1-s}q_{x+t+s} \cdot 1}_{\text{(dies)}} + \underbrace{v^{1-s} \cdot {}_{1-s}p_{x+t+s} \cdot {}_{t+1}V_x}_{\text{(survives)}}$$

$${}_{t+1/3}V_x^{(2)} + v^{1/6} \cdot \frac{P_x^{(2)}}{2} \cdot {}_{(1/6)}p_{x+t+(1/3)} = \underbrace{v^{2/3} \cdot {}_{2/3}q_{x+t+(1/3)}}_{\text{(dies)}} + \underbrace{v^{2/3} \cdot {}_{(2/3)}p_{x+t+(1/3)} \cdot {}_{t+1}V_x}_{\text{(survives)}}$$

Variable, Fully Discrete Life Insurance

Consider a general fully discrete plan of life insurance paying a benefit b_{K+1} at the end of the $(K+1)$st policy year if death occurs in that year. Suppose benefit (net) premiums π_0, π_1, π_2, ... are required at times 0, 1, 2, ... Though the benefit pattern and premium pattern might be non-level the idea is that both streams have the same actuarial present value (i.e. the equivalence principle):

$$\sum_{k=0}^{\omega-x-1} b_{k+1} \cdot v^{k+1} \cdot {}_{k|}q_x = \sum_{k=0}^{\omega-x-1} \pi_k \cdot v^k \cdot {}_kp_x$$

Dividing by ${}_hE_x = v^h\,{}_hp_x$ and rearranging terms this equation is equivalent to

$$\frac{1}{{}_hE_x}\left[\sum_{k=0}^{h-1}\pi_k \cdot v^k \cdot {}_kp_x - \sum_{k=0}^{h-1} b_{k+1}v^{k+1} \cdot {}_{k|}q_x\right] = \sum_{j=0}^{\omega-x-h-1} b_{h+j+1} \cdot v^{j+1} \cdot {}_{j|}q_{x+h} - \sum_{j=0}^{\omega-x-h-1} \pi_{h+j} \cdot v^j \cdot {}_jp_{x+h}.$$

The left side of this equation can be interpreted as a survivor's share at duration h of the accumulation of past premium (insurer inflow) minus past benefits (insurer outflow). This is the retrospective form of the reserve and it can be interpreted as an asset for the insurer. In the aggregate deterministic fund (spreadsheet) approach with a zero beginning fund the first year,

Policy Year	(1) Beginning Fund	(2) Premium Income	(3) Interest Income	(4) Death Benefits	(5) Ending Fund
⋮	⋮	⋮	⋮	⋮	⋮
$k+1$	End Fund$_k$	$\ell_{x+k} \cdot \pi_k$	$((1)+(2))i$ (refers to columns)	$d_{x+k} \cdot b_{k+1}$	$(1)+(2)+(3)-(4)$ (refers to columns)

the left side of the equation above (asset to the insurer for each policy in force at duration h) can be calculated as (End Fund$_h$)/ℓ_{x+h}.

The right hand side looks into the future (i.e. prospectively) and calculates a liability to the insurer for each policy in force, which is equal to the APV at age $x+h$ of future benefits less future premium. This liability is the benefit (net premium) reserve, ${}_hV$, at duration h. Thus the equation says that at each duration assets and liabilities match.

The arithmetic across one row (policy year $k+1$) of the spreadsheet can be written algebraically as

$$\underbrace{\ell_{x+k} \cdot {}_kV}_{\substack{\text{beg. fund} \\ \text{asset = liability}}} + \underbrace{\ell_{x+k} \cdot \pi_k}_{\substack{\text{premium} \\ \text{income}}} + \underbrace{\ell_{x+k}[{}_kV + \pi_k]i}_{\text{interest income}} - \underbrace{d_{x+k} \cdot b_{k+1}}_{\text{death benefits}} = \underbrace{\ell_{x+k+1} \cdot {}_{k+1}V}_{\text{ending fund}}$$

in the aggregate, or, dividing by ℓ_{x+k} and rearranging slightly, as

$$({}_kV + \pi_k)(1+i) - q_{x+k} \cdot b_{k+1} = p_{x+k} \cdot {}_{k+1}V$$

per policy in force at duration k. Both equations can be viewed as forward moving recursion relations for reserves starting with ${}_0V = 0$. Several rearrangements of this equation have useful interpretations:

(i) $_kV + \pi_k$ = "initial reserve" for policy year $(k+1)$ = funds available at the start of the year for each policy in force = APV_{x+k} (year end needs for policy year $k+1$)

$$= \underbrace{v \cdot q_{x+k} \cdot b_{k+1}}_{\substack{\text{(disc.)(prob.)(amt.)} \\ \text{needed if death} \\ \text{occurs}}} + \underbrace{v \cdot p_{x+k} \cdot {}_{k+1}V.}_{\substack{\text{(disc.)(prob.)(amt.)} \\ \text{needed if } (x+k) \\ \text{survives to year end}}}$$

This balancing per in force policy at each duration is equivalent to asset-liability matching.

(ii) Substituting $p_{x+k} = 1 - q_{x+k}$ and rearranging we arrive at

$$\pi_k = \underbrace{(v \cdot {}_{k+1}V - {}_kV)}_{\substack{\text{"savings fund} \\ \text{deposit"}}} + \underbrace{\underbrace{v}_{\text{disc.}} \cdot \underbrace{q_{x+k}}_{\text{prob.}} \underbrace{(b_{k+1} - {}_{k+1}V)}_{\text{"amount at risk"}}}_{\substack{\text{single benefit premium for a} \\ \text{1 year term insurance at} \\ \text{age } x+k \text{ for the amount at risk}}}.$$

The idea of this equation is that through an alternate, equivalent arrangement we can analyze risk in a way that leads to allocating $Var({}_kL)$ (variance (risk) of the kth prospective loss function) to each future policy year (Hattendorf's method - next heading in this outline). This equivalent arrangement works as follows. Instead of paying the full premium, π_k, each year to the insurer, split the premium into two parts (the two terms on the right side of the equation above):

(a) make annual **savings fund deposits** (account assumed to earn same rate used by the insurer in discounting) $v \cdot {}_1V$, $v \cdot {}_2V - {}_1V$, ... at the beginning of policy years (same timing as premium), so that the account balances at durations 1, 2, ... match the year-end reserves, ${}_1V, {}_2V, \ldots$ for the insurance scheme; and

(b) buy a 1 year term insurance at each age $x+k$ for the amount at risk in year $(k+1)$, $b_{k+1} - {}_{k+1}V$, paying a single benefit premium of $v \cdot q_{x+k} \cdot (b_{k+1} - {}_{k+1}V)$.

If you die in year $k+1$ your savings fund at year end has a balance of ${}_{k+1}V$ for your beneficiary, and your beneficiary receives $(b_{k+1} - {}_{k+1}V)$ from the 1 year term insurance for a total of b_{k+1} — same as if all dollars had been spent on the variable insurance. If you survive the year you have your savings fund balance of ${}_{k+1}V$ — the same as the asset held for you by the insurer on the variable insurance plan.

The point of the equation is that there is no risk in the savings fund (you're just accumulating with interest), so all risk in a policy year (i.e. variance) can be viewed in terms of the sequence of 1 year term insurances for the amount at risk. Hattendorf's results, to come next, express this point algebraically.

Example: $b_h = 1 + {}_hV$ if death occurs within n-years; level premium Π to be determined

$$v \cdot {}_hV \;-\; {}_{h-1}V \;=\; \Pi \;-\; (b_h - {}_hV)vq_{x+h-1} \;=\; \Pi \;-\; vq_{x+h-1}$$

$$v^h \cdot {}_hV \;-\; v^{h-1} \cdot {}_{h-1}V \;=\; v^{h-1} \cdot \Pi \;-\; v^h q_{x+h-1} \qquad \text{(multiply by } v^{h-1}\text{)}$$

$$v^n \cdot {}_nV = \ddot{a}_{\overline{n}|} \cdot \Pi - \sum_{h=1}^{n} v^h q_{x+h-1} \qquad \text{(sum } h = 1, \ldots, n\text{)}$$

$$\Rightarrow \Pi \;=\; \frac{v^n \cdot {}_nV + \sum_{h=1}^{n} v^h q_{x+h-1}}{\ddot{a}_{\overline{n}|}}$$

Note: $\sum_{h=1}^{n} \left(v^h \cdot {}_hV - v^{h-1} \cdot {}_{h-1}V \right) = v^n \cdot {}_nV - v^0 \cdot {}_0V$ (telescoping sum, ${}_0V = 0$)

Allocation of Loss and Variance to Policy Years
(Hattendorf's Method)

1. Variance for 1 – Year Term Insurance at Face Value b

$$L \;=\; \text{loss function} \;=\; \begin{cases} bv - bvq_x & K = 0 \\ -\,bvq_x & K \geq 1 \end{cases}$$

$$=\; bv \cdot Y \;-\; bvq_x \quad \text{where} \quad Y \sim B(n = 1,\; p = q_x)$$

$$E[L] \;=\; bv\,E[Y] \;-\; bvq_x \;=\; bvq_x \;-\; bvq_x \;=\; 0$$

$$Var(L) = Var(bvY - bvq_x) \;=\; Var(bvY) \;=\; b^2v^2\,Var(Y) \;=\; b^2v^2 q_x p_x$$

2. General fully discrete model with b_h = benefit in year h and premiums $\Pi_0, \Pi_1, \ldots$, due at times 0,1,2,… . View Π_{h-1} = h^{th} year premium as a savings fund deposit plus a premium for 1-year term for the amount at risk $b_h - {}_hV$. Thus all "risk" (read variance) is with regard to the 1-year term insurance.

Λ_{h-1} = prospective loss at time $h-1$ on 1-year term for amount at risk.

Value	Event	Probability
$0 \;-\; 0$	$K < h-1$	${}_{h-1}q_x$
$(b_h - {}_hV)v \;-\; (b_h - {}_hV)\,vq_{x+h-1}$	$K = h-1$	${}_{h-1\vert}q_x$
$0 \;-\; (b_h - {}_hV)\,vq_{x+h-1}$	$K > h-1$	${}_hp_x$

(The values above are the cases of Λ_{h-1} = { … }.)

Note: This loss is conditional on survival to age x, not to age $x+h-1$.

3. Properties of Λ_{h-1}

(i) $L = {}_0L$ = loss function at issue = $\sum_{h=0}^{\omega-x-1} v^h \Lambda_h$

(ii) $E[\Lambda_h] = 0$; Λ_h and Λ_j uncorrelated if $h \neq j$.

(iii) $\therefore\ Var(L) = \sum_{h=0}^{\omega-x-1} Var(v^h \Lambda_h) = \sum_{h=0}^{\omega-x-1} v^{2h}\, Var(\Lambda_h)$

$$= \sum_{h=0}^{\omega-x-1} v^{2h}\left(v^2\,(b_{h+1} - {}_{h+1}V)^2\ {}_hp_x \cdot q_{x+h} \cdot p_{x+h}\right)$$

$$= \sum_{h=0}^{\omega-x-1} \underbrace{v^{2h} \cdot {}_hp_x}_{{}^2{}_hE_x \text{ - brings value from duration } h \text{ back to issue}} \underbrace{\left([b_{h+1} - {}_{h+1}V]^2\, v^2\, q_{x+h}p_{x+h}\right)}_{\text{variance on one year term for amount at risk - value at start of year } [h,\, h+1] \text{ - see (1) above}}$$

4. Similar expressions can be written for the variance of the prospective loss function at duration k, ${}_kL$:

$$Var({}_kL) = \sum_{j=0}^{\omega-x-k-1} \underbrace{v^{2j} \cdot {}_jp_{x+k}}_{{}^2{}_jE_{x+k}} \underbrace{[(b_{k+j+1} - {}_{k+j+1}V)^2 v^2 q_{x+k+j}p_{x+k+j}]}_{\text{variance on one year term insurance - value at start of year } [k+j,\, k+j+1]}$$

$$\Rightarrow \quad Var({}_kL) = (b_{k+1} - {}_{k+1}V)^2 v^2 q_{x+k}p_{x+k} + v^2 p_{x+k} \cdot Var({}_{k+1}L)$$

which could be viewed as a backward recursion beginning with the final policy year where ${}_{\omega-x}L = 0,\ Var({}_{\omega-x}L) = 0$.

Note: ${}_kL$ is conditional on survival to age $x+k$ although this is not explicitly in the notation.

5. A Numerical Example of Loss Functions and Alternate Variance Calculations

$i = 1 \quad \Rightarrow \quad v = 1/2 = d$

x	70	71	72	73
ℓ_x	24	18	12	6
d_x	6	6	6	

Consider the aggregate deterministic analysis for \$1 of 3 year, fully-discrete, endowment insurance issued to (70) with interest and mortality as above (selected for numerical convenience)

$$A_{70:\overline{3}|} = vq_{70} + v^2\,{}_{1|}q_{70} + \underbrace{v^3\,{}_{2|}q_{70} + v^3\,{}_3p_{70}}_{v^3\,{}_2p_{70}}$$

$$= \left(\tfrac{1}{2}\right)\left(\tfrac{1}{4}\right) + \left(\tfrac{1}{2}\right)^2\left(\tfrac{1}{4}\right) + \left(\tfrac{1}{2}\right)^3\left(\tfrac{1}{2}\right) = \tfrac{1}{4} = .25$$

$${}^2A_{70:\overline{3}|} = \left(\tfrac{1}{2}\right)^2\left(\tfrac{1}{4}\right) + \left(\tfrac{1}{2}\right)^4\left(\tfrac{1}{4}\right) + \left(\tfrac{1}{2}\right)^6\left(\tfrac{1}{2}\right) = \tfrac{11}{128}$$

$$\ddot{a}_{70:\overline{3}|} = (1 - A_{70:\overline{3}|})/d = \tfrac{3}{2} = 1.5$$

$$P_{70:\overline{3}|} = A_{70:\overline{3}|}/\ddot{a}_{70:\overline{3}|} = \tfrac{1}{6}$$

Spreadsheet

Year	Beginning Fund	Premium	Interest	Death Benefits	Ending Fund
1	0	$4 = (24)(\frac{1}{6})$	4	6	2
2	2	$3 = (18)(\frac{1}{6})$	5	6	4
3	4	2	6	6	6*

*** $1 remains as the survival benefit for the 6 survivors**

$${}_1V_{70:\overline{3}|} = \frac{\text{Fund}_1}{\ell_{71}} = \frac{2}{18} = \frac{1}{9}$$

$${}_2V_{70:\overline{3}|} = \frac{\text{Fund}_2}{\ell_{72}} = \frac{4}{12} = \frac{1}{3}$$

$${}_3V_{70:\overline{3}|} = \frac{\text{Fund}_3}{\ell_{73}} = \frac{6}{6} = 1$$

Note: ${}_3V_{70:\overline{3}|}$ **is calculated an instant before a survivor benefit of 1 is paid to each survivor. This is a traditional assumption so that** ${}_nV_{x:\overline{n}|} = 1$ **whereas** ${}_nV^{\;1}_{x:\overline{n}|} = 0$ **(nothing exists in the future after the benefits are paid at time** n**).**

Loss Function At Issue

$$L = \begin{cases} v^{K+1} - P_{70:\overline{3}|}\ddot{a}_{\overline{K+1}|} & K = 0, 1, 2 \\ v^3 - P_{70:\overline{3}|}\ddot{a}_{\overline{3}|} & K \geq 3 \end{cases}$$

$$Var(L) = \left(1 + \frac{P_{70:\overline{3}|}}{d}\right)^2 ({}^2A_{70:\overline{3}|} - A_{70:\overline{3}|}{}^2)$$

$$= \frac{{}^2A_{70:\overline{3}|} - A_{70:\overline{3}|}{}^2}{(1 - A_{70:\overline{3}|})^2} = \frac{\frac{11}{128} - \frac{1}{4}^2}{\frac{3}{4}^2} = \frac{1}{24}$$

$$= \underbrace{v^2(1-{}_1V_{70:\overline{3}|})^2 q_{70}p_{70} + v^2 p_{70}[v^2(1-{}_2V_{70:\overline{3}|})^2 q_{71}p_{71}]}_{\text{Hattendorf: two terms since } b_3 - {}_3V_{70:\overline{3}|} = 1 - 1 = 0}$$

$$= \left(\tfrac{1}{2}\right)^2\left(1 - \tfrac{1}{9}\right)^2\left(\tfrac{1}{4}\right)\left(\tfrac{3}{4}\right) + \left(\tfrac{1}{2}\right)^2\left(\tfrac{3}{4}\right)\left[\left(\tfrac{1}{2}\right)^2\left(1 - \tfrac{1}{3}\right)^2\left(\tfrac{1}{3}\right)\left(\tfrac{2}{3}\right)\right]$$

$$= \frac{1}{24}$$

Loss Function at Duration One

${}_1L$	Probability	Event
$v - P_{70:\overline{3}\vert} = \frac{1}{3}$	$\frac{6}{18} = \frac{1}{3}$	$J = 0$
$v^2 - P_{70:\overline{3}\vert}\ddot{a}_{\overline{2}\vert} = 0$	$\frac{12}{18} = \frac{2}{3}$	$J \geq 1$

$$Var({}_1L) = E[{}_1L^2] - E[{}_1L]^2 \qquad \text{(first principles)}$$

$$= \left(\tfrac{1}{3}\right)^2\left(\tfrac{1}{3}\right) + 0^2\left(\tfrac{2}{3}\right) - \left[\left(\tfrac{1}{3}\right)\left(\tfrac{1}{3}\right) + 0\left(\tfrac{1}{3}\right)\right]$$

$$= \frac{2}{81}$$

$$= v^2(1 - {}_2V_{70:\overline{3}|})^2 q_{71} p_{71} = \left(\tfrac{1}{2}\right)^2\left(1 - \tfrac{1}{3}\right)^2\left(\tfrac{1}{3}\right)\left(\tfrac{2}{3}\right)$$

$$= \frac{2}{81} \qquad \text{(Hattendorf)}$$

$$= \frac{{}^2A_{71:\overline{2}|} - A_{71:\overline{2}|}{}^2}{(1 - A_{70:\overline{3}|})^2} \qquad \text{(algebraic)}$$

$$= \frac{\frac{1}{8} - \left(\frac{1}{3}\right)^2}{\left(1 - \frac{1}{4}\right)^2} = \frac{2}{81}$$

$$A_{71:\overline{2}|} = vq_{71} + v^2\,{}_1|q_{71} + v^2\,{}_2p_{71} = \frac{1}{3}$$

$${}^2A_{71:\overline{2}|} = v^2q_{71} + v^4\,{}_1|q_{71} + v^4\,{}_2p_{71} = \frac{1}{8}$$

Recursion

$$Var(L) = v^2(1 - {}_1V_{70:\overline{3}|})^2 q_{70} p_{70} + v^2 p_{70} Var({}_1L)$$

$$= \left(\tfrac{1}{2}\right)^2\left(1 - \tfrac{1}{9}\right)^2\left(\tfrac{1}{4}\right)\left(\tfrac{3}{4}\right) + \left(\tfrac{1}{2}\right)^2\left(\tfrac{3}{4}\right)\frac{2}{81} = \frac{1}{24}$$

(agrees with earlier calculation)

Variance of the Λ_h's

$$Var(\Lambda_0) = v^2(1 - {}_1V_{70:\overline{3}|})^2 q_{70} p_{70} = \frac{1}{27}$$

$$Var(\Lambda_1) = p_{70} v^2 (1 - {}_2V_{70:\overline{3}|})^2 q_{71} p_{71} = \frac{1}{54}$$

$$Var(\Lambda_2) = {}_2p_{70} v^2 (1 - {}_3V_{70:\overline{3}|})^2 q_{72} p_{72} = 0 \qquad (1 = {}_3V_{70:\overline{3}|})$$

$$Var(L) = Var(\Lambda_0) + Var(\Lambda_1)v^2 + Var(\Lambda_2)v^4 = \frac{1}{27} + \frac{1}{54}\cdot\frac{1}{4} = \frac{1}{24}$$

Premiums and Reserves Determined From Indifference Using an Exponential Utility Function

1. $u(w) = -e^{-\alpha w}$ is the insurer's utility of wealth function where w is the insurer's wealth and $\alpha > 0$.

2. L is the loss at issue on an insurance:

   $L = Z - P \cdot Y$

   $Z =$ random present value of benefit
   $P =$ annual premium amount
   $Y =$ random present value of an annuity of 1/year in the pattern (i.e., continuous, discrete) of premium payment

3. **Exponential premiums** are determined from the equation below which expresses the insurer's indifference to issuing the policy:

$$\underbrace{-e^{-\alpha w}}_{\substack{\text{utility if}\\\text{insurance not}\\\text{issued}}} = \underbrace{E[-e^{-\alpha(w-L)}]}_{\substack{\text{expected utility if the}\\\text{insurance is issued}}}$$

$$\Rightarrow \quad M_L(\alpha) = 1 \quad \text{(algebra)}$$

   Note: L is a function of the unknown annual premium amount P. The equation $M_L(\alpha) = 1$ (left side a complicated function of P) is numerically solved for P. This is the minimum P the insurer would accept. Any smaller P would diminish the insurer's expected utility.

4. The exponential reserve at duration t, ${}_tV^{exp}$, is determined from the indifference equation

$$-e^{-\alpha(w-{}_tV^{exp})} = E[-e^{-\alpha(w-{}_tL)}]$$

   where ${}_tL$ is the prospective loss function at duration t. This equation is equivalent to

$$e^{\alpha({}_tV^{exp})} = M_{{}_tL}(\alpha)$$

   or

$${}_tV^{exp} = \frac{ln(M_{{}_tL}(\alpha))}{\alpha}.$$

CONCEPTUAL REVIEW TEST

1. Write the insurer's prospective loss function at duration t for \$1 of whole life insurance to (x) in the fully continuous, semicontinuous, and fully discrete cases. Explain the symbols U and J with regard to $(x+t)$.

2. Write both the prospective and retrospective reserve formula for the tth year, net level premium reserve (i.e., expected prospective loss) of the models in Question 1.

3. In the context of the models above suppose the insurer has a fund of $\$F_t$ at duration t for a policy still in force. Funds available to the insurer are $\$F_t$ plus future premium and funds needed are for future benefits. If U is "large" funds available will be sufficient to cover future benefits, whereas if U is "small" they may be insufficient. What is the probabilistic interpretation if the fund is the tth year, net level premium reserve?

4. The reserve formula ${}_tV_x = A_{x+t} - P_x\ddot{a}_{x+t}$ for a single policy in force at duration t can be rearranged to give $\ell_{x+t} \cdot {}_tV_x + \sum_{k=0}^{\omega-x-t-1} v^k \cdot \ell_{x+t+k} \cdot P_x = \sum_{k=0}^{\omega-x-t-1} v^{k+1} \cdot d_{x+t+k} \cdot 1$. What is the aggregate deterministic interpretation?

5. If $1000{}_{20}V_{30} = \$250$ and $1000P_{30} = \$7$, is the reserve plus future premium sufficient to cover future benefits if (50) dies at age 55.7? 72.2? Assume $i = .06$. Argue by accumulating the reserve plus future premium until the time at which \$1000 is needed.

6. Explain the relation ${}_tV_x^{(m)} = \left(1 + \beta(m)P_x^{(m)}\right) {}_tV_x$ between $m^{th}ly$ and annual premium reserves for fully discrete whole life.

7. The approximate reserve ${}_{20.25}V_{30} \approx \frac{3}{4} \cdot {}_{20}V_{30} + \frac{1}{4} \cdot {}_{21}V_{30} + \frac{3}{4}P_x$ is a linear interpolation between terminal reserves plus "unearned premium." Write the corresponding exact relation which says that the APV of funds available at duration 20.25 equals the APV of funds needed at duration 21.

8. Give an explanation of the reserve formula ${}_tV_x = \left(1 - \frac{P_x}{P_{x+t}}\right)A_{x+t}$.

9. In Question 1 give expressions for the variance of the prospective loss functions in terms of insurances for the fully continuous and discrete cases.

CONCEPTUAL REVIEW TEST SOLUTIONS

1. (f.c.) ${}_tL = v^U - \overline{P}(\overline{A}_x)\,\overline{a}_{\overline{U}|}$
(s.c.) ${}_tL = v^U - P(\overline{A}_x)\,\ddot{a}_{\overline{J+1}|}$
(f.d.) ${}_tL = v^{J+1} - P_x\,\ddot{a}_{\overline{J+1}|}$
where U is the complete future lifetime of $(x+t)$ and $J = [U]$ (greatest integer) is the corresponding curtate lifetime.

2. (prospective) (retrospective)
(f.c.) ${}_t\overline{V}(\overline{A}_x) = \overline{A}_{x+t} - \overline{P}(\overline{A}_x)\,\overline{a}_{x+t} = \overline{P}(\overline{A}_x)\,\overline{s}_{x:\overline{t}|} - \frac{1}{{}_tE_x}\cdot \overline{A}^{\,1}_{x:\overline{t}|}$
(s.c.) ${}_tV(\overline{A}_x) = \overline{A}_{x+t} - P(\overline{A}_x)\,\ddot{a}_{x+t} = P(\overline{A}_x)\,\ddot{s}_{x:\overline{t}|} - \frac{1}{{}_tE_x}\cdot \overline{A}^{\,1}_{x:\overline{t}|}$
(f.d.) ${}_tV_x = A_{x+t} - P_x\,\ddot{a}_{x+t} = P_x\,\ddot{s}_{x:\overline{t}|} - \frac{1}{{}_tE_x}\cdot A^{1}_{x:\overline{t}|}$

3. "On average" the funds available are exactly equal the funds needed.

4. According to the determinist, there will be exactly ℓ_{x+t+k} survivors at age $x+t+k$ from a group of ℓ_{x+t} lives aged $x+t$, and d_{x+t+k} deaths between ages $x+t+k$ and $x+t+k+1$. Thus, since the left side is the aggregate present value of available funds, and the right side is the aggregate present value of needed funds, the equation says available and needed funds are exactly equal.

5. Death at 55.7: $U = 5.7$, $J = 5$, accumulated value of reserve plus future premium in 6 years (when 1000 is needed) equals $250(1.06)^6 + 7\ddot{s}_{\overline{6}|.06} = 406.39$ – not sufficient. Death at 72.2: $U = 22.2$, $J = 22$, accumulated value of reserve plus future premium in 23 years equals $250(1.06)^{23} + 7\ddot{s}_{\overline{23}|.06} = 1{,}303.65$ – more than sufficient. Notice that the inequality $250(1.06)^{23} + 7\ddot{s}_{\overline{23}|.06} > 1000$ at a time 23 years after age 50 is equivalent to the present value inequality $\underset{\text{(reserve)}}{250} > \underset{\text{(loss function)}}{1000\cdot v^{23} - 7\ddot{a}_{\overline{23}|}}$.

6. With m^{th}-ly premiums there is a "loss of premium" equal $\beta(m)P_x^{(m)}$ in the year of death. Since this is like an extra death benefit one must hold a reserve for face amount $1 + \beta(m)P_x^{(m)}$.

7. ${}_{20.25}V_{30} = {}_{.75}q_{50.25}\cdot v^{.75}\cdot 1 + {}_{.75}p_{50.25}\cdot v^{.75}\cdot {}_{21}V_{30}$.

8. At age $x+t$, premiums of size P_{x+t} are needed to support benefits for $(x+t)$. Since only P_x is being received, $\frac{P_x}{P_{x+t}}$ of the benefit is covered by future premium, so $1 - \frac{P_x}{P_{x+t}}$ of the benefit must be covered by the reserve.

9. (f.c.) ${}_tL = v^U - \overline{P}(\overline{A}_x)\overline{a}_{\overline{U}|} = \left(1+\frac{\overline{P}(\overline{A}_x)}{\delta}\right)v^U - \frac{\overline{P}(\overline{A}_x)}{\delta}$. Since $Var(aX+b) = a^2Var(X)$ we obtain $Var({}_tL) = \left(1+\frac{\overline{P}(\overline{A}_x)}{\delta}\right)^2\cdot Var(v^U)$ where $Var(v^U) = {}^2\overline{A}_{x+t} - \overline{A}_{x+t}{}^2$.
(f.d.) Similarly, $Var({}_tL) = \left(1+\frac{P_x}{d}\right)^2\left({}^2A_{x+t} - A_{x+t}{}^2\right)$

COMPUTATIONAL REVIEW TEST

1. Assume $\delta = .05$ and the lifetimes of newborns follow De Moivre's model with $\omega = 100$. In this case $f_T(t) = \frac{1}{100-x}$ for $0 \le t \le 100 - x$ (i.e., uniform distribution) and $\overline{A}_x = \frac{1}{100-x} \cdot \overline{a}_{\overline{100-x}|}$. Suppose (25) purchases \$1000 of whole life insurance paying a net annual premium of $1000\overline{P}(\overline{A}_{25}) = 17.60$ (i.e., a fully continuous model).

   (a) Write the prospective loss function assuming the policy is still in force when (25) reaches age 50.

   (b) Calculate the net level premium reserve at duration 25 (i.e., age 50).

   (c) What is the probability that the reserve is sufficient (i.e., $Pr(144.36 > {}_{25}L)$); express the inequality in terms of U which is uniformly distributed over [0, 50])

   (d) Find the standard deviation of the prospective loss function.

   (e) For 100 such policies still in force at duration 25, what is the probability that the aggregate reserve is sufficient (i.e., $Pr(100 \cdot 144.36 >$ aggregate loss function))?

   (f) What is the probability that 110% of the aggregate reserve is sufficient?

The following information is given for questions 2 - 3:

(i) $\ddot{a}_{40} = 14.81661$, $\ddot{a}_{45} = 14.11209$, $\ddot{a}_{60} = 11.14535$, $\ddot{a}_{45:\overline{5}|} = 4.42893$, $\ddot{a}_{40:\overline{10}|} = 7.69664$

(ii) $i = .06$, $\alpha(2) = 1.00021$, $\beta(2) = .25739$

(iii) $\ell_{60} = 81{,}880.73$, $\ell_{77} = 48{,}281.81$, $\ell_{78} = 45{,}303.60$

2. Using mortality and interest as above calculate the following reserves:

   (a) $1000{}_{20}V_{40}$

   (b) $1000{}_{20}V_{40}^{(2)}$ (assume UDD)

   (c) $1000{}_{5}^{10}V_{40}$

   (d) $1000{}_{20}^{10}V_{40}$

3. Use the information above to determine the probability that the reserve in problem 2(a) is sufficient.

COMPUTATIONAL REVIEW TEST SOLUTIONS

1. (a) ${}_{25}L = 1000\, e^{-.05U} - 17.60\bar{a}_{\overline{U}|}$, where U is the future lifetime of (50).

(b) $1000\,{}_{25}\bar{V}(\bar{A}_{25}) = 1000\bar{A}_{50} - 17.60\bar{a}_{50} = \left(1000 + \frac{17.60}{.05}\right)\bar{A}_{50} - \frac{17.60}{.05} = 144.36$ since $\bar{A}_{50} = \frac{1}{50}\bar{a}_{\overline{50}|} = .367166$

(c) $144.36 > {}_{25}L = \left(1000 + \frac{17.60}{.05}\right)v^U - \frac{17.60}{.05} \Leftrightarrow U \geq 20.04$. Thus the probability that the reserve is sufficient is $Pr(U \geq 20.04) = \int_{20.04}^{50} f_U(u)\,du = \int_{20.04}^{50} \frac{1}{50}\,du = .60$

(d) $Var({}_{25}L) = \left(1000 + \frac{17.60}{.05}\right)^2 ({}^2\bar{A}_{50} - \bar{A}_{50}{}^2)$ where ${}^2\bar{A}_{50} = \frac{1}{50}\bar{a}_{\overline{50}|}$ at $\delta = .10$. Thus $Var({}_{25}L) = 116{,}708.9$, $\sigma = 341.63$

(e) L_{Agg} is a sum of 100 independent variables having expected value 144.36 and standard deviation 341.63, thus $\mu(Agg) = 14{,}436$, $\sigma_{Agg} = 3416.3$.

$$Pr(\text{Agg Reserve} > \text{Agg Loss}) = Pr\left(100(144.36) > L_{Agg}\right)$$
$$\approx Pr\left(\frac{14{,}436 - 14{,}436}{3416.3} > N(0,1)\right)$$
$$= Pr(0 \geq N(0,1)) = .5.$$

(f) 110% of aggregate reserve is 15,879.60.

$$Pr(15{,}879.60 > L_{Agg}) \approx Pr\left(\frac{15{,}879.60 - 14{,}436}{3416.3} \geq N(0,1)\right) = \Phi(.423) \approx .66$$

2. (a) ${}_{20}V_{40} = A_{60} - P_{40}\,\ddot{a}_{60} = 1 + \frac{\ddot{a}_{60}}{\ddot{a}_{40}} = .24778$, $1000\,{}_{20}V_{40} = 247.78$.

(b) ${}_{20}V_{40}^{(2)} \underset{\text{UDD}}{=} \left(1 + \beta(2)P_{40}^{(2)}\right){}_{20}V_{40}$ and $P_{40}^{(2)} = \frac{A_{40}}{\ddot{a}_{40}^{(2)}} \underset{\text{UDD}}{=} \frac{A_{40}}{\alpha(2)\ddot{a}_{40} - \beta(2)} = .011078.$

So $1000\,{}_{20}V_{40}^{(2)} = (1.002851)247.78 = 248.49$

(c) ${}^{10}_{5}V_{40} = A_{45} - {}_{10}P_{40} \cdot \ddot{a}_{45:\overline{5}|} = .10837$,

so $1000\,{}^{10}_{5}V_{40} = 108.37$.

(d) $1000\,{}^{10}_{20}V_{40} = 1000\,A_{60} = 369.13$

3. $Pr(247.78 > \text{Loss}) = Pr(247.78 > 1000\left(\frac{1}{1.06}\right)^{J+1} - 1000\,P_{40}\ddot{a}_{\overline{J+1}|})$ where J is the future lifetime of 60. Now $1000P_{40} = 10.8881$, so the inequality is equivalent to $247.78 \geq 1192.3558 \cdot v^{J+1} - 192.3588$, or $J \geq 16.10$. Thus the reserve is sufficient if $J \geq 17$ and the probability of this is ${}_{18}p_{60} = \frac{\ell_{78}}{\ell_{60}} = .55.$

UNIT REVIEW QUESTIONS

1. You are given: (i) $1000 _t\overline{V}(\overline{A}_x) = 100$ (ii) $1000\overline{P}(\overline{A}_x) = 10.50$ (iii) $\delta = 0.03$

Calculate $\overline{a}_{x+t}$. (Answer to nearest integer)

(A) 21 (B) 22 (C) 25 (D) 26 (E) 27

2. A four-year term life insurance of 1000 is issued on a fully discrete basis to (82). The insured survives to the end of the second policy year. You are given:

(i) $i = 0$ (ii) net annual premium $= 120$ (iii) $q_{84} = 0.12$ (iv) $q_{85} = 0.13$

Calculate $Var(_2L)$. (Answer to nearest 10)

(A) 202,930 (B) 202,980 (C) 203,030 (D) 203,980 (E) 204,030

3. Mortality follows de Moivre's law with $\omega = 100$. A single premium 10-year life annuity is issued to (80). The benefit is 1 per annum payable continuously. Given that $\delta = \frac{1}{15}$, determine $Var(_5L)$.

(A) $225\left[{}^2\overline{a}_{\overline{5}|} - \overline{a}_{\overline{5}|}{}^2\right]$

(B) $15\left[{}^2\overline{a}_{\overline{5}|} - \overline{a}_{\overline{5}|}{}^2\right]$

(C) $225\left[{}^2\overline{a}_{\overline{5}|} - \overline{a}_{\overline{5}|}{}^2\right] + 150\left[e^{-1/3} - e^{-2/3}\right]$

(D) $15\left[{}^2\overline{a}_{\overline{5}|} - \overline{a}_{\overline{5}|}{}^2\right] + 10\left[e^{-1/3} - e^{-2/3}\right]$

(E) $15^2\overline{a}_{\overline{5}|} - \overline{a}_{\overline{5}|}{}^2 + 10e^{-1/3}\left[5e^{-1/3} - 2\overline{a}_{\overline{5}|}\right]$

4. Which of the following is (are) true statements?

I. If P is the net premium for an insurance, and A_k is the present value of future benefits at duration k, then $Var(_kL) = \left[1 + \frac{P}{d}\right]^2 [{}^2A_k - A_k{}^2]$.

II. Companies A and B each issue only one policy. The policies are issued to different individuals of the same age but otherwise are identical. If risk is measured by the variance of the prospective loss, then both companies can reduce their risk if they agree to (1) pay 50% of any claim regardless of which company issued the policy having the claim, and (2) receive 50% of the premium from each insured.

III. The reserve on the December 31 following the tth policy anniversary of a whole life policy issued to (x) on August 1 with true quarterly premiums is approximately equal to

$$\frac{7}{12} \cdot {}_tV_x^{(4)} + \frac{5}{12} \cdot {}_{t+1}V_x^{(4)} + \frac{1}{6} \cdot P_x^{(4)}.$$

(A) I only (B) II only (C) III only (D) I and II only (E) I, II and III

5. Given that $i = .04$, ${}^{20}_{23}V_{15} = .585$, and ${}^{20}_{24}V_{15} = .600$, calculate p_{38}.

(A) .9025 (B) .9060 (C) .9625 (D) .9790 (E) .9860

6. A fully discrete life insurance to (35) has a death benefit of 2500 in year 10. Reserves are calculated at $i = .10$, and the net annual premium is P. Calculate q_{44}, given that ${}_9V + P = {}_{10}V = 500$.

(A) .017 (B) .020 (C) .025 (D) .033 (E) .040

7. Calculate ${}_{20}V_{45}$, given the following values:

(i) $P_{45} = .014$ (ii) $P_{\overset{1}{45:\overline{20|}}} = .022$ (iii) $P_{45:\overline{20|}} = .030$

(A) .260 (B) .263 (C) .267 (D) .269 (E) .273

8. Let L denote the insurer loss for a fully discrete annual premium 2-year endowment insurance of 10 issued to (x). Premiums are determined by the equivalence principle, but are *not* necessarily level. By Hattendorf's Theorem, $Var(L) = \sum_j v^{2j} \cdot Var(\Lambda_j)$, where Λ_j is the random loss allocated to policy year $j+1$. Using Hattendorf's Theorem, calculate $p_x q_x$, given the following values:

(i) $d = .10$ (ii) $Var(L) = 3.24$ (iii) ${}_1V = 5.00$

(A) 0.09 (B) 0.16 (C) 0.21 (D) 0.24 (E) 0.25

9. What extra rate of mortality will be covered in the twentieth year by a net extra annual premium of 5.00 per thousand on an Ordinary Life policy issued at age 35, if the reserve held at all durations is the same as that on a similar policy issued without an extra premium? Given ${}_{20}V_{35} = .480$ on a 4% basis.

(A) .05 (B) .1 (C) .001 (D) .01 (E) .005

10. For a fully continuous continuously decreasing 25-year term insurance issued to (40), you are given:

(i) $b_t = 1000\bar{a}_{\overline{25-t|}}$ for $0 \le t \le 25$
(ii) Fully continuous net annual premium = 200
(iii) $\bar{A}_{50:\overline{15|}} = .60$
(iv) $i = .05$ and $\delta = .04879$

Calculate the net premium reserve at the end of 10 years for this insurance.

(A) 600 (B) 650 (C) 700 (D) 750 (E) 800

11. A special fully discrete 2-year endowment insurance with a maturity value of 1000 is issued to (x). The death benefit in each year is 1000 plus the net premium reserve at the end of that year.

You are given: (i) $i = 10$ (ii) $q_{x+k} = .10(1.10)^k, \quad k = 0, 1$

Calculate the net level annual premium.

(A) 508 (B) 528 (C) 548 (D) 568 (E) 588

12. For a fully discrete whole life insurance with level annual premiums on the life of (x), you are given:

(i) $i = .05$
(ii) $q_{x+h-1} = .004$
(iii) The initial reserve for policy year h is 200.
(iv) The net amount at risk for policy year h is 1295.
(v) $\ddot{a}_x = 16.2$

Calculate the terminal reserve for policy year $h-1$.

(A) 179 (B) 188 (C) 192 (D) 200 (E) 205

13. You are given:

(i) $A_{\overline{x:n|}} = .20$
(ii) $d = .08$

Calculate ${}_{n-1}V_{\overline{x:n|}}$.

(A) .90 (B) .92 (C) .94 (D) .96 (E) .98

14. A 10-year deferred, life annuity-due on (x) includes a refund feature during the deferral period providing for return of the net single premium with interest at the end of the year of death. Interest is credited at rate i.

You are given:

(i) $i = .05$
(ii) The terminal reserve at the end of 9 years equals 15.238.

Calculate the net single premium for this annuity.

(A) 9.355 (B) 9.823 (C) 14.512 (D) 15.238 (E) 16.000

15. L is the loss-at-issue random variable for a fully continuous whole life insurance of 1 on (30) with net premiums determined by the equivalence principle. You are given:

(i) $\overline{A}_{50} = .7$
(ii) ${}^2\overline{A}_{30} = .3$
(iii) $Var(L) = .2$

Calculate ${}_{20}\overline{V}(\overline{A}_{30})$.

(A) .2 (B) .3 (C) .4 (D) .5 (E) .6

16. You are given:

(i) $A_{35} = .17092, \beta(4) = .38272, \alpha(4) = 1.00019$
(ii) $i = .05$
(iii) Deaths are uniformly distributed over each year of age.
(iv) $1000 {}_5V_{35} = 44.71$
(v) $\ddot{a}_{35}^{(4)} = 17.031204$

Calculate $1000\left({}_5V_{35}^{(4)} - {}_5V_{35} \right)$.

(A) .17 (B) .45 (C) 1.00 (D) 3.72 (E) 3.81

17. A fully discrete 3-year endowment insurance of 1000 is issued on (x). You are given:

(i) $i = .06$
(ii) The following extract from the mortality table:

y	ℓ_y
x	100
$x+1$	90
$x+2$	81

(iii) $1000P_{x:\overline{3}|} = 332.51$

Calculate $1000({}_2V_{x:\overline{3}|} - {}_1V_{x:\overline{3}|})$.

(A) 330.38 (B) 332.86 (C) 334.51 (D) 337.22 (E) 340.74

18. For a special fully discrete whole life insurance on (40), you are given:

(i) The net premium for this insurance is equal to P_{20}.
(ii) ${}_kV = {}_kV_{20}, k = 0, 1, \ldots, 19$
(iii) ${}_{11}V = {}_{11}V_{20} = .08154$
(iv) $q_{40+k} = q_{20+k} + .01, \; k = 0, 1, \ldots, 19$
(v) $q_{30} = .008427$

Calculate b_{11}, the death benefit in year 11.

(A) .457 (B) .468 (C) .480 (D) .491 (E) .502

19. For a fully discrete 10-payment whole life insurance of 1000 on (x), you are given:

(i) $i = .06$
(ii) $q_{x+9} = .01262$
(iii) The annual benefit premium is 32.88.
(iv) The benefit reserve at the end of year 9 is 322.87.

Calculate $1000P_{x+10}$.

(A) 31.52 (B) 31.92 (C) 32.32 (D) 32.72 (E) 33.12

20. For a fully discrete whole life insurance of 1 on (30), you are given:

(i) $Var({}_{10}L|K(x) \geq 10) = y + v^2 Var({}_{11}L|K(x) \geq 10)$
(ii) $q_{30} = .00153 \quad q_{40} = .00278$
$\ddot{a}_{30} = 18.0577 \quad \ddot{a}_{40} = 16.6323$
$\ddot{a}_{41} = 16.4596$
(iii) $i = .05$

Calculate y.

(A) .0019 (B) .0020 (C) .0021 (D) .0022 (E) .0023

Use the following information for Questions 21-24.

An insurance company has 200 3-year term insurance policies, all of which were issued at age x. Each policy is fully discrete with annual premiums and a death benefit of 1000. Of the 200 policies, 100 are at the end of their first policy year and 100 at the end of their second policy year.

You are given:

(i) $i = .10$
(ii) ${}_kL$ is the random variable for the insurer's prospective loss at time k for a single policy.
(iii) The losses are independent
(iv) $Var({}_2L) = 206{,}612$
(v) The premiums were determined using the equivalence principle.

You are also given:

h	q_{x+h}	$1000_{h+1}V^1_{x:\overline{3}|}$
0	.30	95.833
1	.40	120.833
2	.50	0.000

21. Calculate the insurer's aggregate net level premium reserve.

(A) 12,083 (B) 16,752 (C) 19,417 (D) 21,667 (E) 23,422

22. Calculate $Var({}_1L)$.

(A) 102,452 (B) 179,412 (C) 210,179 (D) 243,127 (E) 255,761

23. Calculate the amount which, on the basis of a normal distribution, will give the insurer a probability of .95 of meeting the obligations on these policies.

(A) 30,168 (B) 32,852 (C) 33,879 (D) 35,122 (E) 42,288

24. Suppose there are ten times as many in-force policies at durations one and two. How big would the fund of Question 11 have to be?

(A) 252,039 (B) 275,420 (C) 298,928 (D) 307,461 (E) 328,524

Use the following information for Questions 25-28.

A special deferred annuity on (30) provides the following benefits:

(1) A 20-year deferred whole life annuity of 1000 per year, payable continuously.
(2) The return of all net premiums without interest at the moment of death, in the event of death within the first 20 years.

Premiums are payable continuously for 20 years.

25. Which of the following correctly states the random present value of benefits, where the annual premium amount is π?

(A) $\begin{cases} \pi \bar{a}_{\overline{T}|} & T \leq 20 \\ 1000(\bar{a}_{\overline{T}|} - \bar{a}_{\overline{20}|}) & T > 20 \end{cases}$

(B) $\begin{cases} \pi \bar{a}_{\overline{T}|} & T \leq 20 \\ 1000\bar{a}_{\overline{T}|} & T > 20 \end{cases}$

(C) $\begin{cases} Tv^T & T \leq 20 \\ 1000\bar{a}_{\overline{T}|} & T > 20 \end{cases}$

(D) $\begin{cases} \pi T v^T & T \leq 20 \\ 1000\bar{a}_{\overline{T}|} & T > 20 \end{cases}$

(E) $\begin{cases} \pi T v^T & T \leq 20 \\ 1000(\bar{a}_{\overline{T}|} - \bar{a}_{\overline{20}|}) & T > 20 \end{cases}$

26. Which of the following is a correct expression for π, the fully continuous net annual premium?

(A) $\dfrac{1000\,{}_{20|}\bar{a}_{30}}{\bar{a}_{30:\overline{20}|} + (\bar{I}\bar{A})^{\;1}_{30:\overline{20}|}}$

(B) $\dfrac{1000\bar{a}_{30}}{\bar{a}_{30} - \bar{a}_{30:\overline{20}|}}$

(C) $\dfrac{1000\bar{a}_{30:\overline{20}|}}{\bar{a}_{30:\overline{20}|} - (\bar{I}\bar{A})^{\;1}_{30:\overline{20}|}}$

(D) $\dfrac{1000\,{}_{20|}\bar{a}_{30}}{\bar{a}_{30:\overline{20}|} - (\bar{I}\bar{A})^{\;1}_{30:\overline{20}|}}$

(E) $\dfrac{1000\,{}_{20|}\bar{a}_{30} + (\bar{I}\bar{A})^{\;1}_{30:\overline{20}|}}{\bar{a}_{30:\overline{20}|}}$

27. Which of the following is a correct prospective form for the 10th year net level premium reserve for this plan?

(A) $\pi(\overline{I}\overline{A})^{1}_{40:\overline{10}|} + 1000_{10|}\overline{a}_{40} - \pi\overline{a}_{40}$

(B) $10\pi\overline{A}^{1}_{40:\overline{10}|} + \pi(\overline{I}\overline{A})^{1}_{40:\overline{10}|} + 1000_{10|}\overline{a}_{40} - \pi\overline{a}_{40}$

(C) $(\pi + 10)(\overline{I}\overline{A})^{1}_{40:\overline{10}|} + 1000\overline{a}_{50} - \pi\overline{a}_{40:\overline{10}|}$

(D) $\pi(\overline{I}\overline{A})^{1}_{40:\overline{10}|} + 1000_{10|}\overline{a}_{40} - \pi\overline{a}_{40:\overline{10}|}$

(E) $10\pi\overline{A}^{1}_{40:\overline{10}|} + \pi(\overline{I}\overline{A})^{1}_{40:\overline{10}|} + 1000_{10|}\overline{a}_{40} - \pi\overline{a}_{40:\overline{10}|}$

28. Which of the following is a correct retrospective form for the 10th year net level premium reserve for this plan?

(A) $\pi\overline{s}_{30:\overline{20}|} - \pi(\overline{I}\overline{A})^{1}_{30:\overline{10}|}/_{10}E_{40}$

(B) $\pi\overline{s}_{30:\overline{10}|} - \pi(\overline{I}\overline{A})^{1}_{30:\overline{10}|}/_{10}E_{30}$

(C) $\pi\overline{s}_{30:\overline{10}|} - \left(\pi(\overline{I}\overline{A})^{1}_{30:\overline{10}|} + {}_{10|}\overline{a}_{30}\right)/_{10}E_{30}$

(D) $\pi\overline{s}_{30:\overline{10}|}$

(E) $\pi\overline{s}_{30:\overline{10}|} - \pi\overline{A}^{1}_{30:\overline{10}|}/_{10}E_{30}$

Use the following information for Questions 29 - 34.

${}_kL$ is the prospective loss-at-time k random variable for a fully-discrete, 3-year endowment insurance of 15 issued to (x). You are given:

(i) $i = .20$
(ii) The net level premium reserve at the end of the first year is 3.30.
(iii) The net level premium reserve at the end of the second year is 7.80.

29. The net level annual premium is closest to

(A) 4.40 (B) 4.55 (C) 4.70 (D) 4.85 (E) 5.00

30. q_{x+1} is equal to

(A) .10 (B) .15 (C) .20 (D) .25 (E) .30

31. Compute ${}_1L$ if death occurs in the third policy year.

(A) −7.80 (B) −1.80 (C) 0 (D) 1.80 (E) 7.80

32. $Var({}_1L)$ is equal to

(A) 6.75 (B) 7.00 (C) 7.25 (D) 7.50 (E) 7.75

33. q_x is

(A) .10 (B) .15 (C) .20 (D) .25 (E) .30

34. $Var({}_0L)$ is

(A) 17.88 (B) 18.96 (C) 20.04 (D) 21.12 (E) 22.24

Use the following information for Questions 35 - 38.

The random variable ${}_kL$ is the prospective loss at time k for a fully discrete 3-year endowment insurance of 3 on (x).

You are given:

(i) $i = .10$

(ii) $q_x = .009$

(iii) The premium is $3P_{x:\overline{3}|} = .834$

(iv)

k	$3{}_kV_{x:\overline{3}|}$
1	.898
2	1.893
3	3.000

35. Calculate q_{x+1}.

(A) .007 (B) .011 (C) .015 (D) .019 (E) .023

36. Calculate ${}_0L$, given that (x) dies in the first year.

(A) .08 (B) .23 (C) .63 (D) 1.25 (E) 1.89

37. Calculate $Var({}_1L)$.

(A) .011 (B) .016 (C) .021 (D) .026 (E) .031

38. Calculate $Var(\Lambda_0)$.

(A) .016 (B) .024 (C) .033 (D) .042 (E) .054

Use the following information for Questions 39 - 42.

For a portfolio of 100 deferred life annuities, you are given:

(i) The annuities were issued as 10-year deferred life annuities of 1 per year payable continuously.
(ii) No death benefits are payable.
(iii) Level benefit premiums are payable continuously during the deferral period.
(iv) The composition of the portfolio on January 1, 1996 is:

Age at Issue	Issue Date	Number
40	January 1, 1994	60
50	January 1, 1990	40

(v) $\mu(x) = .03,\ x \geq 0$
(vi) $\delta = .05$

39. Calculate $\overline{P}({}_{10|}\overline{a}_{40})$.

(A) .168 (B) .375 (C) .816 (D) 1.374 (E) 1.815

40. Calculate the benefit reserve on January 1, 1997 for one such annuity issued on (50).

(A) .85 (B) 2.67 (C) 4.96 (D) 6.28 (E) 7.66

41. Calculate the expected aggregate benefit reserve on January 1, 2001.

(A) 358 (B) 459 (C) 502 (D) 765 (E) 826

42. Given one annuitant, age 50 at issue, dies on January 1, 2001, calculate the insurer's loss at issue on this annuity.

(A) −6.42 (B) −5.83 (C) −3.61 (D) −2.45 (E) −1.86

Use the following information for Questions 43 - 46.

For a 5-year endowment insurance of 1 on (35), you are given:

(i) The death benefit is payable at the moment of death.
(ii) Premiums, payable continuously, are determined using the equivalence principle.
(iii) $\mu(35{+}t) = .05,\ t \geq 0$
(iv) $\delta = .04$
(v) ${}_tL$ is the prospective loss at time t.

43. Calculate $1000\overline{P}(\overline{A}_{35:\overline{5}|})$.

(A) 151 (B) 173 (C) 198 (D) 208 (E) 226

44. Calculate ${}^2\overline{A}_{35:\overline{5}|}$.

(A) .606 (B) .638 (C) .706 (D) .739 (E) .839

45. Calculate $E[{}_4L|T(35) > 4]$.

(A) .76 (B) .77 (C) .78 (D) .79 (E) .80

46. Calculate $Var({}_0L)$.

(A) .01 (B) .04 (C) .06 (D) .08 (E) .12

Use the following information for Questions 47 - 51.

For a special fully discrete 20-year endowment insurance on (68), you are given:

(i) $\ddot{a}_{68} = 9.686158$, $\ddot{a}_{70} = 9.075861$ $\ddot{a}_{77} = 6.973059$
$q_{73} = .0433$, ${}_{15|}q_{68} = .0441$, $\ell_{73} = 5{,}920{,}515$
$\ell_{77} = 4{,}828{,}285$, $\ell_{68} = 7{,}018{,}508$

(ii) $i = .05$

(iii) Net premiums, for $k \neq 5$, are given by
$\pi_k = 1000P_{68}$, $k = 0, 1, 2, 3, 4, 6, 7, \ldots, 19$

(iv) $\pi_5 > 0$

(v) Death benefits, for $k + 1 \neq 16$, are given by $b_{k+1} = 1000$, $k + 1 = 1, 2, \ldots, 14, 15, 17, 18, 19, 20$

(vi) $b_{16} > 0$

(vii) The endowment benefit is 1000.

(viii) $1000P_{68} = 55.62$ $\ddot{a}_{68:\overline{20}|} = 9.351599$
$1000A_{68:\overline{20}|} = 554.69$ $\ddot{a}_{85:\overline{3}|} = 2.521820$

47. Calculate ${}_{17}V$.

(A) 504 (B) 524 (C) 602 (D) 730 (E) 740

48. Calculate ${}_2V$.

(A) 63 (B) 71 (C) 84 (D) 95 (E) 103

For question 49 only, you are also given:

(i) ${}_5V = 157.00$
(ii) ${}_6V = 292.00$

49. Calculate π_5.

(A) 150 (B) 155 (C) 160 (D) 165 (E) 170

For Questions 50 and 51 only, you are also given: $\pi_5 = 270$

50. Calculate b_{16}.

(A) 5300 (B) 6300 (C) 7100 (D) 7900 (E) 8100

51. Calculate ${}_9V$.

(A) 420 (B) 600 (C) 640 (D) 650 (E) 680

SOLUTIONS TO UNIT REVIEW QUESTION

1. $${}_t\overline{V}(\overline{A}_x) = \overline{A}_{x+t} - \overline{P}(\overline{A}_x)\overline{a}_{x+t} \quad \text{(prospective form.)}$$
$$= (1 - \delta\overline{a}_{x+t}) - \overline{P}(\overline{A}_x)\overline{a}_{x+t}$$
$$= 1 - \left(\delta + \overline{P}(\overline{A}_x)\right)\overline{a}_{x+t}$$
$$\therefore \ \overline{a}_{x+t} = \frac{1 - {}_t\overline{V}(\overline{A}_x)}{\delta + \overline{P}(\overline{A}_x)} = \frac{1 - .100}{.03 + .0105} = 22.22$$

ANSWER B

2. Let J be the curtate future lifetime of $x+2$. Since $i = 0$

Event	${}_2L^* = 1000v^{J+1} - 120\,\ddot{a}_{\overline{J+1}|} = 1000 - 120(J+1)$	Probability
$J = 0$	$1000 - 120 = 880$	$q_{84} = .12$
$J = 1$	$1000 - 120(2) = 760$	${}_{1|}q_{84} = (.88)(.13) = .1144$
$J \geq 2$	$0 - 120(2) = -240$	${}_2p_{84} = (.88)(.87) = .7656$

$$E[{}_2L] = 880(.12) + 760(.1144) - 240(.7656) = 8.8$$
$$E[{}_2L^2] = (880)^2(.12) + (760)^2(.1144) + (240)^2(.7656) = 203{,}104$$
$$Var({}_2L) = 203{,}104 - 8.8^2 = 203{,}027$$

ANSWER C

* If $J \geq 2$, ${}_2L = 0 - 2(120)$

3. $${}_5L = \begin{cases} \overline{a}_{\overline{T}|} & T \leq 5 \\ \overline{a}_{\overline{5}|} & T > 5 \end{cases} = \begin{cases} \dfrac{1-v^T}{\delta} & T \leq 5 \\ \dfrac{1-v^5}{\delta} & T > 5 \end{cases} = \frac{1-Z}{\delta}$$

where Z is the random present value of benefit for a 5-year endowment insurance to 85. Thus $Var({}_5L) = Var\left(\frac{1-Z}{\delta}\right) = \frac{1}{\delta^2}\left({}^2\overline{A}_{85:\overline{5}|} - \overline{A}_{85:\overline{5}|}{}^2\right)$. By de Moivre's Law $f_T(t) = \frac{1}{15}$, $t \in [0,15]$. So

$$\overline{A}_{85:\overline{5}|} = \int_0^5 e^{-\delta t} f_T(t)\,dt + v^5\,{}_5p_{85} = \int_0^5 e^{-t/15} \cdot \frac{1}{15}\,dt + e^{-5\delta} \cdot \frac{10}{15} = \frac{1}{15}\,\overline{a}_{\overline{5}|} + \frac{2}{3}\,e^{-5/15}.$$

Similarly $${}^2\overline{A}_{85:\overline{5}|} = \int_0^5 e^{-2\delta t} f_T(t)\,dt + v^{10}\,{}_5p_{85} = \frac{1}{15}\,{}^2\overline{a}_{\overline{5}|} + \frac{2}{3}\,e^{-10/15}.$$

Thus $$Var({}_5L) = \frac{1}{(1/15)^2}\left[\frac{1}{15}\,{}^2\overline{a}_{\overline{5}|} + \frac{2}{3}\,e^{-10/15} - \left(\frac{1}{15}\,\overline{a}_{\overline{5}|} + \frac{2}{3}\,e^{-5/15}\right)^2\right]$$
$$= \left(15\,{}^2\overline{a}_{\overline{5}|} - \overline{a}_{\overline{5}|}^2\right) + 150\,e^{-2/3} - 20\,\overline{a}_{\overline{5}|}\,e^{-1/3} - 100\,e^{-2/3}$$
$$= \left(15\,{}^2\overline{a}_{\overline{5}|} - \overline{a}_{\overline{5}|}^2\right) + 10\left(5e^{-2/3} - 2\,\overline{a}_{\overline{5}|}\,e^{-1/3}\right)$$

ANSWER E

4. I. $\quad {}^2A_k \; - \; A_k{}^2$ is $Var(Z)$ only if $b_{K+1} \; = \; 0$ or 1. *False*

II. $\quad Var\left(\frac{1}{2}\,{}_kL\right) \; = \; Var({}_kL)\cdot\left(\frac{1}{2}\right)^2 \; = \; \frac{1}{4}\,Var({}_kL)$. Thus

$2 \times Var\left(\frac{1}{2}\,{}_kL\right) = \frac{1}{2}Var({}_kL) < Var({}_kL)$. *True*

III.

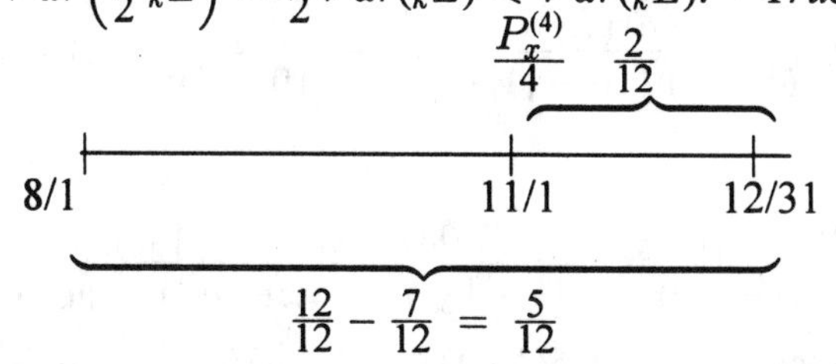

$$_{t+5/12}V_x^{(4)} \; \approx \; \frac{7}{12}\cdot{}_tV_x^{(4)} + \frac{5}{12}\cdot{}_{t+1}V_x^{(4)} \; + \; \frac{1}{12}\,P_x^{(4)}$$

(unearned premium)

since 12/31 is 1 month prior to the end of the quarter. *False* ANSWER B

5. $^{20}_{23}V_{15} = A_{38} - 0$ (prospective – past premium period)

and similarly $^{20}_{24}V_{15} \; = \; A_{39}$. Thus $.585 = {}^{20}_{23}V_{15} = A_{38} = vq_{38} + vp_{38}A_{39} = \frac{1}{1.04}\left(q_{38}+p_{38}(.6)\right)$,

$q_{38} = .021, \;\; p_{38} = .979$ ANSWER D

6. From the basic recursive relation

$$({}_9V+P)(1+i) \; = \; \text{year-end funds available} \; = \; \text{needed funds}$$

$$= \; q_{35+9}(2500) + p_{35+9}({}_{10}V) \; = q_{44}(2500-{}_{10}V) + {}_{10}V$$

(dies) (survives)

Thus

$$q_{44} \; = \; \frac{({}_9V+P)(1+i) - {}_{10}V}{2500 - {}_{10}V} \; = \; \frac{{}_{10}V(1+i) - {}_{10}V}{2500 - {}_{10}V}$$

$$= \; \frac{i\cdot{}_{10}V}{2500 - {}_{10}V} \; = \; \frac{(.10)(500)}{2500 - 500} \; = \; .10\,\frac{1}{4} \; = \; .025$$

ANSWER C

7. A retrospective solution is suggested since $P_{45:\overline{20|}}$ and $P_{\overset{\;1}{45}:\overline{20|}}$ concern ages 45-65, the *past* at age 65. Now $_{20}V_{45} = P_{45}\,\ddot{s}_{45:\overline{20|}} - \frac{A^{1}_{45:\overline{20|}}}{_{20}E_{45}}$. $P^{1}_{45:\overline{20|}} = P_{45:\overline{20|}} - P_{\overset{\;1}{45}:\overline{20|}} = .030 - .022 = .008 = \frac{A^{1}_{45:\overline{20|}}}{\ddot{a}_{45:\overline{20|}}}$.

Also $.022 = P_{\overset{\;1}{45}:\overline{20|}} = \frac{_{20}E_{45}}{\ddot{a}_{45:\overline{20|}}} = \frac{1}{\ddot{s}_{45:\overline{20|}}}$.

So $\frac{A^{1}_{45:\overline{20|}}}{_{20}E_{45}} = \frac{.008}{.022} = \frac{4}{11}$, $P_{45}\ddot{s}_{45:\overline{20|}} = .014\left(\frac{1}{.022}\right) = \frac{7}{11}$

Thus $_{20}V_{45} = \frac{7}{11} - \frac{4}{11} = \frac{3}{11} = .273$ ANSWER E

8. $L = \Lambda_0 + \Lambda_1 \cdot v$ where Λ_0, Λ_1 are the p.v. of losses in policy years 1 and 2 at the beginning of the year. In year two there is no uncertainty since the 10 is paid as either a death benefit or as a pure endowment. Thus $Var(L) = Var(\Lambda_0) + v^2 Var(\Lambda_1) = Var(\Lambda_0)$ since $Var(\Lambda_1) = 0$. Also $Var(\Lambda_0) = v^2(10 - {}_1V)^2 q_x p_x = (1-d)^2(10 - {}_1V)^2 q_x p_x$. Hence

$$q_x p_x = \frac{Var(\Lambda_0)}{(1-d)^2(10-{}_1V)^2} = \frac{Var(L)}{(1-d)^2(10-{}_1V)^2} = \frac{3.24}{.9^2(10-5)^2} = .16$$ ANSWER B

9. For a standard policy, ${}_{20}V_{35} = ({}_{19}V_{35}+P_{35})(1.04) - q_{54}(1-{}_{20}V_{35})$. For the substandard, ${}_{20}V_{35} = ({}_{19}V_{35}+P_{35}+.005)(1.04) - (q_{54}+c)(1-{}_{20}V_{35})$, where c is the extra mortality rate. Subtracting the two lines produces $0 = -.005(1.04) + c(1-{}_{20}V_{35})$, or $c = \dfrac{.005(1.04)}{1-.48} = .01$,

ANSWER D

10. Prospectively the 10th reserve is given by

$${}_{10}V = APV_{50}(\text{benefits for ages 50-65}) - APV_{50}(\text{premiums}). \qquad (*)$$

The easy part is $APV(\text{premiums}) = 200\bar{a}_{50:\overline{15}|} = \dfrac{200(1 - \bar{A}_{50:\overline{15}|})}{\delta} \approx 1640.$

At age 50 the random present value of future benefits is $Z = \begin{cases} v^U \cdot 1000\bar{a}_{\overline{15-U}|} & 0 \le U \le 15 \\ 0 & U > 15 \end{cases}$

where U is the future lifetime of (50). Thus the benefit term in (*) is given by

$$\begin{aligned}
E[Z] &= \int_0^{15} v^u \cdot 1000\,\frac{1-v^{15-u}}{\delta} \cdot f_U(u)\,du \\
&= \frac{1000}{\delta}\left[\int_0^{15} v^t \cdot f_U(u)\,du - \int_0^{15} v^{15} \cdot f_U(u)\,du\right] \\
&= \frac{1000}{\delta}\left[\bar{A}^{\,1}_{50:\overline{15}|} - v^{15} \cdot {}_{15}q_{50}\right] \\
&= \frac{1000}{.04879}\left[\bar{A}^{\,1}_{50:\overline{15}|} - v^{15}(1 - {}_{15}p_{50})\right] \\
&= \frac{1000}{.04879}\left[\bar{A}_{50:\overline{15}|} - v^{15}\right] \\
&= \frac{1000}{.04879}\left[.6 - (1.05)^{-15}\right] \approx 2439.
\end{aligned}$$

Thus, by (*), ${}_{10}V = 2439 - 1640 = 799$, ANSWER E

11. A standard approach to a problem in which the death benefit includes a reserve is the recursive relation between consecutive reserves. In this problem the work is simplified by the fact that the plan covers only 2 years. Note first that ${}_0V = 0$ and that ${}_2V = 1000$ since the reserve must build up enough to pay the endowment benefit. Let P be the net level annual premium.

Year 1 $$\underbrace{({}_0V+P)(1+i)}_{\text{available at } t=1} = \underbrace{q_x \cdot (1000+{}_1V) + p_x \cdot {}_1V}_{APV \text{ of needed funds at } t=1}$$

$$\Rightarrow \quad P(1.10) = .1(1000+{}_1V) + .9({}_1V), \text{ or } 1.10P - 100 = {}_1V$$

Year 2 $$({}_1V+P)(1+i) = q_{x+1} \cdot (1000+{}_2V) + p_{x+1} \cdot 1000$$

$$\Rightarrow \quad (1.10P - 100+P)(1.10) = .11(1000+1000) + .89(1000)$$

$$\Rightarrow \quad P = \frac{(1110/1.10) + 100}{2.1} = 528,$$ ANSWER B

12. The best way to bring the amount at risk into the problem is via the following recursive reserve relation where P is the net level annual premium (notice Face Value B is unknown) and ${}_{h-1}V + P$ is the initial reserve in the hth policy year:

$$\underbrace{({}_{h-1}V+P)}_{\text{initial reserve}}(1+i) = q_{x+h-1} \cdot B + p_{x+h-1} \cdot {}_hV = q_{x+h-1}\underbrace{(B - {}_hV)}_{\text{at risk}} + {}_hV$$

$(200)(1.05) = (.004)(1295) + {}_hV$, so ${}_hV = 204.82$.
Then $B = (B - {}_hV) + {}_hV = 1295 + 204.82 = 1499.82$ and
$P = B \cdot P_x = (1499.82)\left(\frac{1}{\ddot{a}_x} - d\right) = (1499.82)\left(\frac{1}{16.2} - \frac{1}{21}\right) = 21.16.$
Thus ${}_{h-1}V = \text{initial reserve} - P = 200 - 21.16 = 178.84,$ ANSWER A

13. Notice that with $d = .08$ and $A_{x:\overline{n}|} = .20$ being given, we can easily create $\ddot{a}_{x:\overline{n}|}$ and $P_{x:\overline{n}|}$. At duration $n-1$ the reserve plus the premium for the final year must accumulate to 1 by year end, since every policy in force at the start of this year requires 1 by year end:

$$\left({}_{n-1}V_{x:\overline{n}|} + P_{x:\overline{n}|}\right)(1+i) = 1$$

$$\begin{aligned} \Rightarrow \quad {}_{n-1}V_{x:\overline{n}|} &= v - P_{x:\overline{n}|} \\ &= (1-d) - \left(\frac{dA_{x:\overline{n}|}}{1-A_{x:\overline{n}|}}\right) \\ &= .92 - (.08)\left(\frac{.20}{.80}\right) = .90, \end{aligned}$$ ANSWER A

14. The question is poorly stated: one must assume that the annual annuity payment is 1. Now let P be the NSP. The random present value of the refund benefit (NSP plus interest if death is within 10 years) is

$$Y = \begin{cases} (P(1+i)^{K+1})v^{K+1} = P & \text{if } K = 0, 1, \ldots, 9 \\ 0 & \text{otherwise} \end{cases}$$

So $E[Y] = \sum_{k=0}^{9} P \cdot f_K(k) = P\sum_{k=0}^{9} {}_{k|}q_x = P \cdot {}_{10}q_x$.

The basic equation for P is

$$P = NSP(\text{refund benefit}) + NSP(\text{deferred annuity}) = P \cdot {}_{10}q_x + {}_{10|}\ddot{a}_x, \text{ or}$$

$$P = \frac{1}{{}_{10}p_x}({}_{10|}\ddot{a}_x) = \frac{1}{{}_{10}p_x}(v^{10} \cdot {}_{10}p_x \cdot \ddot{a}_{x+10}) = v^{10}\ddot{a}_{x+10}.$$

Finally, the 9th reserve is given as 15.238. So

$$15.238 = {}_9V = \underbrace{\underbrace{P(1+i)^{10}}_{\text{amt.}} \cdot \underbrace{v}_{\text{disc.}} \cdot \underbrace{q_{x+9}}_{\text{prob.}}}_{\text{for death}} + \underbrace{\underbrace{\ddot{a}_{x+10}}_{\text{amt.}} \cdot \underbrace{v}_{\text{disc.}} \cdot \underbrace{p_{x+9}}_{\text{prob.}}}_{\text{for survival}}.$$

From the above $P = v^{10}\ddot{a}_{x+10}$. Substituting this in the last equation gives

$$15.238 = v^{10}\ddot{a}_{x+10}(1+i)^{10} \cdot vq_{x+9} + \ddot{a}_{x+10} \cdot v \cdot p_{x+9} = v\ddot{a}_{x+10},$$

so

$$P = v^{10}\ddot{a}_{x+10} = v^9(15.238) = (.644609)(15.238) = 9.823,$$ ANSWER B

15. The form of the given data suggests using the form of the reserve in terms of insurances:

$${}_{20}\overline{V}(\overline{A}_{30}) = \overline{A}_{50} - \overline{P}(\overline{A}_{30})\overline{a}_{50}$$

$$= \overline{A}_{50} - \frac{\overline{A}_{30}}{\overline{a}_{30}}\overline{a}_{50}$$

$$= \overline{A}_{50} - \frac{\overline{A}_{30}}{(1-\overline{A}_{30})/\delta} \cdot (1-\overline{A}_{50})/\delta = \frac{\overline{A}_{50} - \overline{A}_{30}}{1 - \overline{A}_{30}}$$

We are given $\overline{A}_{50} = .70$ and need to find $\overline{A}_{30}$, which is hidden in the other two pieces of information:

$$.20 = Var(L) = \left(1 + \frac{\overline{P}(\overline{A}_{30})}{\delta}\right)^2 ({}^2\overline{A}_{30} - \overline{A}_{30}{}^2)$$

$$= \left(\frac{1}{\delta\overline{a}_{30}}\right)^2 ({}^2\overline{A}_{30} - \overline{A}_{30}{}^2) = \frac{{}^2\overline{A}_{30} - \overline{A}_{30}{}^2}{(1 - \overline{A}_{30})^2} = \frac{.3 - \overline{A}_{30}{}^2}{(1 - \overline{A}_{30})^2}.$$

Cross multiplying and solving a tedious quadratic equation gives $\overline{A}_{30} = .5$. Thus ${}_{20}\overline{V}(\overline{A}_{30}) = \frac{.7 - .5}{1 - .5} = .40$, ANSWER C

16. Under the UDD assumption there is a standard relation between reserves with m^{th}ly premiums and reserves with annual ones.

$$ {}_5V_{35}^{(4)} = \left(1 + \beta(4)P_{35}^{(4)}\right) {}_5V_{35} $$

Hence the difference in reserves is $\beta(4)P_{35}^{(4)}\,{}_5V_{35}$:

$$ \begin{aligned} \beta(4) &= .38272 \text{ (given)} \\ {}_5V_{35} &= .04471 \text{ (given)} \\ P_{35}^{(4)} &= \frac{A_{35}}{\ddot{a}_{35}^{(4)}} = \frac{.17092}{17.031204} \quad \begin{matrix}\text{(given)}\\ \text{(given)}\end{matrix} \\ &= .010036. \end{aligned} $$

Thus

$$ \begin{aligned} \text{Difference} &= (.38272)(.010036)(.04471) \\ &= .000172 \end{aligned} $$

ANSWER A

17. There is no algebraic simplification of ${}_2V_{x:\overline{3}|} - {}_1V_{x:\overline{3}|}$ which can considerably simplify its calculation. One simply needs to calculate each of the reserves separately and then subtract them. Since you are given complete information on interest and mortality the reserves can be calculated in numerous ways. (Note: You are not given q_{x+2} or p_{x+2} but this is irrelevant since anyone who survives to $x+2$ is certain to be paid the \$1 at the end of the next year. This is a special feature of the final year of an endowment insurance.)

A nice way to solve this particular problem, since the premium is given to you, is to do two years of aggregate deterministic accounting. Since assets and liabilities match at the end of each year in net premium accounting, ${}_1V_{x:\overline{3}|}$ equals EF_1/ℓ_{x+1} and ${}_2V_{x:\overline{3}|} = EF_2/\ell_{x+2}$ where EF_k is the ending fund for year k is the spreadsheet.

Year	Beginning Fund	Premium	Interest Income	Benefits	Ending Fund
1	0	33,251.00	1,995.06	10,000	25,246.06
2	25,246.06	29,925.90	3,310.32	9,000	49,482.28

$$ 1000\,{}_1V_{x:\overline{3}|} = \frac{25{,}246.06}{90} = 280.51 $$

$$ 1000\,{}_2V_{x:\overline{3}|} = \frac{49{,}482.28}{81} = 610.89 $$

Difference $= 330.37$

ANSWER A

18. The key to solving this question is recognizing that you know the reserves at the end and beginning of year 11. So the unknown year 11 benefit is connected with the beginning and ending reserves by a recursion relation. This relation is a reflection of the arithmetic across the 11th row of the aggregate deterministic spreadsheet: (see the Review Notes in this unit)

Whole Life at (20): $${}_{10}V_{20} + P_{20} = vq_{30} \cdot 1 + vp_{30} \cdot {}_{11}V_{30}$$

Special Insurance to (40): $$\underbrace{{}_{10}V}_{\text{generic symbol}} + Prem = vq_{50} \cdot b_{11} + vp_{50} \cdot \underbrace{{}_{11}V}_{\text{generic symbol}} .$$

You are given in (i) and (ii) that the left sides of these two equations are identical. Hence the right sides are identical. Now fill in other given information and you see that b_{11} is the lone unknown. (Cancel the common v.)

$$\underset{\uparrow\ .008427}{v \cdot q_{30}} \cdot 1 + v \cdot \underset{\uparrow\ .991573}{p_{30}} \cdot \underset{\uparrow\ .08154}{{}_{11}V_{20}} = v \cdot \underset{\uparrow\ .018427}{q_{50}} \cdot b_{11} + v \cdot \underset{\uparrow\ .981573}{p_{50}} \cdot \underset{\uparrow\ .08154}{{}_{11}V}$$

$\Rightarrow \quad b_{11} = .50159.$ ANSWER E

19. The key idea is that ${}^{10}_{10}V_x = A_{x+10}$ since no premium is due after age $x+10$. The sought $P_{x+10} = \dfrac{dA_{x+10}}{1 - A_{x+10}}$ and $d = \frac{6}{106}$. Since the 9th reserve and mortality for the 10th year, $q_{x+9} = .01262$, are both given, the recursive relation for year 10 is suggested:

$${}^{10}_{9}V_x + {}_{10}P_x = 1 \cdot v \cdot q_{x+9} + v \cdot p_{x+9} \cdot {}^{10}_{10}V_x$$

$$.32287 + .03288 = \frac{.01262}{1.06} + \frac{.98738}{1.06} \cdot {}^{10}_{10}V_x$$

$$\Rightarrow \quad {}^{10}_{10}V_x = .36913 \quad \Rightarrow \quad P_{x+10} = \frac{(\frac{6}{106})(.36913)}{1 - .36913} = .03312$$ ANSWER E

20. By Hattendorf's principle (see the Unit Condensed Review Notes)

$$Var({}_{10}L|K \geq 10) = v^2(1 - {}_{11}V_{30})^2 q_{40} p_{40} + v^2 p_{40}(\underbrace{Var({}_{11}L|K \geq 11)}_{Var({}_{11}L|K \geq 10)}).$$

So the question is simply asking for the first term on the right side:

$$y = v^2 \underbrace{(1 - {}_{11}V_{30})}_{\left(\frac{\ddot{a}_{41}}{\ddot{a}_{30}}\right)} q_{40} p_{40} = \left(\frac{1}{1.05}\right)^2 \left(\frac{16.46}{18.06}\right)^2 (.00278)(.99722) = .002089$$ ANSWER C

21 - 24.
Since there are 100 in-force policies at each duration, we have

$$\text{Aggregate Reserve} = 100(1000\,{}_1V^{\,1}_{x:\overline{3}|}) + 100(1000\,{}_2V^{\,1}_{x:\overline{3}|}) = 21{,}666.60.$$

Question 21 has ANSWER D.

The quickest method of calculating $Var({}_1L)$ is to employ Hattendorf's formula. After this we will also illustrate a first-principles method which is a bit longer.

$$Var({}_1L) = v^2 q_{x+1} p_{x+1} (\underbrace{1000 - 120.833}_{\text{at risk}})^2 + v^2 p_{x+1}(v^2 q_{x+2} p_{x+2})(\underbrace{1000 - 0}_{\text{at risk}})^2 = 255{,}761.$$

Question 22 has ANSWER E.

The alternate method is based on calculating the values of the discrete variable ${}_1L$ and the associated probabilities. One then calculates $Var({}_1L) = E[{}_1L^2] - (E[{}_1L])^2$ from the table. We first need the net level premium which is hidden in the given information on the reserves at durations one and two:

$${}_1V^{\,1}_{x:\overline{3}|} + P^{\,1}_{x:\overline{3}|} = v\left(q_{x+1} \cdot 1 + p_{x+1} \cdot {}_2V^{\,1}_{x:\overline{3}|}\right),$$

from which we find $P^{\,1}_{x:\overline{3}|} = .333712$, so that $100{,}000P^{\,1}_{x:\overline{3}|} = 333.71$.

${}_1L$	Event	Probability
$1000/1.10 - 333.71\ddot{a}_{\overline{1}|} = 575.38$	$J = 0$	$q_{x+1} = .40$
$1000/(1.10)^2 - 333.71\ddot{a}_{\overline{2}|} = 189.36$	$J = 1$	${}_1|q_{x+1} = (.6)(.5) = .30$
$0 - 333.71\ddot{a}_{\overline{2}|} = -637.09$	$J \geq 2$	${}_2p_{x+1} = (.6)(.5) = .30$

From this data we can find $E[{}_1L^2] = .4(575.38)^2 + .3(189.36)^2 + .3(-637.09)^2$; the value of $E[{}_1L] = 1000\,{}_1V^{\,1}_{x:\overline{3}|}$ is given as 95.833.

L_{Agg}, the insurers aggregate loss function on the 200 policies, is a sum of 100 independent variables like ${}_1L$, and another 100 independent variables like ${}_2L$. Thus L_{Agg} is approximately normal with parameters

$$\mu(Agg) = 100E[{}_1L] + 100E[{}_2L] = 100(95.833) + 100(120.833) = 21{,}666.60$$

and

$$\sigma^2_{Agg} = 100Var({}_1L) + 100Var({}_2L) = 100(255{,}761) + 100(206{,}612) = 46{,}237{,}300$$

so

$$\sigma_{Agg} = \sqrt{46{,}237{,}300} = 6799.8 \approx 6800.$$

The fund sought is the 95th percentile of L_{Agg}, which is $\mu(Agg) + 1.645\sigma_{Agg} = 32{,}852$.

That is,

$$\begin{aligned} .95 &= Pr(32{,}852 > L_{Agg} = PV(\text{future benefit} - \text{future premium})) \\ &= Pr(\underbrace{32{,}852 + PV(\text{future premium}) > PV(\text{future benefit})}_{\text{i.e., obligations are met}}). \end{aligned}$$

Question 23 has ANSWER B.

If there are ten times as many policies, then $\mu(Agg)$ goes up by a factor of 10 whereas σ_{Agg} goes up by a factor of $\sqrt{10}$. Then the needed amount is

$$\text{Fund} = 10(21{,}666.60) + \sqrt{10} \cdot 1.645(6800) = 252{,}039.$$

Question 24 has ANSWER A.

25 -28.

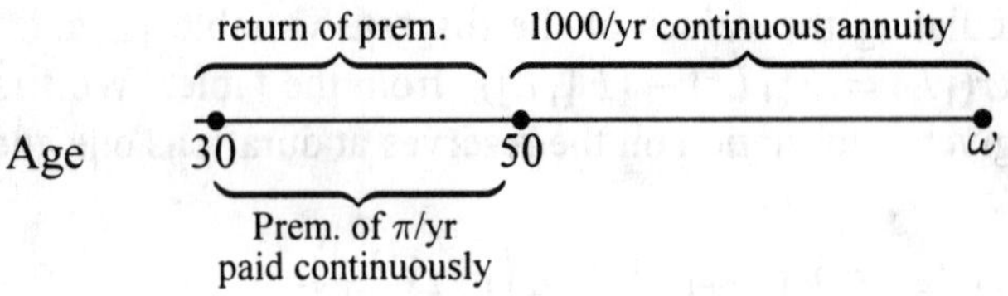

In T years, $T \leq 20$, the amount of premium paid is πT. Hence the random present value is $(\pi T)(v^T)$ if $T \leq 20$ and zero if $T > 20$. The random present value of the 20 year deferred continuous life annuity is

$$\begin{cases} 0 & T \leq 20 \\ 1000(\bar{a}_{\overline{T|}} - \bar{a}_{\overline{20|}}) & T > 20 \end{cases}$$

The total of these two is ANSWER E to Question 25.

The fully continuous net annual premium is the solution of the equation

$$\begin{aligned} \pi \bar{a}_{30:\overline{20|}} &= E[\text{Random P.V. of benefits}] \\ &= E[\text{Return of Premium}] + E[\text{deferred annuity}] = \pi \bar{I}\bar{A}^{\;1}_{30:\overline{20|}} + 1000_{20|}\bar{a}_{30} \\ \Rightarrow \pi &= \frac{1000_{20|}\bar{a}_{30}}{\bar{a}_{30:\overline{20|}} - \bar{I}\bar{A}^{\;1}_{30:\overline{20|}}} \end{aligned}$$

Question 26 has ANSWER D.

Prospectively, the reserve at duration 10 is the APV at 40 of the premium refund benefit (up to age 50) plus the APV at 40 of the 10 year deferred continuous life annuity of 1000/year less the APV at 40 of the remaining 10 years of continuous net premiums. The tricky piece is the refund APV. Let U be the complete future lifetime of 40.

$$\begin{matrix}\text{Random Premium} \\ \text{Refund P.V. at 40}\end{matrix} = \begin{cases} \underbrace{(10+U)\pi}_{\text{amount}} \cdot \underbrace{v^U}_{\text{discount}} & U \leq 10 \\ 0 & U > 10 \end{cases}$$

$$\Rightarrow \; APV_{40}\text{ (refund)} = 10\pi \bar{A}^{\,1}_{40:\overline{10|}} + \pi \bar{I}\bar{A}^{\,1}_{40:\overline{10|}}$$

$$\Rightarrow \; {}_{10}V\text{ (prospective)} = APV_{40}\text{ (refund)} + 1000\,{}_{10|}\bar{a}_{40} - \pi \bar{a}_{40:\overline{10|}}$$

So Question 27 has ANSWER E.

If the same reserve is calculated retrospectively the accumulation of past premium is $\pi \bar{s}_{30:\overline{10|}}$. The only past benefits are 10 years of increasing term insurance so

$$\begin{aligned} {}_{10}V\text{ (retrospective)} &= \text{Accumulated Value(past premium} - \text{past benefits)} \\ &= \pi \bar{s}_{30:\overline{10|}} - \pi \bar{I}\bar{A}^{\,1}_{30:\overline{10|}} / {}_{10}E_{30}. \end{aligned}$$

Question 28 has ANSWER B.

29 - 34.

We are given $i = .20$, $15 \cdot {}_1V_{x:\overline{3|}} = 3.30$ and $15 \cdot {}_2V_{x:\overline{3|}} = 7.80$. Using the recursive reserve relation for the third policy year we have

$$\begin{aligned} (15 \cdot {}_2V_{x:\overline{3|}} + P) = APV \text{ of funds available at year's start} &= APV \text{ of funds needed} \\ &= \underset{\text{(death)}}{v \cdot 15 \cdot q_{x+2}} + \underset{\text{(survival)}}{v \cdot 15 \cdot p_{x+2}} = v \cdot 15 \end{aligned}$$

where $P = 15 \cdot P_{x:\overline{3|}}$ is the net level annual premium. This gives $7.80 + P = \frac{15}{1.20}$, or $P = 4.70$

Question 29 has ANSWER C.

Since q_{x+1} is related to the second policy year we use the relation between the first and second reserves $(15 \cdot {}_1V_{x:\overline{3|}} + P) = v \cdot 15 \cdot q_{x+1} + v^{15} \cdot {}_2V_{x:\overline{3|}} \cdot p_{x+1}$, or
$1.2(3.30{+}4.70) = 15q_{x+1} + 7.80(1 - q_{x+1})$. Hence $q_{x+1} = .25$.

Question 30 has ANSWER D.

At duration 1 the possible losses are

$15 \cdot v - 4.70 = 7.80$ $\quad J = 0$

$15 \cdot v^2 - (4.70{+}4.70/1.2) = 1.80$ $\quad J = 1, 2, \ldots$

since either a survival benefit or death benefit of 15 is paid by the end of the third policy year. J is the curtate future lifetime of $x{+}1$.

Question 31 has ANSWER D.

To compute the variance we need to know the probabilities associated with the losses in (c): $Pr(J = 0) = q_{x+1} = .25$, so $Pr(J = 1, 2, \ldots) = 1 - .25 = .75$. Thus

$$E[Loss] = (7.80)(.25) + (1.80)(.75) = 3.30 \quad \text{(the first reserve)}$$

$$E[Loss^2] = (7.80)^2(.25) + (1.80)^2(.75) = 17.64$$

and $\quad Var(Loss) = 17.64 - (3.30)^2 = 6.75.$

Question 32 has ANSWER A. Hattendorf's method could also have been employed.

Just as in 6 we have a recursive relation for year one: $P = 15v\,q_x + 3.30v\,(1{-}q_x)$. Substituting $P = 4.7$ from above and $v = 1/1.2$ results in $q_x = .20$.

Question 33 has ANSWER C.

By Hattendorf's method

$Var(L) = (15{-}3.3)^2 v^2 q_x p_x + (15{-}7.8)^2 v^4 p_x q_{x+1} p_{x+1} = 15.21 + 3.75 = 18.96.$

There is nothing at risk in the third year since $15\,{}_3V_{x:\overline{3}|} = 15$, so the sum has only two terms.

Question 34 ANSWER B.

35 - 38.

Since you are given reserves at ages $x{+}1$ and $x{+}2$, the benefit for year 2, and $i = 10$, the mortality for year 2, q_{x+1}, can be gotten from the recursion relation between consecutive reserves:

$$3 \cdot {}_1V_{x:\overline{3}|} + 3P_{x:\overline{3}|} = v \cdot q_{x+1} \cdot 3 + v(1{-}q_{x+1}) \cdot 3 \cdot {}_2V_{x:\overline{3}|}.$$

Substituting the given information results in $q_{x+1} = .01102$.

Question 35 has ANSWER B.

${}_0L = 3v^{K+1} - 3P_{x:\overline{3}|}\ddot{a}_{\overline{K+1}|}$ if $K = 0$, 1 or 2 and ${}_0L = 3v^3 - 3P_{x:\overline{3}|}\ddot{a}_{\overline{3}|}$ if $K \geq 3$. Use the first version with $K = 0$ to obtain $\left(\frac{3}{1.1}\right) - .834\ddot{a}_{\overline{1}|} = 1.893$.

Question 36 has ANSWER E.

$Var({}_1L)$ can be calculated in a number of ways:

(i) Use the discrete distribution in the table below having 2-distinct values

${}_1L$ - value	Probability	Event
$\frac{3}{1.1} - .834$	$q_{x+1} = .01102$	$J = 0$
$\frac{3}{1.1^2} - .834\ddot{a}_{\overline{2}|.10}$	$p_{x+1} = .98898$	$J \geq 1$

(ii) Use the standard formula $(3)^2\left(1 + \frac{P_{x:\overline{3}|}}{d}\right)^2\left({}^2A_{x+1:\overline{2}|} - A_{x+1:\overline{2}|}{}^2\right)$

(iii) Use Hattendorf's principle - only one term in the sum since an endowment insurance has nothing at risk in the final year.

$$Var({}_1L) = v^2(3 - 3{}_2V_{x:\overline{3}|})^2 q_{x+1}p_{x+1} = \frac{(3 - 1.893)^2}{1.1^2}(.01102)(.98898) = .011038$$

Question 37 has ANSWER A.

Note: Small differences are noted in the answers since $.834 = 3P_{x:\overline{3}|}$ is rounded!

See the Condensed Review Notes for information on the variables $\Lambda_0, \Lambda_1, \ldots$ etc.

$$Var(\Lambda_0) = (3 - 3{}_1V_{x:\overline{3}|})^2 v^2 q_x p_x = \frac{(3 - .898)^2}{1.21}(.009)(.991) = .03256$$

Question 38 has ANSWER C.

39 - 42.

Notice that the information in the table in (iv) represents in force on 1/1/96, not the number of issues! In general

$$\overline{P}({}_{10|}\overline{a}_{40}) = \frac{{}_{10|}\overline{a}_{40}}{\overline{a}_{40:\overline{10}|}} = \frac{v^{10} \cdot {}_{10}p_{40} \cdot \overline{a}_{50}}{\overline{a}_{40} - v^{10} \cdot {}_{10}p_{40}\overline{a}_{50}}.$$

With constant force any $\overline{a}_x = \frac{1}{\mu+\delta} = \frac{1}{.08} = 12.5$ and $v^n\,{}_np_x = e^{-n\delta}e^{-n\mu} = e^{-(\mu+\delta)n}$. Hence the premium above equals $\frac{e^{-.8}}{1 - e^{-.8}} = .8160$.

Question 39 has ANSWER C.

1/1/97 is duration 7 for an issue to (50) on 1/1/90. Retrospectively, the 7th reserve looks like the accumulation of past premium with interest and survival:

$${}_7\overline{V}({}_{10}|\bar{a}_{50}) = \overline{P}({}_{10}|\bar{a}_{50})\bar{s}_{50:\overline{7}|}$$

Constant force makes age irrelevant so

$$\overline{P}({}_{10}|\bar{a}_{50}) = \overline{P}({}_{10}|\bar{a}_{40}) = .8160.$$

Also

$$\begin{aligned}
\bar{s}_{50:\overline{7}|} &= \frac{\bar{a}_{50:\overline{7}|}}{v^7 \cdot {}_7p_{50}} \\
&= \int_0^7 e^{-\delta t}\,{}_tp_{50}\,dt / v^7 \cdot {}_7p_{50} \\
&= \int_0^7 e^{-(\mu+\delta)t}\,dt / e^{-7(\mu+\delta)} \qquad \text{(Constant force)} \\
&= \frac{1-e^{-(\mu+\delta)7}}{(\mu+\delta)} / e^{-7(\mu+\delta)} = \frac{e^{(\mu+\delta)7}-1}{\mu+\delta} = 9.3834.
\end{aligned}$$

Thus the 7th reserve is (.8160)(9.3834) = 7.6569

Question 40 has ANSWER E.

The diagram below should prove helpful.

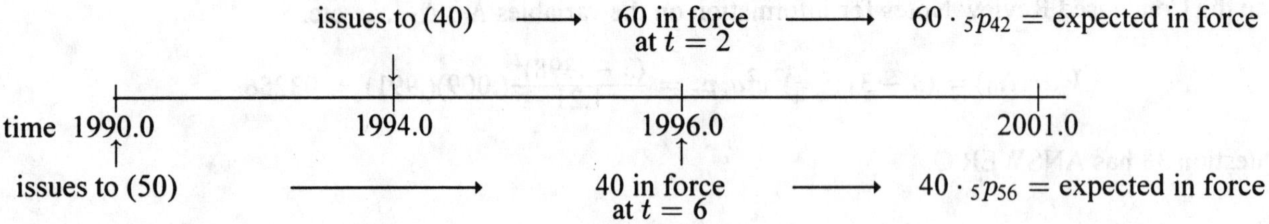

Note: 1/1/2001 is duration 7 for the issues to (40) and duration 11 for the issues to (50).

$$(\text{Expected Benefit Reserve } 1/1/2001) = 60 \cdot \underbrace{{}_5p_{42}}_{e^{-5(.03)}} \cdot \underbrace{{}_7\overline{V}({}_{10}|\bar{a}_{40})}_{7.66 \text{ above}} + 40 \cdot \underbrace{{}_5p_{56}}_{e^{-5(.03)}} \cdot \underbrace{{}_{11}\overline{V}({}_{10}\bar{a}_{50})}_{=\bar{a}_{61} = \frac{1}{\mu+\delta} = 12.5}$$

$$= 395.58 + 430.35 = 825.94$$

Question 41 has ANSWER E.

If death is on 1/1/2001 (age 61) the value of the loss function is

$$L = \underbrace{\text{P.V. money out}}_{\bar{a}_{\overline{11}|} - \bar{a}_{\overline{10}|}} - \underbrace{\text{P.V. money in}}_{\bar{P}({}_{10|}\bar{a}_{50})\bar{a}_{\overline{10}|}}$$

$$= a_{\overline{11}|} - (1+\bar{P}({}_{10|}\bar{a}_{50}))\bar{a}_{\overline{10}|}$$

$$= 8.46 - (1.816)7.87 = -5.83.$$

Question 42 has ANSWER B.

43 - 46.
To obtain the premium you first need

$\bar{a}_{35:\overline{5}|} = \int_0^5 v^t \cdot {}_tp_x dt \underset{\text{c.f.}}{=} \int_0^5 e^{-(\mu+\delta)t} dt = \frac{(1-e^{-5(\mu+\delta)})}{(\mu+\delta)} = 4.0264$. Then $\frac{1}{\bar{a}_{35:\overline{5}|}} = \delta + \bar{P}(\bar{A}_{35:\overline{5}|})$ gives a premium of .20836.

Question 43 has ANSWER D.

One possible way to obtain ${}^2\bar{A}_{35:\overline{5}|}$ is to use the relation $1 = (2\delta)^2\bar{a}_{55:\overline{5}|} + {}^2\bar{A}_{55:\overline{5}|}$ after calculating ${}^2\bar{a}_{55:\overline{5}|} = \frac{(1-e^{-5(\mu+2\delta)})}{(\mu+2\delta)} = 3.6766$. This results in ${}^2\bar{A}_{50:\overline{5}|} = .7059$.

Question 44 has ANSWER C.

The question asks for ${}_4\bar{V}(\bar{A}_{35:\overline{4}|}) = \bar{A}_{39:\overline{1}|} - \bar{P}(\bar{A}_{35:\overline{5}|})\bar{a}_{39:\overline{1}|} = 1 - \frac{\bar{a}_{39:\overline{1}|}}{\bar{a}_{35:\overline{5}|}} = 1 - \frac{.9563}{4.0264} = .7625$, where $\bar{a}_{39:\overline{1}|}$ is calculated in the same manner as $\bar{a}_{35:\overline{5}|}$ in Question 43 above.

Question 45 has ANSWER A

A standard formula (see Condensed Review Notes) for this variance is $\frac{({}^2\bar{A}_{35:\overline{5}|} - \bar{A}_{35:\overline{5}|}{}^2)}{(1-\bar{A}_{35:\overline{5}|})^2}$, which results in .0787 when you plug in

$\bar{A}_{35:\overline{5}|} = 1 - \delta\bar{a}_{35:\overline{5}|} = .83894$ (see above)

${}^2\bar{A}_{35:\overline{5}|} = .7059$ (see above).

Question 46 has ANSWER D.

47 - 51.
The following diagram is useful in organizing the work on this group:

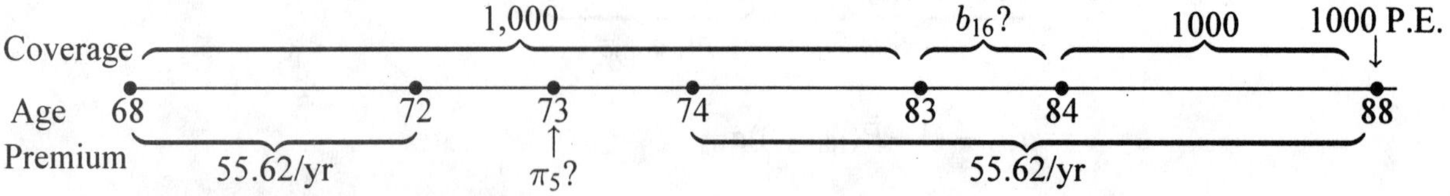

Since $\ddot{a}_{85:\overline{3}|} = 2.521820$ is given we calculate the 17th reserve prospectively as $1000[A_{85:\overline{3}|} - .05562\ddot{a}_{85:\overline{3}|}] = 1000\left[1 - \left(\frac{1}{21} + .05562\right)2.521820\right] = 740$ (nearest dollar)

Question 47 has ANSWER E.

In calculating ${}_2V$ from the given data a very subtle idea is needed. At age 70 when you look backward (i.e., retrospectively) you see the same pattern of benefits and premiums that you would see with 1000 of fully discrete whole life issued to 68. Thus

$${}_2V \underset{\text{(retro)}}{=} 1000\,{}_2V_{68} \underset{\text{(pros)}}{=} 1000\left(1 - \frac{\ddot{a}_{70}}{\ddot{a}_{68}}\right) = 1000\left(1 - \frac{9.076}{9.686}\right) = 63 \text{ (nearest dollar).}$$

Question 48 has ANSWER A.

With ${}_5V$ and ${}_6V$ given it appears a recursive approach is best:

$${}_5V + \pi_5 = 1000 \cdot q_{73} \cdot \left(\frac{1}{1+i}\right) + {}_6V \cdot p_{73} \cdot \left(\frac{1}{1+i}\right)$$

${}_5V = 157$, ${}_6V = 292$, $q_{73} = .0433$, and $i = .05$ are given, thus $\pi_5 = 150$ (nearest dollar).

Question 49 has ANSWER A.

If $\pi_5 = 270$ one can calculate b_{16} from the relation APV_{68}(premium) $= APV_{68}$(benefits). To make these calculations view premium as a 20-year temporary annuity due of 55.62/year plus an extra $(270 - 55.62)$ at age 73, and view the benefits as 20 years of discrete, 1000 endowment insurance with an extra benefit of $b_{16} - 1000$ if death occurs in (83, 84]:

$$55.62\ddot{a}_{68:\overline{20}|} + (270-55.62)v^5 \cdot {}_5p_{68} = 1000A_{68:\overline{20}|} + (b_{16}-1000)v^{16} \cdot {}_{15|}q_{68}.$$

Using the given values of $i = .05$, $\ddot{a}_{68:\overline{20}|} = 9.352$, $A_{68:\overline{20}|} = .55469$, ${}_{15|}q_{68} = .0441$, and ${}_5p_{68} = \frac{\ell_{73}}{\ell_{68}} = .8436$, if follows from the above that $b_{16} = 6300$ (nearest \$100).

Question 50 has ANSWER B.

Another subtle idea is needed to calculate ${}_9V$ retrospectively:

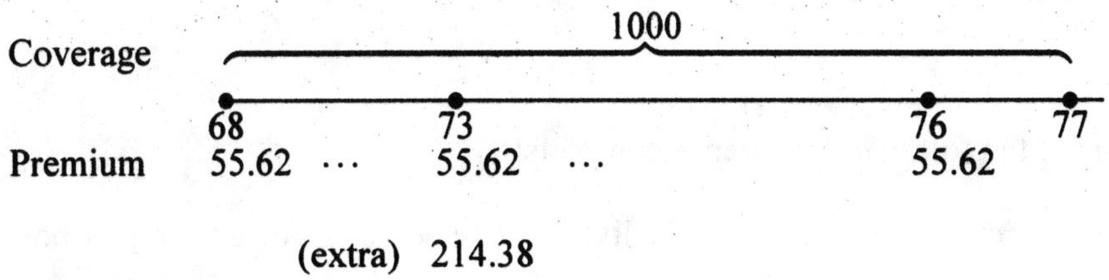

Retrospectively this looks the same as $1000{}_9V_{68}$ plus the accumulation to age 77 of the extra 214.38 at age 73. Thus

$$\begin{aligned} {}_9V &= 1000{}_9V_{68} + \frac{214.38}{v^4\ {}_4p_{73}} \\ &= 1000\left(1-\frac{\ddot{a}_{77}}{\ddot{a}_{68}}\right) + \frac{214.38(1+i)^4\ell_{73}}{\ell_{77}} \\ &= 280.10 + 319.53 = 600 \quad \text{(nearest dollar)} \end{aligned}$$

Question 51 has ANSWER B.

UNIT 5: MULTIPLE LIFE FUNCTIONS

Introduction

Consider the pricing on a net basis of the following insurance contracts:

(i) A continuous annuity of \$1/year to a pair of lives, (60) and (65), for as long as both survive; or

(ii) A \$1 life insurance on the pair (60), (65) payable to a beneficiary of the pair at the time of the second death.

The theoretical framework in which we carry out these pricing calculations is the same as that of Units 1-4, where distributional properties of $T(x)$ or $K(x)$ determined everything. T and K were time until failure or waiting time models (i.e., survival models). In this unit the single life (x) is replaced by a status consisting of several lives, and T is replaced by a variable modeling the waiting time until failure of the status.

Failure is defined in a manner which is convenient for the problem being analyzed. In (i) above we are interested in the waiting time until the first death of (60) and (65) since this is the time period of the annuity payout. The joint life status, denoted $(60, 65)$, is deemed to fail at the first death. The associated waiting time variable, $T(60, 65)$, is thus defined as the minimum of $T(60)$ and $T(65)$. In (ii) the payment is made at the time of the second death. The last-survivor status, denoted by $(\overline{60, 65})$, is deemed to fail at the second death. The associated waiting time variable, $T(\overline{60, 65})$, is thus defined as the maximum of $T(60)$ and $T(65)$.

In the next two sections we look at the joint life and last survivor status in more detail, considering insurances, annuities and "life expectancy" in the case that $T(x)$ and $T(y)$ are assumed to be independent. At each point where independence is used we will make a parenthetical note. After this is finished we will examine the more challenging problem where $T(x)$ and $T(y)$ are dependent.

The Joint Life Status for Independent Lives

Here we have a pair of lives (x) and (y) and $T(x, y)$, the time until the first death, or, failure of the joint life status (x, y), is the minimum of $\{T(x), T(y)\}$. In this section $T(x)$ and $T(y)$ are assumed to be **independent**. Much of the treatment here does not need this assumption so we will indicate wherever it is essential in the development. In any case, $T(x, y)$ is a function of $T(x)$ and $T(y)$, so its distribution can be calculated from the joint density of $T(x)$ and $T(y)$.

Recall from section one of this manual that there are five equivalent ways of specifying a survival model: the density function, the distribution function, the survival function, the force of mortality (hazard rate function), and the life table. For the joint life status and last survivor status we will develop analogues (except for the life table) when $T(x)$, $T(x)$ are independent.

For the joint life status the easiest thing to derive is the survival function. Throughout this section we will use T for $T(x, y) = min\{T(x), T(y)\}$.

$$\begin{aligned} s_T(t) = Pr(T(x,y) > t) &= Pr(\text{first death occurs after } t \text{ years}) \\ &= Pr(\{T(x) > t\} \text{ and } \{T(y) > t\}) \\ &= Pr(T(x) > t) \cdot Pr(T(y) > t) \qquad \text{(independence)} \\ &= {}_tp_x \cdot {}_tp_y. \end{aligned}$$

Just as ${}_tp_x$ is a common shorthand for the single life survival function, $Pr(T(x) > t)$, $s_T(t)$ is commonly written as ${}_tp_{(x,y)}$ or just ${}_tp_{xy}$. The distribution function, $F_T(t)$ or ${}_tq_{xy}$, is given by

$$\begin{aligned} {}_tq_{xy} = Pr(T(x,y) \le t) &= Pr(T(x) \le t \ \text{ or } \ T(y) \le t) \\ &= Pr(T(x) \le t) + Pr(T(y) \le t) - Pr(\{T(x) \le t\} \text{ and } \{T(y) \le t\}) \\ &= {}_tq_x + {}_tq_y - {}_tq_x \cdot {}_tq_y \qquad \text{(independence).} \end{aligned}$$

This could also have been derived from

$$\begin{aligned} {}_tq_{xy} = Pr(T(x,y) \le t) &= 1 - Pr(T(x,y) > t) \\ &= 1 - {}_tp_{xy} \\ &= 1 - {}_tp_x \cdot {}_tp_y \qquad \text{(independence)} \\ &= 1 - (1 - {}_tq_x)(1 - {}_tq_y) \\ &= {}_tq_x + {}_tq_y - {}_tq_x \cdot {}_tq_y \end{aligned}$$

rather than from the additive probability law used above.

In general the density function is the negative derivative of the survival function. So

$$\begin{aligned} \underbrace{f_T(t)}_{\text{density}} &= -\frac{d}{dt}[{}_tp_x \cdot {}_tp_y] \qquad \text{(independence)} \\ &= -\frac{d({}_tp_x)}{dt} \cdot {}_tp_y + {}_tp_x \cdot -\frac{d({}_tp_y)}{dt} \\ &= ({}_tp_x\mu(x+t){}_tp_y + {}_tp_x({}_tp_y\mu(y+t)) \\ &= \underbrace{({}_tp_x \cdot {}_tp_y)}_{\substack{\text{survival} \\ \text{function}}}(\mu(x+t) + \mu(y+t)). \end{aligned}$$

Since a hazard rate or force of mortality is generically the ratio of the density function to the survival function, we see that for independent lives the joint life hazard rate, $\mu_{xy}(t)$, is given by $\mu(x+t)+\mu(y+t)$. Recall that a hazard rate is not itself a probability, but $\mu_{xy}(t)\,dt$ is approximately the probability of failure (i.e., the first death) of (x, y) in the time interval $[t, t+dt]$, given survival at time t.

$$\underbrace{\mu_{xy}(t)\,dt}_{\substack{\approx \text{ probability that} \\ (x+t) \text{ or } (y+t) \text{ fails} \\ \text{in the next instant} \\ \text{(a union)}}} = \underbrace{\mu(x+t)\,dt}_{\substack{\approx \text{ probability that} \\ (x+t) \text{ fails in} \\ \text{the next instant}}} + \underbrace{\mu(y+t)\,dt}_{\substack{\approx \text{ probability that} \\ (y+t) \text{ fails in} \\ \text{the next instant}}}$$

Technically, due to the additive law of probability for a union of events, the right-hand side should include

$$-\,Pr(\text{both } (x+t) \text{ and } (y+t) \text{ fail in the next instant}) = -(\mu(x+t)\,dt)(\mu(y+t)\,dt) \qquad \text{(independence)},$$

but, since dt is "infinitesimal," $(dt)^2$ is too small to matter.

Example 1 Suppose (60) and (65) have independent lifetimes following the de Moivre survival model with $\omega = 100$. Compute the density, survival, and hazard rate functions for the joint life status $(60, 65)$. Find the probability that the first death occurs between 10 and 20 years from now.

Solution With de Moivre's law $\ell_x = \omega - x = 100 - x$ for $0 \le x \le 100 = \omega$. Hence, ${}_tp_x = \left(\frac{\ell_{x+t}}{\ell_x}\right) = \left(\frac{100-x-t}{100-x}\right)$ and $\mu(x+t) = \frac{1}{\omega-(x+t)} = \frac{1}{100-x-t}$. Thus

$${}_tp_{(60,65)} \underset{\text{independence}}{=} {}_tp_{60}\cdot{}_tp_{65} = \left(1-\tfrac{t}{40}\right)\left(1-\tfrac{t}{35}\right)$$

for $0 \le t \le 35$. Note that ${}_tp_{65}$ is zero for $t > 35$. Also

$$\mu_{(60,\,65)}(t) = \mu(60+t) + \mu(65+t) = \left(\frac{1}{40-t}\right) + \left(\frac{1}{35-t}\right)$$

for the range $0 \le t < 35$. Multiplying these functions gives a joint life density of

$$f_T(t) = \frac{35-t}{35}\cdot\frac{1}{40} + \frac{40-t}{40}\cdot\frac{1}{35}$$

for $0 \le t \le 35$.

Finally,

$$Pr(10 \le T(60,65) \le 20) = \int_{10}^{20} f_T(t)\,dt$$

$$= s_T(10) - s_T(20) \qquad \text{(easier)}$$

$$= {}_{10}p_{(60,65)} - {}_{20}p_{(60,65)}$$

$$= {}_{10}p_{60} \cdot {}_{10}p_{65} - {}_{20}p_{60} \cdot {}_{20}p_{65} \qquad \text{(independence)}$$

$$= \left(\frac{30}{40}\right)\left(\frac{25}{35}\right) - \left(\frac{20}{40}\right)\left(\frac{15}{35}\right) = \frac{450}{(40)(35)} = \frac{9}{28}.$$

□

Example 2 Suppose (x) and (y) have independent future lives following constant force models $\mu(x+t) = \mu_1$, $\mu(y+t) = \mu_2$ for all $t \ge 0$. Describe the distribution of $T(x,y)$.

Solution With constant forces we know ${}_tp_x = e^{-\mu_1 t}$, ${}_tp_y = e^{-\mu_2 t}$. So, with independence,

$${}_tp_{xy} = {}_tp_x \cdot {}_tp_y = e^{-\mu_1 t} \cdot e^{-\mu_2 t} = e^{-(\mu_1+\mu_2)t},$$

a constant force model with force $\mu_1 + \mu_1$. In other word, if $T(x) \sim Exp(\mu_1)$ (i.e., $T(x)$ has the exponential distribution with parameter μ_1) and $T(y) \sim Exp(\mu_2)$, then $T(x,y) \sim E(\mu_1+\mu_2)$ if $T(x)$ and $T(y)$ are assumed to be independent. □

Next, we want to look at joint life insurances, annuities and expectancy. Consider first an insurance paying \$1 at the first death of (x) and (y). The random present value variable is $Z = v^{T(x,y)}$. The net single premium or actuarial present value of the benefit, denoted $\overline{A}_{xy}$, is calculated as

$$\overline{A}_{xy} = E[Z] = \int_{t=0}^{min(\omega-x,\,\omega-y)} \underset{\text{(amount)}}{1} \cdot \underset{\text{(discount)}}{v^t} \cdot \underset{\text{(probability)}}{f_{T(x,y)}(t)\,dt}$$

where $f_{T(x,y)}(t) = {}_tp_x \cdot {}_tp_y(\mu(x+t) + \mu(y+t))$. For example, with an assumption $\mu(x+t) = \mu_1$ and $\mu(y+t) = \mu_2$, the integral gives $\overline{A}_{xy} = \dfrac{\mu_1 + \mu_2}{(\mu_1+\mu_2)+\delta}$. This should not be surprising since $\overline{A}_x = \dfrac{\mu_1}{\mu_1+\delta}$ and $\mu_1 + \mu_2$ is the constant force for the status (x,y). Just as in Unit 1, we could calculate $Var(Z)$ as ${}^2\overline{A}_{xy} - (\overline{A}_{xy})^2$.

Now consider a continuous annuity of \$1/year until the first death of (x) and (y). The random present value variable is $Y = \overline{a}_{\overline{T(x,y)}|} = \dfrac{1 - v^{T(x,y)}}{\delta} = \dfrac{1-Z}{\delta}$. The actuarial present value of the annuity, denoted $\overline{a}_{xy}$, could be computed as $E[Y]$ (the aggregate payment method), as

$$\int_{t=0}^{min(\omega-x,\,\omega-y)} \underset{\text{(discount)}}{v^t} \cdot \underset{\text{(probability)}}{{}_tp_x \cdot {}_tp_y} \underset{\text{(amount)}}{dt},$$

or as $E\left[\frac{1-Z}{\delta}\right] = \frac{1-\overline{A}_{xy}}{\delta}$. With constant forces $\mu(x+t) = \mu_1$, $\mu(y+t) = \mu_2$ we obtain $\overline{a}_{xy} = \frac{1}{(\mu_1+\mu_2)+\delta}$ analogous to $\overline{a}_x = \frac{1}{\mu_1+\delta}$.

The expected time until failure of (x,y), denoted $\overset{\circ}{e}_{xy}$, is given by $E[T(x,y)]$. It can be calculated as

$$\overset{\circ}{e}_{xy} = \int_0^{min(\omega-x,\,\omega-y)} t \cdot f_{T(x,y)}(t)\,dt,$$

or

$$\overset{\circ}{e}_{xy} = \int_0^{min(\omega-x,\,\omega-y)} {}_tp_{xy}\,dt \qquad \text{(integration by parts)}$$

just as with single lives. For example,with constant force, $\overset{\circ}{e}_{xy} = \frac{1}{\mu_1+\mu_2}$, analogous with $\overset{\circ}{e}_x = \frac{1}{\mu_1}$.

Note: Sometimes you will simply see integrals in the form "$\int_{t=0}^{\infty}$" for all of the above. This is still technically correct since at least one factor in the integrand is zero if $t > \omega - x$ or $t > \omega - y$.

Example 3 Suppose (60) and (65) have independent future lifetimes following de Moivre's law with $\omega = 100$ and suppose $\delta = .05$. Calculate $\overline{A}_{(60,65)}$, $\overline{a}_{(60,65)}$ and $\overset{\circ}{e}_{(60,65)}$.

Solution Since $\delta\overline{a}_{60,65} + \overline{A}_{60,65} = 1$ we need only calculate one of the first two items by an integration. For completeness, however, we have given both. Only the insurance integral is finished since it is the simpler one.

$$\overline{A}_{60,65} = \int_{t=0}^{35} 1 \cdot e^{-.05t} \cdot \underbrace{\left[\frac{35-t}{35} \cdot \frac{1}{40} + \frac{40-t}{40} \cdot \frac{1}{35}\right]}_{\frac{3}{56} - \frac{t}{700}} dt$$

$$= \frac{3}{56}\int_0^{35} e^{-.05t}dt - \frac{1}{700}\int_0^{35} te^{-.05t}dt$$

$$= .885242 - .298355 = .586887 \quad \text{(one integration by parts)}$$

$$\overline{a}_{60,65} = \int_{t=0}^{35} e^{-.05t} \cdot \frac{35-t}{35} \cdot \frac{40-t}{40} \cdot dt \quad \text{(two integration by parts)}$$

$$= \frac{(1-\overline{A}_{60,65})}{\delta} = 8.262265. \quad \text{(easier)}$$

$$\overset{\circ}{e}_{60:65} = \int_{t=0}^{35} \left(\frac{35-t}{35}\right)\left(\frac{40-t}{40}\right) dt$$

$$= \frac{1}{1400}\left[1400t - \frac{75t^2}{2} + \frac{t^3}{3}\right]_0^{35} = 12.3958$$

□

In addition to calculating insurances, annuities, and life expectancy with the continuous model $T(x, y)$, we could calculate similar things for the discrete model $K(x, y) = [T(x, y)]$ (greatest integer). Integrals are replaced by sums and it is useful to know the density and survival functions:

$$\begin{aligned} f_{K(x,y)}(k) = Pr(K(x,y) = k) &= {}_{k|}q_{xy} \\ &= Pr(k \leq T(x,y) < k+1) \\ &= Pr(k < T(x,y) \leq k+1) && (T \text{ is continuous}) \\ &= s_T(k) - s_T(k+1) \\ &= {}_kp_{xy} - {}_{k+1}p_{xy} \\ &= {}_kp_x \cdot {}_kp_y - {}_{k+1}p_x \cdot {}_{k+1}p_y && \text{(independence)} \\ &= {}_kp_x \cdot {}_kp_y[1 - p_{x+k} \cdot p_{y+k}] \\ &= {}_kp_x \cdot {}_kp_y[q_{x+k} + q_{y+k} - q_{x+k} \cdot q_{y+k}]. \end{aligned}$$

$$\begin{aligned} s_{K(x,y)}(k) = Pr(K(x,y) > k) &= Pr(T(x,y) \geq k+1) \\ &= {}_{k+1}p_{xy} \\ &= {}_{k+1}p_x \cdot {}_{k+1}p_y && \text{(independence).} \end{aligned}$$

An annuity due of \$1/year for as long as both (x) and (y) survive has a random present value variable $Y = \ddot{a}_{\overline{K(x,y)+1}|}$. The actuarial present value, $\ddot{a}_{xy}$, could be calculated by the aggregate payment method as $E[Y] = \sum_{k=0}^{\infty} \ddot{a}_{\overline{K+1}|} f_{K(x,y)}(k)$, or by the current payment method as $\ddot{a}_{xy} = \sum_{k=0}^{\infty} 1 \cdot v^k \cdot {}_kp_{xy}$. One could also calculate $A_{xy} = E[v^{K(x,y)+1}] = 1 - d\ddot{a}_{xy}$ and $e_{xy} = E[K(x,y)]$.

The Last Survivor Status for Independent Lives

Here we have a pair of lives (x) and (y), and $T(\overline{x,y})$, the time until the second death, or, failure of the last survivor status $(\overline{x,y})$, is the maximum of $\{T(x), T(y)\}$. Once again we will assume $T(x)$, $T(y)$ to be independent and a parenthetical note will point out places where this assumption is used.

For the last survivor status it is easiest to develop the distribution function:

$$\begin{aligned} F_{T(\overline{x,y})}(t) &= Pr(T(\overline{x,y}) \leq t) \\ &= Pr(\text{both deaths occur within } t\text{-years}) \\ &= Pr(\{T(x) \leq t\} \text{ and } \{T(y) \leq t\}) \\ &= Pr(T(x) \leq t) \cdot Pr(T(y) \leq t) && \text{(Independence)} \\ &= {}_tq_x \cdot {}_tq_y. \end{aligned}$$

A natural shorthand for this distribution function is ${}_tq_{\overline{xy}}$. So the above can be written as ${}_tq_{\overline{xy}} = {}_tq_x \cdot {}_tq_y$ (with independence), and the corresponding survival function relation is

$$\begin{aligned} {}_tp_{\overline{xy}} &= 1 - {}_tq_{\overline{xy}} \\ &= 1 - {}_tq_x \cdot {}_tq_y \qquad \text{(Independence)} \\ &= 1 - (1 - {}_tp_x)(1 - {}_tp_y) \\ &= {}_tp_x + {}_tp_y - {}_tp_x \cdot {}_tp_y . \end{aligned}$$

The density function can be derived as $\frac{d}{dt}[{}_tq_{\overline{xy}}]$. It satisfies

$$f_{T(\overline{x,y})}(t)dt \approx Prob(2^{nd} \text{ death occurs in } [t, t+dt]) = \underbrace{{}_tq_x \cdot {}_tp_y \cdot \mu(y+t)\, dt}_{\substack{(x) \text{ dies prior to time } t \\ \text{and } (y) \text{ dies in } [t,t+dt]}} + {}_tq_y \cdot {}_tp_x \cdot \mu(x+t)\, dt.$$

The last survivor hazard rate, $\mu_{\overline{xy}}(t) = \dfrac{density}{survival}$, is rather messy.

One can introduce symbols such as $\overline{A}_{\overline{xy}}$, $\overline{a}_{\overline{xy}}$ and $\mathring{e}_{\overline{xy}}$ for the APV of \$1 at the second death, the APV of \$1/year continuously until the second death, or the expected time until the second death respectively. These values can be calculated as expected values of $v^{T(\overline{x,y})}$, $\overline{a}_{\overline{T(x,y)}|}$ or $T(\overline{x,y})$ respectively. All are functions of $T(\overline{x,y})$ so you integrate the function of $T(\overline{x,y})$ times $f_{T(\overline{x,y})}(t)$. These integrations can be avoided due to standard relations involving the joint life, last survivor, and single life functions.

All of these relations can be derived from the simple fact that the set of two numbers $\{T(x,y),\, T(\overline{x,y})\}$ is the same as the set $\{T(x),\, T(y)\}$, and many of them have a simple intuitive explanation as well. For example, since the two sets are equal we would have

$$v^{T(x,y)} + v^{T(\overline{x,y})} = v^{T(x)} + v^{T(y)}.$$

Taking expected values results in the APV relation

$$\overline{A}_{xy} + \overline{A}_{\overline{xy}} = \overline{A}_x + \overline{A}_y.$$

Intuitively, a single premium of $\overline{A}_{xy} + \overline{A}_{\overline{xy}}$ pays for a \$1 benefit at the first death and a \$1 benefit at the second death. A single premium of $\overline{A}_x + \overline{A}_y$ pays for \$1 benefits at the deaths of (x) and (y). This is exactly the same benefit pattern so the single premiums must be equal. Analogously,

$$\overline{a}_{xy} + \overline{a}_{\overline{xy}} = \overline{a}_x + \overline{a}_y$$

and

$$\mathring{e}_{xy} + \mathring{e}_{\overline{xy}} = \mathring{e}_x + \mathring{e}_y.$$

Example 4 Suppose (60) and (65) have independent future lifetimes following de Moivre's law with $\omega = 100$ and suppose $\delta = .05$. Calculate $\overline{A}_{\overline{60,65}}$, $\overline{a}_{\overline{60,65}}$, and $\mathring{e}_{\overline{60,65}}$.

Solution In Example 3 we obtained $\overline{A}_{60,65} = .586887$, $\overline{a}_{60,65} = 8.262265$ and $\mathring{e}_{60,65} = 12.3958$ under the same interest and mortality assumptions. So to calculate the desired last survivor values we need single life values:

$$\overline{A}_{60} = \frac{1}{40}\,\overline{a}_{\overline{40|}} = .432332 \qquad \text{(de Moivre's law)}$$

$$\overline{A}_{65} = \frac{1}{35}\,\overline{a}_{\overline{35|}} = .472129 \qquad \text{(see Unit 1)}$$

$$\overline{a}_{60} = \frac{1-\overline{A}_{60}}{\delta} = 11.3534$$

$$\overline{a}_{65} = \frac{1-\overline{A}_{65}}{\delta} = 10.5574$$

$$\mathring{e}_{60} = \frac{40}{2} = 20 \qquad \left(T(x) \sim U(0, \omega - x) \;\Rightarrow\; \mathring{e}_x = \frac{\omega - x}{2}\right)$$

$$\mathring{e}_{60} = \frac{35}{2} = 17.5$$

Hence

$$\overline{A}_{\overline{60,65}} = \overline{A}_{60} + \overline{A}_{65} - \overline{A}_{60,65} = .317575.$$

$$\overline{a}_{\overline{60,65}} = \overline{a}_{60} + \overline{a}_{65} - \overline{a}_{60,65} = 13.6485.$$

$$\mathring{e}_{\overline{60,65}} = \mathring{e}_{60} + \mathring{e}_{65} - \mathring{e}_{60,65} = 25.1042.$$

□

The Joint Life Status and Last Survivor Status With Dependent Lifetimes

Without independence you lose relations ${}_tp_{xy} = {}_tp_x \cdot {}_tp_y$, ${}_tq_{\overline{xy}} = {}_tq_x \cdot {}_tq_y$, and $\mu_{xy}(t) = \mu(x+t) + \mu(y+t)$, that made it easy to begin with single life models in order to analyze $T(x,y)$ and $T(\overline{x,y})$. The general treatment of (x, y) and $(\overline{x,y})$ must begin with a joint density $f_{T(x),\,T(y)}(t_1, t_2)$ for $T(x)$ and $T(y)$. We could have done our preceding work in terms of this density using $f_{T(x),\,T(y)}(t_1, t_2) = f_{T(x)}(t_1) \cdot f_{T(y)}(t_2)$ to reflect independence. So here we are not assuming the joint density is a product of the two marginal densities.

In general we define the joint distribution function by

$$F_{T(x),\,T(y)}(t_1, t_2) = Pr(\{T(x) \le t_1\} \text{ and } \{T(y) \le t_2\}) = \int_0^{t_1}\int_0^{t_2} f_{T(x),T(y)}(s,t)\,dt\,ds,$$

and the joint survival function by

$$s_{T(x),\,T(y)}(t_1, t_2) = Pr(\{T(x) > t_1\} \text{ and } \{T(y) > t_2\}) = \int_{t_1}^{\infty}\int_{t_2}^{\infty} f_{T(x),T(y)}(s,t)\,dt\,ds.$$

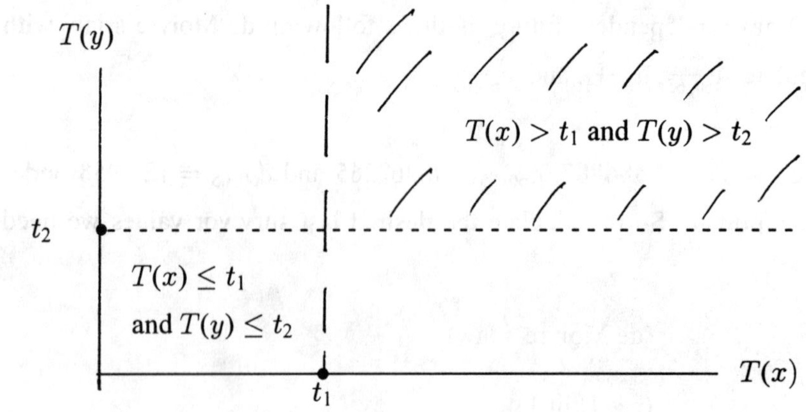

The hashed regions in the figure are the regions of integration in the calculations above. Note that $F_{T(x),T(y)}$ and $s_{T(x),T(y)}$ do not sum to 1 since the regions are not all encompassing. Once these two functions are calculated, we can calculate the last survivor distribution function via

$$_tq_{\overline{xy}} = Pr(\{T(x) \leq t\} \text{ and } \{T(y) \leq t\}) = F_{T(x),T(y)}(t, t),$$

and the joint life survival function via

$$_tp_{xy} = Pr(\{T(x) > t\} \text{ and } \{T(y) > t\}) = s_{T(x),T(y)}(t, t).$$

Alternately,

$$\begin{aligned} _tp_{xy} = 1 - {_tq_{xy}} &= 1 - Pr((T(x) \leq t) \cup (T(y) \leq t)) \\ &= 1 - [Pr(T(x) \leq t) + Pr(T(y) \leq t) - Pr(\text{both} \leq t)] \\ &= 1 - [{_tq_x} + {_tq_y} - {_tq_{\overline{xy}}}] \\ &= {_tp_x} + {_tp_y} - {_tp_{\overline{xy}}} \end{aligned}$$

where $_tp_{\overline{xy}} = 1 - {_tq_{\overline{xy}}}$. These ideas are illustrated in the following example.

Example 5 Suppose the joint density of $T(x)$, $T(y)$ is given by

$$f_{T(x),T(y)}(t_1, t_2) = \frac{t_1 + t_2}{1000}$$

for $0 \leq t_1, t_2 \leq 10$. Calculate the marginal densities and distribution functions (i.e., $_tq_x$, $_tq_y$), the last survivor distribution function (i.e., $_tq_{\overline{xy}}$) and the joint-life survival function (i.e., $_tp_{xy}$).

Solution For t_1, t_2 in $[0, 10]$

$$
\begin{aligned}
F_{T(x),T(y)}(t_1,t_2) &= \int_0^{t_1}\int_0^{t_2} f_{T(x),T(y)}(s,t)\,dt\,ds \\
&= \int_0^{t_1}\int_0^{t_2} \frac{s+t}{1000}\,dt\,ds \\
&= \int_0^{t_1}\left[\frac{st+\frac{t^2}{2}}{1000}\right]_{t=0}^{t_2} ds \\
&= \int_0^{t_1} \frac{st_2+\frac{t_2^2}{2}}{1000}\,ds \\
&= \left.\frac{\frac{s^2t_2}{2}+\frac{st_2^2}{2}}{1000}\right|_{s=0}^{t_1} \\
&= \frac{(t_1^2t_2+t_1t_2^2)}{2000}
\end{aligned}
$$

$\Rightarrow \quad {}_tq_{\overline{xy}} = F_{T(x),T(y)}(t,t) = \dfrac{2t^3}{2000} = \dfrac{t^3}{1000}$

$\Rightarrow \quad {}_tq_x = Pr(\{T(x) \le t\} \text{ and } \{T(y) \le 10\}) = F_{T(x),T(y)}(t,10) = \dfrac{(10t^2+100t)}{2000}$

$\Rightarrow \quad f_{T(x)}(t) = \frac{d}{dt}[{}_tq_x] = \dfrac{20t+100}{2000}$

Note: Because of the symmetry in the joint density $\frac{t_1+t_2}{1000}$, it follows also that ${}_tq_y = {}_tq_x$, etc.... Furthermore,

$$
\begin{aligned}
s_{T(x),T(y)}(t_1,t_2) &= \int_{t_1}^{10}\int_{t_2}^{10} f_{T(x),T(y)}(s,t)\,dt\,ds \\
&= \int_{t_1}^{10}\int_{t_2}^{10} \frac{s+t}{1000}\,dt\,ds \\
&= \int_{t_1}^{10}\left[\left.\frac{st+\frac{t^2}{2}}{1000}\right|_{t=t_2}^{10}\right] ds \\
&= \int_{t_1}^{10} \frac{10s+50-st_2-\frac{t_2^2}{2}}{1000}\,ds \\
&= \frac{1000-50(t_1+t_2)-5(t_1^2+t_2^2)+\frac{(t_1^2t_2+t_1t_2^2)}{2}}{1000}
\end{aligned}
$$

$$\Rightarrow \qquad {}_tp_{xy} = s_{T(x),T(y)}(t,t) = \frac{1000 - 100t - 10t^2 + t^3}{1000} = \frac{(10-t)(100-t^2)}{1000}$$

$$\Rightarrow \qquad {}_tp_x = Pr(\{T(x) > t\} = Pr(T(x) > t \text{ and } \{T(y) > 0\})$$

$$= s_{T(x),T(y)}(t,0) = \frac{1000 - 50t - 5t^2}{1000}$$

We could also have obtained ${}_tp_x$ as

$$1 - {}_tq_x = 1 - \left[\frac{10t^2+100t}{2000}\right], \qquad \text{(compare above)}$$

and ${}_tp_{xy}$ as

$${}_tp_x + {}_tp_y - (1 - {}_tq_{\overline{xy}}) = 2\left[\frac{1000-50t-5t^2}{1000}\right] - \left[1 - \frac{t^3}{1000}\right] \qquad \text{(earlier discussion)}$$

$$= \frac{(2000-1000) - 100t - 10t^2 + t^3}{1000} \qquad \text{(compare above).}$$

If we need the densities of $T(x,y)$ or $T(\overline{x,y})$ they are obtained via

$$\underbrace{f_{T(x,y)}(t)}_{\text{density}} = -\frac{d}{dt}(\underbrace{{}_tp_{xy}}_{\text{survival}}) = \frac{100 + 20t - 3t^2}{1000}, \quad 0 \le t \le 10$$

and

$$\underbrace{f_{T(\overline{x,y})}(t)}_{\text{density}} = \underbrace{\frac{d}{dt}({}_tq_{\overline{xy}})}_{\text{distribution}} = \frac{3t^2}{1000}, \quad 0 \le t \le 10$$

Finally, notice that ${}_tq_x \cdot {}_tq_y = \left[\frac{10t^2+100t}{2000}\right]^2$ is not equal to ${}_tq_{\overline{xy}} = \frac{t^3}{1000}$, so we do not have independence! (Independence $\Rightarrow$ ${}_tq_{\overline{xy}} = {}_tq_x \cdot {}_tq_y$) □

Parametric Models of Dependent Lifetimes

Here we will introduce two parametric models of dependence, Frank's Copula and the Common Shock Model. We begin with Frank's Copula.

In this model one begins with marginal distribution functions $F_{T(x)}(s) = {}_sq_x$, $F_{T(y)}(t) = {}_tq_y$ and a non-zero parameter α. The idea is to use these three items to produce a joint distribution function, $F_{T(x),T(y)}(s,t)$, such that

(i) the marginal distributions are preserved, and

(ii) $T(x)$, $T(y)$ are dependent.

Frank's Copula

$$F_{T(x),T(y)}(s,t) = \frac{1}{\alpha} ln\left[1 + \frac{(e^{\alpha_s q_x} - 1)(e^{\alpha_t q_y} - 1)}{(e^{\alpha} - 1)}\right] \text{ where } 0 \le s \le \omega - x,\ 0 \le t \le \omega - y$$

With this definition it can be shown that $\lim\limits_{\alpha \to 0} f_{T(x),T(y)}(s,t) = f_{T(x)}(s) f_{T(y)}(t)$. This can be interpreted to say that the dependence diminishes toward independence as α approaches zero. Note that for (i) above we have

$$\underset{\text{(marginal from joint)}}{F_{T(x)}(s) = F_{T(x),T(y)}(s, \omega - y)} = \frac{1}{\alpha} ln\left[1 + \frac{(e^{\alpha_s q_x} - 1)(e^{\alpha \cdot 1} - 1)}{(e^{\alpha} - 1)}\right] = \frac{1}{\alpha} \cdot ln\,[e^{\alpha_s q_x}] = \underset{\text{(original marginal)}}{{}_s q_x}$$

since ${}_{\omega - y}q_y = 1$.

Example 6 Suppose $(x) = (50)$, $(y) = (60)$ follow de Moivre's law with $\omega = 100$. Assume $\alpha = .5$. Calculate the following based on Frank's Copula:

(i) ${}_{10}q_{50}$, ${}_{10}q_{60}$;

(ii) ${}_{10}q_{\overline{50,60}}$; and

(iii) ${}_{10}q_{50,60}$.

Solution

(i) Since the marginal distributions are preserved, ${}_t q_{50}$ and ${}_t q_{60}$ are calculated from $\ell_x = 100 - x$ as ${}_t q_{50} = \frac{t}{50}$, ${}_t q_{60} = \frac{t}{40}$. Thus ${}_{10}q_{50} = \frac{10}{50} = .20$ and ${}_{10}q_{40} = \frac{10}{40} = .25$.

(ii) From Frank's formula

$${}_{10}q_{\overline{50,60}} = F_{T(50),T(60)}(10,10) = \frac{1}{.5} ln\left[1 + \frac{(e^{(.5)(.2)} - 1)(e^{(.5)(.25)} - 1)}{(e^{.5} - 1)}\right] = 2 \cdot ln\,[1.021586] = .0427$$

Note: ${}_{10}q_{50} \cdot {}_{10}q_{60} = (.20)(.25) = .05 \ne {}_{10}q_{\overline{50,60}}$ so we have dependence between $T(50)$, $T(60)$.

(iii) In general

$${}_t q_{xy} = Pr(\{T(x) \le t\} \text{ or } \{T(y) \le t\})$$

$$= Pr(T(x) \le t) + Pr(T(y) \le t) - Pr(\text{both} \le t) \qquad \text{(Additive law)}$$

$$= {}_t q_x + {}_t q_y - {}_t q_{\overline{xy}}.$$

Frank's copula preserves the marginal distributions you begin with, hence

$$_{10}q_{50,60} = {_{10}q_{50}} + {_{10}q_{60}} - {_{10}q_{\overline{50,60}}} = .20 + .25 - .0427 = .4073.$$

Note: If $T(50)$, $T(60)$ were independent and $_{10}q_{50} = .20$, $_{10}q_{60} = .25$, we would have

$$_{10}q_{50,60} = {_{10}q_{50}} + {_{10}q_{60}} - {_{10}q_{\overline{50,60}}} = {_{10}q_{50}} + {_{10}q_{60}} - ({_{10}q_{50}})({_{10}q_{60}}) = .40,$$

in contrast with the dependent case above. □

In the common shock model one begins with lifetimes $T^*(x)$ and $T^*(y)$ which are assumed to be independent. In addition, it is assumed that $T^*(x)$, $T^*(y)$, and Z are independent where $f_Z(t) = \lambda e^{-\lambda t}$ (an exponential density). Next, $T(x)$ and $T(y)$ are defined by

$$T(x) = min\{T^*(x), Z\}$$

$$T(y) = min\{T^*(y), Z\}.$$

(We will see that $T(x)$, $T(y)$ are dependent.) This definition models the idea that their "normal" lifetimes might be shortened by some additional hazard such as a plane crash. With these formulas we can calculate the joint survival function via

$$s_{T(x),\,T(y)}(s,t) = Pr(\{T(x) > s\} \text{ and } \{T(y) > s\})$$

$$= Pr(\text{min of } T^*(x) \text{ and } Z \text{ exceeds } s \text{ \underline{and} min of } T^*(y) \text{ and } Z \text{ exceeds } t)$$

$$= Pr(\{T^*(x) > s\} \text{ and } \{T^*(y) > t\} \text{ and } \{Z > max(s,t)\})$$

$$= (s_{T^*(x)}(s))(s_{T^*(y)}(s))e^{-\lambda max(s,t)} \qquad \text{(Independence of } T^*(x), T^*(y), Z)$$

since $s_Z(t) = e^{-\lambda t}$ for an exponential distribution. Thus the joint life survival function, $_tp_{xy} = s_{T(x),T(y)}(t,t)$, is given by

<u>Common Shock Model</u>

$$_tp_{xy} = s_{T^*(x)}(t) \cdot s_{T^*(y)}(t) \cdot e^{-\lambda t}$$

The marginal distributions are obtained as follows:

$$_tp_x = s_{T(x)}(t) \overset{*}{=} s_{T(x),T(y)}(t,0) = s_{T^*(x)}(t)e^{-\lambda t}$$

and

$$_tp_y = s_{T(y)}(t) = s_{T(x),T(y)}(0,t) = s_{T^*(y)}(t)e^{-\lambda t}.$$

$*$ $\{T(x) > t\} = \{T(x) > t \text{ and } T(y) > 0\}$

One clearly sees that $_tp_x \cdot {_tp_y} \neq {_tp_{xy}}$, so we have modified $T^*(x)$ and $T^*(y)$ in such a way that $T(x)$, $T(y)$ are dependent. Using the generic idea that a hazard rate is the negative derivative of the log of the survival function, we see from the above that

Common Shock Relations

$$\mu_{xy}(t) = -(ln\, {_tp_{xy}})' = \mu_x^*(t) + \mu_y^*(t) + \lambda$$

$$\mu_x(t) = -(ln\, {_tp_x})' = \mu_x^*(t) + \lambda$$

$$\mu_y(t) = -(ln\, {_tp_y})' = \mu_y^*(t) + \lambda$$

Example 7 If $T^*(x)$ and $T^*(y)$ are independent exponential distributions with parameters λ_1, λ_2 respectively, calculate the following from the common shock model:

(i) the distributions of $T(x)$, $T(y)$, and $T(x, y)$

(ii) $\overline{A}_x$, $\overline{A}_y$, $\overline{A}_{xy}$ and $\overline{A}_{\overline{xy}}$;

(ii) $\mathring{e}_x$, $\mathring{e}_y$, $\mathring{e}_{xy}$ and $\mathring{e}_{\overline{xy}}$; and

(iv) the probability that the status (x, y) fails due to the common shock (ie., both of $T^*(x)$ and $T^*(y)$ exceed Z).

Solution

(i) From the above we have

$\mu_{xy}(t) = \lambda_1 + \lambda_2 + \lambda$, $\mu(x{+}t) = \lambda_1 + \lambda$, $\mu(y{+}t) = \lambda_2 + \lambda$, all constant force models. Hence $T(x, y)$, $T(x)$, and $T(y)$ are exponentially distributed with parameters $\lambda_1 + \lambda_2 + \lambda$, $\lambda_1 + \lambda$, $\lambda_2 + \lambda$ respectively.

(ii) From (i) and the single life constant force formula $\overline{A}_x = \frac{\mu}{\mu+\delta}$, we obtain

$$\overline{A}_{xy} = \frac{\lambda_1 + \lambda_2 + \lambda}{\lambda_1 + \lambda_2 + \lambda + \delta}, \quad \overline{A}_x = \frac{\lambda_1 + \lambda}{\lambda_1 + \lambda + \delta}, \quad \overline{A}_y = \frac{\lambda_2 + \lambda}{\lambda_2 + \lambda + \delta}, \text{ and } \overline{A}_{\overline{xy}} = \overline{A}_x + \overline{A}_y - \overline{A}_{xy}.$$

(iii) Similarly, from (i), we have $\overset{\circ}{e}_{xy} = \frac{1}{\lambda_1 + \lambda_2 + \lambda}$, $\overset{\circ}{e}_x = \frac{1}{\lambda_1 + \lambda}$, $\overset{\circ}{e}_y = \frac{1}{\lambda_2 + \lambda}$, and $\overset{\circ}{e}_{\overline{xy}} = \overset{\circ}{e}_x + \overset{\circ}{e}_y - \overset{\circ}{e}_{xy}$.

(iv) $$Pr(Z < T^*(x), T^*(y)) = \int_{t=0}^{\infty} \underbrace{\lambda e^{-\lambda t}\, dt}_{Pr(t \le Z \le t+dt)} \cdot \underbrace{s_{T^*(x)}(t)}_{Pr(T^*(x)>t)} \cdot \underbrace{s_{T^*(y)}(t)}_{Pr(T^*(y)>t)}$$

$$= \int_{t=0}^{\infty} \lambda e^{-\lambda t}\, dt \cdot e^{-\lambda_1 t} \cdot e^{-\lambda_2 t}$$

$$= \int_{t=0}^{\infty} \lambda e^{-(\lambda+\lambda_1+\lambda_2)t}\, dt = \frac{\lambda}{\lambda+\lambda_1+\lambda_2}.$$

Note: For the independent continuous variables $T^*(x)$, $T^*(y)$, and Z there are 6 possible size orderings. Ties can be disregarded since the probability of independent continuous random variables being equal is always zero. From the table below is clear that the status fails due to the common shock (i.e., $T(x,y) = Z$) whenever both $T^*(x)$ and $T^*(y)$ exceed Z.

Relation	$T(x)$	$T(y)$	$T(x,y)$
$Z < T^*(x) < T^*(y)$	Z	Z	Z
$Z < T^*(y) < T^*(x)$	Z	Z	Z
$T^*(x) < Z < T^*(y)$	$T^*(x)$	Z	$T^*(x)$
$T^*(x) < T^*(y) < Z$	$T^*(x)$	$T^*(y)$	$T^*(x)$
$T^*(y) < Z < T^*(x)$	Z	$T^*(y)$	$T^*(y)$
$T^*(y) < T^*(x) \le Z$	$T^*(x)$	$T^*(y)$	$T^*(y)$

In (iv) above we showed $\frac{\lambda}{\lambda + \lambda_1 + \lambda_2} = Pr$(status fails due to common shock), and from the table we see this is also equal $Pr(T(x) = T(y))$. The joint density of $T(x)$, $T(y)$ is not only complicated by the dependence of $T(x)$ and $T(y)$. It is also a mixed distribution with a ridge of extra density along the line $T(x) = T(y)$.

In addition to determining ${}_tp_{xy}$, the survival function of $T(x,y) = min\{T(x), T(y)\}$, the survival function of $T(\overline{x,y}) = max\{T(x), T(y)\}$, ${}_tp_{\overline{xy}}$, can be determined from the common shock model via

$${}_tp_{\overline{xy}} = {}_tp_x + {}_tp_y - {}_tp_{xy} = s_{T^*(x)}(t)e^{-\lambda t} + s_{T^*(y)}(t)e^{-\lambda t} - s_{T^*(x)}(t)s_{T^*(y)}(t)e^{-\lambda t}.$$

Gompertz' and Makeham's Laws for the Joint Life Status with Independent Lives

Recall that $\mu(x) = Bc^x$ and $\mu(x) = A+Bc^x$ are known as Gompertz and Makeham's laws respectively. With these laws it is possible to make some simplifications to the joint life status (x, y) when $T(x)$ and $T(y)$ are independent.

With Gompertz's law it is possible to show that $T(x, y)$ has the same distribution as $T(w)$, where $w > x, y$ is the solution of $c^w = c^x + c^y$. As a result there are relations such as $\overline{A}_{xy} = \overline{A}_w$, $\overline{a}_{xy} = \overline{a}_w$, $\mathring{e}_{xy} = \mathring{e}_w$, etc.. One can show two survival models follow the same distribution if their hazard rates are identically equal:

$$\mu_{xy}(t) = \mu(x+t) + \mu(y+t) \qquad \text{(independence)}$$
$$= Bc^{x+t} + Bc^{y+t} \qquad \text{(Gompertz)}$$
$$= Bc^t(c^x+c^y)$$
$$\mu(w+t) = Bc^{w+t} = Bc^t(c^w) \qquad \text{(Gompertz)}$$

Now $T(x, y) \sim T(w)$ if and only if $\mu_{xy}(t) = \mu(w+t)$ for all t, and the last relation clearly holds if and only if $c^x + c^y = c^w$.

Similarly, for Makeham's law, $\mu_{xy}(t) = 2A + Bc^t(c^x+c^y)$ and $\mu_{w,w}(t) = 2A + Bc^t(c^w+c^w)$ are equal for all t if and only if $c^x+c^y = 2c^w$. In this case $\overline{A}_{xy} = \overline{A}_{ww}$, $\overline{a}_{xy} = \overline{a}_{ww}$, $\mathring{e}_{xy} = \mathring{e}_{ww}$, etc..

With both of these laws there is also a uniform seniority property:

Gompertz: $T(x, y) \sim T(w) \Rightarrow T(x+k, y+k) \sim T(w+k)$

$c^x + c^y = c^w \Rightarrow c^{x+k} + c^{y+k} = c^{w+k}$ (mult. both sides by c^k)

Makeham: $T(x, y) \sim T(w, w) \Rightarrow T(x+k, y+k) \sim T(w+k, w+k)$

$c^x + c^y = 2c^w \Rightarrow c^{x+k} + c^{y+k} = 2c^{w+k}$ (same reason)

Special Joint Life Annuities

We begin with the discussion of a so-called reversionary annuity. Consider a continuous annuity of \$1 per year paid to (x) after the death of (y) for as long as (x) survives. The standard actuarial present value symbol for this annuity is $\overline{a}_{y|x}$. It is fairly straightforward to see that $\overline{a}_{y|x} = \overline{a}_x - \overline{a}_{xy}$. One way to see this is to determine that the payment pattern provided by $\overline{a}_x - \overline{a}_{xy}$ is that which is desired. If (x) predeceases (y) then $\overline{a}_x$ and $\overline{a}_{xy}$ provide canceling \$1/year continuous annuities for $T(x)$ years, that is, a net of nothing. On the other hand, if (y) dies first, the difference $\overline{a}_x - \overline{a}_{xy}$ provides \$1/year for $T(x)$ years less \$1/year for $T(y)$ years for a net of \$1/year from time $T(y)$ until time $T(x) > T(y)$.

Another way to see this is to use the 3-factor approach and notice that the probability of payment at time t is the probability that (x) is surviving and y is already deceased. This probability is given by

$$Pr(\{T(x) > t\} \text{ and } \{T(y) \leq t\}) = Pr(T(x) > t) - Pr(\text{both} > t) = {}_tp_x - {}_tp_{xy}.$$

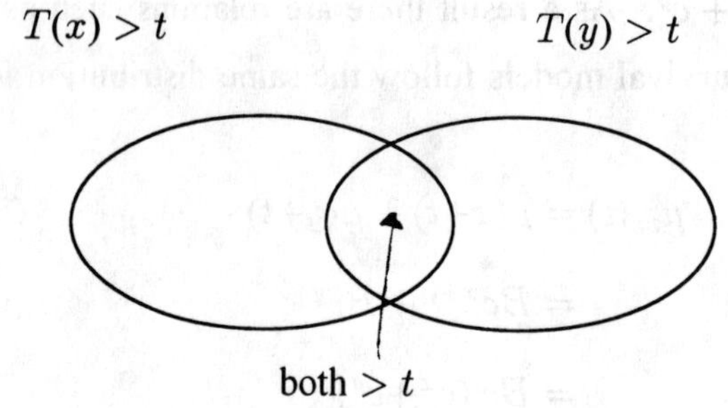

Hence

$$\bar{a}_{y|x} = \int_{t=0}^{\infty} \underbrace{v^t}_{\text{discount}} \cdot \underbrace{({}_tp_x - {}_tp_{xy})}_{\text{probability}} \cdot \underbrace{dt}_{\text{amount}} = \int_0^{\infty} v^t \cdot {}_tp_x\, dt - \int_0^{\infty} v^t \cdot {}_tp_{xy}\, dt = \bar{a}_x - \bar{a}_{xy}.$$

Now consider a continuous joint life annuity to (x, y) of \$1/year while both are surviving which reduces to $\$f$/year after the first death and until the second death. This can be looked at as the total of two distinct annuities:

(i) \$1/year while both are alive with $APV = \bar{a}_{xy}$; and

(ii) $\$f$/year while exactly one is alive with

$$APV = \int_{t=0}^{\infty} \underbrace{v^t}_{\text{discount}} \cdot \underbrace{({}_tp_{\overline{xy}} - {}_tp_{xy})}_{\substack{\text{probability exactly} \\ \text{1 alive in } t \text{ years}}} \cdot \underbrace{f\, dt}_{\text{amount}} = f\bar{a}_{\overline{xy}} - f\bar{a}_{xy}.$$

Thus the composite APV is $\bar{a}_{xy} + f(\bar{a}_{\overline{xy}} - \bar{a}_{xy})$. The key point is that ${}_tp_{\overline{xy}} - {}_tp_{xy}$ is the probability that exactly one of the two is surviving in t years.

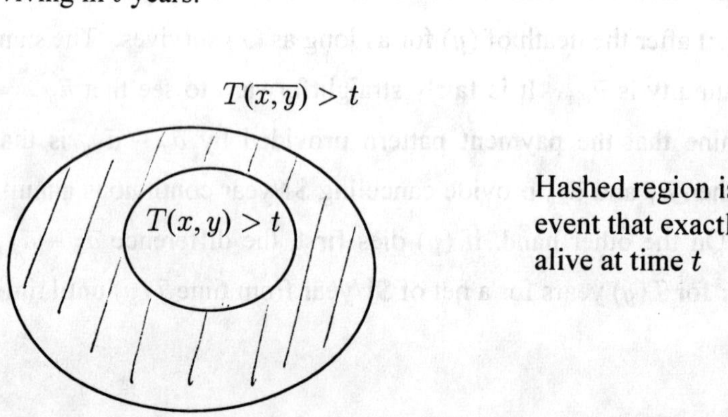

Finally we would like to revisit $\overline{a}_{x:\overline{n|}}$ in the light of the current unit on the joint life status. We can think of "$\overline{n|}$" as being a "life" that is certain to fail in n years, that is, $Pr(T(\overline{n|}) = n) = 1$. Thus $\overline{a}_{x:\overline{n|}}$ can be viewed as the APV of a continuous annuity of \$1/year until the first failure of (x) and $(\overline{n|})$, that is, to the death of (x) if (x) fails before $(\overline{n|})$ (i.e., $T(x) < n$), or to the "death" of $(\overline{n|})$ if $(\overline{n|})$ fails before (x) (i.e., $n < T(x)$). Recalling the general identity $\overline{a}_{\overline{xy}} = \overline{a}_x + \overline{a}_y - \overline{a}_{xy}$, we can now write the current last survivor annuity APV as

$$\overline{a}_{\overline{x,\overline{n|}}} = \overline{a}_x + \overline{a}_{\overline{n|}} - \overline{a}_{x,\overline{n|}} = \overline{a}_{\overline{n|}} + {}_{n|}\overline{a}_x.$$

We saw this annuity in Unit two described as a continuous life annuity of \$1/year to (x) with the first n years guaranteed (i.e., certain for n years, and life contingent thereafter).

CONDENSED REVIEW NOTES AND ADVANCED TOPICS

Joint Life Status/Independent Lives

$(x_1, \dots, x_n)$ – fails at *first* death

$T(x_1, \dots, x_n) = \; min\left\{T(x_1), \dots, T(x_n)\right\}$

$${}_tp_{xy} = S_{T(x,y)}(t) = S_{T(x)}(t) \cdot S_{T(y)}(t) = {}_tp_x \cdot {}_tp_y$$

$${}_tq_{xy} = F_{T(x,y)}(t) = Pr\Big((x) \text{ or } (y) \text{ fails within } t \text{ years}\Big)$$

$$= Pr\Big(\{T(x) \le t\} \cup \{T(y) \le t\}\Big)$$

$$= Pr\Big(T(x) \le t\Big) + Pr\Big(T(y) \le t\Big) - P\Big(\{T(x) \le t\} \cap \{T(y) \le t\}\Big)$$

$$= {}_tq_x + {}_tq_y - {}_tq_x \cdot {}_tq_y$$

$\mu_{xy}(t) = \text{joint life force} = \mu(x{+}t) + \mu(y{+}t)$

$f_{T(x,y)}(t) = S_{T(x,y)}(t)\; \mu_{xy}(t) = {}_tp_x \cdot {}_tp_y \cdot (\mu(x{+}t) + \mu(y{+}t))$

$K(x,y) = \text{curtate time to failure} = [T(x,y)]$

$$f_{K(x,y)}(k) = Pr\Big(K(x,y) = k\Big) = {}_kp_x \cdot {}_kp_y \cdot (q_{x+k} + q_{y+k} - q_{x+k} \cdot q_{y+k})$$

$$= {}_{k|}q_{xy} = {}_kp_{xy} \cdot q_{x+k,y+k}$$

$\bar{a}_{xy} = \text{APV of \$1/year while } x, y \text{ both survive}$

$$= \int_{t=0}^{min(\omega-x,\omega-y)} v^t \cdot {}_tp_x \cdot {}_tp_y dt \qquad \text{(current payment)}$$

$\overline{A}_{xy} = \text{APV of \$1 at first death}$

$$= \int_{t=0}^{min(\omega-x,\omega-y)} v^t \cdot {}_tp_x \cdot {}_tp_y \cdot (\mu(x{+}t){+}\mu(y{+}t))dt$$

Last Survivor Status/Independent Lives

$(\overline{x_1, \dots, x_n})$ – fails at *last* death

$T(\overline{x_1, \dots, x_n}) = max\{T(x_1), \dots, T(x_n)\}$

$${}_tq_{\overline{xy}} = F_{T(\overline{xy})}(t) = F_{T(x)}(t) \cdot F_{T(y)}(t) = {}_tq_x \cdot {}_tq_y$$

$${}_tp_{\overline{xy}} = s_{T(\overline{xy})}(t) = Pr(x \text{ or } y \text{ survives } t \text{ years})$$

$$= Pr\Big(\{T(x) > t\} \cup \{T(y) > t\}\Big)$$

$$= Pr(T(x) > t) + Pr(T(y) > t) - Pr\Big(\{T(x) > t\} \cap \{T(y) > t\}\Big)$$

$$= {}_tp_x + {}_tp_y - {}_tp_x \cdot {}_tp_y$$

$$f_{T(\overline{x,y})}(t) = {}_tq_x \cdot {}_tp_y \cdot \mu(y{+}t) + {}_tq_y \cdot {}_tp_x \cdot \mu(x{+}t) = {}_tp_{\overline{xy}} \cdot \mu_{\overline{xy}}\,(t)$$

$$\mu_{\overline{xy}}(t) = \text{complicated} = \frac{f_{T(\overline{xy})}(t)}{{}_tp_{\overline{xy}}}$$

$$K(\overline{x,y}) = [T(\overline{x,y})]$$

$$f_{K(\overline{x,y})}(k) = Pr(K(\overline{x,y}) = k) = \underbrace{{}_kq_y \cdot {}_kp_x \cdot q_{x+k} + {}_kq_x \cdot {}_kp_y \cdot q_{y+k}}_{\text{one dies prior to time } k \text{ and one dies in } [k,\, k+1]} + \underbrace{{}_kp_{xy} \cdot q_{x+k} \cdot q_{y+k}}_{\text{both die between } k \text{ and } k+1}$$

Relations Between Joint Life and Last Survivor

(Independence used at only one place below)

$$\{T(x,y), T(\overline{x,y})\} = \{T(x), T(y)\} \quad \Rightarrow \quad v^{T(x,y)} + v^{T(\overline{x,y})} = v^{T(x)} + v^{T(y)}$$

$$\Rightarrow \quad \overline{A}_{xy} + \overline{A}_{\overline{xy}} = E\left[v^{T(x,y)} + v^{T(\overline{x,y})}\right] = \overline{A}_x + \overline{A}_y,$$

(*) $\overline{a}_{xy} + \overline{a}_{\overline{xy}} = \overline{a}_x + \overline{a}_y$

$$\begin{aligned} Cov\Big(T(xy), T(\overline{xy})\Big) &= E\,[T(x,y)\,T(\overline{x,y})] - E\,[T(x,y)]E\,[T(\overline{x,y})] \\ &= E\,[T(x)\,T(y)] - \mathring{e}_{xy}\,\mathring{e}_{\overline{xy}} \\ &= \mathring{e}_x \cdot \mathring{e}_y - \mathring{e}_{xy}\,\mathring{e}_{\overline{xy}} \qquad \text{(independence)} \\ &= \mathring{e}_x \cdot \mathring{e}_y - \mathring{e}_{xy}\Big(\mathring{e}_x + \mathring{e}_y - \mathring{e}_{xy}\Big) \qquad \Big((*) \text{ with } i = 0\Big) \\ &= \Big(\mathring{e}_x - \mathring{e}_{xy}\Big)\Big(\mathring{e}_y - \mathring{e}_{xy}\Big) \end{aligned}$$

$$Cov\Big(v^{T(x,y)}, v^{T(\overline{x,y})}\Big) = \Big(\overline{A}_x - \overline{A}_{xy}\Big)\Big(\overline{A}_y - \overline{A}_{xy}\Big)$$

Special Laws — Simplified Joint Life Relations

Gompertz: $\mu(x) = Bc^x$

$\mu_{xy}(t) = \mu(x+t) + \mu(y+t) = Bc^{x+t} + Bc^{y+t} = B(c^x + c^y)\,c^t$

$\mu(w+t) = Bc^{w+t} = Bc^w c^t$

$\mu_{xy}(t) = \mu(w+t)$ all $t \Leftrightarrow c^x + c^y = c^w$

the status (x,y) is equivalent to the single life status (w)

Applications: *uniform seniority* - if (55, 60) is equivalent to (62.6), then (66, 71) is equivalent to $71 + (62.6 - 60) = 73.6$: $c^{55} + c^{60} = c^{62.6} \quad \Rightarrow \quad 1 + c^5 = c^{7.6}$

$\Rightarrow \quad c^{66} + c^{71} = c^{66}(1 + c^5) = c^{66}(c^{7.6}) = c^{73.6}.$

$\overline{A}_{xy} = \overline{A}_w, \quad \overline{a}_{xy} = \overline{a}_w$

Makeham: $\mu(x) = A + Bc^x$

$\mu_{xy}(t) = 2A + B(c^x + c^y)\, c^t$

$\mu_{ww}(t) = 2A + B(c^w + c^w)\, c^t$

$\mu_{xy}(t) = \mu_{ww}(t)$ all $t \Leftrightarrow c^x + c^y = 2c^w$

the status (x,y) is equivalent to (w,w)

Applications: Uniform seniority - if $(55, 60)$ is equivalent to $(57.8, 57.8)$ then $(66, 71) \equiv (68.8, 68.8)$:

$$c^{55} + c^{60} = 2c^{57.8} \quad \Rightarrow \quad 1 + c^5 = 2c^{2.8}$$

$$\Rightarrow \quad c^{66} + c^{71} = c^{66}(1 + c^5) = c^{66}(2c^{2.8}) = c^{68.8} + c^{68.8}.$$

$$\overline{A}_{xy} = \overline{A}_{ww}, \quad \overline{a}_{xy} = \overline{a}_{ww}$$

Evaluation of Joint Life Functions

(UDD on Individual Lives)

$$\overline{A}_{xy} = \tfrac{i}{\delta} A_{xy} + \tfrac{i}{\delta}\left(1 - \tfrac{2}{\delta} + \tfrac{2}{i}\right) A_{both}$$

$$A_{xy}^{(m)} = \tfrac{i}{i^{(m)}} A_{xy} + \tfrac{i}{i^{(m)}}\left(1 + \tfrac{1}{m} - \tfrac{2}{d^{(m)}} + \tfrac{2}{i}\right) A_{both}$$

A_{both} pays 1 at end of policy year if both die during it

Reversionary Annuity

$a_{y|x} = \overline{a}_x - \overline{a}_{xy} =$ APV of \$1/year paid continuously to (x) after death of (y) (if (x) is still surviving)

x	y	$\overline{a}_x - \overline{a}_{yx}$ covers
alive	alive	$1 - 1 = 0$/yr continuously
alive	dead	$1 - 0 = 1$/yr continuously
dead	alive	$0 - 0 = 0$/yr continuously

Statuses With Dependent Lives

If $T(x)$ and $T(y)$ are not necessarily independent, then everything must begin with the joint density, $f_{T(x),T(y)}(t_1, t_2)$, of $T(x)$ and $T(y)$. What follows below still applies to independent lives. In this case the joint density is $f_{T(x)}(t_1) \cdot f_{T(y)}(t_2)$, and simplifications for independent lives such as ${}_tp_{xy} = {}_tp_x \cdot {}_tp_y$, ${}_tq_{\overline{xy}} = {}_tq_x \cdot {}_tq_y$, and $\mu_{xy}(t) = \mu(x+t) + \mu(y+t)$ will follow with a few extra steps.

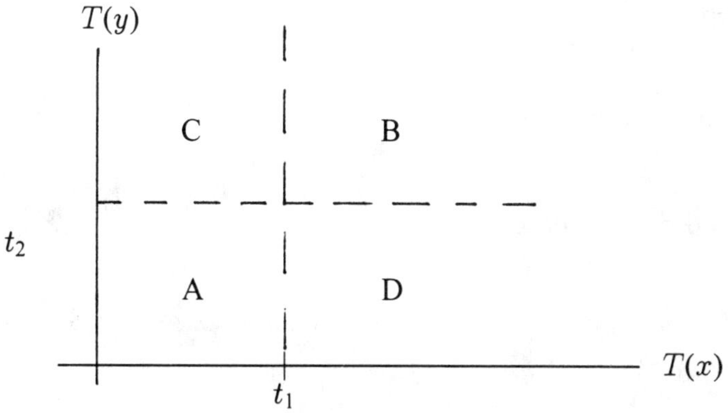

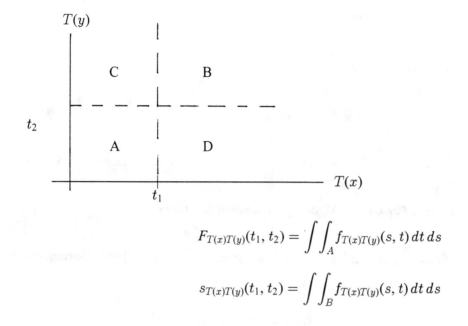

$$F_{T(x)T(y)}(t_1, t_2) = \int\int_A f_{T(x)T(y)}(s, t)\, dt\, ds$$

$$s_{T(x)T(y)}(t_1, t_2) = \int\int_B f_{T(x)T(y)}(s, t)\, dt\, ds$$

Last survivor distribution function: $\quad {}_tq_{\overline{xy}} = Pr(\{T(x) \leq t\} \text{ and } \{T(y) \leq t\}) = F_{T(x)T(y)}(t, t)$

Joint life survivor function: $\quad {}_tp_{xy} = Pr(\{T(x) > t\} \text{ and } \{T(y) > t\}) = s_{T(x)T(y)}(t, t)$

Distribution and survival functions of $T(x)$ ($T(y)$ similar)

$$\begin{cases} {}_tq_x = Pr(\{T(x) \leq t)\} = Pr(\{T(x) \leq t\} \text{ and } \{T(y) < \infty\}) \\ \qquad = F_{T(x),\,T(y)}(t, \infty) = \int\int_A f_{T(x)T(y)} + \int\int_C f_{T(x)T(y)} \\ {}_tp_x = Pr(T(x) > t) = 1 - {}_tq_x, \text{ or} \\ s_{T(x)T(y)}(t, 0) = Pr(\{T(x) > t\} \text{ and } \{T(y) > 0\}) = \int\int_D f_{T(x)T(y)} + \int\int_B f_{T(x)T(y)} \end{cases}$$

Application of Additive Probability law

$$\begin{cases} {}_tq_{xy} = 1 - {}_tp_{xy} \\ \qquad = Pr(\{T(x) \leq t\}) + Pr(\{T(y) \leq t\}) - Pr(\text{both } T(x), T(y) \leq t) \\ \qquad = {}_tq_x + {}_tq_y - {}_tq_{\overline{xy}} \end{cases}$$

Application of Additive Probability law

$$\begin{cases} {}_tp_{\overline{xy}} = 1 - {}_tq_{\overline{xy}} \\ \qquad = Pr(\{T(x) > t\}) + Pr(\{T(y) > t\}) - Pr(\text{both } T(x), T(y) > t) \\ \qquad = {}_tp_x + {}_tp_y - {}_tp_{xy} \end{cases}$$

Note: One can deal with $T(\overline{x,y})$ using its distribution function, ${}_tq_{\overline{xy}}$, derived by a double integral above. One can deal with $T(x,y)$ using its survival function, ${}_tp_{xy}$, derived by a double integral above. In addition, one could use the two relations immediately above to avoid repetitious double integrals. In other words, to deal with both $T(x,y)$ and $T(\overline{x,y})$ it is only necessary to compute $F_{T(x)T(y)}(t_1, t_2)$ **or** $s_{T(x)T(y)}(t_1, t_2)$ by integration. For example, suppose you calculate $F = F_{T(x)T(y)}$ by integration. Then

$$ {}_tq_{\overline{xy}} = F(t,t), $$

$$ {}_tq_x = F(t,\infty),\ {}_tq_y = F(\infty,t), $$

and

$$ {}_tq_{xy} = {}_tq_x + {}_tq_y - {}_tq_{\overline{xy}}, $$

are sufficient to study $T(\overline{x,y})$, $T(x)$, $T(y)$ and $T(x,y)$.

Frank's Copula/Parametric Model of Dependent Lifetimes

Given distribution functions ${}_tq_x$, ${}_tq_y$ and a non-zero parameter α, define a joint distribution function

$$ F_{T(x),T(y)}(s,t) = \frac{1}{\alpha} ln\left[1 + \frac{(e^{\alpha_s q_x}-1)(e^{\alpha_t q_y}-1)}{(e^{\alpha}-1)}\right] $$

where $0 \leq x \leq \omega - x$, $0 \leq t \leq \omega - x$. $T(x)$, $T(y)$ are dependent and the marginal distributions are preserved (i.e., ${}_sq_x = F_{T(x),T(y)}(s,\infty)$ and ${}_tq_y = F_{T(x),T(y)}(\infty,t)$). Use this F and relations in the preceding section of the outline to study $T(\overline{x,y})$, $T(x)$, $T(y)$ and $T(x,y)$.

Common Shock Model of Dependent Lifetimes

Begin with $T^*(x)$, $T^*(y)$, Z assumed to be independent, and with $f_Z(t) = \lambda e^{-\lambda t}$ for $t > 0$ (i.e., Z is exponentially distributed). Define

$$ T(x) = min\{T^*(x), Z\}, T(y) = min\{T^*(y), Z\} $$

Then the joint survival function is given by

$$ s_{T(x),T(y)}(s,t) = (s_{T^*(x)}(s))(s_{T^*(y)}(t))e^{-\lambda max\{s,t\}}, $$

and the joint life status survival function is thus

$$ {}_tp_{xy} = s_{T(x),T(y)}(t,t) = s_{T^*(x)}(t) \cdot s_{T^*(y)}(t) \cdot e^{-\lambda t}. $$

The survival functions for the marginal distributions are

$$ {}_tp_x = s_{T(x)}(t) = s_{T^*(x)}(t) \cdot e^{-\lambda t} $$

$$ {}_tp_y = s_{T(y)}(t) = s_{T^*(y)}(t) \cdot e^{-\lambda t} $$

$T(x)$, $T(y)$ are dependent since ${}_tp_x \cdot {}_tp_y \neq {}_tp_{xy}$. The corresponding forces are

$$ \mu_{xy}(t) = \mu_x^*(t) + \mu_y^*(t) + \lambda $$

$$ \mu_x(t) = \mu_x^*(t) + \lambda $$

$$ \mu_y(t) = \mu_y^*(t) + \lambda. $$

$T(\overline{x,y})$ can be studied using ${}_tp_{\overline{xy}} = {}_tp_x + {}_tp_y - {}_tp_{xy}$ and the above to calculate the right side.

Contingent Function Examples

1. $$ {}_nq^{\;1}_{xy} = Pr((x) \text{ dies before } (y) \text{ and within } n \text{ years}) $$

$$ = \int_{t=0}^{n} \underbrace{{}_tp_y}_{\substack{\text{prob. that} \\ (y) \text{ is alive} \\ \text{at } (x)\text{'s death}}} \cdot \underbrace{{}_tp_x \mu(x+t)\,dt}_{\substack{\approx \text{ prob. that } (x) \\ \text{dies in } [t,\, t+dt]}} $$

2. $$ \overline{A}^{\;1}_{xy} = APV(\$1 \text{ at the death of } (x) \text{ if } (y) \text{ is still alive}) $$

$$ = \int_{t=0}^{\infty} \underbrace{1}_{\text{amount}} \cdot \underbrace{e^{-\delta t}}_{\text{discount}} \cdot \underbrace{{}_tp_y({}_tp_x \mu(x+t)dt)}_{\substack{\approx \text{ prob. that } (x) \text{ fails} \\ \text{in } [t,\, t+dt] \text{ and } (y) \\ \text{is still alive}}} $$

Note: Both of the above assume that $T(x)$ and $T(y)$ are independent.

CONCEPTUAL REVIEW TEST

1. Suppose a pair of lives has ages 58 and 62 today, from which their future lifetimes are measured. If their deaths occur at ages 65.2 and 68.4 respectively, then what value is taken on by $T = T(58,62)$, the waiting time until the failure of the joint life status?

   What value is taken by $T = T(\overline{58, 62})$?

2. Use a Riemann sum analysis to explain why the integral $\int_0^{min\{\omega-x,\omega-y\}} v^t \cdot {}_tp_x \cdot {}_tp_y dt$ is the APV of a continuous annuity of \$1/year while both (x) and (y) survive. Assume $T(x)$ and $T(y)$ are independent.

3. Let $K = K(x,y)$ be the curtate time until failure for the joint life status (x,y). Express $Pr(K=5)$ in terms of single life p's and q's. What assumption do you make?

4. Write an integral to express the APV of an insurance paying $\$b_t$ upon the last death of (x), (y) if it occurs in t years. Assume $T(x)$ and $T(y)$ are independent.

5. Give an intuitive explanation of the APV identity $\overline{A}_{xy} + \overline{A}_{\overline{xy}} = \overline{A}_x + \overline{A}_y$.

6. Explain the relations ${}_tq_{xy} + {}_tq_{\overline{xy}} = {}_tq_x + {}_tq_y$ and ${}_tp_{xy} + {}_tp_{\overline{xy}} = {}_tp_x + {}_tp_y$ that hold even when $T(x)$ and $T(y)$ are dependent.

7. Explain how to obtain ${}_tq_{\overline{xy}}$ and ${}_tp_{xy}$ from the joint density $f_{T(x),T(y)}(t_1, t_2)$.

8. Explain how to obtain ${}_tq_x$ and ${}_tp_x$ from $F_{T(x),T(y)}(s, t)$.

CONCEPTUAL REVIEW TEST SOLUTIONS

1. $T(58{,}62) = min\{65.2 - 58, 68.4 - 62\} = min\{7.2, 6.4\} = 6.4$

   $T(\overline{58, 62}) = \max\{7.2, 6.4\} = 7.2$

2. The APV of the amount paid during a short interval $[t, t{+}\Delta t]$ is approximately the expected value of the following distribution:

Random P.V.	Event	Probability
$v^t \cdot \Delta t$	x, y both surviving	${}_tp_x \cdot {}_tp_y$ (independence)
$v^t \cdot 0$	not both surviving	$1 - {}_tp_x \cdot {}_tp_y$

   $E\,$[Random P.V.] $= v^t \cdot {}_tp_x \cdot {}_tp_y \cdot \Delta t + 0$. Thus, partitioning $[0, min\{\omega{-}x, \omega - y\}]$, we obtain APV of annuity $= \sum_{i=1}^{n}$ APV of portion in $[t_{i-1}, t_i] \approx \sum_{i=1}^{n} v^{t_i} \cdot {}_{t_i}p_x \cdot {}_{t_i}p_y \cdot \Delta t_i$, a Reiman sum for the given integral.

3. If $K = 5$, both (x) and (y) survive 5 years (probability $= {}_5p_x \cdot {}_5p_y$ assuming x, y have independent future lifetimes) and then either $(x{+}5)$ or *$(y{+}5)$ succumbs within 1 year (probability $= q_{x+5} + q_{y+5} - q_{x+5} \cdot q_{y+5}$, since * is a mathematical "or," i.e., union of 2 sets; $Pr(A \cup B) = Pr(A) + Pr(B) - Pr(A \cap B)$). Since both of these events must happen the multiplicative law gives $Pr(K = 5) = {}_5p_x \cdot {}_5p_y(q_{x+5} + q_{y+5} - q_{x+5} \cdot q_{y+5})$.

4. $$APV = \int_{t=0}^{max\{\omega-x,\,\omega-y\}} \underbrace{\underbrace{v^t \cdot b_t}_{\substack{\text{present value}\\ \text{of benefit}}} \cdot \underbrace{\underbrace{({}_tq_x \cdot {}_tp_y \cdot \mu(y{+}t)dt}_{\substack{\text{prob. } x \text{ dies before}\\ \text{time } t \text{ and } y \text{ dies in}\\ \text{instant after time } t}} + \underbrace{{}_tq_y \cdot {}_tp_x \cdot \mu(x{+}t)dt}_{\substack{\text{prob. } y \text{ dies before}\\ \text{time } t \text{ and } x \text{ dies in}\\ \text{instant after time } t}}}_{\text{prob. last death occurs in time interval } [t,\, t+dt]}}_{\text{portion of APV corresponding to time interval } [t,\, t+dt]}$$

5. $\overline{A}_{xy} + \overline{A}_{\overline{xy}}$ is enough to provide \$1 on both the first and last deaths of (x) and (y). In any case (i.e., irrelevant of who dies first), this is \$1 at death of (x) and \$1 at death of (y), whose APV is $\overline{A}_x + \overline{A}_y$.

6. Additive probability law:

$$ {}_tq_{xy} = Pr(T(x) \text{ or } T(y) \le t) = Pr(T(x) \le t) + Pr(T(y) \le t) - Pr(\text{both} \le t) $$
$$ = {}_tq_x + {}_tq_y - {}_tq_{\overline{xy}}. $$

Note that ${}_tq_{\overline{xy}} = {}_tq_x \cdot {}_tq_y$ if you add an assumption of independence. The explanation for the other relation follows from the additive law applied to ${}_tp_{\overline{xy}} = Pr(T(x) \text{ or } T(y) > t)$ or from ${}_tp_x = 1 - {}_tq_x$, ${}_tp_{xy} = 1 - {}_tq_{xy}$, etc..

7. $$ {}_tq_{\overline{xy}} = Pr(T(x) \le t \text{ and } T(y) \le t) = \int_0^t \int_0^t f_{T(x),T(y)}(t_1, t_2)\, dt_2\, dt_1 \text{ and} $$

$$ {}_tp_{xy} = Pr(T(x) > t \text{ and } T(y) > t) = \int_t^\infty \int_t^\infty f_{T(x),T(y)}(t_1, t_2)\, dt_2\, dt_1 $$

8. The events $\{T(x) \le t\}$ and $\{T(x) \le t,\ T(y) < \infty\}$ are identical. The probability of the first is ${}_tq_x$ and the probability of the second is $F_{T(x),T(y)}(t, \infty)$. Then use ${}_tp_x = 1 - {}_tq_x$.

COMPUTATIONAL REVIEW TEST

For 1, 2 assume $T(x)$, $T(y)$ are independent.

1. Assume $T(x)$ follows de Moivre's law with $\omega - x = 50$ and $T(y)$ follows a constant force model with $\mu = \frac{1}{25}$. Compute the following:

   (a) ${}_tp_{xy}$

   (b) $\mu_{xy}(t)$

   (c) the p.d.f of $T(x,y)$

   (d) $\overline{a}_{xy}$ (assume δ=.05)

   (e) $\overline{A}_{xy}$ (use the relation with annuity values)

2. Assume $T(x)$ follows de Moivre's law with $\omega - x = 50$ and $T(y)$ follows de Moivre's law with $\omega - y = 40$. Compute the following:

   (a) ${}_tp_{\overline{xy}}$ (different form for $0 \leq t \leq 40$ and $40 \leq t \leq 50$)

   (b) the p.d.f of $T(\overline{x,y})$ (note: ${}_tq_y$=0, ${}_tp_y$=1 for $40 \leq t \leq 50$)

   (c) $\overline{A}_{\overline{xy}}$ (assume δ=.05)

   (d) $\overline{a}_{\overline{xy}}$

   (e) $\overline{A}_{xy}$ and $\overline{a}_{xy}$ (from relation with joint life & single life values).

COMPUTATIONAL REVIEW TEST SOLUTIONS

1. de Moivre's law: ${}_tp_x = \frac{\omega - x - t}{\omega - x} = \frac{50-t}{50}$, $\mu(x+t) = \frac{1}{\omega - x - t} = \frac{1}{50-t}$, $t < 50$

Constant force: ${}_tp_y = e^{-\mu t} = e^{-t/25}$, $\mu(x+t) = \frac{1}{25}$, $0 < t < \infty$

(a) $${}_tp_{xy} = {}_tp_x \cdot {}_tp_y = \begin{cases} \frac{50-t}{50} \cdot e^{-t/25} & 0 \le t \le 50 \\ 0 & 50 < t \end{cases}$$

(b) $$\mu_{xy}(t) = \mu(x+t) + \mu(y+t) = \begin{cases} \frac{1}{50-t} + \frac{1}{25} & 0 < t < 50 \\ \frac{1}{25} & 50 \le t \end{cases}$$

(c) $$f(t) = {}_tp_{xy} \cdot \mu_{xy}(t) = \frac{50-t}{50} \cdot e^{-t/25}\left[\frac{1}{50-t} + \frac{1}{25}\right],\ 0 \le t < 50$$

(d) $$\bar{a}_{xy} = \int_{t=0}^{min\{50,\infty\}} e^{-.05t}\,\frac{50-t}{50} \cdot e^{-t/25} \cdot dt \quad \text{(current payment method)}$$

$$= \frac{1}{50}\int_{t=0}^{50} (50-t)\,e^{-.09t}dt = \frac{e^{-.09t}}{-.09} - \frac{1}{50}\left[\frac{te^{-.09t}}{-.09} - \frac{e^{-.09t}}{(.09)^2}\right]\Bigg|_0^{50}$$

$$= e^{-4.5}\left(\frac{-1}{.09} + \frac{1}{.09} + \frac{1}{50(.09)^2}\right) - \left[\frac{-1}{.09} + \frac{1}{.09^2} \cdot \frac{1}{50}\right]$$

$$= 8.6694$$

(e) $\overline{A}_{xy} = 1 - \delta\overline{A}_{xy} = .5665$

2. de Moivre's law: ${}_tp_x = \frac{50-t}{50}$, ${}_tq_x = \frac{t}{50}$, $\mu(x+t) = \frac{1}{50-t}$, $0 \le t < 50$

${}_tp_y = \frac{40-t}{40}$, ${}_tq_y = \frac{t}{40}$, $\mu(y+t) = \frac{1}{40-t}$, $0 \le t < 40$

Note: ${}_tq_y = 1$ if $40 \le t \le 50$, ${}_tp_y = 0$

(a) $${}_tp_{\overline{xy}} = 1 - {}_tq_{\overline{xy}} = 1 - {}_tq_x \cdot {}_tq_y = \begin{cases} 1 - \frac{t^2}{2000} & 0 \le t \le 40 \\ 1 - \frac{t}{50} \cdot 1 & 40 \le t \le 50 \end{cases}$$

(b) $$f(t) = \begin{Bmatrix} \frac{t}{50} \cdot \frac{1}{40} & 0 \le t < 40 \\ 0 & 40 \le t \le 50 \end{Bmatrix} + \begin{cases} \frac{t}{40} \cdot \frac{1}{50} & 0 \le t \le 40 \\ 1 \cdot \frac{1}{50} & 40 \le t \le 50 \end{cases} = \begin{cases} \frac{t}{1000} & 0 \le t \le 40 \\ \frac{1}{50} & 40 \le t \le 50 \end{cases}$$

(c) $$\overline{A}_{\overline{xy}} = \int_{t=0}^{50} e^{-.05t} \cdot f(t)dt = \int_0^{40} e^{-.05t} \cdot \frac{t}{1000}dt + \int_{40}^{50} e^{-.05t}/50dt$$

$$= \frac{1}{1000}\left[\frac{te^{-.05t}}{-.05} - \frac{e^{-.05t}}{.05^2}\right]_0^{40} + \frac{e^{-.05t}}{-2.5}\Bigg|_{40}^{50}$$

$$= .2589$$

(d) $\bar{a}_{\overline{xy}} = \dfrac{1 - \bar{A}_{\overline{xy}}}{\delta} = 14.822$

(e) $\bar{A}_{xy} + \bar{A}_{\overline{xy}} = \bar{A}_x + \bar{A}_y$ and by de Moivre's law

$\bar{A}_x = \dfrac{1}{\omega - x}\, \bar{a}_{\overline{\omega - x|}} = \dfrac{1}{50}\, \bar{a}_{\overline{50|}} = .3672,\ \bar{A}_y = \dfrac{1}{40}\, \bar{a}_{\overline{40|}} = .4323.$

Hence $\bar{A}_{xy} = .4323 + .3672 - .2589 = .5406,$

$\bar{a}_{xy} = (1 - \bar{A}_{xy})/\delta = 9.188$

UNIT REVIEW QUESTIONS

1. You are given:

(i) $\ddot{a}_{xy} = 10$

(ii) ${}^2\ddot{a}_{xy} = 7$

(iii) $Var\left(\ddot{a}_{\overline{K+1}|}\right) = 27$, where K is the number of years completed to the failure of the status (xy).

Calculate the discount rate d.

(A) $\frac{3}{127}$ (B) $\frac{1}{20}$ (C) $\frac{6}{127}$ (D) $\frac{1}{10}$ (E) $\frac{13}{127}$

2. In a population, nonsmokers have a force of mortality one-half that of smokers at each age x, $x \geq 50$. For nonsmokers, $\ell_x = 1000(75 - x)$, $0 \leq x \leq 75$. If (65) is a nonsmoker and (55) is a smoker, calculate $\overset{\circ}{e}_{65:55}$. Assume $T(65)$ and $T(55)$ are independent.

(A) $\frac{569}{160}$ (B) $\frac{85}{24}$ (C) 3 (D) $\frac{47}{16}$ (E) $\frac{35}{12}$

3. The force of mortality for females is given by $\mu(x) = 0.001 + (10^{-5.1})c^x$, where $\log_{10}c = 0.04$. The force of mortality for males is given by $\mu'(y) = 0.001 + (10^{-4.9})c^y$, where $\log_{10}c = 0.04$. The joint status of two females, both age f, is equivalent to the joint status of two males, both age m. Assume the lives are independent.

Calculate $f - m$.

(A) 5 (B) 7 (C) 8 (D) 10 (E) 12

4. A mortality table follows Makeham's Law with $c^{10} = 2$. The multiple life status 20:30 can be replaced by the multiple life status w:w. The multiple life status 10:w can be replaced by multiple life status z:z. Find z. Assume the lives are independent.

(A) 16 (B) 17 (C) 18 (D) 19 (E) 20

5. $T(x)$ and $T(y)$ are independent and each is uniformly distributed over each year of age. Simplify $18({}_{1/3}q_{xy}) - 12({}_{1/2}q_{xy})$.

(A) 0 (B) $\frac{1}{2}(q_{xy})$ (C) $\frac{1}{2}(q_{\overline{xy}})$ (D) q_{xy} (E) $q_{\overline{xy}}$

6. What is the present value of a continuous annuity which starts on the death of y and continues for 5 years, or until the death of x, whichever happens first? Assume the lives are independent.

(A) $\bar{a}_{x:\overline{5|}} - \bar{a}_{xy}$

(B) $\bar{a}_{x:\overline{5|}} - \bar{a}_{xy:\overline{5|}}$

(C) $\bar{a}_{x:\overline{5|}} - [\bar{a}_{xy} \; - \; \bar{a}_{x+5:y}]$

(D) $\bar{a}_{x:\overline{5|}} + {}_5E_x\, \bar{a}_{x+5:y}$

(E) $\bar{a}_{x:\overline{5|}} - [\bar{a}_{xy} \; - \; {}_5E_x\, \bar{a}_{x+5:y}]$

7. Y is the present-value random variable for an annual life annuity-due of 1 issued on the lives of (x) and (y). For the first 15 years, a payment is made if at least one of (x) and (y) is alive. Thereafter, a payment is made only if exactly one of (x) and (y) is alive. You are given:

(i) $\ddot{a}_{xy} = 7.6$ (ii) $\ddot{a}_x = 9.8$ (iii) $\ddot{a}_y = 11.6$ (iv) ${}_{15|}\ddot{a}_{xy} = 3.7$

Calculate $E[Y]$.

(A) 9.7 (B) 9.9 (C) 10.1 (D) 10.3 (E) 10.5

8. Z is the present-value random variable for a discrete whole life insurance of 1 issued to (x) and (y) which pays 1 at the first death and 1 at the second death. You are given:

(i) $a_x = 9$ (ii) $a_y = 13$ (iii) $i = .04$

Calculate $E[Z]$.

(A) .08 (B) .28 (C) .69 (D) 1.08 (E) 1.15

9. A fully discrete last-survivor insurance of 1 is issued on two independent lives each age x. Net annual premiums are reduced by 25% after the first death.

You are given: (i) $A_x = .40$ (ii) $A_{xx} = .55$ (iii) $\ddot{a}_x = 10.0$

Calculate the initial net annual premium.

(A) .019 (B) .020 (C) .022 (D) .024 (E) .025

10. You are given:

(i) $T(x)$ and $T(y)$ are independent.

(ii)

k	q_{x+k}	q_{y+k}
0	.08	.10
1	.09	.15
2	.10	.20

Calculate ${}_{2|}q_{xy}$.

(A) .179 (B) .192 (C) .205 (D) .218 (E) .231

11. You are given:

(i) Mortality follows de Moivre's law with $\omega = 100$.
(ii) $T(80)$ and $T(85)$ are independent.
(iii) G is the probability that the second death takes place more than 5 years from now.
(iv) H is the probability that the first death occurs after 5 and before 10 years from now.

Calculate $G + H$.

(A) $\frac{41}{144}$ (B) $\frac{7}{24}$ (C) $\frac{1}{3}$ (D) $\frac{53}{144}$ (E) $\frac{5}{4}$

12. S is the actuarial present value of a continuous annuity of 1 per annum payable while at least one of (30) and (45) is living, but not if (30) is alive and under age 40. Assume that $T(30)$ and $T(45)$. Which of the following is equal to S?

I. $\bar{a}_{45} + \bar{a}_{30} - \bar{a}_{30:45:\overline{10|}}$

II. $\bar{a}_{45} + {}_{10|}\bar{a}_{30} - \bar{a}_{30:45}$

III. $\bar{a}_{45} + {}_{10|}\bar{a}_{30} - {}_{10|}\bar{a}_{30:45}$

IV. $\bar{a}_{45} + {}_{10|}\bar{a}_{30} - \bar{a}_{30:45:\overline{10|}}$

(A) None (B) I only (C) II only (D) III only (E) IV only

13. (x) and (y) buy a fully discrete life insurance paying a benefit on the policy anniversary following the second death.

Net annual premiums are 110 per year while both survive, and 40 per year after the first death. You are given:

(i) $i = 1/19$
(ii) $\ddot{a}_x = 8$
(iii) $a_y = 6$
(iv) $A_{xy} = .80$

Calculate the benefit amount.

(A) 1100 (B) 1200 (C) 1300 (D) 1450 (E) 1600

14. For a fully continuous last-survivor whole life insurance of 1 on (x) and (y), you are given:

(i) $T(x)$ and $T(y)$ are independent.
(ii) $\mu(x+t) = \mu(y+t) = .06, t > 0$
(iii) $\delta = .04$
(iv) Premiums are payable until the first death.

Calculate the annual benefit premium.

(A) .033 (B) .042 (C) .055 (D) .072 (E) .120

15. The future lifetimes of (60) and (70) follow de Moivre's Law with $\omega = 100$. Their bivariate distribution is given by Frank's copula with $\alpha = -2$.

Determine ${}_{10}q_{\overline{60:70}}$.

(A) .083 (B) .125 (C) .458 (D) .500 (E) .583

16. Suppose $\delta = .05$ and $\ell_x = 100 - x$. Then $\overline{a}_{\overline{60:\overline{20|}}}$ is closest to

(A) 11 (B) 12 (C) 13 (D) 14 (E) 15

Use the following information for Questions 17 -19.
You are given:
(i) ${}_tp_x = 1 - t^2 q_x,\ 0 \le t \le 1$
(ii) ${}_tp_y = 1 - t^2 q_y,\ 0 \le t \le 1$
(iii) $q_x = .080$
(iv) $q_y = .004$
(v) $T(x)$ and $T(y)$ are independent.

17. Calculate the value of $\mu_{xy}(t)$ when $t = .50$.

(A) .0812 (B) .0825 (C) .0856 (D) .0868 (E) .0886

18. Calculate the value of ${}_tp_{xy}\mu_{xy}(t)$ when $t = .50$.

(A) .0838 (B) .0856 (C) .0868 (D) .0886 (E) .0902

19. Which of the following is a correct expression for ${}_tp_y\mu(y+t)$?

(A) $\dfrac{.008t^2}{1-.08t}$ (B) $\dfrac{.008t}{1-.08t}$ (C) $\dfrac{.032t}{1-.08t}$ (D) $.008t^2$ (E) $.008t$

Use the following information for Questions 20-22.

$T(x)$ and $T(y)$ are not independent; specifically,

$$_tp_{xy} = \frac{1}{2}(_tp_x) + \frac{1}{2}(_tp_x \cdot {_tp_y}).$$

Each of $T(x)$ and $T(y)$ are based on a constant force of mortality of $\mu = .10$. You are also given that $\delta = .05$.

20. Calculate $\overline{a}_{xy}$.

(A) $\frac{11}{3}$ (B) $\frac{14}{3}$ (C) $\frac{16}{3}$ (D) $\frac{19}{3}$ (E) $\frac{22}{3}$

21. Calculate $\overline{A}_{xy}$.

(A) $\frac{7}{15}$ (B) $\frac{9}{15}$ (C) $\frac{11}{15}$ (D) $\frac{12}{15}$ (E) $\frac{13}{15}$

22. Calculate $\overline{A}_{\overline{x:y}}$.

(A) $\frac{7}{15}$ (B) $\frac{9}{15}$ (C) $\frac{11}{15}$ (D) $\frac{12}{15}$ (E) $\frac{13}{15}$

Use the following information for Questions 23 - 26.

You are given:

(i) (30) and (50) are independent lives, each subject to a constant force of mortality, $\mu = .05$.
(ii) $\delta = .03$

23. Calculate $_{10}q_{\overline{30:50}}$.

(A) .155 (B) .368 (C) .424 (D) .632 (E) .845

24. Calculate $\overset{\circ}{e}_{\overline{30:50}}$.

(A) 10 (B) 20 (C) 30 (D) 40 (E) 50

25. Calculate $Var[T(\overline{30:50})]$.

(A) 50 (B) 100 (C) 150 (D) 200 (E) 400

26. Calculate $Cov[T(30{:}50), T(\overline{30{:}50})]$.

(A) 10 (B) 25 (C) 50 (D) 100 (E) 200

Use the following information for Questions 27-30.

You are given that the joint density for $T(x)$, $T(y)$ is

$$f_{T(x),\,T(y)}(t_1, t_2) = \frac{4}{(1+t_1+2t_2)^3}$$

for $t_1, t_2 \geq 0$.

27. Calculate $F_{T(x),\,T(y)}(1,2)$.

(A) $\frac{13}{30}$ (B) $\frac{14}{30}$ (C) $\frac{15}{30}$ (D) $\frac{16}{30}$ (E) $\frac{17}{30}$

28. Calculate $s_{T(x),\,T(y)}(1,2)$.

(A) $\frac{5}{30}$ (B) $\frac{8}{30}$ (C) $\frac{11}{30}$ (D) $\frac{14}{30}$ (E) $\frac{16}{30}$

29. Calculate ${}_tp_x$, the marginal survival function of $T(x)$.

(A) $\frac{2}{2+t}$ (B) $\left(\frac{2}{2+t}\right)^2$ (C) $\frac{1}{(1+t)^2}$ (D) $\frac{1}{1+t}$ (E) $\frac{1}{1+2t}$

30. Calculate ${}_tq_{xy}$, the joint life distribution function.

(A) $\frac{1}{1+3t}$ (B) $\frac{1}{1+2t}$ (C) $\frac{2t}{1+3t}$ (D) $\frac{3t}{1-3t}$ (E) $\frac{3t}{1+3t}$

Use the following information for Questions 31 - 34.

The future lifetimes of (x) and (y), $T^*(x)$ and $T^*(y)$, are exponentially distributed with forces $\mu^*(x+t) = \mu^*(y+t) = .10$. The independent lives (x) and (y) are subjected to a common shock with force $\lambda = .05$. Define $T(x) = min\{T^*(x), Z\}$ and $T(y) = min\{T^*(y), Z\}$ where $T^*(x)$, $T^*(y)$ and Z are assumed independent and $f_Z(z) = .05e^{-.05z}$.

31. Calculate ${}_{10}p_{\overline{xy}}$.

(A) .356 (B) .358 (C) .360 (D) .362 (E) .364

32. Calculate $\overset{\circ}{e}_{\overline{xy}} = E[T(\overline{x,y})]$.

(A) $\frac{28}{3}$ (B) $\frac{26}{3}$ (C) $\frac{24}{3}$ (D) $\frac{21}{3}$ (E) $\frac{12}{3}$

33. Calculate $\overline{A}_{xy}$ if $\delta = .08$.

(A) $\frac{20}{33}$ (B) $\frac{21}{33}$ (C) $\frac{23}{33}$ (D) $\frac{24}{33}$ (E) $\frac{25}{33}$

34. What is the probability that the joint life status (x, y) fails due to the common shock?

(A) $\frac{1}{6}$ (B) $\frac{1}{5}$ (C) $\frac{1}{4}$ (D) $\frac{2}{5}$ (E) $\frac{2}{3}$

SOLUTIONS TO UNIT REVIEW QUESTIONS

1. $27 = Var\left(\ddot{a}_{\overline{K+1|}}\right) = Var\left(\frac{1-v^{K+1}}{d}\right) = \frac{1}{d^2}\left({}^2A_{xy} - A_{xy}{}^2\right)$

From $1 = d\ddot{a}_{xy} + A_{xy}$ we get $A_{xy} = 1 - 10d$, and from $1 = {}^2d\ {}^2\ddot{a}_{xy} + {}^2A_{xy}$ (${}^2d = 2d - d^2$ = rate of disc at twice original force) we get ${}^2A_{xy} = 1 - (2d - d^2)\cdot 7$. Substituting these results into the first equation gives $27d^2 = {}^2A_{xy} - A_{xy}{}^2 = (1-14d+7d^2) - (1-20d+100d^2)$, $120d^2 - 6d = 0$; $d = \frac{6}{120} = \frac{1}{20}$. ANSWER B

2. $\mu^n(x) = \frac{1}{75-x} = \frac{1}{2}\ \mu^s(x) \Rightarrow \mu^s(x) = \frac{2}{75-x} \Rightarrow \ell_x^s = (75-x)^2$.

Thus ${}_tp_{55}^s = \frac{\ell_{55+t}^s}{\ell_{55}^s} = \left(\frac{20-t}{20}\right)^2$ and ${}_tp_{65}^n = \frac{\ell_{65+t}^n}{\ell_{65}^n} = \frac{10-t}{10}$. Let $T = T(55,65)$.

Then

$$\mathring{e}_{55^s,65^n} = E[T] = \int_0^{10} t\ f_{T(55,65)}(t)dt$$
$$= \int_0^{10} {}_tp_{55,65}dt$$
$$= \int_0^{10} {}_tp_{55}^s \cdot {}_tp_{65}^n dt$$
$$= \int_0^{10} \left(\frac{20-t}{20}\right)^2 \cdot \frac{(10-t)}{10}dt$$
$$= \frac{1}{4000}\left[\int_0^{10} (20-t)^2\cdot(20-t-10)dt\right]$$
$$= \frac{1}{4000}\left[\int_0^{10} (20-t)^3dt - 10\int_0^{10}(20-t)^2dt\right]$$
$$= \frac{1}{4000}\left[-\frac{(20-t)^4}{4} + 10\cdot\frac{(20-t)^3}{3}\Bigg|_0^{10}\right]$$
$$= \frac{1}{4000}\left[14{,}166.\overline{66}\right] = 3.541\overline{6} = \frac{85}{24}$$

ANSWER B

3. Both mortality laws are Makeham. Now $\mu_{f,f}(t) = \mu_{m,m}(t)$ for all t means $2\left(.001+10^{-5.1}\cdot 10^{.04(f+t)}\right) = 2\left(.001+10^{-4.9}\cdot 10^{.04(m+t)}\right)$. Subtracting .002 and dividing by $2\cdot 10^{.04t}$ yields $10^{-5.1}\cdot 10^{.04f} = 10^{-4.9}\cdot 10^{.04m}$, or $-5.1 + .04f = -4.9 + .04m$. Hence $f - m = \frac{.20}{.04} = 5$ ANSWER A

4. Under Makeham's Law 20:30 is equivalent to $w{:}w$ if $c^{20}+c^{30} = 2c^w$. Thus $c^w = \frac{1}{2}[(c^{10})^2 + (c^{10})^3] = \frac{1}{2}[2^2+2^3] = 6$. Now $10{:}w$ equivalent to $z{:}z$ means $2c^z = c^{10} + c^w = 2+6$ or $c^z = 4$. Thus $4 = c^z = (c^{10})^{z/10} = 2^{z/10}$: $z/10 = 2$ ANSWER E

5. $$_{1/3}q_{xy} = 1 - {}_{1/3}p_{xy} = 1 - ({}_{1/3}p_x)({}_{1/3}p_y) = 1 - \left(1-\tfrac{1}{3}q_x\right)\left(1-\tfrac{1}{3}q_y\right)$$
$$= 1-\left(1-\tfrac{1}{3}q_x - \tfrac{1}{3}q_y+\tfrac{1}{9}q_xq_y\right) = \tfrac{1}{3}q_x+\tfrac{1}{3}q_y - \tfrac{1}{9}\,q_xq_y.$$
Similarly $_{1/2}q_{xy} = \tfrac{1}{2}q_x+\tfrac{1}{2}q_y - \tfrac{1}{4}\,q_xq_y.$

Thus $18({}_{1/3}q_{xy}) - 12({}_{1/2}q_{xy}) = (6q_x+6q_y-2q_xq_y)-(6q_x+6q_y-3q_xq_y) = q_xq_y = q_{\overline{xy}}$

ANSWER E

6. Payment is made if (x) is alive and (y) is dead, but died within the preceding 5 years. Thus $APV = \int_0^\infty v^t\,{}_tp_x({}_{t-5}p_y - {}_tp_y)dt$. Now $_{t-5}p_y = 1$ for $t \le 5$, so we write

$$APV = \int_0^5 v^t\,{}_tp_x\,(1-{}_tp_y)dt + \int_5^\infty v^t\,{}_tp_x\,({}_{t-5}p_y - {}_tp_y)dt$$
$$= \bar{a}_{x:\overline{5}|} - \bar{a}_{xy:\overline{5}|} + \int_0^\infty v^{r+5}\,{}_{r+5}p_x({}_rp_y - {}_{r+5}p_y)dr$$
$$= \bar{a}_{x:\overline{5}|} - \bar{a}_{xy:\overline{5}|} + {}_5E_x\cdot\bar{a}_{x+5:y} - {}_5E_{xy}\cdot\bar{a}_{x+5:y+5} = \bar{a}_{x:\overline{5}|} - \bar{a}_{xy} + {}_5E_x\cdot\bar{a}_{x+5:y},$$

ANSWER E

7. Using the current payment method and the description of the annuity yields

$$APV = E[Y] = \sum_{k=0}^{14} v^k\cdot{}_kp_{\overline{xy}} + \sum_{k=15}^{\infty} v^k\cdot({}_kp_{\overline{xy}} - {}_kp_{xy})$$

since $_kp_{\overline{xy}}$ is the probability that at least one is surviving and $_kp_{\overline{xy}} - {}_kp_{xy}$ is the probability that exactly one is surviving. Combining the first term in the second sum with the first sum results in

$$E[Y] = \sum_{k=0}^{\infty} v^k\cdot{}_kp_{\overline{xy}} - \sum_{k=15}^{\infty} v^k\cdot{}_kp_{xy}$$
$$= \ddot{a}_{\overline{xy}} - {}_{15|}\ddot{a}_{xy}$$
$$= (\ddot{a}_x+\ddot{a}_y-\ddot{a}_{xy}) - {}_{15|}\ddot{a}_{xy}$$
$$= 11.6+9.8-7.6-3.7 = 10.1,$$

ANSWER C

Note: No independence assumptions such as $_tp_{xy} = {}_tp_x\cdot{}_tp_y$, $_tq_{\overline{xy}} = {}_tq_x\cdot{}_tq_y$, or $\mu_{xy}(t) = \mu(x+t)+\mu(y+t)$ was used in the solution. So the problem and solution are valid whether $T(x)$, $T(y)$ are dependent or independent.

8. According to the description $E[Z] = A_{xy} + A_{\overline{xy}}$ which is equal to $A_x + A_y$ since this sum of NSP's provides the same benefits. Hence $E[Z] = A_x + A_y = (1-d\ddot{a}_x)+(1-d\ddot{a}_y)$. Since $i = \frac{1}{25}$, then $d = \frac{1}{26}$. Using this, along with $\ddot{a}_x = 1 + a_x$, results in
$E[Z] = \left(1-\frac{1+9}{26}\right)+\left(1-\frac{1+13}{26}\right) = \frac{28}{26} = 1.077,$

ANSWER D

Note: Relations such as $\bar{A}_{xy} + \bar{A}_{\overline{xy}} = \bar{A}_x + \bar{A}_y$ do not require independence of $T(x)$ and $T(y)$.

9. A key point here is that $\ddot{a}_{\overline{xy}} - \ddot{a}_{xy}$ is the APV of a dollar per year annuity due which pays the survivor for as long as she lives after the first death. This follows since $\ddot{a}_{\overline{xy}}$ provides one dollar annually when both are alive or when just (x) or just (y) is surviving, and $-\overline{a}_{xy}$ cancels the payment when both are surviving. Thus the basic equation for this problem is

$$\underbrace{P\ddot{a}_{xx}}_{\substack{APV \text{ while} \\ \text{both living}}} + \underbrace{.75P(\ddot{a}_{\overline{xx}} - \ddot{a}_{xx})}_{\substack{APV \text{ while only} \\ \text{one is living}}} = APV(\text{net premium}) = APV(\text{benefit}) = A_{\overline{xx}}.$$

Values for $\ddot{a}_{xx}$, $\ddot{a}_{\overline{xx}}$ and $A_{\overline{xx}}$ can be found as follows from standard annuity-insurance relations and joint life-last survivor-single life relations:

$$d = \frac{1-A_x}{\ddot{a}_x} = \frac{1-.4}{10} = .06, \ \ddot{a}_{xx} = \frac{1-A_{xx}}{d} = \frac{1-.55}{.06} = 7.5$$

$$\ddot{a}_{\overline{xx}} + \ddot{a}_{xx} = \ddot{a}_x + \ddot{a}_x \ \Rightarrow \ \ddot{a}_{\overline{xx}} = 10 + 10 - 7.5 = 12.5$$

$$A_{\overline{xx}} + A_{xx} = A_x + A_x \ \Rightarrow \ A_{\overline{xx}} = .4 + .4 - .55 = .25$$

Substituting these values in the first equation results in $P[(7.5) + (.75)(12.5 - 7.5)] = .25$, or $P = \frac{.25}{11.25} = .022$, ANSWER C

Note: The independence assumptions here was unnecessary.

10. ${}_{2|}q_{xy}$ is the symbol for the probability that both (x) and (y) survive two years, and then the first death occurs in the next year. So

$$\begin{aligned} {}_{2|}q_{xy} &= \underbrace{{}_2p_x \cdot {}_2p_y}_{\substack{\text{both survive} \\ \text{two years}}} \cdot \underbrace{q_{x+2:y+2}}_{\substack{\text{first death in} \\ \text{next year}}} \\ &= (p_x)(p_{x+1})(p_y)(p_{y+1}) \underbrace{(q_{x+2} + q_{y+2} - q_{x+2} \cdot q_{y+2})}_{\substack{\text{Additive Law: } Pr((x+2) \text{ or} \\ (y+2) \text{ dies in 1 year})}} \\ &= (1-.08)(1-.09)(1-.10)(1-.15)(.10+.20-(.10)(.20)) = .179, \text{ ANSWER A} \end{aligned}$$

Note: One could also ask for ${}_{2|}q_{\overline{xy}} = Pr(2 \le T(\overline{x,y}) < 3) = {}_3q_{\overline{xy}} - {}_2q_{\overline{xy}}$ (${}_tq_{\overline{xy}}$ is the distribution function of $T(\overline{xy})$). Independence could then be used to obtain ${}_{2|}q_{\overline{xy}} = {}_3q_x \cdot {}_3q_y - {}_2q_x \cdot {}_2q_y = (1-{}_3p_x)(1-{}_3p_y) - (1-{}_2p_x)(1-{}_2p_y)$ (easiest). In general ${}_{2|}q_{\overline{xy}} \neq {}_2p_{\overline{xy}} \cdot q_{\overline{x+2,\, y+2}}$. The subtle problem is that if $T(\overline{x,y}) > 2$ you could have both surviving at $t = 2$ or just one surviving. The notation $q_{\overline{x+2,\, y+2}}$ assumes both are surviving.

11. Notice that $G = Pr(T(\overline{x,y}) > 5) = {}_5p_{\overline{xy}} = 1 - {}_5q_{\overline{xy}} = 1 - ({}_5q_x)({}_5q_y)$ (independence), and $H = Pr(5 < T(x,y) \le 10) = s_{T(x,\,y)}(5) - s_{T(x,\,y)}(10) = {}_5p_{xy} - {}_{10}p_{xy} = {}_5p_x \cdot {}_5p_y - {}_{10}p_x \cdot {}_{10}p_x$ (independence). With de Moivre's law $\ell_x = 100 - x$, so ${}_5p_{80} = \frac{15}{20}$, ${}_{10}p_{80} = \frac{10}{20}$, ${}_5q_{80} = \frac{5}{20}$, ${}_5p_{85} = \frac{10}{15}$, ${}_{10}p_{85} = \frac{5}{15}$, and ${}_5q_{85} = \frac{5}{15}$. Thus

$$G + H = \left[1 - \left(\tfrac{5}{20}\right)\left(\tfrac{5}{15}\right)\right] + \left[\left(\tfrac{15}{20}\right)\left(\tfrac{10}{15}\right) - \left(\tfrac{10}{20}\right)\left(\tfrac{5}{15}\right)\right] = \tfrac{275}{300} + \tfrac{100}{300} = \tfrac{375}{300} = \tfrac{5}{4}.$$

ANSWER E.

12. Take the approach that views the APV as the integral over all possible times of payment of the product of payment amount, discount factor, and probability of payment:

$$APV = \int_{t=0}^{10} \underset{\text{amount}}{(1 \cdot dt)} \; \underset{\text{discount}}{(v^t)} \; \underset{\text{probability}^*}{({}_tp_{45\,t}q_{30})} + \int_{t=10}^{\infty} (1 \cdot dt)\,(v^t)\,({}_tp_{\overline{30,45}})$$

*{at least one living} ∩ {30 not living} = {30 dead, 45 alive}

Substituting ${}_tq_{30} = 1 - {}_tp_{30}$ into the first integral and ${}_tp_{\overline{30,45}} = {}_tp_{30} + {}_tp_{45} - {}_tp_{30} \cdot {}_tp_{45}$ into the second, one arrives at

$$APV = \int_0^{10} v^t \cdot {}_tp_{45} \cdot dt - \int_0^{10} v^t \cdot {}_tp_{30} \cdot {}_tp_{45}\,dt + \int_{10}^{\infty} v^t \cdot {}_tp_{45} \cdot dt$$

$$+ \int_{10}^{\infty} v^t \cdot {}_tp_{30} \cdot dt - \int_{10}^{\infty} v^t \cdot {}_tp_{30} \cdot {}_tp_{45} \cdot dt$$

$$= \underset{\substack{\uparrow \\ \text{1st+3rd} \\ \text{integrals}}}{\bar{a}_{45}} + \underset{\substack{\uparrow \\ \text{4th} \\ \text{integral}}}{{}_{10|}\bar{a}_{30}} - \underset{\substack{\uparrow \\ \text{2nd \& 5th} \\ \text{integrals}}}{\bar{a}_{30:45}} \; .$$

Thus II is correct. Since the possible answers indicate at most one of the four is correct, we see that the answer is C. ANSWER C

13. The subtle point here is that $\ddot{a}_{\overline{xy}} - \ddot{a}_{xy}$ is the APV of an annuity-due of 1 per year while exactly one of the two is alive. This can be derived from the 3-factor approach:

$$\begin{aligned} Pr(\text{exactly one alive}) &= Pr[\{(x)\text{ alive}\} \cup \{(y)\text{ alive}\} - \{\text{both alive}\}] \\ &= Pr[(x)\text{ alive}] + Pr[(y)\text{ alive}] - 2 \cdot Pr[\text{both alive}] \\ &= {}_tp_x + {}_tp_y - 2 \cdot {}_tp_{xy} = {}_tp_{\overline{xy}} - {}_tp_{xy}\,, \end{aligned}$$

or from the observation that $\ddot{a}_{\overline{xy}}$ pays 1 until the 2nd death and $-\ddot{a}_{xy}$ cancels off the 1 until the first death (the difference is 1 while exactly one lives). The equivalence relation says

$$110\ddot{a}_{xy} + 40(\ddot{a}_{\overline{xy}} - \ddot{a}_{xy}) = F \cdot A_{\overline{xy}}.$$

From the given information

$$\ddot{a}_{xy} = \frac{1 - A_{xy}}{d} = \frac{.20}{(1/20)} = 4 \qquad \left(d = \frac{1}{n+1} \text{ if } i = \frac{1}{n}\right)$$

$$\ddot{a}_{\overline{xy}} = \ddot{a}_x + \ddot{a}_y - \ddot{a}_{xy} = 8 + 7 - 4 = 11$$

$$A_{\overline{xy}} = 1 - d\ddot{a}_{\overline{xy}} = .45$$

Therefore $F = (440 + 280)/.45 = 1600$, ANSWER E.

14. If P is the annual premium rate then $P\overline{a}_{xy} = \overline{A}_{\overline{xy}}$ since premiums are payable to the first death and the benefit is paid at the second death. With independence of $T(x)$, $T(y)$ and constant forces μ_1 and μ_2 respectively

$$\begin{aligned}\overline{a}_{xy} &= \int_0^\infty v^t \cdot {}_tp_{xy}\,dt \\ &= \int_0^\infty e^{-\delta t} \cdot {}_tp_x \cdot {}_tp_y\,dt \\ &= \int_0^\infty e^{-\delta t} \cdot e^{-\mu_1 t} \cdot e^{-\mu_2 t}\,dt = \frac{1}{\mu_1 + \mu_2 + \delta} = \frac{1}{.06 + .06 + .04} = \frac{1}{.16}.\end{aligned}$$

Similarly, $\overline{A}_{xy} = \dfrac{\mu_1 + \mu_2}{\mu_1 + \mu_2 + \delta} = \dfrac{.12}{.16} = .75$

and $\overline{A}_{\overline{xy}} = \overline{A}_x + \overline{A}_y - \overline{A}_{xy} = \dfrac{.06}{.06+.04} + \dfrac{.06}{.06+.04} - .75 = .45.$

Finally, $P = \dfrac{\overline{A}_{\overline{xy}}}{\overline{a}_{xy}} = (.45)(.16) = .072.$ ANSWER D

Note: One possible variation would have $\$P$/year paid until the first death and reducing to $\$P/2$ per year after the first death and until the second one. In this case $APV(\text{premium}) = P\overline{a}_{xy} + \left(\frac{1}{2}P\right)(\overline{a}_{\overline{xy}} - \overline{a}_{xy}) = \left(\frac{1}{2}P\right)\overline{a}_{\overline{xy}} + \left(\frac{1}{2}P\right)\overline{a}_{xy}.$

15. From Frank's formula with $\alpha = -2$

$${}_{10}q_{\overline{60:70}} = \frac{1}{\alpha} \cdot ln\left[1 + \frac{(e^{\alpha\,{}_{10}q_{60}} - 1)(e^{\alpha\,{}_{10}q_{70}} - 1)}{(e^{\alpha} - 1)}\right] = \frac{1}{-2} \cdot ln(.7786) = .125$$

after using de Moivre's law, $\ell_x = 100 - x$, to compute ${}_{10}q_{60} = \frac{10}{40} = .25$, ${}_{10}q_{70} = \frac{10}{30} = \frac{1}{3}$.

ANSWER B

Note: One could also be asked to compute the following:

$${}_{10}p_{\overline{60:70}} = 1 - {}_{10}q_{\overline{60:70}};\ \text{or}$$

$${}_{10}p_{60:70} = {}_{10}p_{60} + {}_{10}p_{70} - {}_{10}p_{\overline{60:70}};\ \text{or}$$

$${}_{10}q_{60:70} = 1 - {}_{10}p_{60:70} = {}_{10}q_{60} + {}_{10}q_{70} - {}_{10}q_{\overline{60:70}}.$$

16.

$$\begin{aligned}\overline{a}_{\overline{60:\overline{20|}}} &= \overline{a}_{60} + \overline{a}_{\overline{20|}} - \overline{a}_{60:\overline{20|}} = {}_{20|}\overline{a}_{60} + \overline{a}_{\overline{20|}} \\ &= \int_{t=20}^{40} e^{-.05t} \cdot {}_tp_{60}\,dt + \overline{a}_{\overline{20|}} \\ &= \int_{20}^{40} e^{-.05t} \cdot \frac{40-t}{40}\,dt + \overline{a}_{\overline{20|}} \\ &= \int_{20}^{40} e^{-.05t}\,dt - \frac{1}{40}\int_{20}^{40} te^{-.05t}\,dt + \int_0^{20} e^{-.05t}\,dt \\ &= \overline{a}_{\overline{40|}} - \frac{1}{40}\int_{20}^{40} te^{-.05t}\,dt = 17.29 - 3.30 = 13.99.\end{aligned}$$

ANSWER D.

17 - 19.
The expression ${}_tp_{xy}\mu_{xy}(t)$ is the density function. In general the density function is the negative derivative of the survival function,

$S(t) = {}_tp_{xy} = {}_tp_x \cdot {}_tp_y \ = \ (1-t^2q_x)(1-t^2q_y) \ = \ 1-t^2(q_x+q_y)+t^4q_xq_y$ and the force is given by

the ratio of the density function to the survival function:

Therefore, $f(t) \ = \ {}_tp_{xy}\mu_{xy}(t) \ = \ -S'(t) \ = \ 2t(q_x+q_y)-4t^3q_xq_y \ = \ .168t-.00128t^3$,

$$\mu_{xy}(t) \ = \ \frac{f(t)}{S(t)} \ = \ \frac{.168t-.00128t^3}{1-.084t^2+.00032t^4}$$

Plugging in $t=\frac{1}{2}$ gives $f\left(\frac{1}{2}\right) \ = \ .0838$, $\mu_{xy}\left(\frac{1}{2}\right) \ = \ .0856$.

Question 17 has ANSWER C and Question 18 has ANSWER A.

For the single life (y) the density ${}_tp_y\mu_y(t)$ is the negative derivative of the survival function:

$${}_tp_y\mu_y(t) \ = \ -\frac{d}{dt}({}_tp_y) \ = \ 2tq_y \ = \ .008t,$$

Question 19 has ANSWER E.

20 - 22.
The idea is to imitate the current payment formula $\bar{a}_x = \int_{t=0}^{\omega-x} v^t \cdot {}_tp_x\, dt$ for a single life annuity. The analogous result here is $\bar{a}_{xy} = \int_{t=0}^{\infty} v^t \cdot {}_tp_{xy}\, dt$. Substituting $v^t = e^{-\delta t} = e^{-.05t}$ and

$${}_tp_{xy} = \frac{1}{2}(e^{-\mu t})+\frac{1}{2}(e^{-\mu t}\cdot e^{-\mu t}) = .5e^{-.10t}+.5e^{-.20t}$$

into the preceding results in

$$\bar{a}_{xy} = \int_0^\infty e^{-.05t}[.5e^{-.10t}+.5e^{-.20t}]dt = (.5)\frac{1}{.15}+(.5)\frac{1}{.25} = \frac{16}{3}.$$

Question 20 has ANSWER C.

From $\bar{A}_{xy}+\delta\bar{a}_{xy}=1$ it follows quickly that $\bar{A}_{xy}=\frac{11}{15}$.

Question 21 has ANSWER C.

From $\bar{A}_x = \bar{A}_y = \dfrac{\mu}{\mu+\delta} \ = \ \dfrac{.10}{.15}$ and the relation

$$\bar{A}_{\overline{xy}} + \bar{A}_{xy} \ = \ \bar{A}_x + \bar{A}_y$$

it follows that $\bar{A}_{\overline{xy}} = \frac{2}{3}+\frac{2}{3}-\frac{11}{15} = \frac{9}{15}$.

Question 22 has ANSWER B.

23 - 26.
From the independence of lives and the assumption of constant forces we have ${}_{10}q_{\overline{30:50}} = {}_{10}q_{30} \cdot {}_{10}q_{50} = (1 - {}_{10}p_{30})(1 - {}_{10}p_{50}) = (1 - e^{-10(.05)})^2 = .1548.$

Question 23 has ANSWER A.

For independent lives $\mu_{xy}(t) = \mu(x+t) + \mu(y+t)$. Here, with constant forces $\mu_{xy}(t) = \mu + \mu = .10$. Thus $T(x,y)$ has an exponential distribution with parameter $2\mu = .10$, and $\overset{\circ}{e}_{xy} = E[T(x,y)] = \frac{1}{.10} = 10$. Furthermore

$$\overset{\circ}{e}_{\overline{xy}} + \overset{\circ}{e}_{xy} = \overset{\circ}{e}_x + \overset{\circ}{e}_y = \frac{1}{.05} + \frac{1}{.05},$$

so $\overset{\circ}{e}_{\overline{xy}} = 40 - 10 = 30$.

Question 24 has ANSWER C.

From the discussion above, $Var(T(x,y)) = \frac{1}{(.10)^2} = 100$ since $T(x,y)$ follows an exponential distribution.

Question 25 has ANSWER B.

Since $\{T(x,y), T(\overline{x,y})\} = \{T(x), T(y)\}$ it follows that $T(x,y) \cdot T(\overline{x,y}) = T(x) \cdot T(y)$. Thus

$$\begin{aligned} Cov(T(x,y), T(\overline{x,y})) &= E[T(x,y) \cdot T(\overline{x,y})] - E[T(x,y)]E[T(\overline{x,y})] \\ &= E[T(x) \cdot T(y)] - E[T(x,y)]E[T(\overline{x,y})] \\ &= \underbrace{E[T(x)] \cdot E[T(y)]}_{\text{independent of } T(x),\, T(y)} - E[T(x,y)]E[T(\overline{x,y})] \\ &= \left(\tfrac{1}{.05}\right)\left(\tfrac{1}{.05}\right) - (10)\underbrace{(30)}_{\text{Question 24}} = 100 \end{aligned}$$

Question 26 has ANSWER D.

27 - 29.
The joint distribution of $T(x)$, $T(y)$ is calculated as

$$\begin{aligned} F_{T(x),\,T(y)}(t_1,t_2) &= \int_0^{t_1}\int_0^{t_2} \frac{4}{(1+s+2t)^3}\,dt\,ds = \int_0^{t_1}\left[\frac{-1}{(1+s+2t)^2}\right]_{t=0}^{t_2} ds \\ &= \int_0^{t_1}\left(\frac{1}{(1+s)^2} - \frac{1}{(1+s+2t_2)^2}\right)ds \\ &= \frac{-1}{1+s} + \frac{1}{1+s+2t_2}\Big|_{s=0}^{t_1} \\ &= \frac{-1}{1+t_1} + \frac{1}{1+t_1+2t_2} - (-1) - \frac{1}{1+2t_2} \\ &= 1 - \left[\frac{1}{1+t_1} + \frac{1}{1+2t_2}\right] + \frac{1}{1+t_1+2t_2}. \end{aligned}$$

Hence $F_{T(x),\,T(y)}(1,2) = 1 - \left[\frac{1}{2}+\frac{1}{5}\right] + \frac{1}{6} = \frac{14}{30}$.

Question 27 has ANSWER B.

Similarly

$$s_{T(x),\,T(y)}(t_1,t_2) = \int_{t_1}^{\infty}\int_{t_2}^{\infty} \frac{4}{(1+s+2t)^3}\,dt\,ds$$

$$= \int_{t_1}^{\infty}\left[\frac{-1}{(1+s+2t)^2}\right]_{t=t_2}^{\infty} ds$$

$$= \int_{t_1}^{\infty} \frac{1}{(1+s+2t_2)^2}\,ds$$

$$= \frac{-1}{1+s+2t_2}\Big|_{t_1}^{\infty}$$

$$= \frac{1}{1+t_1+2t_2}$$

So $s_{T(x),\,T(y)}(1,2) = \frac{1}{6}$.

Question 28 has ANSWER A.

In general ${}_tp_x = 1 - {}_tq_x = 1 - F_{T(x),\,T(y)}(t,\infty) = 1 - \left[1 - \left(\frac{1}{1+t} + \frac{1}{\infty}\right) + \frac{1}{\infty}\right] = \frac{1}{1+t}$.

Question 29 has ANSWER D.

Note: One could also use ${}_tp_x = s_{T(x),\,T(y)}(t,0) = \frac{1}{1+t+0}$ to accomplish the same result.

In general ${}_tq_{xy} = 1 - {}_tp_{xy} = 1 - s_{T(x),\,T(y)}(t,t) = 1 - \left[\frac{1}{1+t+2t}\right] = \frac{3t}{1+3t}$.

Question 30 has ANSWER E.

31 - 34.
In the common shock model ${}_tp_{xy} = s_{T^*(x)}(t)s_{T^*(y)}(t)e^{-\lambda t} = e^{-.10t}e^{-.10t}e^{-.05t} = e^{-.25t}$. Similarly ${}_tp_x = s_{T^*(x)}(t)e^{-\lambda t} = e^{-.15t}$ and ${}_tp_y = e^{-.15t}$. Thus ${}_tp_{\overline{xy}} = {}_tp_x + {}_tp_y - {}_tp_{xy} = 2e^{-.15t} - e^{-.25t}$; ${}_{10}p_{\overline{xy}} = .364$.

Question 31 has ANSWER E.

$T(x)$ and $T(y)$ are exponentially distributed with parameter $.10 + .05$, and $T(x,y)$ is exponentially distributed with parameter $.10 + .10 + .05$. Thus $\mathring{e}_{\overline{xy}} = \mathring{e}_x + \mathring{e}_y - \mathring{e}_{xy} = \frac{1}{.15} + \frac{1}{.15} - \frac{1}{.25} = \frac{28}{3}$.

Question 32 has ANSWER A.

Since $T(x, y)$ is exponential with parameter .25 it follows that $\overline{A}_{xy} = \frac{.25}{.25 + \delta} = \frac{25}{33}$.

Question 33 has ANSWER E.

From (iv) of Example 7 (see Unit introductory reading) the probability is $\frac{\lambda}{\mu_1 + \mu_2 + \lambda}$ if $T^*(x)$ and $T^*(y)$ are exponentially distributed with parameters μ_1, and μ_2. Here $\frac{\lambda}{\mu_1 + \mu_2 + \lambda} = \frac{.05}{.25} = \frac{1}{5}$.

Question 34 has ANSWER B.

UNIT 6: MULTIPLE-DECREMENT (COMPETING RISK) MODELS

Introduction

In Units 1 - 4 we developed a survival model for a life subject to a single contingent event - death. We begin the discussion here with a life subject to multiple contingencies (decrements) that might remove it from a group. It is certain that the life will eventually depart the group so there is competition among the causes (decrements) to "claim" each life. For example, consider a group of insured lives. They might depart this group by either dying while the policy is in force or by surrendering the policy for a cash value prior to death. Members of a pension plan (employee benefit plan) might depart the group by death, disability, retirement or withdrawal (i.e., downsized, laid off, etc.). This model will be developed in a manner analogous to the single decrement (survival) models of Units 1 - 4, employing similar techniques and notation. Eventually these ideas will be extended to stochastic process models where an entity in a current state may eventually make a transition to a number of other possible states.

Tabular Multiple-Decrement Models

A quick introduction to the basic ideas can be achieved through a tabular (discrete) model analogous to the life tables of Section 1 of this manual. Below is a portion of a table illustrating death and surrender as two modes of departure (decrement) from a group of insured lives aged 25 at issue.

Age	Number Active	Deaths	Surrenders	Total
x	$\ell_x^{(\tau)}$	$d_x^{(1)}$	$d_x^{(2)}$	$d_x^{(\tau)} = d_x^{(1)} + d_x^{(2)}$
25	1000	10	50	60
26	940	12	40	52
27	888	14	30	44

The symbol $\ell_x^{(\tau)}$ denotes the number in the group at age (x), and $d_x^{(i)}$ is the number of members of this group departing by cause (i) in the age interval $[x, x+1)$. Just as in the earlier tabular survival models ratios of various table values can be interpreted as probabilities:

$$q_{25}^{(1)} = Pr((25) \text{ departs in next year by cause } (1)) = \frac{d_{25}^{(1)}}{\ell_{25}^{(\tau)}} = \frac{10}{1000}$$

$$q_{25}^{(2)} = Pr((25) \text{ departs in next year by cause } (2)) = \frac{d_{25}^{(2)}}{\ell_{25}^{(\tau)}} = \frac{50}{1000}$$

$$q_{25}^{(\tau)} = Pr((25) \text{ departs in the next year}) = \frac{d_{25}^{(\tau)}}{\ell_{25}^{(\tau)}} = \frac{60}{1000} = q_{25}^{(1)} + q_{25}^{(2)}$$

$$p_{25}^{(\tau)} = Pr((25) \text{ remains active at least one year}) = \frac{\ell_{26}^{(\tau)}}{\ell_{25}^{(\tau)}} = \frac{940}{1000} = 1 - q_{25}^{(\tau)}$$

$${}_{1|}q_{25}^{(1)} = Pr((25) \text{ departs in age interval } (26,27) \text{ by cause } (1)) = \frac{d_{26}^{(1)}}{\ell_{25}^{(\tau)}} = \frac{12}{1000} = p_{25}^{(\tau)} \cdot q_{26}^{(1)}$$

In this model there are two discrete random variables of interest.

(i) $K = K(25)$, the curtate time until decrement (i.e., (25) departs in the time interval $[K, K+1)$); and

(ii) J, the mode of decrement (e.g., $J = 1$ if (25) eventually departs by death while the policy is in force)

The joint and marginal densities of K and J are basically sitting in the $d_x^{(1)}$, $d_x^{(2)}$ columns as frequencies rather than relative frequencies (i.e., probabilities). Notice that

$$f_{K,J}(k,j) = Pr(K = k \text{ and } J = j) = Pr((25) \text{ departs in } [K, K+1) \text{ by cause } j) = \frac{d_{25+k}^{(j)}}{\ell_{25}^{(\tau)}}.$$

In other words, dividing the $d_x^{(1)}$, $d_x^{(2)}$ columns by $\ell_{25}^{(\tau)}$ will result in the joint density. Summing across the rows will produce the K-marginal density, that is,

$$f_K(k) = \sum_j f_{K,J}(k,j) = \frac{d_{25+k}^{(1)} + d_{25+k}^{(2)}}{\ell_{25}^{(\tau)}} = \frac{d_{25+k}^{(\tau)}}{\ell_{25}^{(\tau)}}.$$

Summing down the columns leads to the J-marginal density:

$$f_J(j) = Pr((25) \text{ eventually leaves by cause } (j)) = \sum_{k=0}^{\infty} f_{K,J}(k,j) = \sum_{k=0}^{\infty} \frac{d_{25+k}^{(j)}}{\ell_{25}^{(\tau)}} = \frac{\overbrace{\sum_{k=0}^{\infty} d_{25+k}^{(j)}}^{\text{Total of } d_x^{(j)} \text{ column}}}{\ell_{25}^{(\tau)}}$$

K is a discrete survival model with distribution function ${}_{k+1}q_x^{(\tau)} = Pr(K \leq k)$ and survival function ${}_{k+1}p_x^{(\tau)} = Pr(K > k)$.

Ideas discussed in the insured lives example above can be easily extended to tabular models including more than two modes of decrement. Dealing with a continuous waiting time until decrement, however, is a more delicate matter and leads to the idea of associated single decrement models. This comes next. A brief glimpse of the ideas can be obtained by considering the data across the first row of the insured lives example above: $\ell_{25}^{(\tau)} = 1000$, $d_{25}^{(1)} = 10$, and $d_{25}^{(2)} = 50$. There is a subtle difference between $q_{25}^{(1)} = \frac{10}{1000}$ and our old friend q_{25}, the probability that (25) dies in the next year. Technically, $q_{25}^{(1)}$ is the probability (25) dies in the next year *while the policy is in force*. In general $q_{25}^{(1)}$ is smaller than q_{25} since some of the $d_{25}^{(2)} = 50$ lapses between ages 25 and 26 might die after lapsing and before age 26! They would be counted in the q_{25} calculation. Thus death gets cheated in the $q_{25}^{(1)}$ calculation due to the competition with cause (2). The idea of an associated single decrement model is to study a particular decrement with the competing effect of the other decrements removed.

Continuous Multiple Decrement Models and the Associated Single Decrement Models

A life age x is assumed to be a member of some group from which there are n possible modes of departure (decrement). We would like to describe the joint distribution of T, the (continuous) time until decrement, and J, a numerical code for the mode of decrement. The starting point is a list of n independent, continuous, waiting time variables $T_1, T_2, \ldots, T_n$. T_i is the waiting time until decrement (i) (event i) claims the life (x). The occurrence of these events is independent of one another. Then T and J are described by

$$T = min\{T_i\}$$

$$J = j \text{ if } T = T_j.$$

With independent continuous random variables the probability of a tie such as $T_1 = T_2$ is zero, so J is well defined (we simply pretend ties don't occur). A multiple decrement model concerns the joint distribution of T and J, whereas an associated single decrement model concerns the distribution of one of the T_i. Each survival model can be specified by a hazard rate (force of decrement) which we denote here by $h_i(t)$ or $\mu^{(i)}(x+t)$.

Next we will introduce the standard notation and relations for the associated single decrement model, followed by the analogous ideas for the multiple decrement model and the relations between the two.

The Associated Single-Decrement Models

T_i = time until decrement (i) claims life (x) (no interference of other causes)

$h_i(t) = \mu^{(i)}(x+t)$ = hazard rate notation

${}_tp_x'^{(i)} = s_{T_i}(t) = exp\left(-\int_0^t \mu^{(i)}(x+s)\,ds\right)$ = survival function

${}_tq_x'^{(i)} = F_{T_i}(t) = Pr(T_i \leq t) = 1 - {}_tp_x'^{(i)}$

$= Pr((x)$ claimed by decrement (i) in next t years where no other decrements are present$)$ = distribution function

${}_tp_x^{\prime(i)}\,\mu^{(i)}(x+t) = f_{T_i}(t) =$ probability density function

Note: The $(\ )^{\prime(i)}$ notation is used to indicate that only decrement (i) is operating on the life (x)

$${}_tq_x^{\prime(i)} = Pr(T_i \le t) = \int_0^t f_{T_i}(s)\,ds = \int_0^t {}_sp_x^{\prime(i)}\mu^{(i)}(x+s)\,ds$$

The Multiple Decrement Model

$$T = min\{T_i\} = \text{time until decrement}$$

$$J = j = \text{mode of decrement if } T = T_j$$

T-distribution

Survival function: $\quad {}_tp_x^{(\tau)} = Pr(T > t) = Pr(\text{all } T_i > t)$

$$= \underbrace{\prod_i Pr(T_i > t)}_{\text{(independence of } \{T_i\})} = {}_tp_x^{\prime(1)} \cdots {}_tp_x^{\prime(n)}$$

Hazard rate: $\quad \mu^{(\tau)}(x+t) = -ln({}_tp_x^{(\tau)})' = \sum_{i=1}^{n} -ln({}_tp_x^{\prime(i)})' = \sum_{i=1}^{n} \mu^{(i)}(x+t)$

Distribution function: $\quad {}_tq_x^{(\tau)} = Pr(T \le t) = 1 - {}_tp_x^{\tau}$

$$= Pr((x) \text{ is decremented within } T \text{ years})$$

Density function: $\quad f_T(t) = {}_tp_x^{(\tau)}\mu^{(\tau)}(x+t)$

Joint Distribution of T, J

Joint density: $f_{T,J}(t, j) = {}_tp_x^{\tau} \cdot \mu^{(j)}(x+t)$

Note: $f_{T,J}(t, j) \approx Pr((x)$ departs by cause j during the time interval $[t, t+dt])$

$$= \underbrace{{}_tp_x^{\tau}}_{\substack{\text{probability } (x) \\ \text{survives all causes} \\ \text{for } t \text{ years}}} \cdot \underbrace{\mu^{(j)}(x+t)\,dt}_{\substack{\text{probability } (x+t) \\ \text{departs in next instant} \\ \text{due to cause } j}}$$

$${}_tq_x^{(j)} = Pr(T \le t \text{ and } J = j) = \int_0^t f_{T,J}(s, j)\,ds$$

$$= \int_0^t {}_sp_x^{(\tau)}\mu^{(j)}(x+t)\,dt = Pr((x) \text{ departs by cause } j \text{ within } t \text{ years})$$

Note: (1) $\quad {}_tq_x^{(\tau)} = \sum_{i=1}^{n} {}_tq_x^{(j)}$

(2) In the ${}_tq_x^{(j)}$ calculation there is competition with the other causes. In general, ${}_tp_x^{\tau} = \prod_i {}_tp_x^{\prime(i)} < {}_tp_x^{\prime(j)}$ so that

$${}_tq_x^{(j)} = \int_0^t {}_sp_x^{(\tau)} \cdot \mu^{(j)}(x+s)\,ds \le \int_0^t {}_sp_x^{\prime(j)} \cdot \mu^{(j)}(x+s)\,ds = {}_tq_x^{\prime(j)}$$

(i.e., competition with other causes diminishes the unfettered effect of decrement (j).)

J-Distribution

Density: $f_J(j) = Pr(J = j) = Pr((x)$ decremented by cause $j)$

$$= \int_{t=0}^{\infty} f_{T,J}(t, j)\,dt = \int_{t=0}^{\infty} {}_tp_x^{(\tau)} \cdot \mu^{(j)}(x+t)dt = {}_\infty q_x^{(j)}$$

One relation we have seen on the previous page is the important idea that ${}_tq_x^{(i)} < {}_tq_x'^{(i)}$ due to the competition of causes in the multiple decrement context. One other general relation always holding between these quantities is the following:

$$1 - \sum_{i=1}^{n} {}_tq_x^{(i)} = 1 - {}_tq_x^{\tau} = {}_tp_x^{\tau} = \prod_i {}_tp_x'^{(i)} = (1 - {}_tq_x'^{(1)})\cdots(1 - {}_tq_x'^{(n)})$$

$$\Rightarrow \begin{cases} {}_tq_x^{(1)} + {}_tq_x^{(2)} = {}_tq_x'^{(1)} + {}_tq_x'^{(2)} - ({}_tq_x'^{(1)} \cdot {}_tq_x'^{(2)}) & \text{2 decrements} \\ {}_tq_x^{(1)} + {}_tq_x^{(2)} + {}_tq_x^{(3)} = {}_tq_x'^{(1)} + {}_tq_x'^{(2)} + {}_tq_x'^{(3)} & \text{3 decrements} \\ \quad - ({}_tq_x'^{(1)} \cdot {}_tq_x'^{(2)} + {}_tq_x'^{(1)} \cdot {}_tq_x'^{(3)} + {}_tq_x'^{(2)} \cdot {}_tq_x'^{(3)}) & \\ \quad + {}_tq_x'^{(1)} \cdot {}_tq_x'^{(2)} \cdot {}_tq_x'^{(3)} & \end{cases}$$

As usual, when $t = 1$ symbols such as ${}_1q_x^{(i)}$, ${}_1q_x'^{(i)}$, ${}_1p_x'^{(i)}$, etc. are shortened to $q_x^{(i)}$, $q_x'^{(i)}$, $p_x'^{(i)}$, etc.

Example 1 Suppose decrement (1) has hazard rate $h_1(t) = \mu^{(1)}(x+t) = \frac{1}{40-t}$ for $0 \le t < 40$ and decrement (2) has hazard rate $h_2(t) = \mu^{(2)}(x+t) = \frac{1}{60-t}$ for $0 \le t < 60$. View T_1 as the time until death of (x) and T_2 as the time until (x) will lapse an insurance contract. Assume T_1, T_2 are independent waiting time models. Calculate the following

(i) ${}_tp_x'^{(i)}, {}_tq_x'^{(i)}$ for $i = 1, 2$

(ii) ${}_tp_x^{(\tau)}$, $f_{T,J}(t, j)$, ${}_tq_x^{(j)}$ for $j = 1, 2$

(iii) $f_J(j)$

Solution

(i) We saw earlier that $\mu(x) = \frac{p'(x)}{p(x)}c$ results in

$${}_xp_0 = s(x) = exp\left(-\int_0^x \frac{p'(y)}{p(y)}c\,dy\right) = exp\left(-ln\,(p(y))\Big|_0^x \cdot c\right) = exp\left(ln\left(\frac{p(0)}{p(x)}\right)c\right) = \left[\frac{p(0)}{p(x)}\right]^c.$$

This same shortcut here with $\mu^{(1)}(x+t) = \frac{1}{40-t}$ and $\mu^{(2)}(x+t) = \frac{1}{60-t}$ results in ${}_tp_x'^{(1)} = s_{T_1}(t) = \left(\frac{40}{40-t}\right)^{-1} = \left(1 - \frac{t}{40}\right)$ for $0 \le t \le 40$ and ${}_tp_x'^{(2)} = s_{T_2}(t) = \left(1 - \frac{t}{60}\right)$ for $0 \le t \le 60$. Hence

$${}_tq_x'^{(1)} = 1 - {}_tp_x'^{(1)} = \frac{t}{40} \qquad 0 \le t \le 40$$

and

$${}_tq_x'^{(2)} = 1 - {}_tp_x'^{(2)} = \frac{t}{60} \qquad 0 \le t \le 60$$

One could also calculate ${}_tq_x'^{(1)}$ as

$\int_0^t {}_sp_x'^{(1)}\mu^{(1)}(x+s)\,ds = \int_0^t \left(1 - \frac{s}{40}\right)\left(\frac{1}{40-s}\right)ds = \int_0^t \frac{1}{40}ds = \frac{t}{40}$. Notice that the ${}_tq_x'^{(i)}$ are distribution functions of the T_i. Differentiating one sees that T_1 is uniformly distributed on [0, 40] while T_2 is uniformly distributed on [0, 60].

(ii) ${}_tp_x^{(\tau)}$ can be constructed by either ${}_tp_x'^{(1)} \cdot {}_tp_x'^{(2)}$ or via $exp\left(-\int_0^t \mu^{(\tau)}(x+s)ds\right)$:

$$ {}_tp_x^{(\tau)} = \left(\frac{40-t}{40}\right)\left(\frac{60-t}{60}\right) \quad 0 \le t \le 40 $$

Notice that ${}_tp_x'^{(1)} = 0$ for $t > 40$ so ${}_tp_x^{(\tau)}$ must also be zero for $t > 40$. Hence

$$ f_{T,J}(t,j) = {}_tp_x^{(\tau)} \cdot \mu^{(j)}(x+t) = \begin{cases} \dfrac{60-t}{(40)(60)} & 0 \le t \le 40, j=1 \\ \dfrac{40-t}{(40)(60)} & 0 \le t \le 40, j=2 \end{cases} $$

Finally, for $0 \le t \le 40$

$$ {}_tq_x^{(1)} = \int_0^t \frac{60-s}{(40)(60)}ds = \frac{60t - \frac{t^2}{2}}{(40)(60)} = \underbrace{\left(\frac{t}{40}\right)}_{{}_tq_x'^{(1)}}\underbrace{\left(1-\frac{t}{120}\right)}_{\text{factor}<1} $$

and

$$ {}_tq_x^{(2)} = \int_0^t \frac{40-s}{(40)(60)}ds = \frac{40t - \frac{t^2}{2}}{(40)(60)} = \underbrace{\left(\frac{t}{60}\right)}_{{}_tq_x'^{(2)}}\underbrace{\left(1-\frac{t}{80}\right)}_{\text{factor}<1}. $$

From the above one sees ${}_tq_x^{(i)} < {}_tq_x'^{(i)}$, and ${}_tq_x^{(1)} = {}_tq_x'^{(1)}\left(1-\frac{1}{2}\,{}_tq_x'^{(2)}\right)$, ${}_tq_x^{(2)} = {}_tq_x'^{(2)}\left(1-\frac{1}{2}\,{}_tq_x'^{(1)}\right)$ is consistent with ${}_tq_x^{(1)} + {}_tq_x^{(2)} = {}_tq_x'^{(1)} + {}_tq_x'^{(2)} - {}_tq_x'^{(1)} \cdot {}_tq_x'^{(2)}$ as promised by the general theory.

(iii) Now $f_J(1) = {}_\infty q_x^{(1)} = {}_{40}q_x^{(1)} = \frac{40}{40}\left(1-\frac{40}{120}\right) = \frac{2}{3}$ and
$f_J(2) = {}_\infty q_x^{(2)} = {}_{40}q_x^{(2)} = \frac{40}{60}\left(1-\frac{40}{80}\right) = \frac{2}{3}\cdot\frac{1}{2} = \frac{1}{3}$. □

One additional point of interest concerns the conditional distribution of J given $T = t$:

$$ f_J(j|T=t) = \frac{f_{T,J}(t,j)}{f_T(t)} = \frac{{}_tp_x^{(\tau)}\mu^{(j)}(x+t)}{{}_tp_x^{(\tau)}\mu^{(\tau)}(x+t)} = \frac{\mu^{(j)}(x+t)}{\mu^{(\tau)}(x+t)} = Pr(j \text{ is mode given } t \text{ is the time of decrement}). $$

In certain cases one sees no t's in this formula or domain. In these cases T and J are independent and $f_J(j|T=t) = f_J(j)$. For instance, in the following cases we see no t's in $\frac{\mu^{(j)}(x+t)}{\mu^{(\tau)}(x+t)}$:

(i) $\mu^{(i)}(x+t) = \mu^{(i)} \quad \Rightarrow \quad f_J(j|T=t) = \frac{\mu^{(j)}}{\mu^{(\tau)}}$

Constant forces mean that T_1, T_2 are independent and exponentially distributed. T is also exponentially distributed.

(ii) $\mu^{(i)}(x+t) = k_i t^n \quad \Rightarrow \quad f_J(j|T=t) = \dfrac{k_j}{\sum\limits_i k_i}$

All T_i are Weibull distributions with the same n.

(iii) $\mu^{(i)}(x+t) = \frac{r_i}{\omega - t} \quad \Rightarrow \quad f_J(j|T=t) = \dfrac{r_j}{\sum\limits_i r_i}$

One final comment is in order here. It should be noted that ${}_tp_x^{(\tau)} = {}_tp_x^{\prime(1)} \cdot {}_tp_x^{\prime(2)}$, $\mu^{(\tau)}(x+t) = \mu^{(1)}(x+t) + \mu^{(2)}(x+t)$ and $T = min\{T_1, T_2\}$ (with T_1, T_2 assumed independent) is exactly the same mathematically as the joint life status for independent lives (x), (y) (i.e., $T(x)$, $T(y)$ independent). Recall that

$$T(x,y) = min\{T(x), T(y)\}$$

$${}_tp_{xy} = {}_tp_x \cdot {}_tp_y$$

$$\mu_{xy}(t) = \mu(x+t) + \mu(y+t).$$

Tabular Multiple Decrement Models With Interpolation Assumptions

The typical problem here concerns a tabular multiple decrement model which allows the calculation of $q_x^{(i)}$ as $\frac{d_x^{(i)}}{\ell_x^{(\tau)}}$. The curtate time until decrement in this model is a discrete random variable. If we would like to compute the $q_x^{\prime(i)}$ or something like ${}_{1.5}q_x^{(i)}$ we need to extend the discrete model to a continuous one by some type of interpolation method. The three most common methods, discussed in this section are:

1. Constant forces over each year of age
   $\mu^{(i)}(x+t) = \mu_x^{(i)}$ for $0 \le t \le 1$, $x =$ whole age

2. Uniform distribution of decrement within each year of age in each single decrement model
   ${}_tq_x^{\prime(i)} = t \cdot q_x^{\prime(i)}$ (called SUDD here)

3. Uniform distribution of each decrement within each year of age in the multiple decrement table
   ${}_tq_x^{(i)} = t \cdot q_x^{(i)}$ (called MUDD here)

For each of these interpolation methods we want to determine relations between $\{q_x^{(i)}\}$ and $\{q_x'^{(i)}\}$ that would allow calculation of the $q_x'^{(i)}$ from $q_x^{(1)} = \frac{d_x^{(1)}}{\ell_x^{(\tau)}}, \ldots, q_x^{(n)} = \frac{d_x^{(n)}}{\ell_x^{(\tau)}}$ (i.e., determined from a multiple decrement table). Recall that there is always one relation between these quantities given by rearranging.

$$(1 - q_x'^{(1)}) \cdots (1 - q_x'^{(n)}) = p_x'^{(1)} \cdots p_x'^{(n)} = p_x^{(\tau)} = 1 - q_x^{(\tau)} = 1 - (q_x^{(1)} + \cdots + q_x^{(n)})$$

into

$$\sum_{i=1}^{n} q_x^{(i)} = 1 - \prod_{i=1}^{n} (1 - q_x'^{(i)})$$

(e.g., $n = 2 \quad \Rightarrow \quad q_x^{(1)} + q_x^{(2)} = q_x'^{(1)} + q_x'^{(2)} - q_x'^{(1)} \cdot q_x'^{(2)}$).

Before embarking on this mission it is worth pointing out the subtle difference between SUDD and MUDD, which, naively, sound like the same thing. Under the SUDD (in each single decrement assumption), with two decrements, we have for $0 \le t \le 1$

$$\begin{aligned} {}_tp_x^{(\tau)} = {}_tp_x'^{(1)} \cdot {}_tp_x'^{(2)} &= (1 - {}_tq_x'^{(1)})(1 - {}_tq_x'^{(2)}) \\ &= (1 - t \cdot q_x'^{(1)})(1 - t \cdot q_x'^{(2)}) && \text{(SUDD)} \\ &= 1 - t(q_x'^{(1)} + q_x'^{(2)}) + t^2(q_x'^{(1)} \cdot q_x'^{(2)}) && \text{(quadratic in } t\text{),} \end{aligned}$$

whereas with MUDD we have

$$\begin{aligned} {}_tp_x^{(\tau)} = 1 - {}_tq_x^{(\tau)} &= 1 - {}_tq_x^{(1)} - {}_tq_x^{(2)} \\ &= 1 - t \cdot q_x^{(1)} - t \cdot q_x^{(2)} && \text{(MUDD)} \\ &= 1 - t(q_x^{(1)} + q_x^{(2)}) && \text{(linear in } t\text{)} \end{aligned}$$

Constant Forces

We assume here that $\mu^{(i)}(x+t) = \mu_x^{(i)}$ for all t between 0 and 1. This means ${}_tp_x'^{(i)} = e^{-\mu_x^{(i)} \cdot t}$ and ${}_tp_x^{(\tau)} = e^{-\mu_x^{(\tau)} \cdot t}$ where $\mu_x^{(\tau)} = \sum_i \mu_x^{(i)}$. Thus

$$q_x^{(i)} = \int_0^1 {}_tp_x^{(\tau)} \mu^{(i)}(x+t)\, dt = \int_0^1 e^{-\mu_x^{(\tau)} \cdot t} \cdot \mu_x^{(i)}\, dt = \frac{1 - e^{-\mu_x^{(\tau)}}}{\mu_x^{(\tau)}} \cdot \mu_x^{(i)} = \frac{\mu_x^{(i)}}{\mu_x^{(\tau)}} \cdot q_x^{(\tau)},$$

or, equivalently

$$\mu_x^{(i)} = \frac{q_x^{(i)}}{q_x^{(\tau)}} \cdot \mu_x^{(\tau)}.$$

In turn, this means

$$q_x^{\prime(i)} = 1 - p_x^{\prime(i)} = 1 - e^{-\mu_x^{(i)}} = 1 - exp\left(-\mu_x^{(\tau)} \cdot \frac{q_x^{(i)}}{q_x^{(\tau)}}\right) = 1 - \left[p_x^{(\tau)}\right]^{(q_x^{(i)}/q_x^{(\tau)})}$$

Example 2

Suppose $n = 2$, $q_x^{(1)} = .02$ and $q_x^{(2)} = .05$. Calculate $q_x^{\prime(1)}$ and $q_x^{\prime(2)}$ assuming constant forces over each year of age.

Solution

$q_x^{(\tau)} = .02 + .05 = .07$, $p_x^{(\tau)} = .93$, hence

$$q_x^{\prime(1)} = 1 - (.93)^{2/7} = .020521$$

and

$$q_x^{\prime(2)} = 1 - (.93)^{5/7} = .050516.$$

SUDD (in each single decrement table)

Here we assume ${}_tq_x^{\prime(i)} = t \cdot q_x^{\prime(i)}$ (distribution function) so ${}_tp_x^{\prime(i)}\mu^{(i)}(x+t) = density$ $function = \frac{d}{dt}(t \cdot q_x^{\prime(i)}) = q_x^{\prime(i)}$. Thus

$$\begin{aligned} q_x^{(i)} &= \int_0^1 {}_tp_x^{(\tau)}\mu^{(i)}(x+t)\,dt = \int_0^1 (\prod_{j\neq i}(1 - {}_tp_x^{\prime(j)})({}_tp_x^{\prime(i)}\mu^{(i)}(x+t))\,dt \\ &= \int_0^1 (\prod_{j\neq i}(1 - t \cdot q_x^{\prime(j)}))q_x^{\prime(i)}\,dt \\ &= q_x^{\prime(i)} \cdot \int_0^1 \underbrace{\prod_{j\neq i}(1 - t \cdot q_x^{\prime(j)})}_{\text{polynomial of degree } n-1}\ dt \end{aligned}$$

Evaluation with $n = 2$ produces

$$q_x^{(i)} = q_x^{\prime(i)}[1 - \tfrac{1}{2}q_x^{\prime(j)}] \qquad \{i, j\} = \{1, 2\},$$

or with $n = 3$

$$q_x^{(i)} = q_x^{\prime(i)}\left[1 - \frac{1}{2}\left(q_x^{\prime(j)} + q_x^{\prime(k)}\right) + \frac{1}{3}\left(q_x^{\prime(j)} \cdot q_x^{\prime(k)}\right)\right] \qquad \{i, j, k\} = \{1, 2, 3\}.$$

Example 3 Suppose $n = 2$, $q_x^{(1)} = .02$ and $q_x^{(2)} = .05$. Calculate $q_x'^{(1)}$ and $q_x'^{(2)}$ assuming UDD over each year of age in the single decrement models.

Solution From the above we need to solve the system

$$.02 = q_x^{(1)} = q_x'^{(1)}\left[1 - \tfrac{1}{2}q_x'^{(2)}\right]$$

$$.05 = q_x^{(2)} = q_x'^{(2)}\left[1 - \tfrac{1}{2}q_x'^{(1)}\right]$$

for the $q_x'^{(i)}$. The typical method to obtain an exact answer is to solve the 2nd equation for $q_x'^{(2)}$, substitute it in the first, and then clear denominators to obtain a quadratic:

$a = q_x'^{(1)}, b = q_x'^{(2)}$

$$.05 = b\left[1 - \frac{1}{2}a\right] \quad \Rightarrow \quad b = \frac{.05}{1 - \frac{1}{2}a}$$

$$\Rightarrow \quad .02 = a\left[1 - \frac{1}{2}b\right] = a\left[1 - \frac{.05}{2-a}\right]$$

$$\Rightarrow \quad 0 = .04 - 1.97a + a^2 \quad \Rightarrow \quad a = 1.95 \text{ or } .020518$$

$$\Rightarrow \quad a = q_x'^{(1)} = .020518 \quad \text{(other solution } > 1 \text{ is impossible!)}$$

Note: Compare this with $q_x'^{(1)}$ in Example 2 using a constant force assumption.

An approximate answer is readily obtained from the Famous School Criss Cross Iteration Method illustrated below:

$$q_x'^{(1)} = \frac{.02}{1 - \frac{1}{2} \cdot q_x'^{(2)}}$$

$$q_x'^{(2)} = \frac{.05}{1 - \frac{1}{2} \cdot q_x'^{(1)}}$$

A first guess $q_x^{\prime(2)} = .05$ is substituted into the first equation giving a first guess at $q_x^{\prime(1)}$. This is substituted into the 2nd equation to get a new guess at $q_x^{\prime(2)}$, which is then substituted back into the first and so on. The successive approximations to $q_x^{\prime(1)}$ obtained this way (to six decimal places) are

$$.020513, .020518, .020518, \ldots.$$

The iteration rapidly converges to the same result above obtained by an exact solution of a quadratic equation.

MUDD

Here we assume ${}_tq_x^{(i)} = t \cdot q_x^{(i)}$ for each decrement, (x) integral and $0 \le t \le 1$. Thus $t \cdot q_x^{(i)} = {}_tq_x^{(i)} = \int_0^t {}_sp_x^{(\tau)} \cdot \mu^{(i)}(x+s)\,ds$. Differentiating both sides of this equation with respect to t and employing the second fundamental theorem of calculus (i.e., $\frac{d}{dt}\int_0^t f(s)\,ds = f(t)$) we obtain $q_x^{(i)} = {}_tp_x^{(\tau)}\mu^{(i)}(x+t)$. This in turn results in

$$\mu^{(i)}(x+t) = \frac{q_x^{(i)}}{{}_tp_x^{\tau}} = \frac{q_x^{(i)}}{1 - {}_tq_x^{(\tau)}} \overset{\text{(MUDD)}}{=} \frac{q_x^{(i)}}{1 - t \cdot q_x^{(\tau)}} = \frac{p'(t)}{p(t)} \cdot c,$$

where $p(t) = 1 - t \cdot q_x^{(\tau)}$ and $c = \frac{-q_x^{(i)}}{q_x^{(\tau)}}$. Thus ${}_tp_x^{\prime(i)} = \left[\frac{p(0)}{p(t)}\right]^c = \left[\frac{1}{1 - t \cdot q_x^{\tau}}\right]^{-q_x^{(i)}/q_x^{(\tau)}}$. Substituting $t = 1$ and rearranging slightly gives

$$1 - q_x^{\prime(i)} = p_x^{\prime(i)} = \left(p_x^{(\tau)}\right)^{q_x^{(i)}/q_x^{(\tau)}},$$

the exact same relation resulting from an interpolation assumption of constant forces over each year of age! This is truly unexpected.

Tabular Multiple Decrement Models With Discrete Decrement Patterns

In all of the preceding the T_i were assumed to be continuous random variables. In both the multiple decrement table and the associated single decrement table this results in the annual decrement amount being spread continuously over the year. Here we examine the case where one or more of the T_i are discrete. Suppose we have $q_x^{(1)} = .02$, $q_x^{(2)} = .05$ and decrement 1 is UDD in the single decrement model whereas 2/3 of the annual decrement (2) takes places at mid year and the other 1/3 at year end. How do we calculate $q_x'^{(1)}$ and $q_x'^{(2)}$?

We again need two equations in the $q_x'^{(i)}$. Note first that

$$ {}_tp_x'^{(2)} = 1 - {}_tq_x'^{(2)} = \begin{cases} 1 & 0 \le t < \frac{1}{2} \\ 1 - \frac{2}{3}q_x'^{(2)} & \frac{1}{2} \le t < 1 \\ 1 - q_x'^{(2)} & t = 1 \end{cases} $$

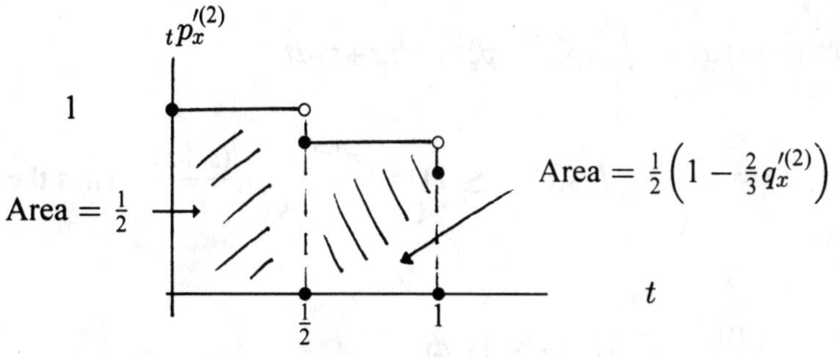

One equation is obtained from

$$ .02 = q_x^{(1)} = \int_0^1 {}_tp_x^{\tau}\mu^{(1)}(x+t)\,dt $$

$$ = \int_0^1 {}_tp_x'^{(2)} \cdot \underbrace{{}_tp_x'^{(1)}\mu^{(1)}(x+t)}_{q_x'^{(1)} \text{ by UDD}}\,dt $$

$$ = q_x'^{(1)} \int_0^1 {}_tp_x'^{(2)}\,dt $$

$$ = q_x'^{(1)}\left[\frac{1}{2} + \frac{1}{2}\left(1 - \frac{2}{3}q_x'^{(2)}\right)\right] \qquad \text{(figure)} $$

$$ = q_x'^{(1)}\left[1 - \frac{1}{3}q_x'^{(2)}\right] $$

We could use $.07 = q_x^{(\tau)} = q_x'^{(1)} + q_x'^{(2)} - q_x'^{(1)} \cdot q_x'^{(2)}$ as the other equation. This gives us a pair of expressions

$$ q_x'^{(1)} = \frac{.02}{1 - \frac{1}{3}q_x'^{(2)}} $$

and

$$ q_x'^{(2)} = \frac{.07 - q_x'^{(1)}}{1 - q_x'^{(1)}} $$

suitable for criss cross iteration:

$$
\begin{array}{llllll}
q_x'^{(1)}: & .020339 & .020344 & & .020344 & \\
 & \uparrow & \searrow \ \uparrow & \searrow & \uparrow & \searrow \\
q_x'^{(2)}: & .05 & .050692 & & .050687 & .050687.
\end{array}
$$

Another technique for obtaining the second equation is based on the idea that the conditional density of T_2 given $T_2 \leq 1$ is discrete with $f_{T_2}\left(\frac{1}{2}\,|\,T_2 \leq 1\right) = \frac{2}{3}$ and $f_{T_2}(1\,|\,T_2 \leq 1) = \frac{1}{3}$ (i.e., $\frac{2}{3}$ of the annual decrement for decrement 2 is at mid-year and the other $\frac{1}{3}$ is at year end). We need to take a new look at the standard relation

$$.05 = q_x^{(2)} = \int_0^1 {}_tp_x^{(\tau)}\mu^{(2)}(x+t)\,dt = \int_0^1 {}_tp_x'^{(1)} \cdot {}_tp_x'^{(2)}\mu^{(2)}(x+t)\,dt.$$

Now $f_{T2}(t) = {}_tp_x'^{(2)} \cdot \mu^{(2)}(x+t)$ and $Pr(T_2 \leq 1) = q_x'^{(2)}$, so $f_{T2}(t\,|\,T_2 \leq 1) = \dfrac{{}_tp_x'^{(2)} \cdot \mu^{(2)}(x+t)}{q_x'^{(2)}}$. Thus the equation displayed above can be rewritten as

$$.05 = q_x^{(2)} = q_x'^{(2)} \int_0^1 \underbrace{\underbrace{{}_tp_x'^{(1)}}_{\text{function of } t} \cdot \underbrace{f_{T2}(t\,|\,T_2 \leq 1)}_{\text{disc. density}}}_{\substack{\text{Expected value of } {}_tp_x'^{(1)} \text{ with} \\ \text{respect to a discrete density}}} dt$$

$$= q_x'^{(2)}\left[{}_{\frac{1}{2}}p_x'^{(1)} \cdot \underbrace{f_{T2}(\tfrac{1}{2}\,|\,T_2 \leq 1)}_{2/3} + {}_1p_x'^{(1)} \cdot \underbrace{f_{T2}(1\,|\,T_2 \leq 1)}_{1/3}\right]$$

$$= q_x'^{(2)}\left[(1-\tfrac{1}{2}q_x'^{(1)})\tfrac{2}{3} + (1-q_x'^{(1)})\tfrac{1}{3}\right]$$

$$= q_x'^{(2)}[1-\tfrac{2}{3}q_x'^{(1)}].$$

Note the consistency of the two equations

$$.02 = q_x'^{(1)}\left[1 - \tfrac{1}{3}q_x'^{(2)}\right]$$

and

$$.05 = q_x'^{(2)}\left[1-\tfrac{2}{3}q_x'^{(1)}\right]$$

we now have, in contrast to the first of the above and $.07 = q_x'^{(1)} + q_x'^{(2)} - q_x'^{(1)} \cdot q_x'^{(2)}$. The sum of the two equations above is exactly the latter.

In general we see that

$$q_x^{(i)} = \int_0^1 \Big(\prod_{j \neq i} {}_tp_x'^{(j)}\Big)({}_tp_x'^{(i)}\mu^{(i)}(x+t))\,dt = q_x'^{(i)} \int_0^1 \underbrace{\Big(\prod_{j \neq i} {}_tp_x'^{(j)}\Big) f_{T_i}(t|T_i \leq 1)\,dt}_{\substack{\text{Expected value of } \prod_{j\neq i} {}_tp_x'^{(j)} \text{ with respect} \\ \text{to the conditional distribution } T_i|_{T_i \leq 1}.}}$$

Central Rates of Decrement

The term central rate always refers to a weighted average of the force (hazard rate) over some period of time. For a force $\mu^{(i)}(x+t)$ the averaging can take place in either the multiple decrement or single decrement context:

$$ {}_n m_x^{(i)} = \frac{\int_0^n {}_t p_x^{(\tau)} \mu^{(i)}(x+t)\, dt}{\int_0^n {}_t p_x^{(\tau)} dt}, \quad {}_n m_x'^{(i)} = \frac{\int_0^n {}_t p_x'^{(i)} \mu^{(i)}(x+t)\, dt}{\int_0^n {}_t p_x'^{(i)} dt} $$

Note that $g(t) = \dfrac{{}_t p_x^{(\tau)}}{\int_0^n {}_t p_x^{(\tau)} dt}$ and $g^{(i)}(t) = \dfrac{{}_t p_x'^{(i)}}{\int_0^n {}_t p_x'^{(i)} dt}$ can be viewed as continuous densities on $[0, n]$ since $\int_0^n g(t)\, dt = 1 = \int_0^n g^{(i)}(t)\, dt$. The relations above can be rewritten as

$$ {}_n m_x^{(i)} = \frac{{}_n q_x^{(i)}}{\mathring{e}_{x:\overline{n}|}^{(\tau)}} \text{ and } {}_n m_x'^{(i)} = \frac{{}_n q_x'^{(i)}}{\mathring{e}_{x:\overline{n}|}^{(i)}} $$

where

$\mathring{e}_{x:\overline{n}|}^{(\tau)}$ = expected years in the next n years that (x) survives all causes

and

$\mathring{e}_{x:\overline{n}|}^{(i)}$ = expected years in the next n years that (x) survives cause (i).

Notice that if a force $\mu^{(i)}(x+t) = \mu_x^{(i)}$ is constant over an n year period, then ${}_n m_x^{(i)} = {}_n m_x'^{(i)} = \mu_x^{(i)}$.

If one has a tabular model with some convenient interpolation assumption, then the central rates are closely related to the $\{q_x^{(i)}\}$ and $\{q_x'^{(i)}\}$. For example, if the total decrement $d_x^{(\tau)}$ is spread uniformly and continuously over a year of age then ${}_t p_x^{(\tau)} = 1 - {}_t q_x^{\tau} = 1 - t \cdot q_x^{\tau}$, and

$$ m_x^{(i)} = \frac{q_x^{(i)}}{\int_0^1 {}_t p_x^{(\tau)}\, dt} = \frac{q_x^{(i)}}{\int_0^1 1 - t \cdot q_x^{\tau}\, dt} = \frac{q_x^{(i)}}{1 - \frac{1}{2} q_x^{\tau}}. $$

On the other hand if $d_x'^{(i)}$ is spread uniformly and continuously over the year of age in the single decrement model then ${}_t p_x'^{(i)} = 1 - {}_t q_x'^{(i)} = 1 - t \cdot q_x'^{(i)}$, and

$$ m_x'^{(i)} = \frac{q_x'^{(i)}}{\int_0^1 {}_t p_x'^{(i)}\, dt} = \frac{q_x'^{(i)}}{1 - \frac{1}{2} q_x'^{(i)}}. $$

Multiple Decrement Models In Stochastic Processes

In a stochastic process a person or entity is in some "state" and as time advances he may transfer to some other "state". Let T_i be the random time from the time he arrived in the current state until he transfers from the current state to a state (i). Assume the T_i are independent. Then $T = min\{T_i\}$ is the time until transfer and $J = j$ if $T = T_j$ is the mode of transfer. This is exactly the same set of assumptions used to introduce multiple decrement models above. These ideas will be explored in more detail in the section of this manual dealing with stochastic processes. In this context the hazard rate function, $h_i(t) = \dfrac{f_{T_i}(t)}{s_{T_i}(i)}$, is known as an intensity function or force of transition. Due to the independence of the T_i we have $h_T(t) = \sum_i h_i(t)$. Then $h_T(t)dt$ is approximately the probability that transfer occurs in the time interval $[t, t+dt]$ given that the entity is still in the current (i.e., the one at $t = 0$) state at time t. Also $s_T(t)h_i(t)dt = f_{T,J}(t, i)\,dt$ is approximately the probability that the entity remains in the current state until time t and then transfers to state (i) in the next instant.

CONDENSED REVIEW NOTES AND ADVANCED TOPICS

Tabular Multiple Decrement Models

$\ell_x^{(\tau)}$ = expected number in the group at age x (whole number)

$d_x^{(i)}$ = expected number departing in age interval $(x, x+1]$ by cause (i)

$q_x^{(i)} = \frac{d_x^{(i)}}{\ell_x^{(\tau)}} = Pr((x)$ departs in next year by cause (i) with competition from other causes$)$

$q_x^{(\tau)} = \sum_i q_x^{(i)} = Pr((x)$ departs in next year$)$

$p_x^{(\tau)} = \frac{\ell_{x+1}^{(\tau)}}{\ell_x^{(\tau)}} = 1 - q_x^{(\tau)} = Pr((x)$ remains in the group at age $x+1)$

${}_{k|}q_x^{(j)} = \frac{d_{x+k}^{(j)}}{\ell_x^{(\tau)}} = Pr((x)$ departs in the age interval $(x+k,\ x+k+1]$ by cause $j)$

K = curtate time until decrement of (x)

J = mode of decrement

Joint density: $$f_{K,\,J}(k, j) = Pr(K = k \text{ and } J = j) = {}_{k|}q_x^{(j)} = \frac{d_{x+k}^{(j)}}{\ell_x^{(\tau)}}$$

Marginal densities: $$\begin{cases} f_K(k) = Pr(K = k) = \dfrac{d_{x+k}^{(\tau)}}{\ell_x^{(\tau)}} \\ f_J(j) = \dfrac{\sum_k d_{x+k}^{(j)}}{\ell_x^{(\tau)}} \end{cases}$$

Continuous Multiple Decrement Models and the Associated Single Decrement Models

$T_1, \ldots T_n$ independent, continuous, waiting time variables

T_i = waiting time until decrement (i) claims the life (x) with no interference of other causes

$h_i(t) = \mu^{(i)}(x+t)$ = hazard rate $= \frac{-[s_{T_i}(t)]'}{s_{T_i}(t)}$

$T = min\{T_i\}$ = time until life (x) is decremented with all causes competing

$J = j$ if $T = T_j$ Note: The probability of ties among the T_j is zero.

The Single Decrement Models

Survival Function: $\quad {}_tp_x^{\prime(i)} = s_{T_i}(t) = Pr(T_i > t) = exp\left(-\int_0^t \mu^{(i)}(x+s)\, ds\right)$

Distribution Function: $\quad {}_tq_x^{\prime\,(i)} = F_{T_i}(t) = Pr(T \le t_i)$

$= 1 - {}_tp_x^{\prime(i)}$

$= Pr((x)$ claimed in next t years by cause (i) when no other decrements are present$)$

Density Function: $\quad {}_tp_x^{\prime(i)} \cdot \mu^{(i)}(x+t) = f_{T_i}(t)$

$${}_tq_x^{\prime(i)} = Pr(T_i \le t) = \int_0^t f_{T_i}(s)\, ds = \int_0^t {}_sp_x^{\prime(i)}\, \mu^{(i)}(x+s)\, ds = \underbrace{1 - {}_tp_x^{\prime(i)}}_{\text{alternate calculation}}$$

Note: The $(\ )^{\prime(i)}$ notation always indicates that only decrement (i) is operating on life (x).

The Multiple Decrement Model

a. The T-Distribution

Survival Function: $\quad {}_tp_x^{(\tau)} = Pr(T > t) = \prod_i {}_tp_x^{\prime(i)} = exp\left(-\int_0^t \mu^{(\tau)}(x+s)\, ds\right)$

Distribution Function: $\quad {}_tq_x^{(\tau)} = Pr(T \le t) = 1 - {}_tp_x^{(\tau)}$

Hazard Rate: $\quad \mu^{(\tau)}(x+t) = \sum_{i=1}^{n} \mu^{(i)}(x+t)$

Density Function: $\quad {}_tp_x^{(\tau)} \cdot \mu^{(\tau)}(x+t) = \frac{-d}{dt}[{}_tp_x^{(\tau)}]$

b. Joint Distribution of T, J

Density: $\quad f_{T,J}(t,j) = {}_tp_x^{(\tau)} \cdot \mu^{(j)}(x+t)$

$${}_tq_x^{(j)} = \int_0^t {}_sp_x^{(\tau)} \cdot \mu^{(j)}(x+s)\, ds = Pr(T \le t \text{ and } J = j)$$

$${}_tq_x^{(\tau)} = Pr(T \le t) = \sum_j {}_tq_x^{(j)}$$

$${}_tq_x^{(j)} = \int_0^t {}_sp_x^{(\tau)} \cdot \mu^{(j)}(x+s)\, ds < \int_0^t {}_sp_x^{\prime(j)} \cdot \mu^{(j)}(x+s)\, ds = {}_tq_x^{\prime(j)}$$ because

${}_sp_x^{(\tau)} = \prod_i {}_sp_x^{\prime(i)} < {}_sp_x^{\prime(j)}$. Competition of causes reduces the effect of decrement (j) in the multiple decrement model.

c. The J-distribution

Density: $$f_J(j) = Pr(J = j) = \int_{t=0}^{\infty} f_{T,J}(t,j)\,dt = {}_\infty q_x^{(j)}$$

Conditional Density: $$f_J(j|T = t) = \frac{f_{T,J}(t,j)}{f_T(t)} = \frac{\mu^{(i)}(x+t)}{\mu^{(\tau)}(x+t)}$$

Note: T and J are independent if $f_J(j|T = t)$ has no t's in the expression; i.e., $f_J(j|T = t) = f_J(j)$. Possible cases include all forces constant, all $\mu^{(i)}(x+t) = k_i t^n$, or all $\mu^{(i)}(x+t) = \frac{r_i}{\omega - x - t}$.

Relation of $\{{}_tq_x^{(j)}\}$ with $\{{}_tq_x^{\prime(j)}\}$

$$1 - \sum_i {}_tq_x^{(i)} = 1 - {}_tq_x^{(\tau)} = {}_tp_x^{(\tau)} = \prod_{i=1}^{n} {}_tp_x^{\prime(1)} = \prod_{i=1}^{n} (1 - {}_tq_x^{\prime(i)})$$

$$n = 2:\ {}_tq_x^{(1)} + {}_tq_x^{(2)} = {}_tq_x^{\prime(1)} + {}_tq_x^{\prime(2)} - {}_tq_x^{\prime(1)} \cdot {}_tq_x^{\prime(2)}$$

Tabular Multiple Decrement Models With Interpolation Assumptions: the Relation Between the $q_x^{(i)}$ and $q_x^{\prime(i)}$

(a) Constant Forces over each year of age:
x = whole age, $0 \le t \le 1$, $\mu^{(i)}(x+t) = \mu_x^{(i)}$

$$\Rightarrow \qquad q_x^{\prime(i)} = 1 - p_x^{\prime(i)} = 1 - [p_x^{(\tau)}]^{q_x^{(i)}/q_x^{(\tau)}}$$

(b) MUDD - Uniform Distribution of each decrement within each year of age in the multiple decrement model: ${}_tq_x^{(i)} = t \cdot q_x^{(i)}$

$$q_x^{\prime(i)} = 1 - p_x^{\prime(i)} = 1 - [p_x^{(\tau)}]^{q_x^{(i)}/q_x^{(\tau)}}$$

$\Rightarrow$

$${}_tp_x^{(\tau)} = 1 - {}_tq_x^{(\tau)} = 1 - t \cdot q_x^{\tau} \qquad \text{(linear in } t\text{)}$$

(c) SUDD - Uniform Distribution of each decrement within each year of age in each single decrement model: $\;{}_tq_x^{\prime(i)} = t \cdot q_x^{\prime(i)}$

$$\Rightarrow \qquad q_x^{(i)} = \int_0^1 {}_tp_x^{(\tau)}\,\mu^{(i)}(x+t)dt = \int_0^1 \prod_{j\neq i}(1 - t\cdot q_x^{\prime(j)})(\underbrace{{}_tp_x^{\prime(i)}\,\mu^{(i)}(x+t)}_{q_x^{\prime(i)}})\,dt$$

$$= q_x^{\prime(i)} \cdot \int_0^1 \prod_{j\neq i}(1 - t\cdot q_x^{\prime(j)})\,dt$$

$n = 2$: $\quad q_x^{(i)} = q_x^{\prime(i)}[1 - \tfrac{1}{2}q_x^{\prime(j)}] \qquad \{i, j\} = \{1, 2\}$

$n = 3$: $\quad q_x^{(i)} = q_x^{\prime(i)}\left[1 - \tfrac{1}{2}\left(q_x^{\prime(j)} + q_x^{\prime(k)}\right) + \tfrac{1}{3}\left(q_x^{\prime(j)}\cdot q_x^{\prime(k)}\right)\right] \qquad \{i, j, k\} = \{1, 2, 3\}$

Note: When given the $q_x^{(i)}$, the $q_x^{\prime(i)}$ can be obtained from the n equation in n unknowns by solving and substituting or by the SOFA criss-cross iteration.

(d) Discrete Decrement Patterns

$$q_x^{(i)} = q_x^{\prime(i)} \underbrace{\int_0^1 \left[\prod_{j\neq i} {}_tp_x^{\prime(j)}\right] f_{T_i}(t|T_i \le 1)\,dt}_{\substack{\text{Expected value of } \prod_{j\neq i} {}_tp_x^{\prime(j)} \text{ with respect} \\ \text{to the conditional distribution of } T_i}}$$

Example: Decrement 1 is always assumed to be at mid-year and all other decrements are UDD in the single decrement table ($n = 3$)

$$q_x^{(1)} = q_x^{\prime(1)} E[(1 - t\cdot q_x^{\prime(2)})(1 - t\cdot q_x^{\prime(3)})]$$

where the expected value is with respect to $T_1|_{T_1 \le 1}$. Since $f_{T_1}(\tfrac{1}{2}|T_1 \le 1) = 1$, this gives $q_x^{(1)} = q_x^{\prime(1)}\left(1 - \tfrac{1}{2}q_x^{\prime(2)})(1 - \tfrac{1}{2}q_x^{\prime(3)}\right)$.

Central Rates of Decrement

$$_n m_x^{(i)} = \frac{\int_0^n {}_tp_x^{(\tau)}\, \mu^{(i)}(x+t)\, dt}{\int_0^n {}_tp_x^{(\tau)}\, dt} = \frac{{}_nq_x^{(i)}}{\overset{\circ}{e}{}_{x:\overline{n}|}^{(\tau)}} = \frac{{}_nd_x^{(i)}}{{}_nL_x^{(\tau)}}$$

where $\overset{\circ}{e}{}_{x:\overline{n}|}^{(\tau)}$ = expected years in the next n years that (x) survives all causes

$${}_nL_x^{(\tau)} = \int_0^n \ell_{x+t}^{(\tau)}\, dt = \text{people years exposure to all causes over next } n \text{ years}$$

$$_n m_x^{\prime(i)} = \frac{\int_0^n {}_tp_x^{\prime(i)}\, \mu^{(i)}(x+t)\, dt}{\int_0^n {}_tp_x^{\prime(i)}\, dt} = \frac{{}_nq_x^{\prime(i)}}{\overset{\circ}{e}{}_{x:\overline{n}|}^{(i)}}$$

where $\overset{\circ}{e}{}_{x:\overline{n}|}^{(i)}$ = expected years in the next n years that (x) survives cause (i) with no other causes competing

SUDD in single decrement table for cause (i) $\Rightarrow$ $m_x^{\prime(i)} = \dfrac{q_x^{\prime(i)}}{1 - \frac{1}{2} \cdot q_x^{\prime(i)}}$

MUDD $\Rightarrow$ $m_x^{(i)} = \dfrac{q_x^{(i)}}{1 - \frac{1}{2} \cdot q_x^{(\tau)}}$

Insurances Providing Benefits at the Time of Decrement That Depend on the Mode

Suppose an insurance provides a benefit of $B(t, j)$ at time t, the time of decrement, if j is the mode of decrement. Then the NSP is given by

$$NSP = E[B(t,j)\, v^t] = \sum_{j=1}^{m} \int_{t=0}^{\omega-x} B(t,j) \cdot v^t\, f_{T,J}(t,j)\, dt$$

$$= \sum_{j=1}^{m} \underbrace{\int_{t=0}^{\omega-x} B(t,j) \cdot v^t\, {}_tp_x^{(\tau)} \cdot \mu_x^{(j)}(t)\, dt}_{\substack{\text{Portion of NSP for Benefits} \\ \text{Due to Decrement by Cause}jj}}$$

where $J = 1, 2, \ldots, m$ (i.e., m possible modes of decrement).

CONCEPTUAL REVIEW TEST

1. Let T, J be the waiting time until decrement and the mode of decrement for (x). Give the joint density function, the T marginal density and interpret.

2. Give ${}_2q_x^{(1)}$ as an integral in terms of the joint density of T and J, and a Riemann sum type explanation.

3. What is the significance of $\int_0^{\omega-x} {}_tp_x^{(\tau)} \cdot \mu^{(2)}(x+t)\,dt$?

4. For the following portion of a double decrement table, set up ratios to compute the following probabilities and note any assumptions that you make:

x	$\ell_x^{(\tau)}$	$d_x^{(1)}$	$d_x^{(2)}$
25	1000	10	65
26	925	13	12
27	900	17	10
28	873	20	11

(A) $q_{25}^{(2)}$ (B) $m_{25}^{(2)}$ (C) ${}_{2|}q_{25}^{(2)}$

5. In the expression $m_x^{(i)} = \dfrac{d_x^{(i)}}{\int_0^1 \ell_{x+t}^{(\tau)}\,dt}$ for a central rate of decrement, what is the interpretation of the denominator?

6. If there are two modes of decrement in a table, what is the most basic relation between the $q_x^{(i)}$ and $q_x^{\prime(i)}$?

7. Explain why $q_x^{\prime(i)}$ is greater than $q_x^{(i)}$.

CONCEPTUAL REVIEW TEST SOLUTIONS

1. $f_{T,J}(t,j) = {}_tp_x^{(\tau)} \cdot \mu^{(j)}(x+t)$: $f_{T,J}(t,j)dt$ is approximately the probability that (x) departs between t and $t+dt$ years from now. This means she must survive all causes for t years (prob. $= {}_tp_x^{(\tau)}$) and (i.e., intersection) then depart in the next instant due to cause j (prob. $\approx \mu^{(j)}(x+t) \cdot dt$). Thus the multiplicative law gives $f(t,j) = {}_tp_x^{(\tau)} \cdot \mu^{(j)}(x+t)$. $f_T(t) = {}_tp_x^{(\tau)} \cdot \mu^{(\tau)}(x+t)$;

2. $${}_2q_x^{(1)} = \int_{t=0}^{2} f(t,1)dt = \int_{t=0}^{2} {}_tp_x^{(\tau)} \cdot \mu^{(1)}(x+t)dt$$

$$\begin{aligned} {}_2q_x^{(1)} &= Pr\Big((x) \text{ departs within 2 years via cause 1}\Big) \\ &= \sum_{i=1}^{n} Pr\Big((x) \text{ departs in the time interval } [t_{i-1}, t_i] \text{ via cause 1}\Big) \\ &\qquad\qquad (\text{where } t_0 = 0 < t_1 < \cdots < t_n = 2) \\ &\approx \sum_{i=1}^{n} \underbrace{{}_{t_{i-1}}p_x^{(\tau)}}_{\substack{\text{survives for} \\ t_{i-1} \text{ years}}} \cdot \underbrace{\left(\mu^{(1)}(x+t_{i-1}) \cdot \Delta t_{i-1}\right)}_{\substack{\text{departs in next} \\ \text{instant via cause 1}}}, \end{aligned}$$

which converges to the integral above.

3. This is the probability that (x) departs by cause (2) between ages x and ω, that is, the probability that (x) departs by cause (2), $f_J(2) = {}_\infty q_x^{(2)}$.

4. $q_{25}^{(2)} = \frac{65}{1000}$, $m_{25}^{(2)} = \frac{65}{1000 - \frac{1}{2}(10+65)}$ (total decrement is spread uniformly over the year), ${}_{2|}q_{25}^{(2)} = \frac{10}{1000}$.

5. $\int_0^1 \ell_{x+t}^{(\tau)}dt$ is the number of people-years of exposure to all causes of decrement between ages x and $x+1$ for the $\ell_x^{(\tau)}$ active lives at age (x). Riemann sum approach: the $\ell_{x+t}^{(\tau)}$ active lives at age $x+t$ are exposed to decrements for approximately $\ell_{x+t}^{(\tau)} \cdot \Delta t$ people-years between ages $x+t$ and $x+t+\Delta t$.

6. $$\begin{aligned} q_x^{(1)} + q_x^{(2)} = q_x^{(\tau)} = 1 - p_x^{(\tau)} = 1 - p_x'^{(1)} \cdot p_x'^{(2)} &= 1 - (1-q_x'^{(1)})(1-q_x'^{(2)}) \\ &= q_x'^{(1)} + q_x'^{(2)} - q_x'^{(1)} \cdot q_x'^{(2)} \end{aligned}$$

7. $q_x^{(i)}$ is smaller because in the multiple decrement context, some of the $\ell_x^{(\tau)}$ are gobbled up in the next year by other competing causes before cause (i) gets a chance to work its magic.

COMPUTATIONAL REVIEW TEST

1. Suppose $\mu^{(1)}(x+t) = \frac{1}{75-t}$ for $0 \leq t < 75$ and $\mu^{(2)}(x+t) = \frac{2}{50-t}$ for $0 \leq t < 50$. Compute the following:

(a) ${}_tp_x^{\prime(i)}$, ${}_tp_x^{(\tau)}$ (be careful with t domains)

(b) $f_{T,J}(t,j)$

(c) $q_x^{(1)}$, $q_x^{(2)}$, $q_x^{(\tau)}$

(d) $q_x^{\prime(1)}$, $q_x^{\prime(2)}$ (compare magnitudes with (c))

(e) $f_J(1)$, $f_J(2)$, and interpret

(f) $f_J(1\,|\,T{=}1)$, $f_J(2\,|\,T{=}1)$

(g) $m_x^{(1)}$, $m_x^{(2)}$, $m_x^{(\tau)}$

2. If $q_x^{\prime(1)} = .015$, $q_x^{\prime(2)} = .030$, single decrement table for cause 1 satisfies the UDD, and decrement 2 all occurs at midyear, then calculate:

(a) ${}_tp_x^{\prime(\tau)}$ for $0 \leq t \leq 1$

(b) $q_x^{(1)}$ and $q_x^{(2)}$

COMPUTATIONAL REVIEW TEST SOLUTIONS

1. (a) $\int_0^t \mu^{(1)}(x+s)\, ds = ln\left(\frac{75}{75-t}\right)$, $\int_0^t \mu^{(2)}(x+s)\; ds = ln\left(\frac{50}{50-t}\right)^2$, so ${}_tp_x'^{(1)} = \frac{75-t}{75}$ for $0 \le t \le 75$ and ${}_tp_x'^{(2)} = \left(\frac{50-t}{50}\right)^2$ for $0 \le t \le 50$. Thus ${}_tp_x^{(\tau)} = \frac{75-t}{75} \cdot \frac{(50-t)^2}{50^2}$ for $0 \le t \le 50$ (it is zero for $t > 50$)

(b) $$f(t,j) = {}_tp_x^{(\tau)} \cdot \mu^{(j)}(x+t) = \begin{cases} \dfrac{(50-t)^2}{75 \cdot 50^2} & j=1 \\ \dfrac{2(75-t)(50-t)}{75 \cdot 50^2} & j=2 \end{cases} \quad 0 \le t \le 50$$

(c) $$q_x^{(1)} = \int_0^1 f(t,1)dt = \int_0^1 \frac{(50-t)^2}{75 \cdot 50^2}dt = \frac{-(50-t)^3}{3 \cdot 75 \cdot 50^2}\Bigg|_0^1 = .013068$$

$$q_x^{(2)} = \int_0^1 f(t,2)dt = \int_0^1 \frac{2(75-t)(50-t)}{75 \cdot 50^2}dt$$
$$= \frac{2}{75 \cdot 50^2}\left(75 \cdot 50t - \frac{125}{2}t^2 + \frac{t^3}{3}\right)\Bigg|_0^1 = .039337$$

(d) $$q_x'^{(1)} = 1 - p_x'^{(1)} = 1 - \frac{75-1}{75} = \frac{1}{75} = .013333 > .013068 = q_x^{(1)}$$
$$q_x'^{(2)} = 1 - p_x'^{(2)} = 1 - \left(\frac{50-1}{50}\right)^2 = 1 - \left(\frac{49}{50}\right)^2 = .039600 > .039337 = q_x^{(2)}$$

(e) $$f_J(1) = \int_{t=0}^{50} f(t,1)dt = \int_0^{50} \frac{(50-t)^2}{75 \cdot 50^2}dt = \frac{-(50-t)^3}{3 \cdot 75 \cdot 50^2}\Bigg|_0^{50} = \frac{50^3}{3 \cdot 75 \cdot 50^2} = \frac{2}{9}$$
$f_J(2) = 1 - f_J(1) = \frac{7}{9}$

Interpretation: (x) is 3.5 times as likely to be caught by cause (2) as by cause (1).

(f) $f_J(j\,|\,T{=}t) = \dfrac{\mu^{(j)}(x+t)}{\mu^{(\tau)}(x+t)}$ so $f_J(1\,|\,T{=}1) = \dfrac{\frac{1}{74}}{\frac{1}{74}+\frac{2}{49}} = .2487$,

$f_J(2\,|\,T{=}1) = 1 - .2487 = .7513$

(g) $\ell_{x+t}^{(\tau)} = \ell_x \cdot {}_tp_x^{(\tau)}$; for convenience let $\ell_x = 50^2 \cdot 75$ so that $\ell_{x+t}^{(\tau)} = (75-t)(50-t)^2$. Thus $\ell_x^{(\tau)} = 187{,}500$, $\ell_{x+1}^{(\tau)} = 177{,}674$, so $d_x^{(\tau)} = 9826$,

$d_x^{(1)} = \ell_x^{(\tau)} \cdot q_x^{(1)} = (187{,}500)(.013068) = 2450.\bar{3}$, and $d_x^{(2)} = 7375.\bar{6}$. Furthermore

$L_x^{(\tau)} = \int_0^1 \ell_{x+t}^{(\tau)}dt = 182{,}558$. Hence $m_x^{(1)} = \dfrac{2450.\bar{3}}{182{,}558} = .013422$,

$m_x^{(2)} = \dfrac{7375.\bar{6}}{182{,}558} = .040401$, $m_x^{(\tau)} = .053823$

2. (a) ${}_tp_x^{\prime(1)} = 1 - tq_x^{\prime(1)} = 1 - .015t$ for $0 \le t \le 1$ (UDD),

$${}_tp_x^{\prime(2)} = \begin{cases} 1 & 0 \le t < .5 \\ .97 & .5 \le t \le 1 \end{cases}, \quad {}_tp_x^{(\tau)} = \begin{cases} 1 - .015t & 0 \le t < .5 \\ .97 - .01455t & .5 \le t \le 1 \end{cases}$$

(b)

$$q_x^{(1)} = \int_{t=0}^{1} ({}_tp_x^{\prime(1)}\mu^{(1)}(x+t))({}_tp_x^{\prime(2)})dt = \int_{t=0}^{1} .015\,({}_tp_x^{\prime(2)})dt$$

$$= .015\left(\int_0^{.5} 1dt + \int_{.5}^{1} .97dt\right) = .015\,(.985) = .014775$$

$$q_x^{(2)} = q_x^{(\tau)} - q_x^{(1)} = 1 - p_x^{(\tau)} - q_x^{(1)} = 1 - (.97)(.985) - .014775 = .029775$$

UNIT REVIEW QUESTIONS

1. Consider a multiple-decrement table with two causes of decrement. In the single decrement table associated with cause (1), $q_{50}^{\prime(1)} = 0.120$ and decrements are uniformly distributed over the year. In the single decrement table associated with cause (2), $q_{50}^{\prime(2)} = 0.15$ and decrements occur at only two points during the year: two-thirds of the decrements occur at time $t = \frac{1}{6}$, and the remaining one-third occur at time $t = \frac{2}{3}$. Determine $q_{50}^{(2)}$.

(A) 0.138 (B) 0.140 (C) 0.142 (D) 0.144 (E) .0146

2. An individual age 20 is exposed to two causes of death. The force of mortality for the first cause is constant at 0.01. The second force follows de Moivre's Law with $\omega = 100$. Determine $q_{20}^{(2)}$, in terms of $q_{20}^{\prime(1)}$.

(A) $0.80\, q_{20}^{\prime(1)}$ (B) $0.125 - 0.2625\, q_{20}^{\prime(1)}$ (C) $0.0125(1 - q_{20}^{\prime(1)})$ (D) $1.25\, q_{20}^{\prime(1)}$ (E) 0.0125

3. In a triple-decrement table, lives in state T are subject to decrements $d, w,$and r. Once a life suffers from any decrement, it cannot return to state T. The total decrement is uniformly distributed over the year of age. You are given:

(i) $\ell_x^{(\tau)} = 100{,}000$ (ii) $\ell_{x+1}^{(\tau)} = 90{,}000$ (ii) $q_x^{(d)} = 0.02$ (iv) $d_x^{(r)} = 0.6 d_x^{(w)}$

Calculate $m_x^{(w)} - m_x^{(d)}$. (Answer to nearest 0.001)

(A) 0.011 (B) 0.019 (C) 0.021 (D) 0.029 (E) 0.032

4. Determine the joint p.d.f. of T and J, given $\mu^{(1)}(x+t) = x+t$, $\mu^{(2)}(x+t) = \frac{1}{1+x+t}$.

(A) $\frac{1+x}{1+x+t}\, exp\left[-\frac{1}{2}(x+t)^2\right] \cdot \mu^{(j)}(x+t)$

(B) $\frac{1}{1+x+t}\, exp\left[-\frac{1}{2}(2xt+t^2)\right] \cdot \mu^{(j)}(x+t)$

(C) $exp\left[-\frac{1}{2}(2xt+t^2)\right] \cdot \mu^{(1)}(x+t)$ for $j = 1$; $\frac{1+x}{1+x+t} \cdot \mu^{(2)}(x+t)$ for $j = 2$

(D) $\frac{1+x}{1+x+t}\, exp\left[-\frac{1}{2}(2xt+t^2)\right] \cdot \mu^{(j)}(x+t)$

(E) $\frac{1}{1+x+t}\, exp\left[-\frac{1}{2}(x+t)^2\right] \cdot \mu^{(j)}(x+t)$

5. A multiple decrement table has three decrements, each of which is uniformly distributed over each year of age. Calculate $q_{95}^{\prime(1)}$, given the following values:

(i) $q_{95}^{(1)} = .48$ (ii) $q_{95}^{(2)} = .32$ (iii) $q_{95}^{(3)} = .16$

(A) .50 (B) .60 (C) .70 (D) .80 (E) .90

6. For a triple-decrement table, you are given:

(i) $q_{50}^{(1)} = q_{50}^{(3)}$ (ii) $q_{50}^{(2)} = 2q_{50}^{(1)}$ (iii) $\mu^{(1)}(50+t) = \log 2, \quad 0 < t < 1$

Assume a constant force of decrement for each decrement over each year of age.

Calculate $1000q_{50}^{\prime(2)}$.

(A) 531 (B) 630 (C) 750 (D) 766 (E) 794

7. For a double-decrement table, you are given:

(i) $q_{71}^{(1)} = .02$
(ii) $q_{71}^{(2)} = .06$
(iii) Each decrement is uniformly distributed over each year of age in the single-decrement table.

Calculate $1000q_{71}^{\prime(1)}$.

(A) 20.57 (B) 20.59 (C) 20.61 (D) 20.63 (E) 20.65

8. For a double-decrement table, you are given:

(i) $q_x^{\prime(2)} = 2q_x^{\prime(1)}$
(ii) $q_x^{\prime(1)} + q_x^{\prime(2)} = q_x^{(\tau)} + .18$

Calculate $q_x^{\prime(2)}$.

(A) .20 (B) .30 (C) .40 (D) .60 (E) .70

9. For a double-decrement table, you are given:

x	$\ell_x^{(\tau)}$	$d_x^{(1)}$	$d_x^{(2)}$
35	1000	39	41
36	–	–	69
37	828	–	–

Assume each decrement is uniformly distributed over each year of age in the double-decrement table. Calculate $q_{36}^{\prime(1)}$.

(A) .026 (B) .050 (C) .064 (D) .080 (E) .100

10. For a multiple-decrement table, you are given:

(i) ${}_tp_x^{(\tau)} = 1 - .03t,\ 0 \le t \le 1$ (ii) $\mu^{(1)}(x+t) = .02t,\ 0 \le t \le 1$

Calculate $m_x^{(1)}$.

(A) .00970 (B) .00985 (C) .00995 (D) .01000 (E) .01015

11. For a double-decrement table, you are given:

(i) $\mu^{(1)}(x+t) = .02,\ t \ge 0$ (ii) $\mu^{(2)}(x+t) = .04,\ t \ge 0$

Which of the following are true?

I. ${}_tp_x^{(\tau)} = e^{-.06t},\quad t \ge 0$ II. $f_{T,J}(t,1) = .5,\quad t \ge 0$ III. $f_J(2) = 2/3$

(A) I and II only (B) I and III only (C) II and III only (D) I, II and III
(E) The correct answer is not given by (A), (B), (C) or (D).

12. For a double-decrement table, you are given:

(i) $q_x^{\prime(2)} = \frac{1}{8}$

(ii) ${}_{1|}q_x^{(1)} = \frac{1}{4}$

(iii) $q_{x+1}^{(1)} = \frac{1}{3}$

Calculate $q_x^{\prime(1)}$.

(A) $\frac{1}{4}$ (B) $\frac{1}{5}$ (C) $\frac{1}{6}$ (D) $\frac{1}{7}$ (E) $\frac{1}{8}$

13. A multiple-decrement table has two causes of decrement:

(1) accident
(2) other than accident

You are given:

(i) $\mu^{(1)}(y) = .0010$
(ii) $\mu^{(2)}(y) = .0005(10^{.05})^y$

Determine the probability of death by accident for (x) in terms of $\mathring{e}_x$.

(A) $.0005\mathring{e}_x$ (B) $.0010\mathring{e}_x$ (C) $.0050\mathring{e}_x$ (D) $.0100\mathring{e}_x$ (E) $.0500\mathring{e}_x$

14. For a double-decrement table, you are given:

(i) $m_x^{(1)} = .1$
(ii) $m_x^{\prime(2)} = .2$
(iii) Each decrement has a constant force of decrement over each year of age.

Calculate $q_x^{(1)}$.

(A) .086 (B) .095 (C) .100 (D) .106 (E) .115

15. For a double-decrement table, you are given:

(i) $\mu^{(1)}(x+t) = \dfrac{1}{60-t}$ $0 \le t < 60$
(ii) $\mu^{(2)}(x+t) = \dfrac{k}{60-t}$ $0 \le t < 60$
(iii) $f_J(2|\,T=t) = .75$ $0 \le t < 60$

Calculate $f_T(30)$.

(A) $\frac{1}{30}$ (B) $\frac{1}{60}$ (C) $\frac{1}{90}$ (D) $\frac{1}{120}$ (E) $\frac{1}{150}$

16. For a double-decrement table, you are given:

(i)

x	$\ell_x^{(\tau)}$	$d_x^{(1)}$	$d_x^{(2)}$
65	100	–	–
66	–	3	13
67	–	1	3

(ii) $q_{65}^{\prime(1)} = .1$
(iii) $q_{65}^{\prime(2)} = .6$
(iv) The force of mortality is constant for each decrement over the year of age 67.

Calculate $q_{67}^{\prime(1)}$.

(A) .0500 (B) .0543 (C) .0674 (D) .0714 (E) .0807

17. For a triple-decrement table, you are given:

(i) Each decrement has a constant force of decrement over each year of age.
(ii) The following table of values:

j	$\mu^{(j)}(x)$
1	.2
2	.4
3	.6

Calculate $q_x^{(2)}$.

(A) .20 (B) .23 (C) .26 (D) .30 (E) .33

18. For a triple-decrement table, you are given:

(i) Each decrement is uniformly distributed over each year of age in its associated single decrement table.
(ii) $q_x^{\prime(1)} = .1000$ (iii) $q_x^{\prime(2)} = .0400$ (iv) $q_x^{\prime(3)} = .0625$

Calculate $1000q_x^{(1)}$.

(A) 94.00 (B) 94.55 (C) 94.96 (D) 95.00 (E) 100.50

19. In the given table decrement (1) is death and decrement (2) is surrender. The associated single decrement model for death satisfies the UDD assumption. All lapses occur 2/3 of the way through a year of age.

x	$\ell_x^{(\tau)}$	$d_x^{(1)}$	$d_x^{(2)}$
60	1000		80
61		25	
62	835		

The number of lapses between ages 61 and 62 is twice the number of deaths between ages 60 and 61.

Calculate $q_{60}^{\prime(1)}$.

(A) .020542 (B) .020548 (C) .020556 (D) .020564 (E) .020572

20. From a double-decrement table, you are given:

(i) $\ell_{30}^{(\tau)} = 1000$
(ii) $q_{30}^{\prime(1)} = .10$
(iii) $q_{30}^{\prime(2)} = .20$
(iv) ${}_{1|}q_{30}^{(1)} = .05$
(v) $\ell_{32}^{(\tau)} = 562$

Calculate $q_{31}^{(2)}$.

(A) .125 (B) .130 (C) .145 (D) .150 (E) .170

21. You are given the following extract from a triple-decrement table:

x	$q_x^{(1)}$	$q_x^{(2)}$	$q_x^{(3)}$	$q_x^{(\tau)}$	$\ell_x^{(\tau)}$	$q_x^{\prime(1)}$	$q_x^{\prime(2)}$	$p_x^{\prime(3)}$
60	.010	.050	.020	--	10,000	--	--	--
61	--	--	--	.076	--	--	--	--
62	--	--	--	--	--	.023	.033	.990
63	--	--	--	.098	--	--	--	--

Calculate $\ell_{63}^{(\tau)}$.

(A) 7172 (B) 7175 (C) 7951 (D) 7954 (E) 8031

22. For a triple-decrement model, you are given:

(i) Decrement 1 is uniformly distributed over each year of age.
(ii) Decrement 2 occurs only at the end of the year.
(iii) Decrement 3 occurs only at the beginning of the year.
(iv)

x	$\ell_x^{(\tau)}$	$q_x^{\prime(1)}$	$q_x^{\prime(2)}$	$q_x^{\prime(3)}$
60	100,000	.14	.10	.10
61	--	--	.10	.20
62	45,516	--	--	--

Calculate $q_{61}^{(1)}$.

(A) .070 (B) .074 (C) .078 (D) .082 (E) .086

23. For a double-decrement model, you are given:

(i) $\mu^{(1)}(10+t) = \frac{1}{30-t}$, $0 \le t < 30$

(ii) $\mu^{(\tau)}(10+t) = \frac{50-2t}{600-50t+t^2}$, $0 \le t < 20$

Calculate the probability that (10) will terminate from cause 2 during the 6th year.

(A) .0225 (B) .0242 (C) .0392 (D) .0408 (E) .0650

24. You are given the following double-decrement model for students writing actuarial exams:

(i)

x	$q_x^{(1)}$	$q_x^{(2)}$
21	.008	.15
22	.015	.20
23	.025	.25

(ii) $q_x^{(1)}$ denotes the probability of decrement due to attaining fellowship.
(iii) $q_x^{(2)}$ denotes the probability of decrement due to all other causes.
(iv) Decrements occur at the end of the year.

You are also given:

(i) After attaining fellowship, the only decrement is mortality.
(ii) After attaining fellowship, $\mu = .04$.

Calculate the probability that a student writing exams now age 21, will be living and a Fellow three years later.

(A) .031 (B) .036 (C) .038 (D) .043 (E) .046

25. A double-decrement table is constructed from two single decrement tables. You are given:

(i) The force of decrement for cause 1 is constant.
(ii) Decrement 2 is uniformly distributed over each year of age in the single-decrement table.

Which of the following are true?

I. $m_x^{\prime(1)} = m_x^{(1)}$

II. $m_x^{\prime(2)} = \dfrac{q_x^{\prime(2)}}{(1 - .5q_x^{(\tau)})}$

III. $m_x^{\prime(\tau)} = \mu_x^{(1)} + \dfrac{q_x^{\prime(2)}}{(1-.5q_x^{\prime(2)})}$

(A) I and II only (B) I and III only (C) II and III only (D) I, II and III
(E) The correct answer is not given by (A), (B), (C) or (D).

Use the following information for Questions 26 - 29.

A multiple-decrement model with n causes of decrement has forces of decrement:

$$\mu^{(k)}(x+t) = \frac{k}{n+1} \cdot \frac{1}{100-x-t},\ k = 1, 2, \ldots, n \text{ and } t < 100 - x$$

26. Express ${}_tp_x^{(\tau)}$ in terms of j, n, t and x.

(A) $\left(\frac{100-x-t}{100-x}\right)^{n/2}$ (B) $\left(\frac{100-x-t}{100-x}\right)^{n}$ (C) $exp\left(\frac{100-x-t}{100-x}\right)^{n}$

(D) $\frac{n}{2(100-x-t)}$ (E) $\frac{n}{100-x-t}$

27. Express the joint p.d.f. of T and J in terms of j, n, t, and x.

(A) $\frac{j}{n+1}\left(\frac{100-x-t}{100-x}\right)^{n/2}$ (B) $\left(\frac{j}{n+1}\right)\left(\frac{1}{100-x-t}\right)\left(\frac{100-x-t}{100-x}\right)^{n/2}$ (C) $\frac{2j}{n(n+1)}$

(D) $\frac{j}{(n+1)}\left(\frac{1}{100-x-t}\right)$ (E) $\frac{n}{2}\left(\frac{1}{100-x-t}\right)\left(\frac{100-x-t}{100-x}\right)^{n/2}$

28. Express the p.d.f. of T in terms of j, n, t, and x.

(A) $\frac{j}{n+1}\left(\frac{100-x-t}{100-x}\right)^{n/2}$ (B) $\left(\frac{j}{n+1}\right)\left(\frac{1}{100-x-t}\right)\left(\frac{100-x-t}{100-x}\right)^{n/2}$ (C) $\frac{2j}{n(n+1)}$

(D) $\frac{j}{(n+1)}\left(\frac{1}{100-x-t}\right)$ (E) $\frac{n}{2}\left(\frac{1}{100-x-t}\right)\left(\frac{100-x-t}{100-x}\right)^{n/2}$

29. If $n = 5$, calculate $f_J(3 \mid T = 5)$.

(A) .10 (B) .20 (C) .30 (D) .40 (E) .50

Use the following information for Questions 30 - 33.

For a double-decrement model, you are given:

(i) $\mu^{(1)}(40+t) = \frac{2}{60+t},\ t \geq 0$
(ii) $\mu^{(2)}(40+t) = \frac{3}{60+t},\ t \geq 0$
(iii) T is the time-until-decrement random variable for (40).
(iv) J is the cause-of-decrement random variable for (40).

30. Calculate $f_{T,J}(20, 2)$.

(A) .0059 (B) .0066 (C) .0076 (D) .0089 (E) .0099

31. Calculate $f_T(20)$.

(A) .0127 (B) .0136 (C) .0148 (D) .0159 (E) .0165

32. Calculate $f_J(2)$.

(A) .33 (B) .40 (C) .50 (D) .60 (E) .67

33. Calculate $f_{J|T}(1|10)$.

(A) .33 (B) .40 (C) .50 (D) .60 (E) .67

SOLUTIONS TO UNIT REVIEW QUESTIONS

1. One is tempted to calculate $q_{50}^{(2)}$ directly, however, the discontinuous nature of decrement (2) makes this difficult. On the other hand

$q_{50}^{(1)} + q_{50}^{(2)} = q_{50}^{\prime(1)} + q_{50}^{\prime(2)} - q_{50}^{\prime(1)} \cdot q_{50}^{\prime(2)} = .12 + .15 - (.12)(.15) = .252$, so it suffices to calculate $q_{50}^{(1)}$ and get $q_{50}^{(2)} = .252 - q_{50}^{(1)}$.

From the description of single decrements

$$_tp_{50}^{\prime(1)} \cdot \mu^{(1)}(50+t) = q_{50}^{\prime(1)} = .12, \text{ and } _tp_{50}^{\prime(2)} = \begin{cases} 1.00 & t \in (0, \frac{1}{6}] \\ .90 & t \in (\frac{1}{6}, \frac{2}{3}] \\ .85 & t \in (\frac{2}{3}, 1] \end{cases}.$$

Thus
$$\begin{aligned} q_{50}^{(1)} &= \int_0^1 {}_tp_{50}^{\prime(2)} \cdot {}_tp_{50}^{\prime(1)} \cdot \mu^{(1)}(50+t)\,dt \\ &= .12 \int_0^1 {}_tp_{50}^{\prime(2)}\,dt \\ &= .12\left(1\left(\tfrac{1}{6}\right) + .90\left(\tfrac{2}{3} - \tfrac{1}{6}\right) + .85\left(1-\tfrac{2}{3}\right)\right) = .12(.9) = .108 \end{aligned}$$

Hence $q_{50}^{(2)} = .252 - q_{50}^{(1)} = .252 - .108 = .144$ ANSWER D

2. Since $\mu^{(1)}(20+t) = .01$, $_tp_{20}^{\prime(1)} = e^{-.01t}$. Since the 2nd force follows de Moivre's Law $_tp_{20}^{\prime(2)} \cdot \mu^{(2)}(20+t) = \frac{1}{80}$ (i.e., $U(0, 80)$ density). Thus

$$\begin{aligned} q_{20}^{(2)} &= \int_0^1 {}_tp_{20}^{\prime(1)} \cdot {}_tp_{20}^{\prime(2)} \cdot \mu^{(2)}(20+t)\,dt \\ &= \int_0^1 e^{-.01t} \cdot \frac{1}{80}\,dt \\ &= \frac{1}{80}\left(\frac{1}{.01}\right)\left(1 - e^{-.01}\right) \\ &= 1.25\left(1 - p_{20}^{\prime(1)}\right) = 1.25\, q_{20}^{\prime(1)} \end{aligned}$$

ANSWER D

3. $m_x^{(w)} - m_x^{(d)} = \dfrac{d_x^{(w)}}{\ell_x^{(\tau)} - \frac{1}{2}d_x^{(\tau)}} - \dfrac{d_x^{(d)}}{\ell_x^{(\tau)} - \frac{1}{2}d_x^{(\tau)}} = \dfrac{d_x^{(w)} - d_x^{(d)}}{\ell_x^{(\tau)} - \frac{1}{2}d_x^{(\tau)}} = \dfrac{q_x^{(w)} - q_x^{(d)}}{1 - \frac{1}{2} \cdot q_x^{(\tau)}}$.

Note that $L_x^{(\tau)} = \ell_x^{(\tau)} - \frac{1}{2}d_x^{(\tau)}$ since the total decrement is uniformly distributed. From the given information, $\dfrac{10{,}000}{100{,}000} = q_x^{(\tau)} = q_x^{(d)} + q_x^{(r)} + q_x^{(w)} = .02 + q_x^{(w)} + (.6q_x^{(w)})$, or $q_x^{(w)} = .05$.

Substituting into the above gives $m_x^{(w)} - m_x^{(d)} = \dfrac{.05 - .02}{1 - \frac{1}{2}(.10)} = \dfrac{.03}{.95} = .03158$. ANSWER E

4. $f_{T,J}(t,j) = {}_tp_x^{(\tau)} \cdot \mu^{(j)}(x+t)$ where ${}_tp_x^{(\tau)} = e^{-\int_0^t \mu^{(\tau)}(x+s)\,ds}$,
$\int_0^t \mu^{(\tau)}(x+s)\,ds = \int_0^t x + s + \frac{1}{1+x+s}\,ds = xt + \frac{t^2}{2} + \ln\left(\frac{1+x+t}{1+x}\right)$.
Thus ${}_tp_x^{(\tau)} = e^{-(xt+t^2/2) - \ln\left(\frac{1+x+t}{1+x}\right)} = \frac{1+x}{1+x+t} \cdot e^{-(xt+t^2/2)}$. ANSWER D

5. Because the forces of decrements are constant within each year of age we have

$$p_{95}^{\prime(1)} = \left(p_{95}^{(\tau)}\right)^{q_{95}^{(1)}/q_{95}^{(\tau)}} = (1 - .48 - .32 - .16)^{.48/.96} = (.04)^{1/2} = .20.$$

(see Condensed Review Notes). Thus $q_{95}^{\prime(1)} = .80$. ANSWER D

6. With constant forces the expression $q_x^{(i)} = \int_0^1 {}_tp_x^{(\tau)} \cdot \mu^{(i)}(x+t)\,dt$ simplifies to
$\int_0^1 e^{-\mu^{(\tau)} \cdot t} \mu^{(i)}\,dt = \frac{\mu^{(i)}}{\mu^{(\tau)}}\left(1 - e^{-\mu^{(\tau)}}\right) = \frac{\mu^{(i)}}{\mu^{(\tau)}} \cdot q_x^{(\tau)}$. Hence $\frac{q_x^{(i)}}{q_x^{(j)}} = \frac{\mu^{(i)}}{\mu^{(j)}}$. So the given information says $\mu^{(1)} = \mu^{(3)} = \frac{1}{2}\mu^{(2)}$. Since $\log(2) = \mu^{(1)}$, $2\log(2) = \mu^{(2)}$. Finally

$$1000q_{50}^{\prime(2)} = 1000\left(1 - p_{50}^{\prime(2)}\right) = 1000\left(1 - e^{-\mu^{(2)}}\right) = 1000\left(1 - e^{-2\ln 2}\right) = 1000\left(1 - \frac{1}{4}\right) = 750,$$

ANSWER C

7. We are given $q_x^{(1)} = .02$, $q_x^{(2)} = .06$, so from the UDD in single decrement tables (see Condensed Review Notes)

$$.02 = q_x^{(1)} = q_x^{\prime(1)}[1 - \tfrac{1}{2}q_x^{\prime(2)}]$$

and

$$.06 = q_x^{(2)} = q_x^{\prime(2)}[1 - \tfrac{1}{2}q_x^{\prime(1)}].$$

Successive iteration (SoFA Criss-cross; see Unit Introduction or Condensed Review Notes) results in $1000q_{71}^{\prime(1)} = 20.625$. ANSWER D.

8. This problem depends on the general relation

$$\begin{aligned} q_x^{(1)} + q_x^{(2)} = q_x^{(\tau)} = 1 - p_x^{(\tau)} &= 1 - \left(p_x^{\prime(1)}\right)\left(p_x^{\prime(2)}\right) \\ &= 1 - \left(1 - q_x^{\prime(1)}\right)\left(1 - q_x^{\prime(2)}\right) \\ &= q_x^{\prime(1)} + q_x^{\prime(2)} - q_x^{\prime(1)} \cdot q_x^{\prime(2)}. \end{aligned}$$

The given information indicates that $.18 = q_x^{\prime(1)} \cdot q_x^{\prime(2)} = q_x^{\prime(1)}\left(2q_x^{\prime(1)}\right)$, which has the solution $q_x^{\prime(1)} = .30$, $q_x^{\prime(2)} = .60$, ANSWER D

9. The formula $p_x'^{(i)} = \left(p_x^{(\tau)}\right)^{q_x^{(i)}/q_x^{(\tau)}}$ applies to either (i) decrements uniformly distributed in the multiple decrement table, or (ii) constant forces of decrement. The problem asks for $q_{36}'^{(1)}$ which can be expressed as $q_{36}'^{(1)} = 1 - p_{36}'^{(1)} = 1 - \left(p_{36}^{(\tau)}\right)^{q_{36}^{(1)}/q_{36}^{(\tau)}}$. From the given information

$$\ell_{36}^{(\tau)} = \ell_{35}^{(\tau)} - d_{35}^{(1)} - d_{35}^{(2)} = 1000 - 39 - 41 = 920.$$

$$d_{36}^{(1)} = \ell_{36}^{(\tau)} - d_{36}^{(2)} - \ell_{37}^{(\tau)} = 920 - 69 - 828 = 23.$$

Hence $p_{36}^{(\tau)} = \frac{828}{920}$ and $\frac{q_{36}^{(1)}}{q_{36}^{(\tau)}} = \frac{23}{92} = .25$. So $q_{36}'^{(1)} = 1 - \left(\frac{828}{920}\right)^{.25} = .02599$, ANSWER A

10. By definition the central rate $m_x^{(1)}$ is given by

$$m_x^{(1)} = \frac{\int_0^1 {}_tp_x^{(\tau)} \cdot \mu^{(1)}(x+t)\,dt}{\int_0^1 {}_tp_x^{(\tau)}\,dt} = \frac{\int_0^1 \ell_{x+t}^{(\tau)} \cdot \mu^{(1)}(x+t)\,dt}{\int_0^1 \ell_{x+t}^{(\tau)}\,dt} = \frac{d_x^{(1)}}{L_x^{(\tau)}}$$

where $d_x^{(1)}$ is the decrement due to cause 1 in the year of age x to $x+1$ and $L_x^{(\tau)}$ is the number of people-years of exposure to all causes during the same period. The solution involves the straightforward integrations

$$m_x^{(1)} = \frac{\int_0^1 (1-.03t)(.02t)\,dt}{\int_0^1 (1-.03t)\,dt} = \frac{.01-.0002}{.985} = .00995,$$

ANSWER C

11. This problem is a straightforward test of relations involving the joint density of T, J (time and mode of decrement).

I. ${}_tp_x^{(\tau)} = {}_tp_x'^{(1)} \cdot {}_tp_x'^{(2)} = (e^{-.02t})(e^{-.04t}) = e^{-.06t}$, *true*

II. $f_{T,J}(t,1) = {}_tp_x^{(\tau)} \cdot \mu^{(1)}(x+t) = (e^{-.06t})(.02)$, *false*

III. $f_J(2) = Pr(J=2) = {}_\infty q_x^{(2)} = 1 - {}_\infty q_x^{(1)}$

$$= 1 - \int_0^\infty f_{T,J}(t,1)dt$$

$$= 1 - \int_0^\infty .02e^{-.06t}\,dt = 1 - \frac{.02}{.06} = \frac{2}{3}, \textit{ true},$$

ANSWER B

12. From (ii) and (iii) we can deduce that $q_x^{(\tau)} = \frac{1}{4}$ as follows:

$$\frac{1}{4} = {}_{1|}q_x^{(1)} = p_x^{(\tau)} \cdot q_{x+1}^{(1)} = p_x^{(\tau)} \cdot \left(\frac{1}{3}\right) \Rightarrow p_x^{(\tau)} = \frac{3}{4}.$$

The final step is to use the general relation

$$q_x^{(1)} + q_x^{(2)} = q_x^{(\tau)} = q_x'^{(1)} + q_x'^{(2)} - q_x'^{(1)} \cdot q_x'^{(2)}$$

to obtain $\frac{1}{4} = q_x'^{(1)} + \frac{1}{8} - \frac{1}{8}q_x'^{(1)}$, which solves for $q_x'^{(1)} = \frac{1}{7}$, ANSWER D

13. With decrement (1) representing accident, the probability of death by accident is

$$_{\infty}q_x^{(1)} = \int_0^{\infty} {}_tp_x^{(\tau)} \cdot \mu^{(1)}(x+t)\,dt.$$

The trick here is that $\mu^{(1)}(x+t) = .001$ is constant, so the above integral reduces to $.001\int_0^{\infty} {}_tp_x^{(\tau)}\,dt$, which is $(.001)(\mathring{e}_x)$ since surviving the two causes of death is "surviving" in the single-decrement death sense. ANSWER B

14. With an assumption of constant forces of decrement, it follows easily that central rates equal the corresponding force in both the multiple decrement model and the associated single decrement ones:

$$m_x^{(i)} = \frac{\int_0^1 {}_tp_x^{(\tau)} \cdot \mu^{(i)}dt}{\int_0^1 {}_tp_x^{(\tau)}dt} = \mu^{(i)} \qquad \text{(factor } \mu^{(i)} \text{ from top integral and cancel)}$$

$$m_x'^{(i)} = \frac{\int_0^1 {}_tp_x'^{(i)} \cdot \mu^{(i)}dt}{\int_0^1 {}_tp_x'^{(i)}dt} = \mu^{(i)}.$$

Thus $\mu^{(1)} = m_x^{(1)} = .1$ and $\mu^{(2)} = m_x'^{(2)} = .2$. With an assumption of constant forces it also follows that (see Condensed Review Notes in this Unit)

$$q_x^{(i)} = \frac{\mu^{(i)}}{\mu^{(\tau)}} \cdot q_x^{(\tau)} = \frac{\mu^{(i)}}{\mu^{(\tau)}}\left[1 - e^{-\mu^{(\tau)}}\right].$$

Hence $q_x^{(1)} = \frac{.10}{.30}\left[1 - e^{-.30}\right] = .0864$, ANSWER A

15. Recall that $f_T(t) = {}_tp_x^{(\tau)}\mu^{(\tau)}(x+t)$ is the density of T, the time until decrement, and $f_J(j)$ is the notation for the density of J, the mode of decrement. In general

$$f_J(j|\,T=t) = \frac{f_{T,J}(t,j)}{f_T(t)} = \frac{\text{joint}}{T\text{-marginal}} = \frac{{}_tp_x^{(\tau)} \cdot \mu^{(j)}(x+t)}{{}_tp_x^{(\tau)} \cdot \mu^{(\tau)}(x+t)} = \frac{\mu^{(j)}(x+t)}{\mu^{(\tau)}(x+t)}.$$

So from the given (i), (ii) and (iii)

$$.75 = f_J(2|\,T=t) = \frac{k/(60-t)}{(k+1)/(60-t)} = \frac{k}{k+1} \qquad \Rightarrow \qquad k = 3.$$

The sought $f_T(30)$ is ${}_{30}p_x^{(\tau)} \cdot \mu^{(\tau)}(x+30)$. Since $\mu^{(\tau)}(x+30) = 4/(60-30)$, and

$${}_{30}p_x^{(\tau)} = e^{-\int_0^{30}\mu^{(\tau)}(x+s)ds} = e^{-\int_0^{30}4/(60-s)ds} = \left(\frac{60-30}{60}\right)^4 = \frac{1}{16},$$

if follows that $f_T(30) = \frac{1}{16} \cdot \frac{4}{30} = \frac{1}{120}$, ANSWER D

16. In order to obtain $q_{67}^{\prime(1)}$ we need $\ell_{67}^{(\tau)}$, which must come somehow from the partial information at ages 65 and 66. Since $d_{66}^{(\tau)} = 3 + 13 = 16$ we can get $\ell_{67}^{(\tau)}$ if we have $\ell_{66}^{(\tau)}$. Finally $\ell_{66}^{(\tau)} = \ell_{65}^{(\tau)} \cdot p_{65}^{(\tau)} = \ell_{65}^{(\tau)} \cdot p_{65}^{\prime(1)} \cdot p_{65}^{\prime(2)} = 100(1 - .1)(1 - .6) = 36$. So $\ell_{67}^{(\tau)} = \ell_{66}^{(\tau)} - d_{66}^{(\tau)} = 36 - 16 = 20$. From $d_{67}^{(1)} = 1$ and $d_{67}^{(2)} = 3$ it follows that

$$q_{67}^{(1)} = \frac{1}{20}, \quad q_{67}^{(2)} = \frac{3}{20}, \quad q_{67}^{(\tau)} = \frac{4}{20},$$

and from the constant force assumption

$$q_{67}^{\prime(1)} = 1 - p_{67}^{\prime(1)} = 1 - \left(p_{67}^{(\tau)}\right)^{q_x^{(1)}/q_x^{(\tau)}} = 1 - \left(\frac{16}{20}\right)^{1/4} = .0543,$$

ANSWER B

17. With an assumption of constant forces the standard relation needed is

$$q_x^{(i)} = q_x^{(\tau)}\left[\frac{\ln p_x^{\prime(i)}}{\ln p_x^{(\tau)}}\right] = q_x^{(\tau)}\left[\frac{\ln e^{-\mu^{(i)}}}{\ln e^{-\mu^{(\tau)}}}\right] = q_x^{(\tau)} \cdot \frac{\mu^{(i)}}{\mu^{(\tau)}},$$

where $q_x^{(\tau)} = 1 - p_x^{(\tau)} = 1 - \prod_{i=1}^{3} p_x^{\prime(i)} = 1 - \prod_{i=1}^{3} e^{-\mu^{(i)}} = 1 - e^{-\mu^{(\tau)}} = 1 - e^{-1.2} = .6988$

So $q_x^{(2)} = \dfrac{(.6988)\mu^{(2)}}{\mu^{(\tau)}} = (.6988)\dfrac{.04}{(.02 + .04 + .06)} = .233.$

ANSWER B

18. With UDD in each single decrement table we have

$$_tp_x^{\prime(1)}\mu^{(1)}(x+t) = q_x^{\prime(1)} = .10$$

$$_tp_x^{\prime(2)} = 1 - tq_x^{\prime(2)} = 1 - .04t$$

$$_tp_x^{\prime(3)} = 1 - tq_x^{\prime(3)} = 1 - .0625t.$$

Hence

$$q_x^{(1)} = \int_0^1 {}_tp_x^{(\tau)}\mu^{(1)}(x+t)dt = \int_0^1 {}_tp_x^{\prime(2)}\,{}_tp_x^{\prime(3)}\,{}_tp_x^{\prime(1)}\mu^{(1)}(x+t)dt$$

$$= \int_0^1 (1 - .04t)(1 - .0625t)(.10)dt$$

$$= (.10)\int_0^1 1 - .1025t + .0025t^2 dt$$

$$= (.10)\left(t - .1025t^2/2 + .0025t^3/3\Big|_0^1\right) = (.10)(.9496) = .09496.$$

ANSWER C

19. Since $d_{61}^{(2)} = 2d_{60}^{(1)}$ we see from $835 = 1000 - d_{60}^{(1)} - 80 - 25 - d_{61}^{(2)}$ that $d_{60}^{(1)} = 20$. So $q_{60}^{(1)} = .020$, and $q_{60}^{(2)} = .080$. Next we must examine the relation between the $q_{60}^{(j)}$ and the $q_{60}^{\prime(j)}$. Since decrement (1) is UDD, we know that

$$_tp_{60}^{\prime(1)} = 1 - {_tq_{60}^{\prime(1)}} = 1 - tq_{60}^{\prime(1)}, \text{ and } {_tp_{60}^{\prime(1)}}\mu^{(1)}(60+t) = q_{60}^{\prime(1)} \text{ for } t \in (0,\,1).$$

For decrement (2) the entire decrement occurs 2/3 of the way through a year, so

$$_tp_{60}^{\prime(2)} = 1 - {_tq_{60}^{\prime(2)}} = \begin{cases} 1 & 0 \le t < 2/3 \\ 1 - q_{60}^{\prime(2)} & 2/3 \le t \le 1 \end{cases}$$

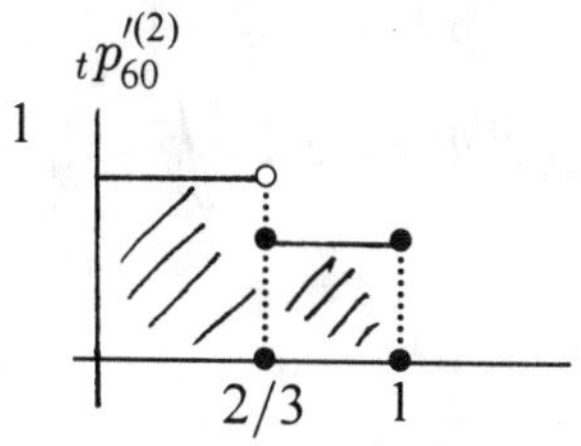

Substitute these results into the standard relation below:

$$.02 = q_{60}^{(1)} = \int_0^1 {_tp_{60}^{(\tau)}}\mu^{(1)}(60+t)dt = \int_0^1 {_tp_{60}^{\prime(2)}} \cdot {_tp_{60}^{\prime(1)}}\mu^{(1)}(60+t)dt$$

$$= \int_0^1 {_tp_{60}^{\prime(2)}} \cdot q_{60}^{\prime(1)} dt$$

$$= q_{60}^{\prime(1)} \cdot \int_0^1 \underbrace{{_tp_{60}^{\prime(2)}}dt}_{\text{hashed area}}$$

$$= q_{60}^{\prime(1)}\left[\frac{2}{3} + \frac{1}{3}\left(1 - q_{60}^{\prime(2)}\right)\right] = q_{60}^{\prime(1)}\left(1 - \frac{1}{3}q_{60}^{\prime(2)}\right).$$

There is also a general relation $.02 + .08 = q_{60}^{(\tau)} = q_{60}^{\prime(1)} + q_{60}^{\prime(2)} - q_{60}^{\prime(1)} \cdot q_{60}^{\prime(2)}$. Solving these two simultaneously for $q_{60}^{\prime(1)}$ leads to a quadratic where

$$q_{60}^{\prime(1)} = \frac{2.96 \pm \sqrt{2.96^2 - .48}}{4} = .020556 \text{ or } \underbrace{1.4594}_{\text{impossible}}.$$

ANSWER C

20. First $q_{30}^{(\tau)} = q_{30}^{\prime(1)} + q_{30}^{\prime(2)} - q_{30}^{\prime(1)} \cdot q_{30}^{\prime(2)} = .28$, so $p_{30}^{(\tau)} = .72$ and $\ell_{31}^{(\tau)} = \ell_{30}^{(\tau)} \cdot p_{30}^{(\tau)} = 720$. Thus $720 - 562 = \ell_{31}^{(\tau)} - \ell_{32}^{(\tau)} = d_{31}^{(1)} + d_{31}^{(2)} = 50 + d_{31}^{(2)}$, or $d_{31}^{(2)} = 108$. We used $.05 = {_{1|}q_{30}^{(1)}} = \dfrac{d_{31}^{(1)}}{1000}$ to obtain $d_{31}^{(1)} = 50$. Finally, $q_{31}^{(2)} = \dfrac{d_{31}^{(2)}}{\ell_{31}^{(\tau)}} = \dfrac{108}{720} = .150$.

ANSWER D

21. From the first row of the table $q_{60}^{(\tau)} = .08$, $p_{60}^{(\tau)} = .92$ and thus $\ell_{61}^{(\tau)} = 10{,}000(.92) = 9{,}200$. Also $p_{62}^{(\tau)} = \prod_i p_{62}^{\prime(i)} = .935311$. $\ell_{62}^{(\tau)} = 9200p_{61}^{(\tau)} = 9200(1 - .076) = 8500.8$,

$\ell_{63}^{(\tau)} = 8500.8 \cdot p_{62}^{(\tau)} = (8500.8)(.935311) = 7950.895$.

ANSWER C

22. First we need to calculate $\ell_{61}^{(\tau)}$ and $q_{61}^{\prime(1)}$:

$$\ell_{61}^{(\tau)} = \ell_{60}^{(\tau)} \cdot p_{60}^{(\tau)} = \ell_{60}^{(\tau)}[\prod_i(1 - q_{60}^{\prime(i)})] = 100{,}000(.86)(.90)(.90) = 69{,}660$$

$$\frac{45{,}516}{69{,}660} = p_{61}^{(\tau)} = (1 - q_{61}^{\prime(1)})(1 - .1)(1 - .2) \qquad \Rightarrow \qquad q_{61}^{\prime(1)} = .0925.$$

Next,

$$q_{61}^{(1)} = \int_0^1 {}_tp_{61}^{(\tau)}\mu^{(1)}(61{+}t)\,dt = \int_0^1 {}_tp_{61}^{\prime(3)} \cdot {}_tp_{61}^{\prime(2)} \cdot {}_tp_{61}^{\prime(1)}\mu^{(1)}(61{+}t)\,dt$$

$$= \int_0^1 {}_tp_{61}^{\prime(3)} \cdot {}_tp_{61}^{\prime(2)} \cdot q_{61}^{\prime(1)}\,dt \qquad \text{(UDD decrement (1))}$$

$$= q_{61}^{\prime(1)} \int_0^1 {}_tp_{61}^{\prime(3)} \cdot {}_tp_{61}^{\prime(2)}\,dt = .0925\int_0^1 {}_tp_{61}^{\prime(3)} \cdot {}_tp_{61}^{\prime(2)}\,dt.$$

From the description of decrements,

$${}_tp_{61}^{\prime(3)} = \begin{cases} 1 & t = 0 \\ .8 & 0 < t \le 1 \end{cases} \quad \text{and} \quad {}_tp_{61}^{\prime(2)} = \begin{cases} 1 & 0 \le t < 1 \\ .9 & t = 1 \end{cases},$$

so the final integral is the area under the piecewise continuous curve in the figure below:

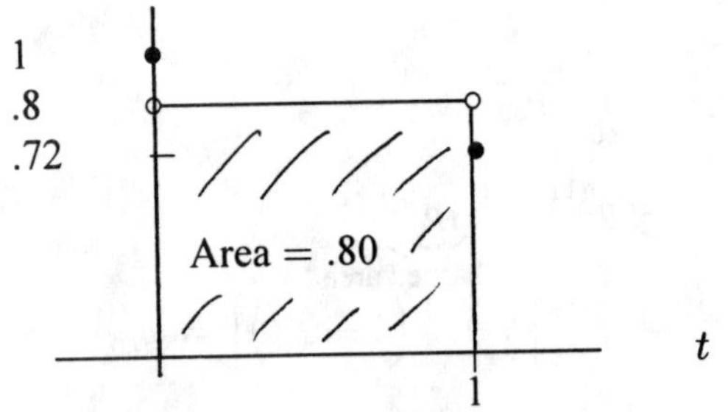

Thus $q_{61}^{(1)} = .0925(.80) = .074.$ ANSWER B

23. Note first that

$$\mu^{(2)}(10{+}t) = \mu^{(\tau)}(10{+}t) - \mu^{(1)}(10{+}t) = \frac{50 - 2t}{(30{-}t)(20{-}t)} - \frac{1}{(30{-}t)} = \frac{1}{20{-}t}.$$

Hence ${}_tp_{10}^{\prime(1)} = \left(1 - \frac{t}{30}\right), {}_tp_{10}^{\prime(2)} = \left(1 - \frac{t}{20}\right)$ using the trick, force $= \frac{p'(t)}{p(t)}c$ $\Rightarrow$ survival function $= \left[\frac{p(0)}{p(t)}\right]^c$. Hence

Pr((10) departs by cause (2) during the 6th year) $= {}_{5|}q_{10}^{(2)}$

$$= \int_5^6 {}_tp_{10}^{(\tau)}\mu^{(2)}(10{+}t)\,dt$$

$$= \int_5^6 \left(1 - \tfrac{t}{30}\right)\left(1 - \tfrac{t}{20}\right)\left(\tfrac{1}{20 - t}\right)dt$$

$$= \frac{30t - \frac{t^2}{2}\big|_5^6}{600} = .0408.$$

ANSWER D

24. Since decrements occur at year-end the probability that (21) is alive and a Fellow in 3 years is given by

$$q_{21}^{(1)} \cdot {}_2p_{22} + {}_1|q_{21}^{(1)} \cdot p_{23} + {}_2|q_{21} \cdot 1 = (.008)e^{-2(.04)} + (1-.008-.150)(.015)e^{-.04}$$
$$+ (1-.008-.150)(1-.015-.200).025$$
$$= .0074 + .0121 + .0165 = .0361$$

ANSWER B

25. I. $\mu^{(i)}(x+t) = \mu^{(i)}$ always results in $m_x'^{(i)} = m_x^{(i)} = \mu^{(i)}$. So I is true.

II. From the UDD for decrement (2) we know ${}_tp_x'^{(2)} = 1 - {}_tq_x'^{(2)} = 1 - t \cdot q_x'^{(2)}$. Thus

$$m_x'^{(2)} = \frac{q_x'^{(2)}}{\int_0^1 {}_tp_x'^{(2)}\,dt} = \frac{q_x'^{(2)}}{\int_0^1 1 - t \cdot q_x'^{(2)}\,dt} = \frac{q_x'^{(2)}}{1 - \frac{1}{2}q_x'^{(2)}}.$$

II is false.

III. In general, $m_x^{(\tau)} = m_x^{(1)} + m_x^{(2)}$. Here $m_x^{(1)} = \mu_x^{(1)}$ due to constant force, but $m_x^{(2)} \neq m_x'^{(2)} = \dfrac{q_x'^{(2)}}{1 - \frac{1}{2}q_x'^{(2)}}$. III is false.

Note: If the total decrement is UDD in the multiple decrement table then

$$m_x^{(i)} = \frac{q_x^{(i)}}{\int_0^1 {}_tp_x^{(\tau)}\,dt} = \frac{q_x^{(i)}}{\int_0^1 1 - t \cdot q_x^{(\tau)}\,dt} = \frac{q_x^{(i)}}{1 - \frac{1}{2}q_x^{(\tau)}}.$$

26 - 29.

Using $1 + 2 + \cdots + n = \dfrac{n(n+1)}{2}$ we can first compute

$$\mu^{(\tau)}(x+t) = \sum_{k=1}^{n} \mu^{(k)}(x+t) = \frac{1}{(n+1)(100-x-t)} \cdot \frac{n(n+1)}{2} = \frac{n}{2(100-x-t)}.$$

A common trick to speed up calculation of the survival function is:

$$\mu^{(\tau)}(x+t) = \frac{p'(t)}{p(t)} \cdot c \;\Rightarrow\; {}_tp_x^{(\tau)} = \left[\frac{p(0)}{p(t)}\right]^c.$$

Here $p(t) = 100 - x - t$, $p'(t) = -1$, so $c = \frac{-n}{2}$. Thus

$${}_tp_x^{(\tau)} = \left[\frac{100 - x}{100 - x - t}\right]^{-n/2},$$

which gives ANSWER A for Question 26.

In general the joint density for T and J is

$$f_{T,J}(t,j) = {}_tp_x^{(\tau)}\,\mu^{(j)}(x+t) = \left[\frac{100-x-t}{100-x}\right]^{n/2}\left(\frac{j}{n+1}\right)\frac{1}{(100-x-t)},$$

which results in ANSWER B for Question 27.

Also, the marginal density for T is

$$f_T(t) = {}_tp_x^{(\tau)}\,\mu^{(\tau)}(x+t) = \left[\frac{100-x-t}{100-x}\right]^{n/2}\cdot\frac{n}{2(100-x-t)},$$

which gives ANSWER E for Question 28.

The conditional distribution of the mode of decrement given the time of decrement, $f_J(j|\,T=t)$, is the ratio of the joint density to the T-marginal, which simplifies to

$$f_J(j|\,T=t) = \frac{f_{T,J}(t,j)}{f_T(t)} = \frac{{}_tp_x^{(\tau)}\mu^{(j)}(x+t)}{{}_tp_x^{(\tau)}\mu^{(\tau)}(x+t)} = \frac{\mu^{(j)}(x+t)}{\mu^{(\tau)}(x+t)} = \frac{j/(n+1)}{n(n+1)/2(n+1)} = \frac{2j}{n(n+1)},$$

so $f_J(3\,|\,T=5) = 6/5(6) = .20$. Question 29 has ANSWER B.

Note: When $f_J(j|T=t)$ involves no t's then T and J are independent and the conditional density is the same as $f_J(j)$.

30 - 33.

Using force $= \dfrac{p'(t)}{p(t)}\cdot c$ to calculate survival function $= \left[\dfrac{p(0)}{p(t)}\right]^c$ we arrive at

$${}_tp_{40}^{\prime(1)} = \left[\frac{60}{60+t}\right]^2,\; {}_tp_{40}^{\prime(2)} = \left[\frac{60}{60+t}\right]^3,\; {}_tp_{40}^{(\tau)} = \left[\frac{60}{60+t}\right]^5.$$

Hence

$$f_{T,J}(20,2) = {}_{20}p_{40}^{\tau}\cdot\mu_{40}^{(2)}(20) = \left(\frac{60}{80}\right)^5\cdot\left(\frac{3}{60+20}\right) = .0089.$$

Question 30 has ANSWER D.

$$f_T(20) = {}_{20}p_{40}^{(\tau)}\cdot\mu_{40}^{(\tau)}(20) = \left(\frac{60}{80}\right)^5\left[\frac{5}{60+20}\right] = .0148.$$

Question 31 has ANSWER C.

Note: $\mu_{40}^{()}(20)$ is the same as $\mu^{()}(40+20) = \mu^{()}(60)$.

The next two questions are closely related since

$$f_J(j|T=t) = \underbrace{\frac{\mu^{(j)}(40+t)}{\mu^{(\tau)}(40+t)}}_{\text{general}} = \underbrace{\frac{\frac{a}{60+t}}{\frac{5}{60+t}}}_{\text{here}} = \frac{a}{5}$$

where $a = 2$ if $j = 1$, $a = 3$ if $j = 2$. The fact that no t's remain means T and J are independent and $f_J(j|T = t) = f_J(j)$. By this result $f_J(2) = \frac{3}{5}$.

Question 32 has ANSWER D.

By the above, $f_J(1) = f_J(1|T = 10) = \frac{2}{5}$.

Question 33 has ANSWER B.

APPENDIX 1

ACTUARIAL PRESENT VALUE EXPRESSIONS

Scan the pages of any text on life contingencies or actuarial mathematics and you will see countless expressions for actuarial present values or net single premiums. It is unfortunate that authors fail to point out that there is just one simple idea that makes it routine to write down correct APV-expressions. There is really no need to memorize the endless list!

Consider first the APV of a very simple, contingent cash flow: a single payment P is made at time t if an event E takes place, otherwise nothing is paid. The random present value of this contingent flow, Y, is a discrete variable with the following probability function:

$Y = y$	$Pr(Y = y)$
0	$Pr(E')$
$P \cdot v^t$	$Pr(E)$

The APV, which is the expected value of Y, is given by

$$E[Y] = \sum_y y \cdot Pr(Y = y) = \underset{\text{(payment)}}{P} \cdot \underset{\text{(discount)}}{v^t} \cdot \underset{\text{(probability)}}{Pr(E)} .$$

Notice the three factors: payment *amount* at time t, a *discount* factor from time t, and the *probablity* that the payment at time t is made.

A more complicated contingent cashflow has possible payments at more than just a single point in time. Since its random present value can be viewed as a sum over all possible payment times, of the present value variables corresponding to single-payment, contingent cashflows, a similar relation holds between the APVs due to the linearity of expected value.

Discrete Version

possible payments: P_i at time t_i, if E_i occurs

$$APV = \sum_{i=1}^{n} P_i \cdot v^{t_i} \cdot Pr(E_i)$$

Continuous Version

possible payments: P_t at time t, $a \le t \le b$, if E_t occurs

$$APV = \int_a^b P_t \cdot v^t \cdot Pr(E_t)$$

Note: sometimes the "dt" is part of P_t and other times it is part of the probability factor.

The expressions simply state that the APV of a contingent cashflow is either the sum or integral, over all possible times of payment, of the product of the three factors: payment amount, discount factor, and probability of payment.

Now let's look at this general idea using examples.

INSURANCE NSP

1. Term insurance to (x) for amount 1, covering the next n years, and payable at death.

Possible times of payment are $0 \le t \le n$. The payment at time t is the unit death benefit, and, for it to be paid, (x) must survive to time t and then expire in the "next instant," which is dt. The probability of this is

$$\underset{\substack{\text{survives}\\ t \text{ years}}}{{}_tp_x} \qquad \underset{\substack{(x+t)\text{ dies in}\\ \text{next instant}}}{(\mu(x+t)dt).}$$

Remember that $\mu(x+t)$ is an instantaneous annual mortality rate at age $x+t$. So the approximate probability that $(x+t)$ dies in the next small fraction of a year, dt, is that fraction of $\mu(x+t)$, i.e., $\mu(x+t)\,dt$. Hence

$$\underset{NSP\text{ symbol}}{\bar{A}^{\,1}_{x:\overline{n}|}} = \int_0^n \underset{(\text{amount})}{1} \cdot \underset{(\text{discount})}{v^t} \cdot \underset{(\text{probability})}{{}_tp_x\,\mu(x+t)\,dt}$$

For a general n-year term insurance paying b_t at death if $0 \le t \le n$, the only change in the above expression would be to replace the 1 by b_t.

2. Increasing, n-year term insurance to (x), beginning at 1 and payable on the policy anniversary following death.

Possible times of payment are $K+1$, where $K = 0, 1, \ldots, n-1$ is the curtate lifetime of (x). For a payment to be made at time $k+1$ we must have (x) surviving to age $x+k$ and then expiring prior to age $x+k+1$, so that the probability is ${}_{k|}q_x = {}_kp_x \cdot q_{x+k}$. Hence we have the NSP expression

$$\underset{NSP\text{ symbol}}{(IA)^1_{x:\overline{n}|}} = \underset{\substack{\text{possible}\\ \text{times}}}{\sum_{k+1=1}^{n}} \underset{\text{amount}}{\left(k+1\right)} \underset{\text{discount}}{\left(v^{k+1}\right)} \underset{\text{probability}}{\left({}_{k|}q_x\right)}.$$

Notice that if $k+1$ goes from 1 to n, then k goes from 0 to $n-1$, which is the more common notation.

ANNUITY APV

Consider a continuous life annuity to (x) payable over the next n years while (x) is surviving, where the annual rate at time t is P_t.

At any exact time t the amount paid is 0; however, over an infinitesimal period from t to $t+dt$ the approximate payment amount is

$$P_t\,dt = (\textit{annual rate})(\textit{fraction of year}).$$

For this to be paid, (x) must be surviving at age $x+t+dt$, which has approximately the same probability, ${}_tp_x$, that (x) survives to age $x+t$. Hence

$$APV(\textit{Variable Annuity}) = \underset{\text{times}}{\int_0^n} \underset{\text{amount}}{(P_t\,dt)} \quad \underset{\text{discount}}{(v^t)} \quad \underset{\text{probability}}{({}_tp_x)} .$$

The special case when $P_t = 1$ is the level, one per year, n year temporary, continuous life annuity to (x), whose APV is denoted by $\overline{a}_{x:\overline{n}|}$. Substituting $P_t = 1$ into the above expression results in

$$\overline{a}_{x:\overline{n}|} = \int_0^n (dt)\,(v^t)\,({}_tp_x),$$

the standard current payment expression for $\overline{a}_{x:\overline{n}|}$. Notice that, in contrast with continuous insurances where "dt" was part of the probability factor, here it is part of the payment factor!

APPENDIX 2

SPECIAL MORTALITY CASES

de MOIVRE'S LAW

I. *Distribution of* X (lifetime of a newborn)

$\ell_x = c(\omega - x)$, $0 \le x \le \omega$, leading to $\mu(x) = \frac{-\ell'_x}{\ell_x} = \frac{1}{\omega - x}$. The value of c is irrelevant.

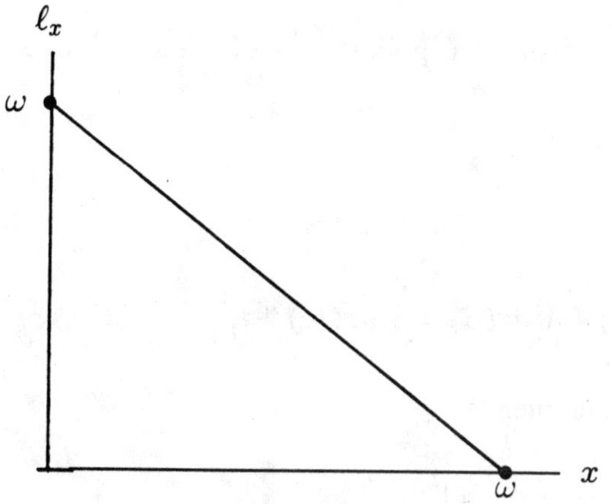

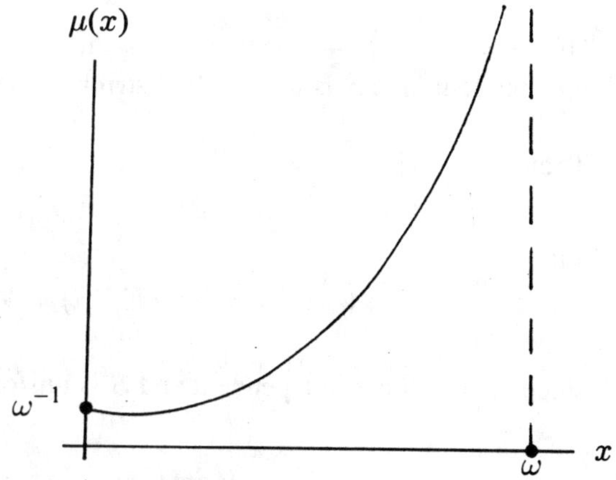

density: $f(x) = {}_x p_0 \mu(x) = \frac{\omega - x}{\omega - 0} \cdot \frac{1}{\omega - x} = \frac{1}{\omega}$, a constant!
therefore X is uniform on $[0, \omega]$

life expectancy: $\overset{\circ}{e}_0 = E[X] =$ midpoint for uniform $= \frac{\omega}{2}$
mean = mode = median, since $f(x)$ is symmetric
$Var(X) = \frac{\text{length}^2}{12}$ for uniform $= \frac{\omega^2}{12}$.

II. *Distribution of* T (future lifetime of (x))

density: $f_T(t) = {}_t p_x \mu(x+t) = \frac{\ell_{x+t}}{\ell_x} \cdot \mu(x+t) = \frac{\omega - (x+t)}{\omega - x} \cdot \frac{1}{\omega - (x+t)} = \frac{1}{\omega - x}$, for $0 \le t \le \omega - x$. Therefore T is uniform over $[0, \omega - x]$.

life expectancy: $\overset{\circ}{e}_x = E[T] =$ midpoint for uniform $= \frac{\omega - x}{2}$

$Var(T) = \frac{\textit{length}^2}{12}$ for uniform $= \frac{(\omega - x)^2}{12}$

III. Distribution of K (curtate future lifetime of (x))

density: $f_K(k) = Pr(K = k) = {}_{k|}q_x = \dfrac{\ell_{x+k} - \ell_{x+k+1}}{\ell_x} = \dfrac{1}{\omega - x}$, a constant!

for $K = 0, 1, \ldots, \omega - x - 1$

This is the "equally likely" model; the K-values $0, 1, \ldots, \omega - x - 1$ all have the same probability $\frac{1}{\omega - x}$. This is a discrete analogue to the continuous uniform distribution.

IV. Relation of T to K

De Moivre's law is an especially strong form of the UDD (uniform distribution of deaths) assumption. UDD means ℓ_x is piecewise linear, whereas de Moivre's law is exactly linear.

UDD $\Rightarrow$ $T = K + S$, where S is the fractional part of final policy year of life, K and S are independent, and S is uniformly distributed on $[0, 1)$.

Then

$$\mathring{e}_x = E[T] = E[K{+}S] = E[K] + E[S] = e_x + \tfrac{1}{2},$$

and

$$Var(T) = Var(K{+}S) = Var(K) + Var(S) = Var(K) + \tfrac{1}{12},$$

since K and S are independent and S is uniform, which means

$$Var(K) = Var(T) - \tfrac{1}{12} = \frac{(\omega - x)^2}{12} - \frac{1}{12}.$$

V. Insurance Values

1. $\displaystyle \bar{A}_x = \int_0^{\omega - x} e^{-\delta t} f_T(t)\,dt = \int_0^{\omega - x} e^{-\delta t} \cdot \frac{1}{\omega - x}\,dt = \frac{1}{\omega - x} \int_0^{\omega - x} e^{-\delta t}\,dt = \frac{1}{\omega - x} \cdot \bar{a}_{\overline{\omega - x|}}$,

   where $\bar{a}_{\overline{\omega - x|}}$ is a continuous annuity certain.

   Explanation: $(\omega - x)\bar{A}_x = \ell_x \bar{A}_x$ is the total pool of money at issue for ℓ_x fully continuous, whole life policies. Since the $\omega - x$ deaths are spread out uniformly and continuously over $(\omega - x)$ years, the aggregate benefits amount to 1 per year, paid continuously for the next $(\omega - x)$ years. This is exactly the payout provided by $\bar{a}_{\overline{\omega - x|}}$.

2. $A_x \underset{\text{UDD}}{=} \frac{\delta}{i} \cdot \bar{A}_x = \frac{\delta}{i}\left(\frac{1}{\omega - x} \cdot \bar{a}_{\overline{\omega - x|}}\right) = \frac{1}{\omega - x} \cdot a_{\overline{\omega - x|}}$ (Note similar explanation)

3. Other similar values: $\bar{A}^{1}_{x:\overline{n|}} = \frac{1}{\omega - x} \cdot \bar{a}_{\overline{n|}}$; $A^{1}_{x:\overline{n|}} = \frac{1}{\omega - x} \cdot a_{\overline{n|}}$

VI. Annuity Values

1. $$\bar{a}_x = \underset{\text{current payment}}{\int_0^{\omega-x} v^t\, {}_tp_x\, dt} = \int_0^{\omega-x} v^t \cdot \frac{\omega-x-t}{\omega-x}\, dt$$

$$= \frac{1}{\omega-x} \underset{\substack{\text{cont. decreasing}\\ \text{cont. paid annuity}\\ \text{certain}}}{(\overline{D}\bar{a})_{\overline{\omega-x}|}}$$

note similarity $$\begin{cases} (Da)_{\overline{n}|} = \dfrac{n-a_{\overline{n}|}}{i} \\ (D\ddot{a})_{\overline{n}|} = \dfrac{n-a_{\overline{n}|}}{d} \\ (\overline{D}\bar{a})_{\overline{n}|} = \dfrac{n-\bar{a}_{\overline{n}|}}{\delta} \end{cases}$$

2. $$\ddot{a}_x = \sum_{k=0}^{\omega-x-1} v^k \cdot {}_kp_x = \sum_{k=0}^{\omega-x-1} v^k \cdot \frac{\omega-x-k}{\omega-x} = \frac{1}{\omega-x} \underset{\text{decreasing annuity due}}{(D\ddot{a})_{\overline{\omega-x}|}}$$

VII. Annual Premiums

1. $P_x = \dfrac{A_x}{\ddot{a}_x} = \dfrac{dA_x}{1-A_x}$; substitute $A_x = \dfrac{1}{\omega-x} \cdot a_{\overline{\omega-x}|}$

2. $P(\overline{A}_x) = \dfrac{\overline{A}_x}{\ddot{a}_x} \underset{\text{UDD}}{=} \dfrac{i}{\delta} \cdot \dfrac{A_x}{\ddot{a}_x} = \dfrac{i}{\delta} \cdot P_x$

3. $\overline{P}(\overline{A}_x) = \dfrac{\overline{A}_x}{\bar{a}_x} = \dfrac{\delta \overline{A}_x}{1-\overline{A}_x}$; substitute $\overline{A}_x = \dfrac{1}{\omega-x} \cdot \bar{a}_{\overline{\omega-x}|}$

VIII. Reserve

$${}_tV_x = 1 - \frac{\ddot{a}_{x+t}}{\ddot{a}_x} = 1 - \frac{\omega-x}{\omega-x-t} \cdot \frac{(D\ddot{a})_{\overline{\omega-x-t}|}}{(D\ddot{a})_{\overline{\omega-x}|}}$$

CONSTANT FORCE

I. Distribution of X

$\mu(x) = \mu$, so $S(x) = e^{-\int_0^x \mu\, ds} = e^{-\mu x}$ (exponential decay). Then $\ell_x = \ell_0 \cdot e^{-\mu x}$

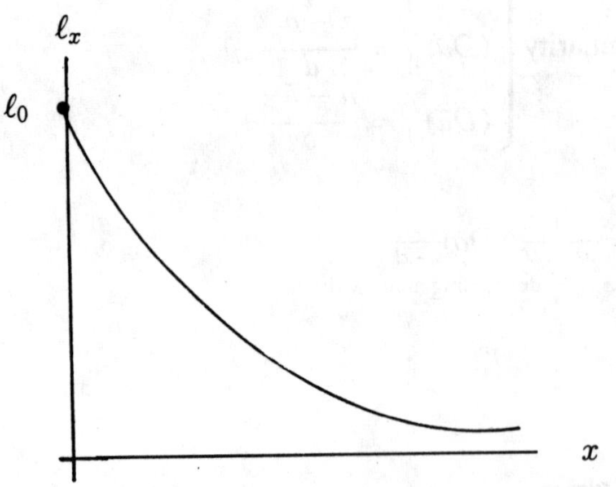

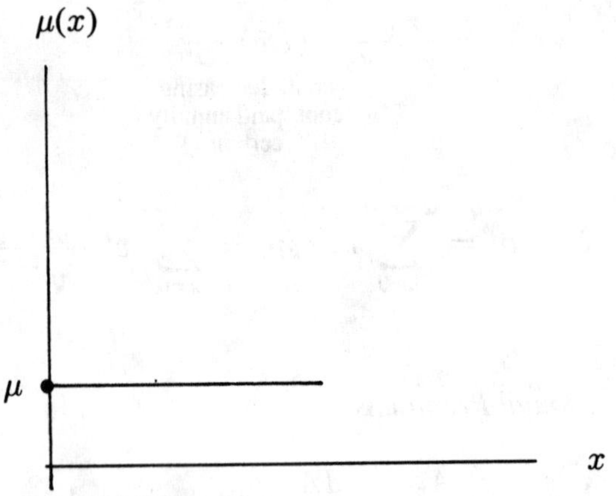

density: $f(x) = -S'(x) = \mu \cdot e^{-\mu x}$, $x > 0$ (exponential density)

Then $E[X] = \mathring{e}_0 = \frac{1}{\mu}$; $Var(X) = \frac{1}{\mu^2}$

II. Distribution of T

density: $f_T(t) = {}_tp_x \mu(x+t) = e^{-\mu t} \cdot \mu$, $t > 0$ (same exponential density)

$\mathring{e}_x = E[T] = \frac{1}{\mu}$; $Var(T) = \frac{1}{\mu^2}$ (Note that age is irrelevant)

III. Distribution of K

density: $f_K(k) = Pr(K = k) = {}_{k|}q_x = {}_kp_x \cdot q_{x+k} = e^{-\mu k}(1 - e^{-\mu})$

This is a geometric distribution. Each year of future life is a Bernoulli trial: success means death in the year, and $p = Pr(\text{success}) = 1 - e^{-\mu}$; failure means survival over the year, and $q = r(\text{failure}) = 1 - p = e^{-\mu}$. K is the number of "failures" before the first "success" in a series of trials.

Geometric distribution facts:

$$e_x = E[K] = \frac{Pr(\text{failure})}{Pr(\text{success})} = \frac{e^{-\mu}}{1 - e^{-\mu}}$$

$$Var(K) = \frac{Pr(\text{failure})}{Pr(\text{success})^2} = \frac{e^{-\mu}}{(1 - e^{-\mu})^2}$$

IV. *Relation of T to K*

Constant force models do not satisfy the UDD assumption. We still have $T = K+S$, but K and S are dependent and the distribution of S is a truncated exponential over $[0, 1)$.

If $0 \leq s \leq 1$

$$F_S(s) = Pr(S \leq s) = Pr\left(\bigcup_{k=0}^{\infty} \underbrace{\left\{K = k \text{ and } S \leq s\right\}}_{\text{i.e., } k \leq T \leq k+s} \right)$$

$$= \sum_{k=0}^{\infty} {}_{k|s}q_x = \sum_{k=0}^{\infty} {}_kp_x \cdot {}_sq_{x+k} = \sum_{k=0}^{\infty} \left(e^{-\mu k}\right)\left(1 - e^{-\mu s}\right)$$

$$= \left(1 - e^{-\mu s}\right) \underbrace{\sum_{k=0}^{\infty} \left(e^{-\mu}\right)^k}_{\text{geometric series}} = \frac{1 - e^{-\mu s}}{1 - e^{-\mu}}$$

Then $f_S(s) = \dfrac{1}{1 - e^{-\mu}} \cdot \mu \cdot e^{-\mu s}$, for $0 \leq s < 1$

and $E[S] = \displaystyle\int_0^1 s \cdot f_S(s)\, ds = \int_0^1 \frac{\mu}{1 - e^{-\mu}} \cdot s e^{-\mu s}\, ds$

$$= \frac{1 - e^{-\mu} - \mu \cdot e^{-\mu}}{(1 - e^{-\mu})\mu} \approx \underbrace{\frac{1}{2}}_{\substack{\uparrow \\ \text{value if } S \\ \text{were uniform}}} - \frac{\mu}{3} \qquad \text{(power series approximation)}$$

V. *Insurance Values*

1. $\displaystyle \overline{A}_x = \int_0^{\infty} e^{-\delta t} f_T(t)\, dt = \int_0^{\infty} e^{-\delta t} (\mu \cdot e^{-\mu t})\, dt = \int_0^{\infty} \mu \cdot e^{-(\mu+\delta)t}\, dt$

   $= \dfrac{\mu}{\mu + \delta}$ (same for all ages)

2. $$A_x = \sum_{k=0}^{\infty} v^{k+1} \cdot {}_{k|}q_x = v^1 \cdot {}_0p_x \cdot q_x + v^2 \cdot {}_1p_x \cdot q_{x+1} + \cdots$$

$$= e^{-\delta} \cdot 1 \cdot (1 - e^{-\mu}) + (e^{-\delta})^2 \cdot e^{-\mu} \cdot (1 - e^{-\mu}) + (e^{-\delta})^3 \cdot (e^{-\mu})^2 \cdot (1 - e^{-\mu}) + \cdots$$

$$= e^{-\delta}\,(1 - e^{-\mu}) \underbrace{\sum_{k=0}^{\infty} (e^{-\delta} \cdot e^{-\mu})^k}_{\text{geometric series}}$$

$$= e^{-\delta}(1 - e^{-\mu}) \cdot \frac{1}{1 - e^{-(\delta+\mu)}}$$

$$= \frac{1 - e^{-\mu}}{e^{\delta} - e^{\mu}} = \frac{q_x}{1 + i - e^{-\mu}} = \frac{q_x}{i + q_x}$$

(Note similarity to $\overline{A}_x = \dfrac{\mu}{\delta + \mu}$)

VI. Annuity Values

1. $\bar{a}_x = \frac{1-\bar{A}_x}{\delta} = \frac{1-(\mu/\mu+\delta)}{\delta} = \frac{1}{\mu+\delta}$

2. $\ddot{a}_x = \frac{1-A_x}{d} = \frac{1-(q_x/i+q_x)}{d} = \frac{i/i+q_x}{d} = \frac{1+i}{i+q_x}$

VII. Annual Premiums

1. $\bar{P}(\bar{A}_x) = \frac{\bar{A}_x}{\bar{a}_x} = \frac{\mu/\mu+\delta}{1/\mu+\delta} = \mu$

2. $P_x = \frac{A_x}{\ddot{a}_x} = \frac{q_x/i+q_x}{1+i/i+q_x} = \frac{q_x}{1+i}$

VIII. Reserves

$${}_t\bar{V}(\bar{A}_x) = 1 - \frac{\bar{a}_{x+t}}{\bar{a}_x} = 1 - 1 = 0; \quad {}_tV_x = 1 - \frac{\ddot{a}_{x+t}}{\ddot{a}_x} = 1 - 1 = 0.$$

APPENDIX 3

A SHORT-TERM WHOLE LIFE EXAMPLE

The purpose of this appendix is to illustrate the main ideas of Units 3 and 4 in a numerical example, to contrast the aggregate deterministic and loss-function approaches to net premiums and reserves, and to briefly introduce net premium accounting.

Suppose all 100 lives age 90 in the table below purchase fully discrete, whole life insurance of 1000 face value for net annual premium $P = 1000P_{90}$. We assume $i = 10\%$ in present value calculations.

x	90	91	92	93
ℓ_x	100	70	40	0
d_x	30	30	40	

Aggregate Deterministic[1] Cashflow

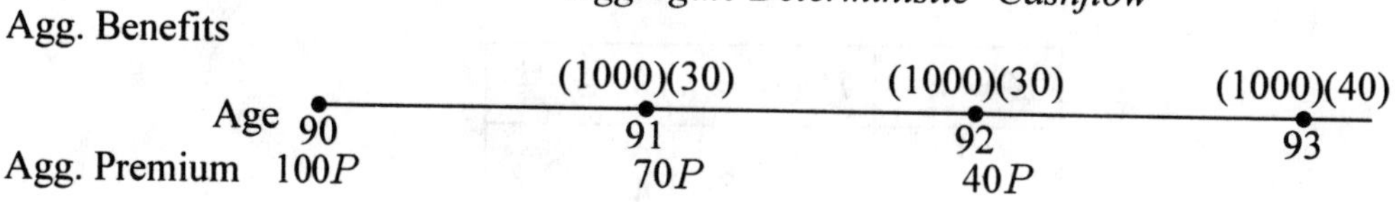

I. Determination of the Net Level Annual Premium

1. Aggregate Deterministic Method.

The present values at $i = 10\%$ of the aggregate benefits and aggregate premiums are equated yielding

$$100P + \frac{70P}{1.1} + \frac{40P}{1.1^2} = PVP = PVB = \frac{(30)(1000)}{1.1} + \frac{(30)(1000)}{1.1^2} + \frac{(40)(1000)}{1.1^3},$$

producing $P = \frac{82,118.7077}{196.6942} = 417.49.$

[1] people cooperate and die exactly as in the table

Notice that when the first equation is divided by $\ell_{90} = 100$ we obtain a balancing equation for a single policy:

(left side)

$$P\left(1+\frac{70}{100}\cdot\frac{1}{1.1}+\frac{40}{100}\cdot\frac{1}{1.1^2}\right) = P(1+p_{90}\cdot v+{}_2p_{90}\cdot v^2) = P\cdot \ddot{a}_{90}$$

(right side)

$$1000\left(\frac{30}{100}\cdot\frac{1}{1.1}+\frac{30}{100}\cdot\frac{1}{1.1^2}+\frac{40}{100}\cdot\frac{1}{1.1^3}\right) = 1000\left({}_{0|}q_{90}\cdot v+{}_{1|}q_{90}\cdot v^2+{}_{2|}q_{90}\cdot v^3\right) = 1000A_{90}.$$

When these algebraic forms are solved for P we obtain the more familiar expression

$$P = 1000\cdot\frac{A_{90}}{\ddot{a}_{90}} = 1000P_{90}.$$

2. The Loss Function Approach

In this method we consider the insurer's loss on a single policy (random present value of outflow minus inflow)

$$L = 1000v^{K+1} - P\cdot\ddot{a}_{\overline{K+1|}} = 1000v^{K+1} - P\cdot\frac{1-v^{K+1}}{d} = \left(1000+\frac{P}{d}\right)v^{K+1} - \frac{P}{d}$$

where K, the curtate lifetime of (90), has the discrete distribution given by

$K = k$	$Pr(K=k) = \frac{d_{90+k}}{\ell_{90}}$
0	30/100
1	30/100
2	40/100

P is called the net level annual premium if the expected loss is zero:

$$0 = E[L] = E\left[1000v^{K+1} - P\cdot\ddot{a}_{\overline{K+1|}}\right] = 1000\cdot E\left[v^{K+1}\right] - P\cdot E\left[\ddot{a}_{\overline{K+1|}}\right]$$
$$= 1000A_{90} - P\cdot\ddot{a}_{90},$$

which means $P = \frac{1000A_{90}}{\ddot{a}_{90}}$ as we saw above.

II. *Interpretation of Net Level Annual Premiums*

1. Aggregate Deterministic Approach

Here we assume people live and die exactly as in the table, and we track the progress of a fund over the 3-year period assuming 100 simultaneous issues. At time $t = 0$ the empty fund receives a deposit of 100 premiums (100×417.49), which earns interest until year-end (10% of 41,749) when benefits for the 30 deaths (30×1000) are withdrawn. This pattern of premium deposit, interest earned, and benefits withdrawn is repeated in each of the next two policy years to arrive at the results in the following table:

Aggregate Deterministic Financial Results for 100 Issues

Policy Year	Beginning Assets	(+) Premium Income	(+) Interest Income	(−) Benefits	Ending Assets
1	0	41,749.00	4174.90	30,000	15,923.90
2	15,923.90	29,224.30	4,514.82	30,000	19,663.02
3	19,663.02	16,699.60	3,636.26	40,000	– 1.12

Note:

(i) Ending assets for year $k-1$ equal beginning assets for year k

(ii) Premium income for year k is $(\ell_{90+k})(417.49)$

(iii) Interest income for year k is 10% of beginning assets plus premium income

(iv) Benefits for year k equal $(1000)(d_{90+k-1})$

(v) Year 3 ending assets would be 0 if the exact premium were used. We rounded to the nearest penny (dropping .004), resulting in the loss of 1.12 which is an accumulation of the losses resulting from dropping the premium by a fraction of a cent.

The point of this table is that for the determinist the net level premium is such that the insurer will *exactly* break even on the group of ℓ_{90} lives.

2. Loss Function Approach

In this approach, as we saw above, the net premium is such that the insurer *expects* to break even on each policy (or, by addition, on a group of policies).. Here we go a step further and attempt to measure the insurer's risk by calculating the variance of the loss function. Now that we have calculated the net level annual premium to be 417.49 we can give numerical values and probabilities for this function:

$$L = \frac{1000}{1.1^{K+1}} - 417.49\ddot{a}_{\overline{K+1}|.10}$$

Event	Probability	Loss	
$K=0$	30/100	491.60	Insurer loses
$K=1$	30/100	29.42	Insurer loses
$K=2$	40/100	−390.74	Insurer profits

$$E[Loss] = \sum_{k=0}^{2}(Loss_k)\Big(Pr(K=k)\Big) = (491.60)(.30) + (29.42)(.30) + (-390.74)(.40) = .01$$ [2]

$$E\left[Loss^2\right] = \sum_{k=0}^{2}(Loss_k)^2\Big(Pr(K=k)\Big) = (491.60)^2(.30) + (29.42)^2(.30) + (-390.74)^2(.40)$$

$$= 133{,}831.93$$

$$Var(Loss) = E[Loss^2] - (E[Loss])^2 = E[Loss^2] = 133{,}831.93$$

2 Would be zero if no rounding of premium or intermediate results had been used.

This variance could also have been calculated algebraically from the expression

$$L = \left(1000 + \frac{P}{d}\right)v^{K+1} - \frac{P}{d} = \left(1000 + \frac{417.49}{1/11}\right)v^{K+1} - \frac{417.49}{1/11}$$

via

$$Var(L) = \left(1000 + (11)(417.49)\right)^2 Var(v^{K+1}) = (31{,}274{,}825.91)[{}^2A_{90} - A_{90}{}^2],$$

where

$$A_{90} = \sum_{k=0}^{2} v^{k+1} \cdot {}_{k|}q_x = \left(\frac{1}{1.1}\right)\left(\frac{30}{100}\right) + \left(\frac{1}{1.1}\right)^2\left(\frac{30}{100}\right) + \left(\frac{1}{1.1}\right)^3\left(\frac{40}{100}\right) = .821187$$

$${}^2A_{90} = \sum_{k=0}^{2} (v^2)^{k+1} \cdot {}_{k|}q_x = \left(\frac{1}{1.21}\right)\left(\frac{30}{100}\right) + \left(\frac{1}{1.21}\right)^2\left(\frac{30}{100}\right) + \left(\frac{1}{1.21}\right)^3\left(\frac{40}{100}\right) = .678627.$$

Slight differences will be noted in these variance calculations due to rounding.

To measure risk for the 100 simultaneous issues, we study the aggregate loss function, L_{Agg}, which is a sum of 100 independent identically distributed individual-policy loss functions like L above. L_{Agg} is approximately normal in distribution with

$$\mu(Agg) = E[L_{Agg}] = 100 \cdot E[L] = (100)(0) = 0$$

$$\sigma^2_{Agg} = Var(L_{Agg}) = 100 \cdot Var(L) = (100)(133{,}831.93), \text{ producing } \sigma_{Agg} = 3{,}658.30.$$

The likely range of aggregate results (e.g, with probability .95) is $\mu(Agg) \pm 1.96\sigma_{Agg}$, which is the interval $[-7170, 7170]$. The high side of this range is troublesome to the insurer since it represents a substantial loss to the insurer on the 100 issues. This amounts to 71.70 per policy which the insurer might collect via an annual risk charge $\theta P = \theta(417.49)$ where

$$(\theta P)\ddot{a}_{90} = 71.70$$

Since $\ddot{a}_{90} = \frac{1 - A_{90}}{d} = (11)(1 - .821187) = 1.9669$, and $P = 417.49$, then the relative security loading, θ, is

$$\theta = \frac{71.70}{(417.49)(1.9669)} = .0873.$$

III. Net Level Premium Reserves

1. Aggregate Deterministic Approach

In the accounting table in *II*, 1, above, the insurer has accumulated a fund (asset) of 15,923.90 at the end of the first policy year. However, at this time he looks into the future for the remaining 70 policies and sees the last two years of the aggregate deterministic cashflow.

Benefits:		(30)(1000)	(40)(1000)
Age	91	92	93
Premium:	$70P$	$40P$	

He finds a net present value (i.e., present value of inflow less outflow) of

$$\left(70P+\frac{40P}{1.1}\right)-\left(\frac{30{,}000}{1.1}+\frac{40{,}000}{1.1^2}\right)=-15{,}924.83.$$

Thus (except for a small rounding error) the fund built up at the end of the first year is exactly matched by a future shortfall (liability). Hence the entire fund must be "held in reserve." There is no profit which could be withdrawn from the business. When this fund is allocated to the 70 policies still in force, the number

$$\frac{\text{Aggregate Fund}}{\text{Policies in Force}}=\frac{15{,}923.90}{70}=227.50$$

is called the first year, net level premium reserve for a policy in force at age 91.

2. The Loss Function Approach

Now consider the prospective loss function for a policy still in force at age 91,

$${}_1L=1000v^{J+1}-417.49\ddot{a}_{\overline{J+1}|},$$

where J is the curtate lifetime of 91:

Event	Probability	Loss Value
$J=0$	$\frac{d_{91}}{\ell_{91}}=\frac{30}{70}$	$\frac{1000}{1.1}-417.49=491.60$
$J=1$	$\frac{d_{92}}{\ell_{91}}=\frac{40}{70}$	$\frac{1000}{1.1^2}-417.49\ddot{a}_{\overline{2}|}=29.42$

The expected future loss on such a policy is

$$E[{}_1L]=\left(\tfrac{30}{70}\right)\left(491.60\right)+\left(\tfrac{40}{70}\right)\left(29.42\right)=227.50,$$

which is identical to the result in *III,* 1, as calculated by the determinist. The determinist believes the shortfall is *exactly* 227.50, whereas the probabilist only *expects* a shortfall of this magnitude. She would go on to measure this risk by calculating the variance of ${}_1L$ and a "likely range" of the shortfall for the group of 70 remaining contracts.

An algebraic form of this expected future shortfall is obtained by taking expected values of both sides of the ${}_1L$ expression:

$$E[{}_1L]=E\left[1000v^{J+1}\right]-417.49\,E\left[\ddot{a}_{\overline{J+1}|}\right]=1000A_{91}-(1000P_{90})\ddot{a}_{91}$$

$$=(1000)[A_{91}-P_{90}\cdot\ddot{a}_{91}],$$

denoted by $1000\,{}_1V_{90}$ in standard actuarial notation.